CIVIL ENGINEERING DRAFTING

Roy H. Wirshing
B.I.E. and Registered Professional Engineer
Technical Drafting Instructor
Broward County School System, Florida

James R. Wirshing
B.S., A.A., A.M., A.A.S., A.C.E.
U.S. Air Force
Civil Engineering Squadron

GLENCOE

Macmillan/McGraw-Hill

New York, New York
Columbus, Ohio
Mission Hills, California
Peoria, Illinois

Library of Congress Cataloging in Publication Data

Wirshing, Roy H.
Civil engineering drafting.

Includes index.
1. Engineering drawings. 2. Mechanical drawing.
I. Wirshing, James R. II. Title.
TA175.W57 1983 624'.022'1 82-17195
ISBN 0-07-071127-5

Technical Studio: Technical Graphics

Civil Engineering Drafting

Imprint 1993

Send all inquiries to:
GLENCOE DIVISION
Macmillan/McGraw-Hill
936 Eastwind Drive
Westerville, Ohio 43081

6 7 8 9 10 11 12 13 14 15 BAW 00 99 98 97 96 95 94 93

ISBN 0-07-071127-5

CONTENTS

Preface iv

Acknowledgments iv

Chapter 1: BASIC DRAFTING EQUIPMENT 1

Chapter 2: LETTERING 15

Chapter 3: THE MUNICIPAL KEY MAP 33

Chapter 4: RURAL KEY MAPS 57

Chapter 5: DRAINAGE BASICS 73

Chapter 6: ESSENTIAL ITEMS ON PLAN VIEWS 103

Chapter 7: FUNDAMENTALS FOR USE IN PLAN AND PROFILE DRAWINGS 119

Chapter 8: ROADWAY PLAN AND PROFILE SHEETS 137

Chapter 9: PRODUCING A PLAN AND PROFILE SHEET 159

Chapter 10: TYPICAL ROADWAY CROSS SECTIONS 185

Chapter 11: SUPERELEVATION 213

Chapter 12: EARTHWORK 227

Chapter 13: PROPOSED DRAINAGE STRUCTURES 235

Chapter 14: RIGHT-OF-WAY 243

Chapter 15: MATHEMATICAL PROCEDURES 249

Chapter 16: LAND DEVELOPMENT 257

Chapter 17: SURVEYING EQUIPMENT 283

Chapter 18: DISTANCE MEASUREMENTS 295

Chapter 19: LEVELING 311

Chapter 20: ANGLE AND DIRECTION OBSERVATION 327

Abbreviations 337

Definitions 340

Index 344

PREFACE

Civil Engineering Drafting is for those who are studying all aspects of highway design drafting, and who may (or may not) at the same time be introduced to some elements of surveying. It is the only civil engineering drafting textbook needed, and if its course of study is completed, the user will be fully prepared for an entry-level drafting position in civil engineering.

The textbook can help meet these objectives because, first, it allows the user to work and learn at their own individual speeds, and second, its wide variety of exercises and problems are taken from actual road design cases.

Users of this text work at their own speed by using the learning activity packages (LAP) included in each chapter. These sections supply users the information needed to measure and adjust their own progress. The LAPs indicate which sections of the text must be studied, provide space for recording the date when the activity is completed, contain information that will guide the user through the exercises or drawing problems, and finally, allow them to recognize when they are ready to take the chapter quizzes.

All the drafting exercises and problems have been selected in order to improve understanding by illustrating the new material in each chapter. They are from actual design cases in states' highway department files. At least one problem in each chapter proceeds step-by-step through the topic that is being discussed, and these problems should be done exactly as the instructions say. In early chapters, these problems will have the user learn by tracing, but in later chapters the work is done from reference drawings. The instructions explain what lines to draw, and why they are drawn. Even though they will be working on their own, users will feel as if an experienced civil engineer is assisting them at all times. Through this arrangement, the movement is gradual from simple to more difficult material, and at the same time opportunity is provided to improve drafting technique as errors are discussed and corrected.

It is important that the user work through as many problems as possible. The more problems completed, the more thorough will be the understanding of the field. In addition, some of the problems are based on map features not explained elsewhere in the text. Since they present new information on a case-by-case basis, knowledge of design situations will be broadened if these are undertaken.

The authors are extremely grateful to the Florida Department of Transportation for the use of their Roadway Design Manual and Contract Plan Reading-Plan Book, which were used extensively in preparing this text. These manuals were prepared for use by experienced drafters, but information from them has been simplified for use in this textbook.

The U.S. Army and U.S. Air Force were helpful in allowing us to use materials from their manuals, especially General Drafting, TM 5-230 and TO 00-25-103.

Acknowledgments

Alvin and Co., Inc.; Atlantic Vocational Technical Center; Charles Bruning Co.; Dietzgen Corp.; David White Instruments; Deerfield Beach Engineering Department; Deerfield Beach Senior High School; Florida Department of Transportation; Faber-Castell Corp.; Keuffel and Esser Co.; Koh-I-Noor Rapidograph, Inc.; Mayline Co., Inc.; Teledyne Post; Topcon Instrument Corp. of America.

Roy H. Wirshing
James R. Wirshing

1 BASIC DRAFTING EQUIPMENT

Objectives

a. Understand the use of the various drafting tools
b. Be able to care for the drafting tools properly
c. Become familiar with the variety of desks, tables, and board coverings
d. Understand why T-squares are seldom used in civil drafting in industry
e. Understand why mechanical lead holders and technical pens are used
f. Understand the system for indicating lead hardness
g. Learn about different drawing mediums
h. Learn the drawing sheet sizes

Rationale

Before entering the field of civil engineering drafting the student needs to become acquainted with the tools of the trade. This text assumes the student has had little or no drafting experience, so the first chapter explains the tools, their usage, and sometimes their care.

This text provides a method of learning procedures, symbols, line structures, and many other different mapping features involved in civil drafting. If the student has been exposed to mechanical or architectural drafting, this will be a plus. However, civil engineering drafting is very different from other types of drafting. Adherence to the instruction to *read the text as you draw* will make the course very simple. The text provides both general and specific instructions for each type of map or structure to be drawn. General instructions are of the type provided by consulting engineer or highway department manuals, which would be too intricate for beginning students. Specific instructions give detailed directions or explanation for each line to be drawn.

One of the authors of the text was first a drafting technician and then an engineer with the Florida Department of Transportation (D.O.T.) for many years. The other is a surveyor in the U.S. Air Force. Some of the material in the text comes from the Florida highway design manual and pertains particularly to Florida, but the methods of drafting can be applied anywhere. Most of the drawings and instructions in this text have been provided through the courtesy of the Florida Department of Transportation.

SCOPE AND ORGANIZATION OF THE TEXT

The text covers the use and care of drafting instruments, line weights and conventions, freehand lettering, notes and dimensions, and maps and structures used in highway design. Elementary surveying and land development complete the book. Students who read the text material while doing the drawings will be well prepared to become good entrance-level civil drafting employees and can aspire to projects such as the interchange in Fig. 1–1.

The text will often have review sections, and each chapter (except Chap. 15) has a quiz, which is removable from the book. The reviews are important as they may explain some items not covered in the chapter; they should be considered text material.

Figure 1-1
Interchange near Austin, Texas *(Texas Highway Department).*

LEARNING ACTIVITY PACKAGES

Always look first at the learning activity package (LAP) at the end of each chapter. The LAP will guide the student through the chapter, telling what to read, when to take the quiz, when to do the drawing problems, and which ones to do.

BASIC EQUIPMENT

For the person who intends to draw, the first requirement is something to place the drawing material on. There are two basic types of equipment for this: drawing boards and drafting tables.

Drawing Board

A drawing board (see Fig. 1–2) is made with strips of soft wood, usually white pine or basswood, glued together edge-to-edge to prevent warping. End cleats are attached to the board with tongue-and-groove joints to prevent warping and to allow for expansion. For a right-handed drafter, the outside edge of the left cleat is the working edge of the drawing board. The working edge must be tested periodically for straightness so that work will be accurate.

Drafting Tables

Drafting tables (Figs. 1–3 and 1–4) are made in all shapes and varieties. Though some can be purchased for less than $100, some of the very exotic tables will cost more than $1000. (Some of these have built-in electric motors which raise and lower the table top.) The board surface of a drafting table should measure at least 4 feet (ft) [1.2 m] long by 3 ft [0.9 m] in height.

Figure 1-2
An excellent large drafting table used extensively in industry *(Mayline Co.)*.

Figure 1-3
A type of drafting station used at many vocational and technical schools. Notice the storage area and "throw tables" *(Bruning Co.)*.

Figure 1-4
Student at work with a drafting machine mounted on a drafting board *(Keuffel and Esser Co.)*.

Self-sealing Board Covers

It is advantageous to have a drafting board or drafting table with a self-sealing type of cover. Some linoleum covers are good, but even better is the self-sealing type commonly produced in Denmark and sold in the United States under various trade names. This self-sealing material is green on one side and off-white on the other. If the drawing surface is covered with this material, pointed instruments will not affect the surface, so compass- and divider-point holes will heal as soon as the point is removed. This is a real help to the drafter, since holes in the drawing surface allow the pencil lead to tear through the drawing paper.

Students should never use thumb tacks to pin down a drawing because these will ruin the surface of the drawing board.

TOOLS AND SUPPLIES USED IN CIVIL DRAFTING

Unlike the other drafting fields, civil has little use for tools that produce horizontal and vertical lines. In civil drafting most of the straight-line work consists of joining various points together. These points seldom lie on a horizontal or vertical line, so the parallel-rule, drafting machine, and T-square are seldom required. Some engineering and state transportation offices are filled to capacity with drawing tables, but T-squares are never seen. Parallel-rules seen in the office of a consulting engineer who specializes in highways would only be there because of the dictates of another type of work.

DRAWING TOOLS

A set of regular drawing instruments (see Fig. 1–5) should not be needed by the civil drafting student, although a large compass which can strike a 10-inch (in) [25-cm] circle may be handy to have.

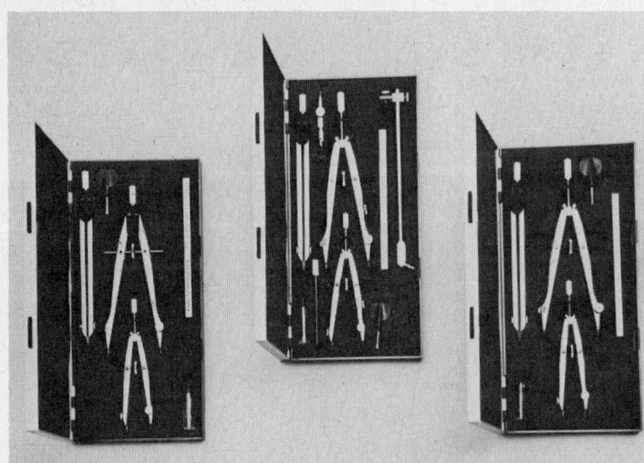

Figure 1-5
Sets of drafting tools *(Keuffel and Esser Co.)*.

Figure 1-6
Beam and bow compasses.

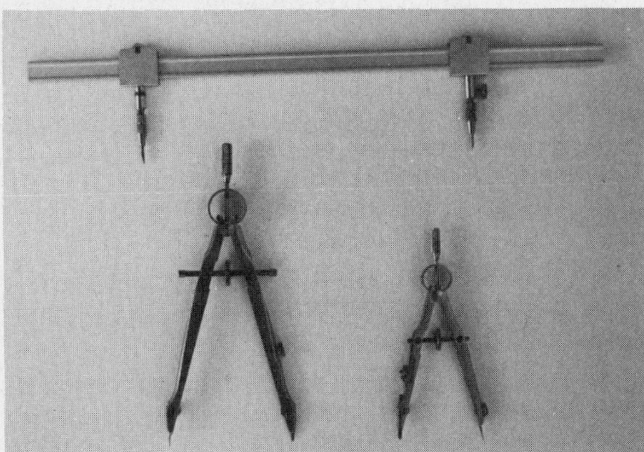

Bow Compass

A bow compass (Fig. 1–6) is an instrument which is nice to have but which is seldom used. It is capable of more precise adjustment than the larger 10-in [25-cm] compass (because of the side adjustment screw arrangement) and may be of some use in designing structures common to drainage.

Beam Compass

A beam compass (see Fig. 1–6) consists of a long bar with a point attached to one end and a pencil or pen attached to the other. All of the attachments are adjustable to permit easy drawing of large circles.

T-square

The student's need for a T-square (Fig. 1–7) will be confined to drawing border lines on the drawings, putting chart boxes into the plans, and so forth. A T-square consists of a straightedge (the blade) that is long enough to span the drawing board, and a shorter crosspiece (the head) that is attached to one end of the blade. The upper edge of the blade and the inner edge of the head are at right angles and are the working edges of the T-square. To prevent warping when not in use, T-squares should be left flat on the drawing board or should be suspended from the hole in the blade. The working edge of a T-square should never be used as a guide for a knife blade.

Test for Straightness. A T-square blade can be tested for straightness by drawing a sharp line along the entire length of the working edge, with the T-square in normal position. The square is then turned over so that the underside is exposed, and the same line is drawn against the same edge. If the edge is not straight, the second line will not coincide with the first. On a T-square with a plastic edge, the error can often be corrected by first scraping the high spots on the edge with a knife and then polishing the edge with fine sandpaper. Check the edge regularly by holding it against the surface of the drawing board.

Figure 1-7
T-square *(Teledyne Post Co.)*.

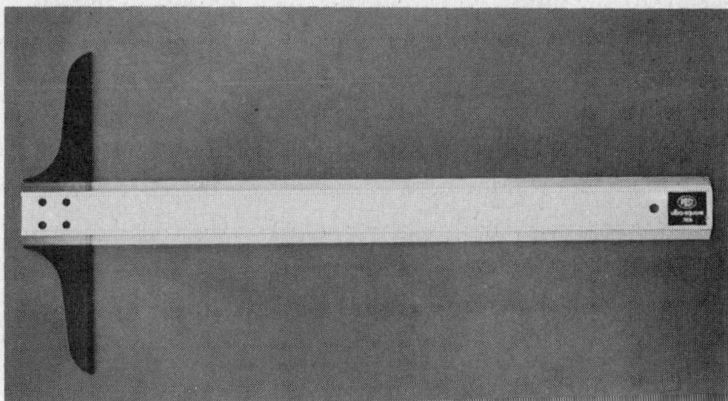

Test for Rigidity. Use the left hand to firmly hold the head of the T-square against the edge of the drawing board in a drawing position. Then test the blade for up-and-down motion or swing. A poor joint can be repaired by regluing the joint and tightening the screws.

Stainless Steel Blade

This is a drafting tool seldom used except by civil drafters. The stainless steel blade comes in several sizes. The most common sizes are 24- or 36-in [61- or 91-cm] lengths. The blades are about ⅛ in [3 mm] thick and 1-in [25 mm] wide with a bevel on both of the top edges.

The most common use of the steel blade is connecting points to make straight lines. This common tool for civil drafters will not be required in this course. Horizontal and vertical border lines will be needed for drawing sheets, but the T-square can do this perfectly. Turning a T-square upside down to connect points which are too far apart to be reached with the triangles will eliminate the need for a steel blade.

Triangles

The two triangles (Fig. 1–8) are made of transparent plastic and will not discolor, distort, or scratch, if handled with reasonable care. One triangle is constructed with angles of 30, 60, and 90°. The other has two 45° angles and one 90° angle.

The standard-size triangles are 10 in [25 cm] long for the longest leg of the 30–60° triangle and 8 in [20 cm] long for each leg of the 45° triangle. Triangles should always be kept flat to avoid warping.

Testing Triangles. The separate edges may be tested for straightness the same way as the working edge of a T-square blade is tested. The 90° angle can be tested for accuracy by setting a side of the triangle against the T-square and, without moving the T-square, drawing a vertical line along the perpendicular side of the triangle. First draw the line with the hypotenuse of the triangle facing away from the head of the T-square, then turn the triangle over and repeat the process with the hypotenuse facing toward the T-square head while keeping the same side of the triangle in contact with the T-square. If the angle is correct, the two lines will coincide.

When the right angle has been proved correct, accuracy of the 45° angles may be tested. Horizontal and vertical legs of equal length are drawn with the T-square and triangle, after which the hypotenuse is drawn with a straightedge. Using the same T-square, the hypotenuse of the 45° triangle can be checked against the hypotenuse thus constructed.

The 60° angle can be checked by drawing a line, with the T-square, of any length shorter than the hypotenuse of the triangle, and then, with the shorter leg of the 30–60° triangle against the T-square, using the 60° angle to draw inclined lines, from both ends of the original line, to form a triangle. If the three sides of the triangle thus drawn are not equal, the 60° angle is incorrect. If the 60° and 90° angles prove correct, then the 30° angle will automatically be accurate.

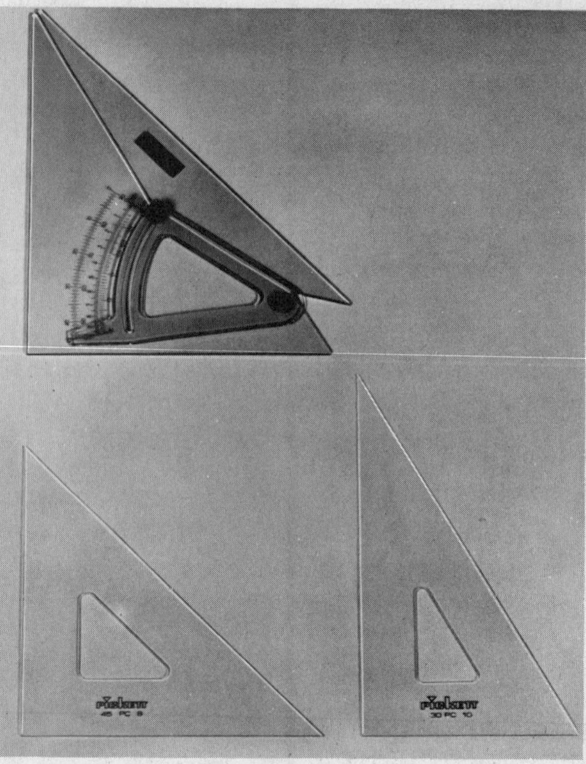

Figure 1-8
Adjustable 45° and 30–60° triangles *(Pickett Co.).*

Correcting Triangles. Triangle edges can be corrected by scraping and sanding. Care must be exercised in deciding which portion of a triangle leg to scrape to true a faulty angle.

Protractor

Protractors are used to measure and set off angles other than those measurable with the drafter's triangles. Protractors usually are numbered at 10° intervals. The smallest graduation is 0.5°. The scale can be read from either end. In setting off an angle to an existing line, the horizontal line on the protractor is placed against the existing line with the vertical line (called the vertex indicator) at the point from which the angle leg is to be drawn (the vertex of the angle). The scale is then used to set off the desired number of degrees.

Drafting Machine

A drafting machine combines the functions of the T-square and triangles with that of a protractor. Drafting machines are especially useful for tool and machine designing saving as much as 30 percent of the drafter's time. They are almost never used for civil drafting.

Scales

In civil drafting, as in architecture, drawings must be rendered with smaller dimensions than the actual size of the project. As an architect cannot make drawings the size of an actual house, so the civil drafter cannot make full-size plans. Many civil jobs are 10 miles (mi) [16 km] long, and a full-size drawing on 10 mi [16 km] of paper is clearly impractical.

For this reason scales are used. The scales have dimensions in accurate proportions to the actual dimensions being represented. The various scales are systematic length ratios that enable drafters to lay out proportional dimensions quickly, easily, and accurately. The scale selected will present a final drawing usually much smaller than the actual object. Engineer's scales (Fig. 1–9) help the drafter select and use appropriate drawing scales.

Irregular Curves

Irregular curves, also known as French curves, are used as mechanical guides for drawing curves other than circles or circle arcs. They are made of transparent plastic and their edges represent successive portions of ellipses, parabolas, spirals, and other standard geometric curves.

Figure 1-9
Various engineering and architectural scales *(Pickett Co.).*

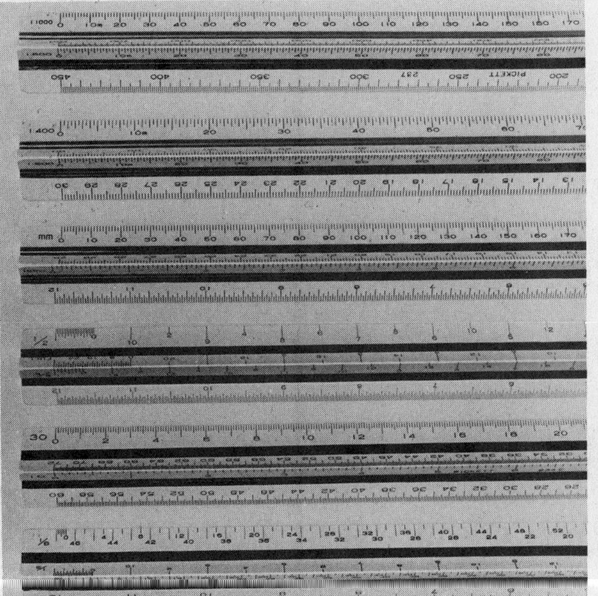

Erasing Shield

The erasing shield is a small plate of thin spring steel, with slots of various shapes stamped out, allowing unwanted lines to be removed while other work is left untouched.

Dustbrush

A drafter's dustbrush is a soft-bristled camel's hair or foxtail brush used for keeping the drawing sheet free of eraser debris. The brush should be kept clean and dry and used only for its intended purpose.

Mechanical Lead Holders

Mechanical lead holders (Figs. 1–10 and 1–11) are so superior to wooden drafting pencils for civil drafting that

Figure 1-10
Students using scale and mechanical lead holders *(Deerfield Beach High School, Florida).*

Figure 1-11
Various mechanical lead holders and lead *(A.W. Faber-Castell Corp.).*

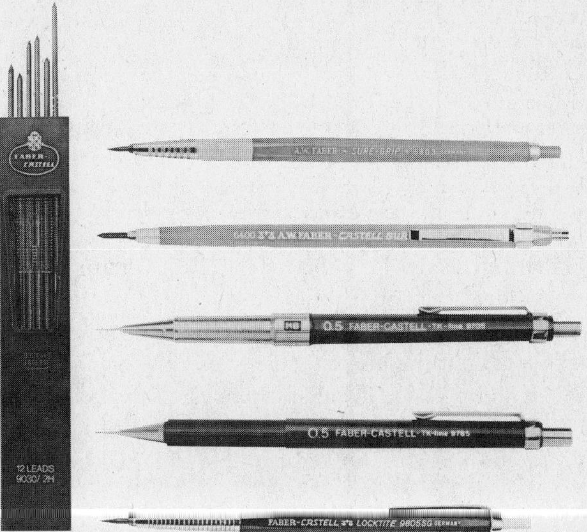

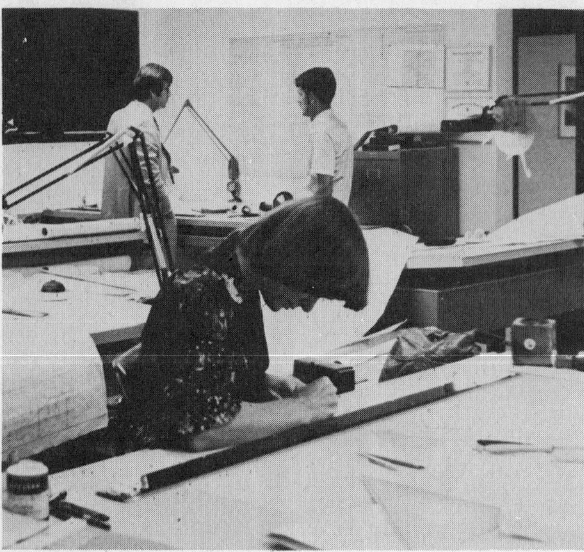

Figure 1-12
Drafting room at a consulting engineering firm *(PRC Harris, Inc.).*

the old style wooden pencil need not be described. The lead holder does exactly as its name implies—it holds a stick of lead. It acts just as the wood does on the old-fashioned pencil. Usually the lead holder, which is the same size as the regular pencil, has a collet to grip the lead, which is inserted from the front of the holder. Pressing on a button at the back of the holder releases the lead so that enough lead feeds out to point, or sharpen, the lead.

Tools in a Drafting Room

Some of the tools discussed here can be seen in the industrial drafting room in Fig. 1–12.

PENCILS, INKS, AND DRAWING MEDIUMS

Lead Hardness

Lead sticks are purchased separately in hardness ranges from 6B (very soft and black) through 5B, 4B, 3B, 2B, B, HB, and F to H, 2H, 3H, 4H, 5H, 6H, 7H, 8H, and the hardest lead 9H.

In this range of lead hardness, the student will find that HB and H are good for lettering, while F, H, and 2H will generally be sufficient for all the drafting work to be done. HB and F are in the middle of the hardness scale. Lead that is on the soft side will give good black drawings, but the disadvantage is that the graphite will smear and produce illegible drawings. The student will have to learn through practice which type of lead will give good linework for reproducible drawings, without the smearing of a too-soft lead.

Electrolytic or filmograph lead (greasy and very black) can be used on mylar. Regular leads cannot be used successfully on mylar. All these leads are available for the mechanical lead holder. Each student should have two lead holders; this makes it possible to set up with the two different types of lead which will be used the most. For example, one holder might hold HB for lettering and the other 2H for linework. This makes it possible to work without continually changing leads in the holder.

REMEMBER When drafting, it is best to choose a lead that is sufficiently hard so as to not blur or smudge, but not so hard that it cuts grooves in the paper when reasonable pressure is applied.

Lead Sharpeners

Lead sharpeners, usually called pointers, come in many varieties (an example is shown in Fig. 1–13). Some have carbide blades inside to sharpen the lead to a very fine point; these last many years and are an excellent buy. Lead is very abrasive and takes the edge off a steel cutter blade very rapidly. Small lead pointers are available for only a few cents, but they last only a few weeks. The better carbide blade type lasts indefinitely. There are many pointers that sit on the side board or drawing table. Some are arranged with clamps so that they fit on the drawing table permanently. The drafter puts the lead holder into the pointer and turns it in a circular direction. The emery cloth inside the pointer is shaped into a conical form. It is this conical shape that puts a sharp point on the lead. These pointers have an indefinite life;

Figure 1-13
Lead pointer for lead used in mechanical lead holders *(A.W. Faber-Castell Corp.).*

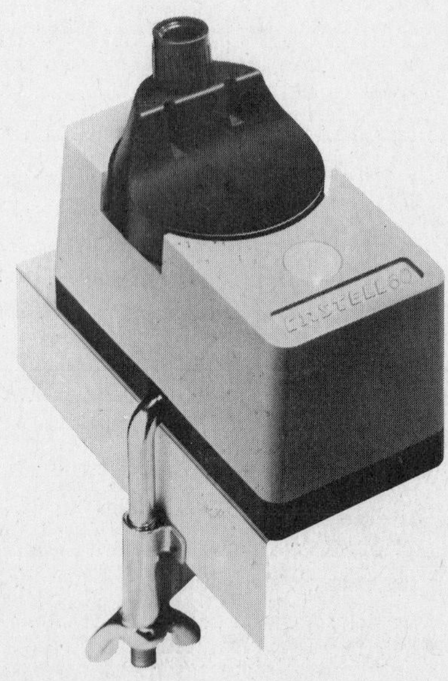

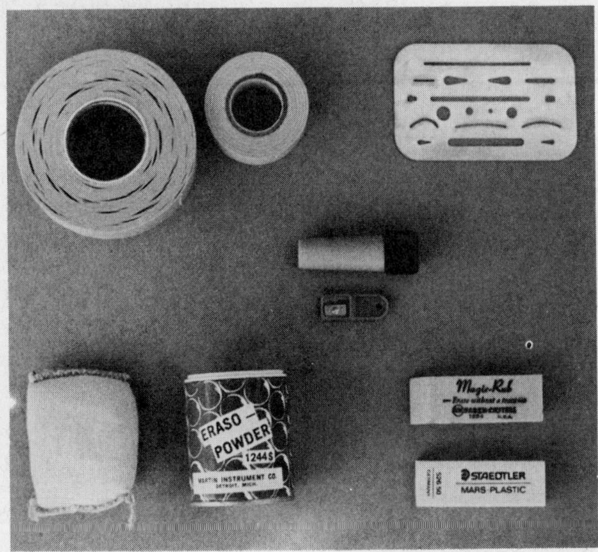

Figure 1-14
Drafting tape, dry cleaner, eraser shield, erasers.

when they no longer produce a good point, the insertion of another emery-paper insert is all that is required.

Paper Fasteners

Use drafting tape (Fig. 1–14) to fasten the drawing paper. The staples and thumb tacks used in the past are out. They ruin the drafting board or drafting table surface, even if the board is covered by some sort of vinyl covering. The drafting tape holds the drawings in the proper position, but be careful when removing the tape. *The tape should be slowly pulled off the drawing first,* then the rest of the tape can be pulled from the drawing board surface. This will keep the drawing from tearing. If the tape is pulled from the board first, a corner will tear off of the drawing nearly every time.

Paper Cleaners

There are many dry cleaning pads and powders (such as those in Fig. 1–14) on the market. They have a rubber-type base, and when sprinkled (or in the case of a little bag, bounced) on the drawing, they leave a powdery debris on the drawing. The drafter works in this powder. This cleaner will remove the excess graphite from the edges of triangles and that which falls from the lead itself. It does a good job of keeping the drawing clean. The disadvantage of the cleaner is that it also removes the graphite from the lines on the drawing. This is caused by the erasing action produced as the triangles slide over the drawing. Sometimes a drawing, which has been produced with too much dry cleaner on its surface, is so faint that it will not reproduce well. Then it must be "heavied up" (darkened) before turning in for printing.

Drawing Mediums

Drawing paper is usually made of rag-content fibers which provide good erasing qualities, can stand frequent handling, and reproduce well. It should have a medium grain, or tooth, to give sharp, clean pencil lines. The paper comes in sheets or rolls. We like to use 20-pound tracing vellum of 100 percent rag. This is available in cut sheets of the following sizes:

Designation	Size (inches)
A	8.5 × 11 or 9 × 12
B	11 × 17 or 12 × 18
C	17 × 22 or 18 × 24
D	22 × 34 or 24 × 36
E	34 × 44 or 36 × 48

Mylar, a plastic film with a matte finish on one or both sides, is available either in rolls or in cut form. Engineering offices buy the cut form, preprinted with borders, boxes, and with the firm's name. Mylar is more expensive than vellum, but lasts virtually forever. This makes it an excellent storage medium. Another advantage of mylar is its erasing quality. It will take ink beautifully and, if an error needs correcting, it can be erased without a trace. In the civil drafting industry mylar is used extensively. Often, there are cases of very complicated drawings, such as plans for a cloverleaf interchange, where the drafting cost has run into the hundreds of dollars in drafter's time. If an improvement to the location is suggested, it may mean redoing about one-third of the entire sheet. On vellum, the erasing process could ruin the entire sheet. With mylar, the part affected can be removed easily with an erasing fluid and eraser. Thus the engineer can save hundreds of dollars by investing an initial few extra dollars on the drafting medium.

Erasers

Generally the Magic Rub (Fig. 1–14) or other trade name white plastic erasers are best for civil drafting. They are soft and very gentle on the vellum or mylar surface. To erase ink from mylar there is a new Pelikan eraser which releases an erasing fluid due to the heat developed by the friction of erasing.

Learn to erase well. In industry it often seems to consume more time than drawing. After several bosses add their suggestions to the final design and the drafter is forced to erase and begin again, the importance of erasing becomes clear.

Inking

Inking was important to the map makers and drafters of the fourteenth through the nineteenth centuries, but the process was slow and laborious. The first pens for inking were the quill-type pens and then the nib pens of the 1920s through the early 1950s. With this kind of inking equipment the quality of the product depended entirely on the ability of the drafter. The pressure of the hand on the quill pen determined the thickness of the line. Many beautiful maps and detail drawings were made in those days, but the time spent to do them was astronomical.

The Technical Pen

In the 1950s, and possibly even earlier in Germany, a new kind of pen, called a *technical pen,* was introduced. One of these pens has a well-known trade name. Just as the trade name Frigidaire brings to mind the domestic refrigerator, so the trade name Rapidograph[1] calls to mind this new type of technical pen (see Fig. 1–15).

The sharp-edged ink lines produced by a Rapidograph technical pen have uniform size and high opacity and are far superior to pencil lines. Pencil line density and width vary with hand pressure, greatly affecting reproduction qualities of the maps made in civil drafting. Pencil line width varies with the wear of the lead point, which can only be corrected by time-consuming, constant, and exact pointing.

Recommended Inking Tools

For training in civil drafting it is recommended that either the student or the technical school provide a technical pen set with the following sizes included: No. 1, 2, and 3. Other materials should include a selected ink in a dropper-stopper or filler squeeze bottle, and erasing materials. The school, if possible, should provide templates, triangles, T-square, and compasses. Some appropriate tools are shown in Fig. 1–16.

Vellum or Drafting Film

The ultimate type of drafting material surface, at this writing, is the Rapidraw film, especially formulated for direct ink drafting. A good vellum will be suitable for our purposes, but it will not accept ink as well and will be more difficult to erase. The student may, for this reason, be permitted to draw in pencil, even though the better medium would be ink. Vellum has one big advantage for the drafting student: It is much cheaper than mylar or any type of drafting film.

Film and Technical Pens Which Are Matched

The Rapidraw film mentioned above is matched to the Rapidograph technical pens and the Pelikan inks. The ultrafine tooth of the Rapidraw film surfaces assures perfect line-edge sharpness, maximum opaqueness of the ink line, and minimal abrasion of pen points. Adhesion developed by surface chemistry assures superior performance of the ink line on the finished drawing unless a deliberate erasure is required. In fact, it is possible to make totally clean erasures without leaving "ghosts" or any other photosensitive mars. The drawing surface remains unaffected even after repeated erasures.

[1] Koh-I-Noor Rapidograph Co.

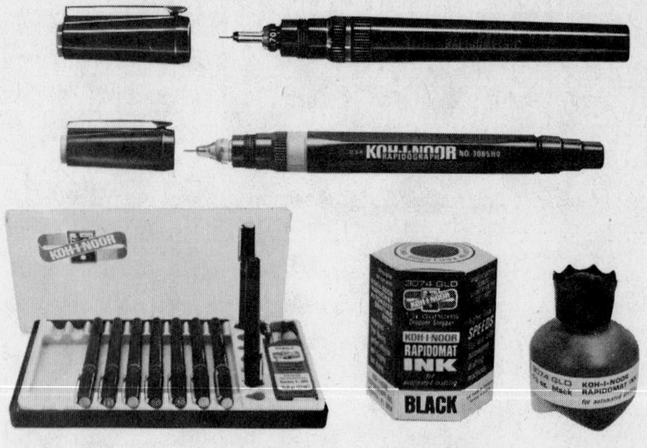

Figure 1-15
Various Rapidograph pens and ink *(Koh-I-Noor Rapidograph Co.).*

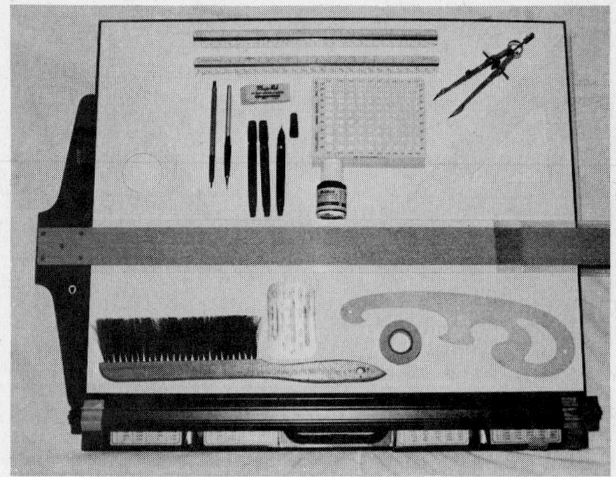

Figure 1-16
Good assortment of tools for civil drafting.

Drafting Ink

Ink must be fast drying, free flowing, and opaque, and must have good adhesion to the vellum or film surface. It must dry with sufficient hardness to resist abrasion, yet remain flexible enough to resist flaking and chipping. Also, it must easily erase at any later date without causing damage to the drawing. Experimentation is perhaps the best method to determine the choice of inks, since not all inks are compatible with all drafting material surfaces.

Scriber Systems

Scriber systems and mechanical lettering devices are available in many varieties (see Figs. 1–17 to 1–19). One has the technical pen attached directly to the scriber, using the main thread of the pen itself, rather than the point sleeve, thus providing more support and stability in action. A plastic bar with letters and figures in the desired size allows mechanical reproduction of the desired lettering. LeRoy, Unitech, Doric, and Rapidometric are a few of the mechanical lettering devices widely used in industry.

DRAFTING PROCEDURES USING INK

To draft with ink the student should have three technical pens available; sizes No. 1, 2, and 3 will be sufficient. Other required materials are ink, drafting film or vellum, and erasing materials.

Set Up

If using drafting film, the first thing a drafter should do to set up is to ensure that the film surface is clean. If it is not clean, then a dry industrial wipe should be used to clean the film of any minor surface soil. More serious soils might require the use of a liquid film cleaner. If vellum is used, this step is not required.

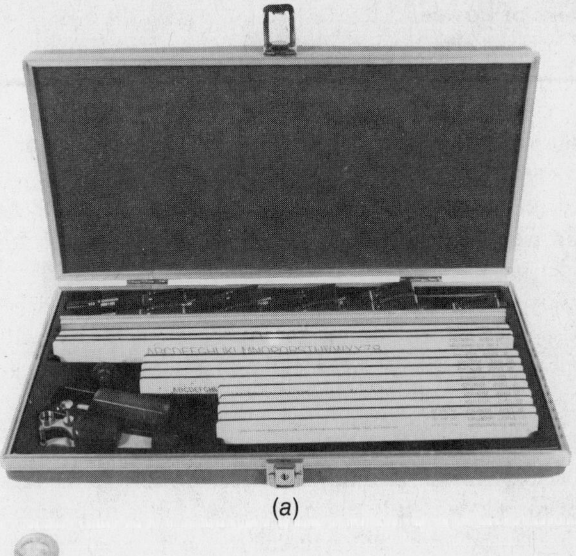

(a)

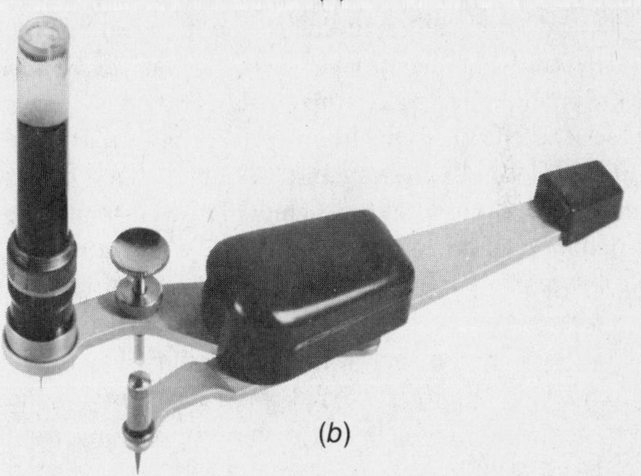

(b)

Figure 1-17
Rapidometric cut through "Z" lettering guide set *(Koh-I-Noor Rapidograph Co.).*

Figure 1-18
(*a*) Lettering set (*b*) Scriber *(Koh-I-Noor Rapidograph Co.).*

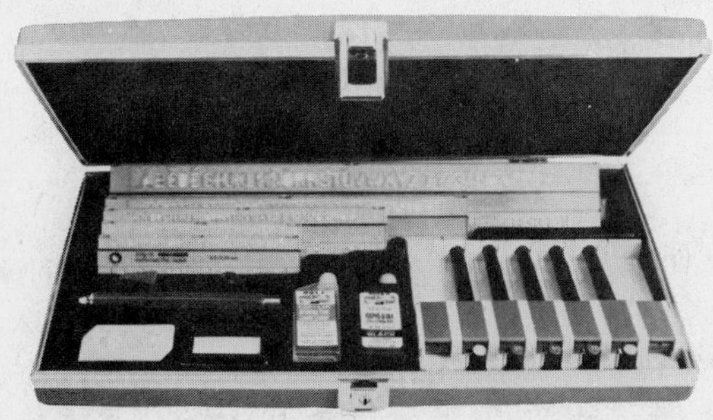

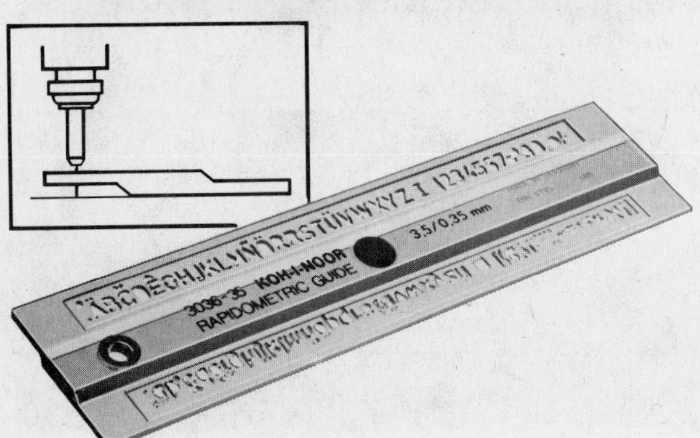

Figure 1-19
Mechanical lettering set *(Teledyne Post Co.).*

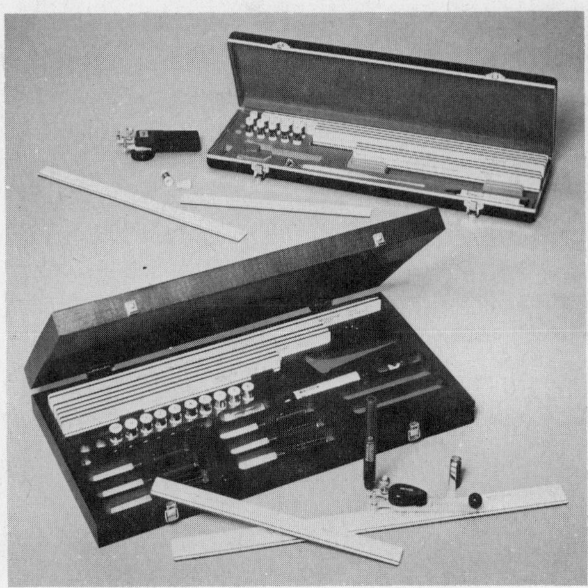

Use of Powder

Under no circumstances should the film surface be cleaned with pounce or powder of any kind. This advice is based on the most current information. A few years ago nothing was inked without the pounce can, a dustbrush, and a rag for wiping off the excess. If powder particles are trapped in the tooth of the film coating, the ink will lie on the surface of these particles without adhering to the film surface coating. As the particles dislodge and fall away, the ink line will flake away as well. These particles also tend to enter the writing tube opening of the technical pens, causing them to clog.

Erasing Ink Details

Ink on film can be easily removed to make corrections or to redraw details and dimensions. Ink is retained on the film by chemically bonding to the film coating, not by penetration of the surface, as in the case of ink on vellum or on other porous materials. The liquid eraser releases the chemical on the ink line, while the friction of the solid vinyl eraser against the film surface results in the formation of fine eraser chips; these chips pick up the ink and can be easily brushed off the film surface.

In the past, drafters working on standard drafting film were accustomed to using water and a facial tissue to remove any ink lines that needed correction. The use of liquid eraser with a plastic solid eraser is less messy and leaves no residue, which might show up on any print reproduced from the drawing. The newest development in erasers, which provides an alternate to the two-step erasing techniques just described, is the Pelikan 9600 PT 20 eraser. It is imbued with an erasing fluid that is released from pores within the eraser by the friction produced when the eraser is rubbed against the drafting film surface. The Pelikan eraser is readily usable with an erasing shield if desired.

An electric eraser is shown in Fig. 1–20.

Setting Up the Drawing Equipment. Drawing equipment should be arranged in an orderly fashion on a flat surface adjacent to the drawing board or drawing desk. If the building has windows, they should be facing north or south in order to avoid the glare of direct sunlight; drawing tables (if there are windows) should be placed so that sunlight enters from the left. The drafting table height should be from 36 to 40 in [91 to 102 cm] above floor level; the drawing surface should be adjusted to a slope of 1 to 8 approximately is appropriately a 7° angle.

Fastening the Drawing Sheet. The left edge of the drawing sheet should be placed approximately 1 in [2.5 cm] from the left edge of the drawing board. If a drawing table serves as the drawing board, the drawing should be centered on the table top so that the drafter can sit comfortably.

Since most of the maps are to be traced, the vellum you are going to trace upon may be taped to the drawing which will be traced. Slant the sheet in any manner that is comfortable to you. The comfort of the drafter is often overlooked, but the drafters who make themselves comfortable will be the ones who do the most and the best work.

Tape the sheet to the drawing board or drafting table with four short pieces of drafting tape. When drawing (not tracing), be sure the paper lines up square with the T-square or parallel rule.

Lettering

The next chapter will be on lettering. The value of good lettering cannot be stressed enough. Drawings which have perfect linework will be spoiled if the lettering is poor. When a drafter goes on a job interview with a portfolio of drawings to show the hiring agent, the agent will look at the lettering. Sometimes the hiring agent can barely read plans—then the lettering really stands out as this may be the only thing this person really recognizes.

Before going on to Chapter 2, look at Figs. 1–21 and 1–22 for examples of other civil engineering jobs and projects.

Figure 1-20
Bruning electric eraser *(Bruning Co.)*.

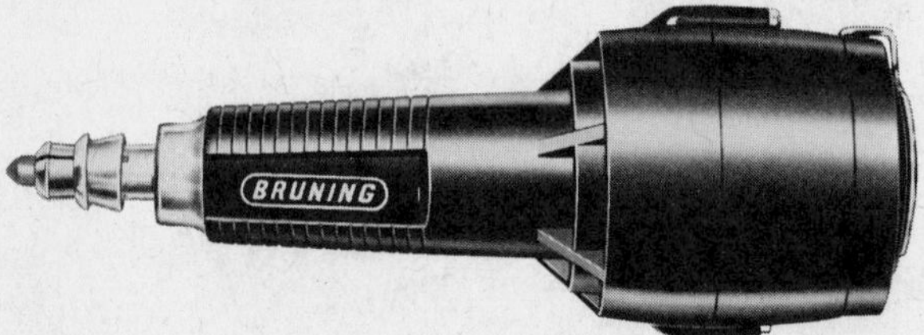

Figure 1-21
Technician working with a computer *(Midsouth Engineering Co.)*.

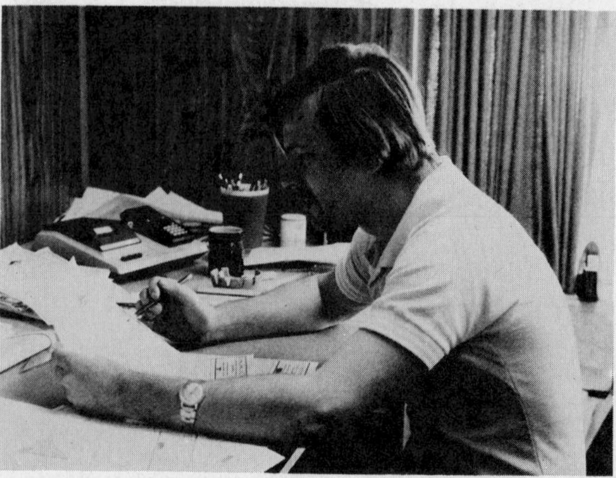

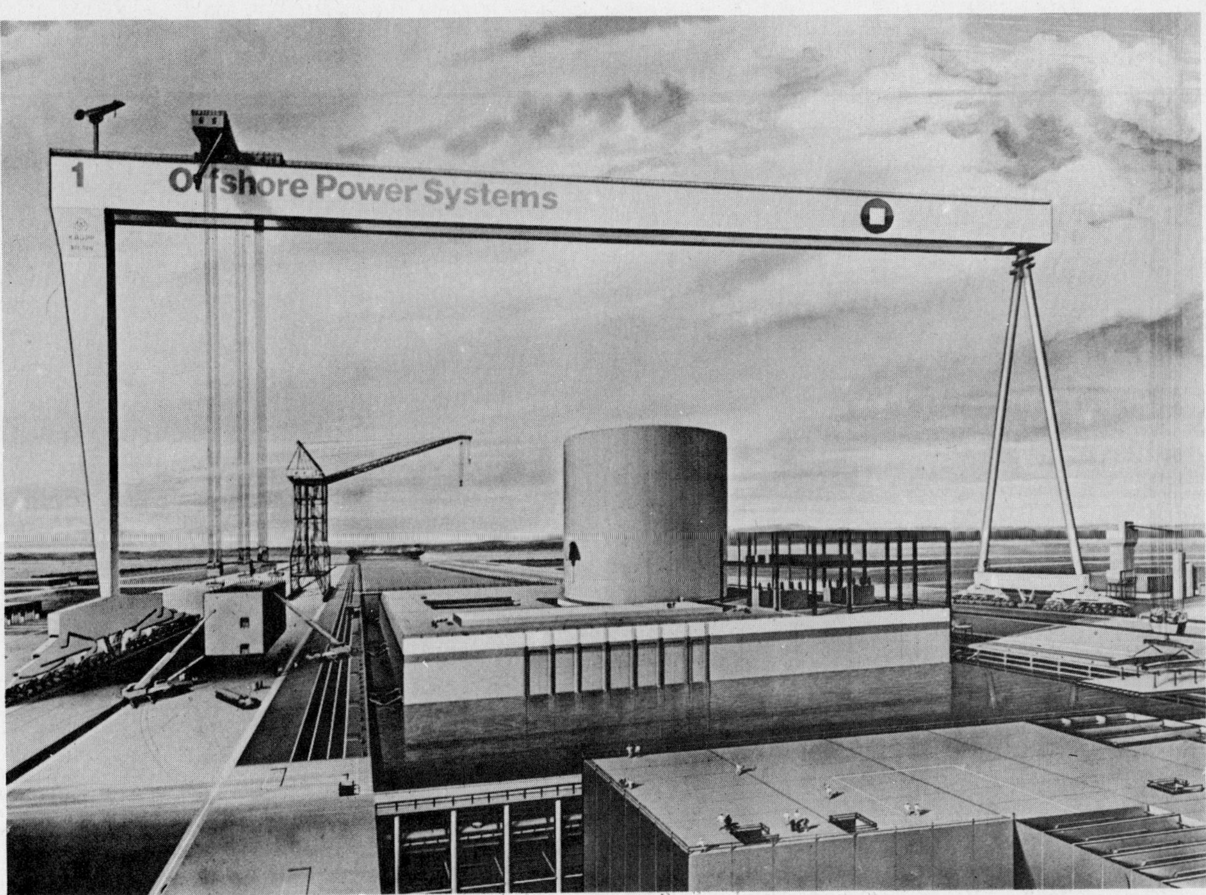

Figure 1-22
Another civil engineering job *(PRC Harris, Inc.).*

LEARNING ACTIVITY PACKAGE

Read Chap. 1 carefully.

Chapter 1 completely read ____________ (*date*).

If the student has not understood some of the objectives (a) through (h), listed on page 1, after completely reading the chapter, the particular portions of the chapter which contain those objectives should be reread. An understanding of the objectives listed above will give a good command of the basic drafting tools that will be used throughout the course.

Objectives read and studied ____________ (*date*).

Now take the removable quiz on Chap. 1. Remove it from the end of the chapter and answer all the questions. (It will be the instructor's decision whether the text may be used during the quiz. The author recommends using the text to find the answers. A drafting technician in industry never depends on memory for any important answer. Everything must be exact, and therefore any question is researched in the proper textbooks. The students now can begin to do things as they are done in industry.)

Quiz completed ____________ (*date*).

1

QUIZ

1. It is a requirement to take mechanical drafting before starting civil drafting. (T or F) False
2. It is most important to read the text while drawing the problems. (T or F) True
3. Which type instructions will the student be closely following, general or specific? General
4. Are drawing boards generally made from oak, maple, white pine, elm, or basswood? There are two correct answers. white pine basswood
5. The top surface of a civil drafting student's table should be a minimum of 4 ft [1.2 m] long. (T or F) true
6. What does a self-sealing board cover do after a compass point has been pulled out? will heal as soon
7. Students should use thumbtacks to fasten their drawings to the drawing surface. (T or F) false
8. T-squares are seldom used in civil drafting, but for students they can be very handy. (T or F) True
9. Students and civil drafters generally can get by nicely without a regular set of drafting instruments. (T or F) ~~F~~ True
10. The T-square can take the place of a stainless steel blade for students. (T or F) True
11. How can a poor joint between the head and blade of a T-square be repaired? ________
12. The steel blade is most commonly used to connect points to form straight lines. (T or F) True
13. The two standard triangles are 45 ° and 60 °.
14. The protractor is used to measure and set off angles.
15. Irregular curves are sometimes known as French curves; their edges represent successive portions of ellipses, parabolas, spirals, and other geometric curves.
16. What is the purpose of an erasing shield? allowing unwanted lines to be removed while other work is left untouched
17. Are lead holders or normal lead pencils more commonly used for civil drafting? lead holders

18. What hardness of lead is in the middle of the hardness scale? ____________

19. What is a major disadvantage of using a very soft lead?
____

20. Why is it important to have two lead holders?
____

21. Why do carbide blades last longer in lead pointers than hard steel blades?
____

22. The student should pull the tape off the drawing first when removing a drawing from the drawing board. (T or F) ____________

23. Will working with dry cleaner on the drawing make the drawing lighter as well as cleaning the drawing surface? ____________

24. What size is a C-size drawing? ____________

25. Mylar is not used extensively in the civil drafting field. (T or F) ____________

26. Mylar is easily erased with a proper erasing fluid and an eraser. (T or F) ____________

27. Scales have dimensions in accurate proportions to the actual dimensions we wish to represent. (T or F) ____________

28. Plastic erasers are more gentle than rubber ones. (T or F) ____________

29. What determines line thickness when using a quill pen? ____________

30. Technical pens produce lines of uniform width. (T or F) ____________

31. The civil drafter or drafting student should ideally have ____________ ____________

32. What is vellum's main big advantage over mylar? ____________

33. Drafting ink needs four qualities: what are they? ____________ ____________ ____________ ____________

34. Scriber systems usually have a scriber and a plastic ____________ with letters and figures on it.

35. When using mylar, it is important to start with a clean surface. (T or F) ____________

36. Should powder be used on mylar before inking? ____________

37. Is ink difficult to remove from mylar? ____________

38. Old-timers often spit on erasers to remove ink from mylar. (T or F) ____________

39. Drawing tables are best faced north or south in a room with windows. (T or F) ____________

2 LETTERING

Objectives

a. Gain proficiency in the use of vertical single stroke Gothic uppercase lettering
b. Learn the proportions and stability of the letters of the alphabet
c. Learn the usefulness of guidelines to maintain letter size and alignment
d. Learn pencil technique in lettering
e. Learn the basic strokes of letters
f. Become acquainted with the lowercase alphabet
g. Learn the figures
h. Learn how to manipulate the scriber and template of mechanical lettering devices

Rationale

Lettering is very important; the student must learn to letter well. Drawings with good linework can be spoiled by poor lettering. In this chapter the student will study the style, proportions, and stability of various letters.

The student will learn the importance of always using guidelines in lettering. A highway like the one in Fig. 2–1 requires carefully lettered plans. The notes on a civil drafting drawing are numerous, and if the lettering is sloppy, the drawing may be misread in the field. (This may bring malpractice law suits against the engineering firm that produced the drawings and pink layoff slips to the technician who drew the drawing with the illegible notes.)

The graphic presentation of civil drafting maps and drawings is supplemented by figured dimensions and notes that also furnish necessary information.[1] Notes and dimensions on drawings must be legible and suitable for easy and rapid execution.

Figure 2-1
A busy highway with over and underpasses near Miami, Fla. Careful lettering is important for all types of highway design *(Florida Department of Transportation).*

STYLE

Lettering style will be single-stroke uppercase commercial Gothic. Vertical lettering (Fig. 2–2) may be used, but only one type should appear in a single drawing. Lowercase letters were used on plan and profile drawings, except for titles, but the modern civil engineering drafting style calls for all uppercase lettering. The expression *single-stroke* means that the width of the lines composing the letters is the width of one stroke of the lettering pencil. It does not mean that each letter is executed with a single, continuous movement of the pencil. Uppercase refers to capital letters, lowercase to small letters.

PROPORTIONS

The ratio of letter width to letter height varies with individual letters. This chapter presents standard pro-

[1]Most of the material for this chapter comes courtesy of the U.S. Army and Air Force. They allowed the use of TM 5-230 and TO 00-25-103.

ABCDEFGHIJKLMNOPQRSTUVWXYZ CAPITALS (UPPER CASE)

abcdefghijklmnopqrstuvwxyz LOWER CASE

1234567890 NUMERALS

Figure 2-2
Vertical letters and figures of the alphabet.

portions that take into consideration the characteristics of the individual letters. Letters using these proportions are called normal letters. When letter width is decreased in relation to letter height to conserve space, the letters are said to be compressed letters. When letter width is increased in relation to letter height, the letters are known as extended letters.

STABILITY

If the areas of the upper and lower portions of certain letters and numerals are made equal, an optical illusion is created which causes them to seem top-heavy. To correct this in order to give the impression of stability, the letters B, E, F, H, K, S, X, and Z and the numbers 2, 3, 5, and 8 must be drawn smaller at the top than at the bottom. The central horizontal strokes of the letters B, E, F, and H are drawn slightly above the center. The upper portions of the letters K, S, X, and Z and the numerals 2, 3, 5, and 8 are made slightly narrower than the lower portions.

UNIFORMITY

Lettering in a drawing should present a uniform appearance. Height, alignment, line weight, and spacing are the principal considerations. Uniform height and alignment are achieved through the use of guidelines. Uniformity in line weight depends on skillful use of the pencil. Uniform spacing of letters in words and of words in sentences is done by eye; good judgment results from practice.

GUIDELINES

Guidelines are always used in executing freehand lettering. They can be horizontal or vertical. Horizontal guidelines determine horizontal alignment, letter height, and spacing between lines of lettering. Two horizontal guidelines are used for uppercase letters. The upper line is called the *cap line,* and the lower line is called the *baseline.* The distance between cap lines and baselines establishes the height of uppercase letters.

Guidelines for lowercase letters, once used in the industry, were constructed in proportion to uppercase sizes. Four horizontal guidelines are used. The cap line and baseline are the same as those for uppercase letters. The two additional lines are called the waistline and the drop-line.

Vertical guidelines keep the verticality of freehand characters uniform. Guidelines are drawn with either standard or lettering triangles and are spaced at random.

SIZE AND SPACING

The size of lettering and the line spacing which should be used on a drawing are controlled by the size of the drawing. The drafter must also consider the percentage of reduction the drawing will require for printing for the field, because this limits the minimum lettering size which can be used. For civil drawings, generally reduced to one-half of the original size for use in the field, lettering should not be less than ⅛ inch (in) [3.2 mm].

LETTERING TRIANGLE

Lettering triangles are made in many sizes and styles. The 45° triangle shown in Fig. 2–3 is a typical example of a triangle used in drafting. It has six columns of countersunk holes numbered 3, 4, 5, 6, 7, and 8 for drawing horizontal guidelines. The triangle is always used with its hypotenuse sliding against the working edge of the T-square (or another straightedge, if the lettering lines are not horizontal). The round hole cut through the center of the triangle has beveled edges to aid in picking up the triangle with the fingernails.

Figure 2-3
The lettering triangle.

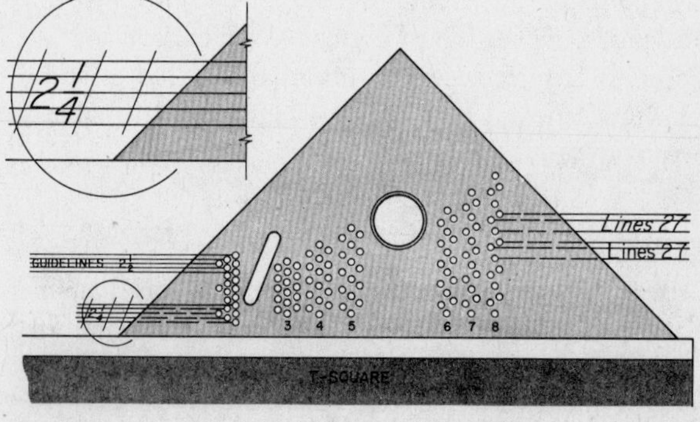

Horizontal Guidelines

The six columns of numbered countersunk holes in the lettering triangle are designed for inserting the cone point of a 6H lead when drawing horizontal guidelines. The horizontal guidelines are drawn by sliding the triangle (with the lead inserted) along the working edge of the T-square. Note that 6H lead is recommended, since the guidelines should be very faint and are used only to guide the lettering. Guidelines will not need to be erased if they are made with very hard lead. Lead from 3H to 6H can be used with good results. The numbers on the lettering triangle indicate, in thirty-seconds of an inch, the distance between cap line and baseline, which will be the size of the capital letters. For example, 8 means 8/32 or 1/4 in [6.4 mm], 6 means 6/32 or 3/16 in [4.8 mm], 5 means 5/32 in [4.0 mm]. Note that the holes are grouped in clusters of three for drawing a cap line, a waistline, and a baseline. No holes are drilled for drawing droplines. The letters requiring a dropline are drawn to size by eye.

The standard spacing between lines of normal lettering is two-thirds the height of the capital letters. Line spacing is one-half capital height for compressed lettering and 1½ times capital height for extended lettering. The holes in the lettering triangle are drilled for normal lettering to give standard spacing between lines, if two or more clusters are used in sequence, without relocating the T-square. The arrows in Fig. 2–3 indicate the method of drawing guidelines for 8/32 or 1/4 in [6.4 mm] lettering. In special cases where the size of lettering varies from line to line, such as in title blocks, the single hole at the top of a column is placed over the baseline of the preceding lettering in order to determine the spacing between lines.

Inclined Guidelines

The standard slope for inclined lettering is an angle of 22½° to the right of vertical or an angle of 67½° with the horizontal (see Fig. 2-4). The elongated slot in the lettering triangle is cut at an angle of 67½° to the hypotenuse for use as a guide in drawing inclined guidelines for slant lettering. The sides of the slot are parallel so that either side may be used for drawing slant guidelines. The triangle rests with its hypotenuse free to slide along the working edge of the T-square to the desired location for the guidelines. As many inclined guidelines may be drawn as experience dictates, but a beginner should draw at least one for each letter, but the more guidelines drawn, the better a beginner's judgment will become.

There are several other methods of obtaining the correct angle for inclined lettering if no lettering triangle is available. One method is to bisect the angle between a vertical line and a 45° line. Another method is to construct a small right triangle with a base of 1 in [25.4 mm] and altitude of 2 7/16 in [61.9 mm]. The hypotenuse of this triangle will make an angle of 67.7° with the horizontal, which is close enough for guidelines. In each case, having established a line at 67½°, all slant guidelines are drawn parallel to it by using two triangles sliding against each other.

Figure 2-4
Angle at which inclined letters and figures are slanted.

Lettering Instrument

The Ames lettering instrument (Fig. 2–5) works on the same principle as the lettering triangle. The main differ-

Figure 2-5
Ames lettering instrument.

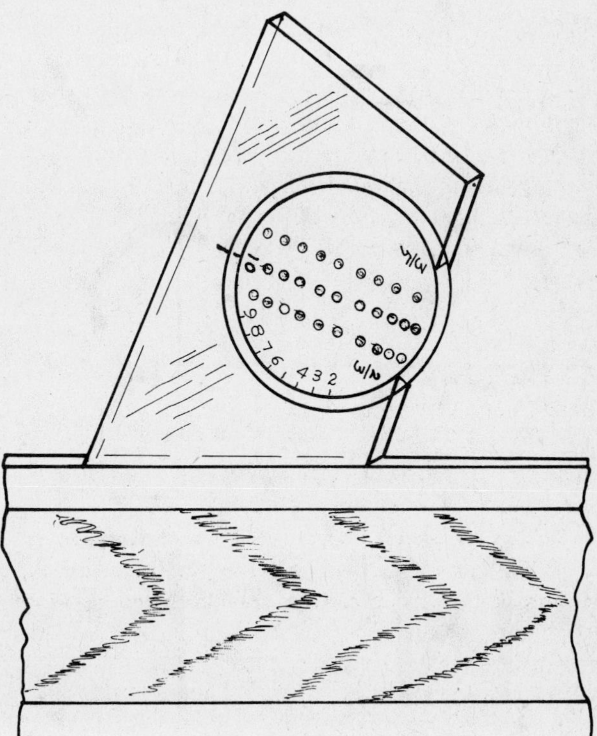

ence is that it has angles of 68 and 75°. The numbers 2 through 10 are numerators of a fraction with a denominator of 32. If the circular disk is turned so that numerator 9 is matched with the line on the frame, the total height of the resultant capital letter would be 9⁄32 in [7.1 mm].

PENCIL TECHNIQUE

All letters and figures are drawn with the basic strokes illustrated in Fig. 2–6. To execute satisfactory letters, a drafter must learn and practice the direction and sequence of strokes used to form each letter.

Position

Rest the forearm on the drawing board below the edge of the paper. Hold the pencil between the thumb, forefinger, and second finger so that each rests against a flat side. The third and fourth fingers and the ball of the palm rest on the drawing sheet.

Basic Strokes

Vertical strokes are drawn from the top down with an even finger movement. Inclined strokes are drawn in the same way and are slanted in the desired direction.

Horizontal strokes are drawn from left to right with a movement of the entire hand, pivoting at the wrist.

Figure 2-6
Basic lettering strokes.

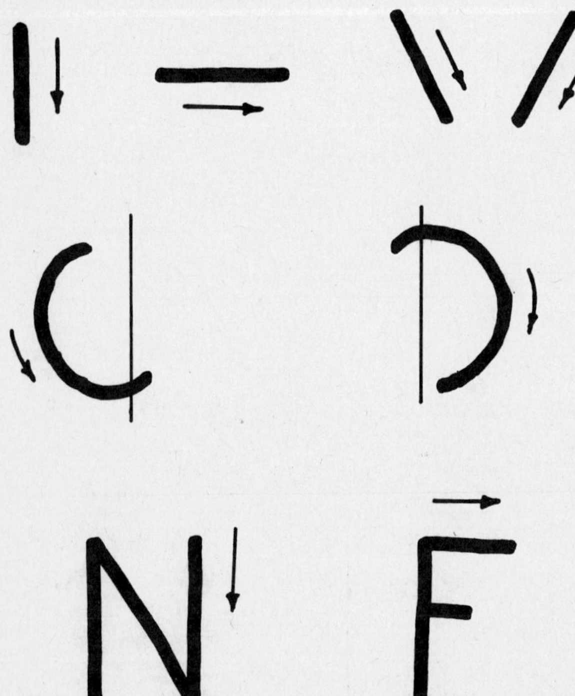

Curved strokes proceed downward, moving in the desired direction, and are produced with a combined finger and wrist motion. Lettering strokes are drawn, not sketched. The uniform, single-stroke appearance required of lettering can be achieved only by practicing the fundamental strokes in the manner described.

VERTICAL LETTERS AND NUMERALS

Figure 2–2 illustrates the required shape of vertical letters and numerals. Figures 2–7 to 2–9 illustrate the construction of characters against a square background, with each side divided into six equal units (except for the letters I and W). The background serves as a reference framework for comparing the height of the various characters to their width, as well as for locating the individual lines that compose the characters. A smaller drawing below each character in Figs. 2–7 and 2–8 shows the direction and sequence of the strokes used in the formation of the character.

Straight Line Capitals

I, A, L, T. The letter I is the basic vertical stroke. Stroke 3 of the A is located one-third of the distance up from the baseline. Inclined strokes 1 and 2 intersect just above the cap line. The horizontal stroke of the T is drawn first; the vertical stroke, or stem, is drawn from the center. With both L and T, the horizontal stroke may be lengthened or shortened to balance the letters in a word. If, for example, L precedes A, its horizontal stroke is reduced slightly; if T precedes A, its horizontal stroke is extended slightly.

H, F, E. In H, F, and E, the central horizontal bar is placed slightly above the center for stability. In both E and F, the cap line stroke is four units long and the central stroke is three-fifths of this length. The baseline of E is one-half unit longer than its cap line.

V, W, M, N. The two inclined strokes of the V intersect just below the baseline. The W is 1⅓ times the width of a normal letter; note that it is wider than the M. Strokes 1 and 2 and strokes 3 and 4 of the W intersect below the baseline. Strokes 3 and 4 of the M and 2 and 3 of the N intersect on the baseline. Note that the outside strokes of the M and N are drawn first.

Z, X, Y, K. Stroke 2 of the Z is longer than stroke 1. The inclined strokes of the *X* are closer together at their starting than at their finishing points. The three strokes of the Y intersect slightly below the center of the square. Stroke 2 of the K intersects stroke 1 at a point one-third of the distance above the baseline. Stroke 3, if extended, would intersect stroke 1 at the top.

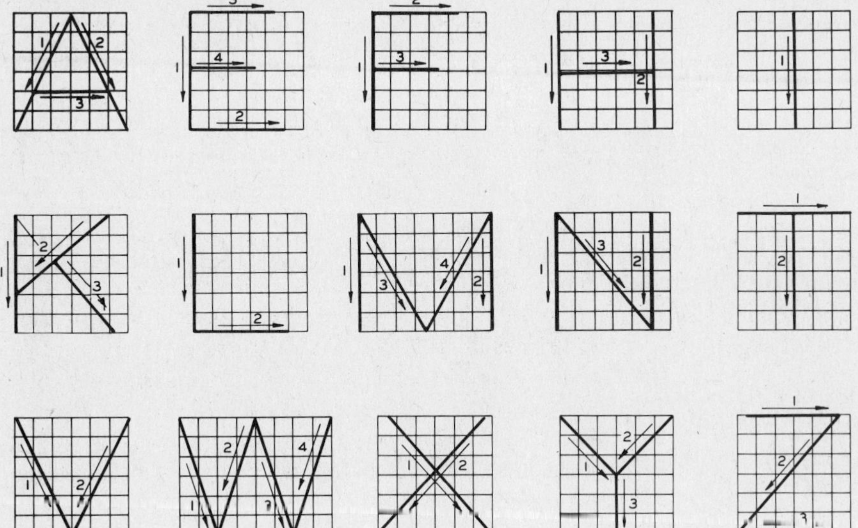

Figure 2-7
Strokes on vertical straight-line capitals.

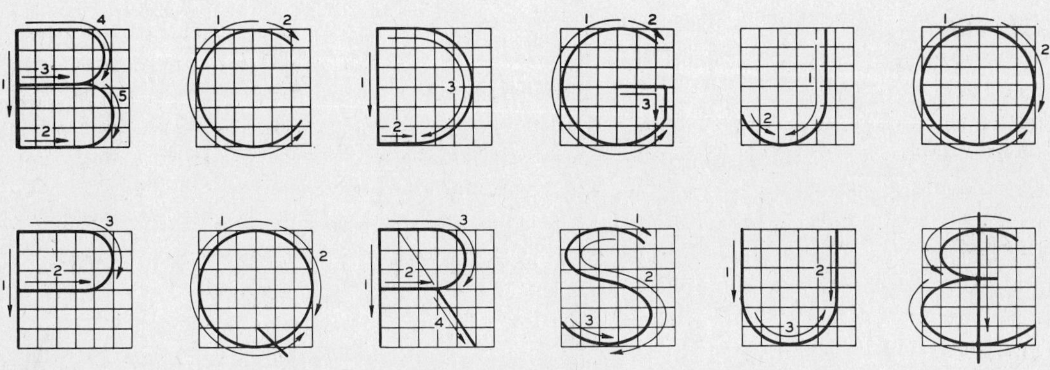

Figure 2-8
Vertical capitals, curved and straight-line combinations.

Figure 2-9
Figures.

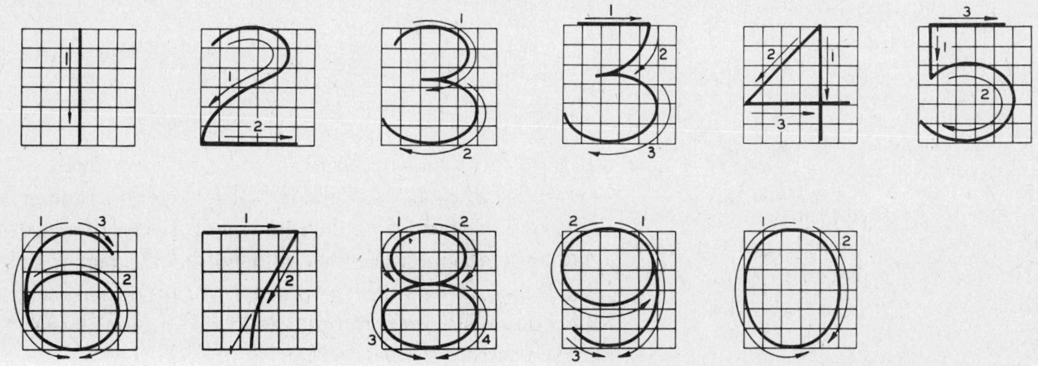

Curved and Straight-line Combinations

O, Q, C, G. The O and Q are complete circles. C and G are not the full width of the square because they are not full circles. The tail of Q, if extended, would intersect the center of the circle. Stroke 4 of G begins at the center of the circle.

U, J, D. Stroke 3 of U is elliptical and connects two parallel vertical lines one-third of the distance above the baseline. Stroke 2 of J is similar, but not so broad. Stroke 4 of D is circular, joining two horizontal segments.

P, R, B. The horizontal midstrokes of P and R lie just below the midpoint, and the horizontal midstroke of B lies just above the midpoint. The horizontal stroke 4 in B is slightly longer than strokes 2 and 3, which are the same length.

S and &. The upper and lower portions of S are ellipses, the upper being slightly smaller than the lower. The ampersand is basically similar despite a greater difference in the sizes of the ellipses.

LOWERCASE LETTERS

Guidelines

In order to give a complete overview of the lettering guidelines, lowercase guidelines are included, though the industry rarely uses lowercase lettering.[2]

The waistline is two-thirds the distance from the baseline to the cap line (Fig. 2–10). The waistline establishes the body height of lowercase letters. Extensions of lowercase letters above the waistline are called ascenders. The dropline is drawn below the baseline at a distance equal to the distance between the waistline and cap line. Extensions of lowercase letters below the baselines are called descenders. The dropline is used to establish the length of descenders and can be eliminated once a drafter is able to visually judge this distance. All ascenders, except that of t, extend to the cap line. All descenders extend to the dropline. As with capital letters, vertical guidelines are drawn at random.

Characteristics

The crosses of f and t are on the waistline and extend the same distance on either side of stroke 1. The horizontal stroke of e is just above midheight. The, bodies of a, b, g, p, and q, are circular, and the vertical strokes of these letters do not increase their width at the points of tangency. The vertical strokes of p and q terminate at the dropline. The vertical strokes of g, j, and y terminate in curves that are tangent to the dropline.

[2]Practicing and following through in the learning of how to render lowercase letters will help perfect your style.

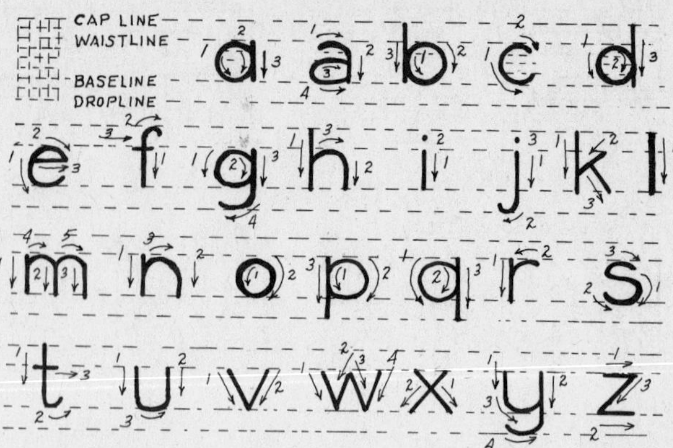

Figure 2-10
Lowercase letters showing cap line, waistline, baseline, and dropline.

NUMERALS AND FRACTIONS

The need for carefully drawing numerals (Fig. 2–9) cannot be overstressed, particularly in the preparation of civil drawings. A poorly drawn numeral can disorganize an entire road operation, causing very costly delays.

Guidelines

Numerals are drawn using the same guidelines as capital letters. Vertical guidelines are spaced at random. Numerals should not be rendered so small or so crowded that legibility is impaired.

Characteristics

The vertical stroke of 4 is placed two units from the right side. The horizontal bar is one-quarter of the height of the number above the baseline. Note that the closed curves of 0, 6, and 9 are elliptical, not circular. The 6 is an inverted 9. The 8 is composed of two ellipses, tangent slightly above the center point. Notice that the top ellipse also is narrower. The 3 is the same as the 8 with the left portions of the loops cut off. The curved lines of 2 follow the elliptical contours of 8. The top portion of the 5 is slightly narrower than the bottom. The bottom ellipse is two-thirds of the height of the figure from the baseline.

Fractions

The division sign in a common fraction is parallel to the direction in which the dimension reads. The complete height of a fraction is twice that of a whole number. The division bar is centered midway between the baseline and cap line. The top guideline of the numerator and the bottom guideline of the denominator are spaced a full number height from the division bar. The numbers composing a fraction are three-quarters of the height of a full number. The clear space on either side of the division bar is one-quarter of a full number. Numbers in a fraction are centered about a vertical guideline that cuts the fraction bar in half.

INCLINED LETTERS

Figure 2–11 illustrates the required formation of inclined letters. The angle of inclination is 67½° with the horizontal. Inclined guidelines may be drawn with the lettering triangle as described, or by measuring the angle with the protractor and then constructing lines parallel to the measured angle. Horizontal guidelines and sequence of strokes are the same as those for vertical letters. Rules of stability, proportion, and balance are similar. The circles and circle arcs used in vertical letters become elliptic in inclined letters, their major axes making angles of 45° with the horizontal. Letters such as A, M, and Y should be made symmetrically about a guideline. Inclined lowercase letters follow the same principles as inclined capitals; but as with the inclined uppercase letters, lowercase letters are now rarely used in the industry.

WORDS

Proper spacing of uppercase letters in words requires that the areas occupied by the letters appear equal, rather than the actual clearance between the letters be equal. In the word MELT, for example, the actual spacing between the L and T can be so close that a vertical dropped from the left end of the horizontal stroke of the T will touch the right end of the horizontal stroke of the L. The areas enclosed in the letters by their vertical strokes give the appearance of adequate clearance. The actual clearance between M and E must be such that the areas enclosed by their adjacent vertical strokes are roughly equivalent to those between the vertical strokes of the L and the imaginary vertical connecting the horizontal strokes of L and T. Actual clearance between E and L can be slightly less than that between M and E. The spacing between words should be equivalent to the basic width of the letters M and O.

SPACING BETWEEN SENTENCES

Spacing between sentences should be uniform for the entire drawing, but this is a matter of personal choice. The space necessary to insert a capital M between the period at the end of a sentence and the first letter of the next sentence is satisfactory.

MECHANICAL LETTERING

Mechanical lettering is executed with a special pen which is held in a scriber and guided by a template. Guidelines are not required. With such tools, uniform legible char-

Figure 2-11
Inclined letters showing the angle of inclination.

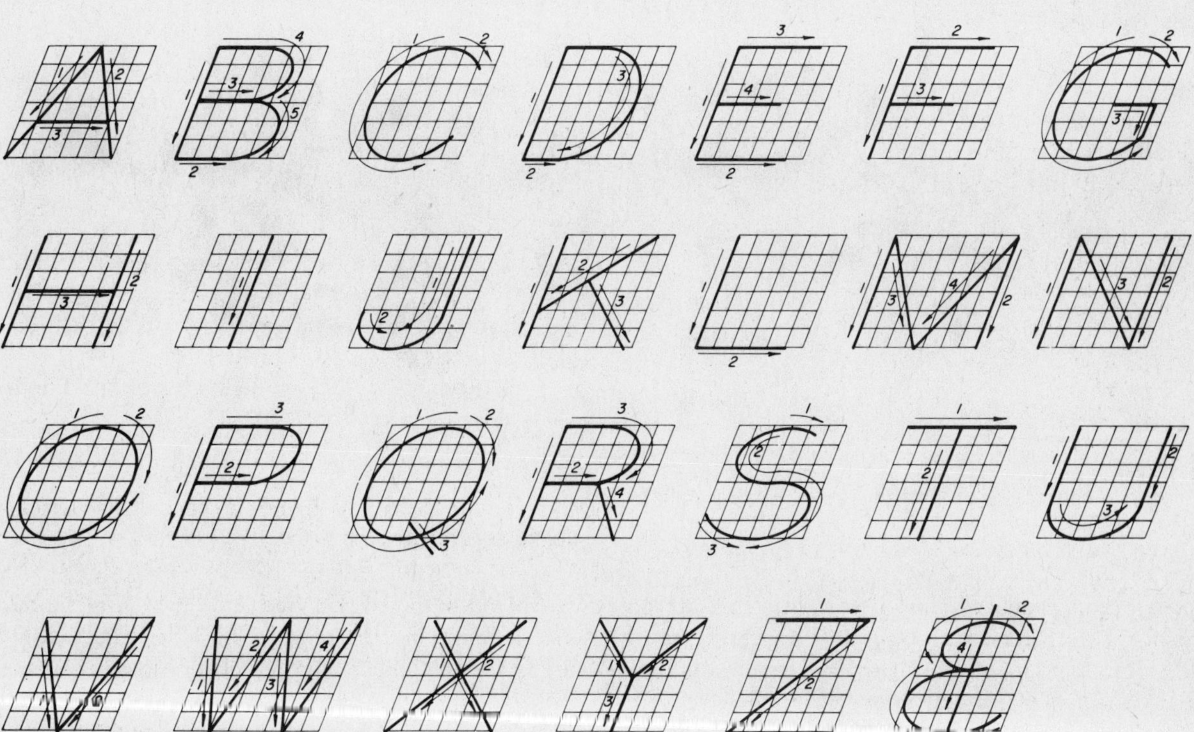

Figure 2-12
Chalkboard drafting machine commonly used to make guidelines for lettering on the board *(Keuffel and Esser Co.).*

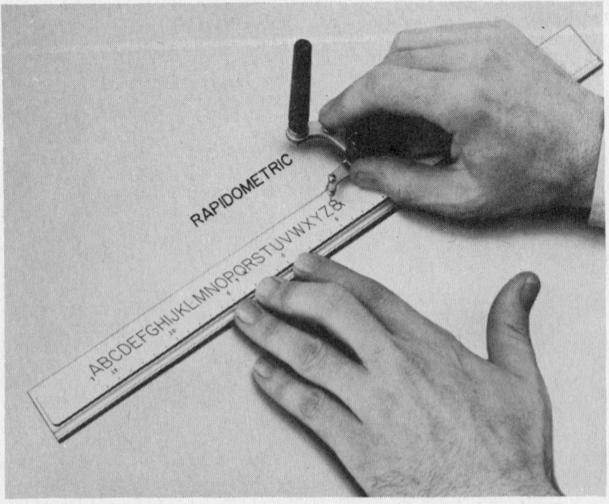

Figure 2-13
Using a mechanical lettering device *(Koh-I-Noor Rapidograph Corp.).*

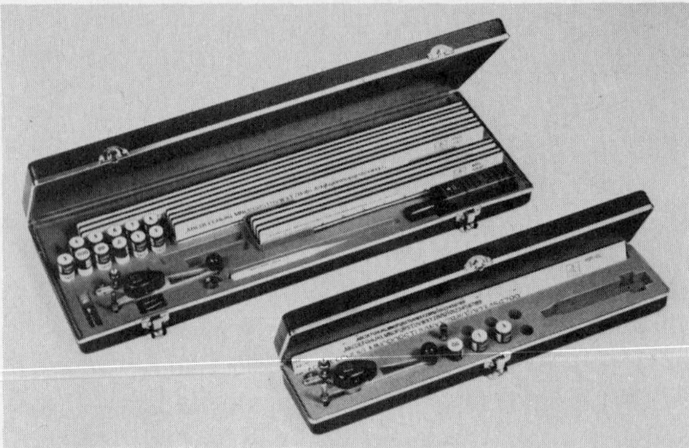

Figure 2-14
Leroy mechanical lettering sets *(Faber-Castell Corp.).*

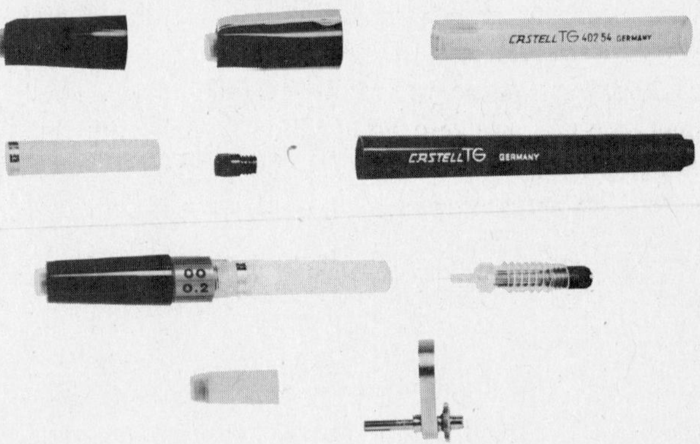

Figure 2-15
Inking pens used in some mechanical lettering sets *(Faber-Castell Corp.).*

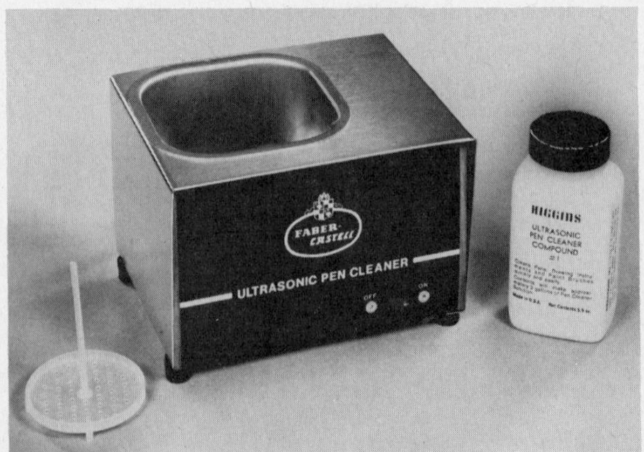

Figure 2-16
Ultrasonic pen cleaner used to clean pens of mechanical lettering sets *(Faber-Castell Corp.).*

acters can be produced more rapidly than by freehand methods. Mechanical lettering is used principally for title blocks, data for maps, charts, and graphs, and for road job titles. Figures 2–12 through 2–16 show a variety of mechanical lettering equipment.

It should be noted that freehand lettering is the required lettering in drafting; mechanical lettering is confined to the special uses just described. However, some consulting engineering firms require that all lettering be done with a mechanical lettering device in order to make

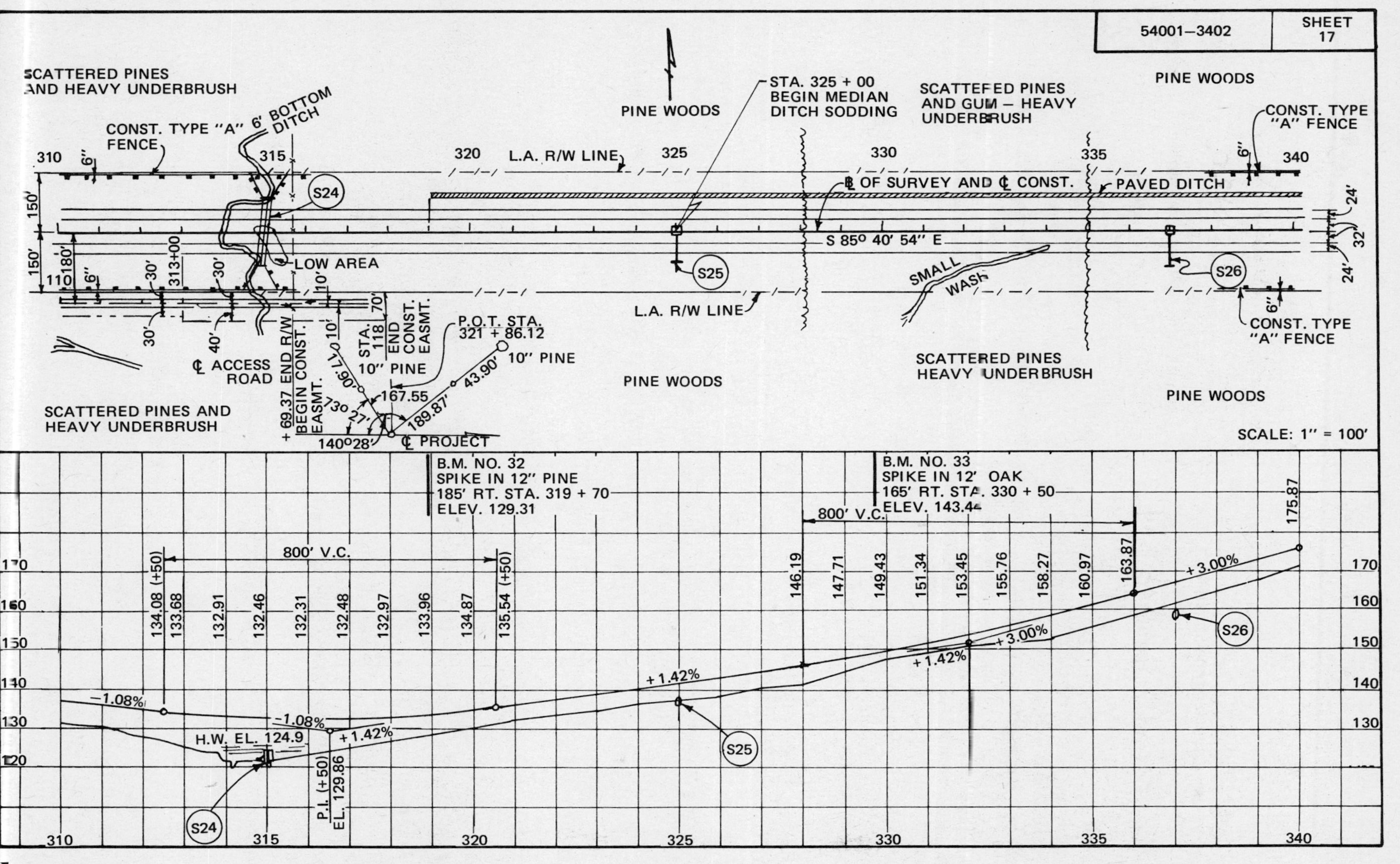

Figure 2-17
Plan and profile drawing to illustrate the importance of good lettering. There is at least this much lettering on most plan and profile sheets.

all drawings appear similar. In this case the company provides a mechanical lettering set for every drafter. The availability of mechanical lettering devices should not deter drafters from the daily practice required to execute freehand lettering. In fact, drafters going on job interviews with their portfolios of drawings will often find the hiring personnel scrutinizing the lettering carefully.

IMPORTANCE OF GOOD LETTERING

Lettering is so important that mastery of this phase of drafting cannot be stressed enough. Figure 2–17 shows how much lettering is required on a typical plan and profile sheet. Some drafting courses require that 10 minutes be spent each day in lettering practice.

A good linework drawing will be ruined automatically if the lettering is poor. In addition, much of the information contained in a civil drawing appears in the notes that accompany the drawing. If poor lettering causes a building contractor to misread the intent of the drawing, a great deal of time and money can be lost.

In the past few years malpractice suits have occurred against engineering firms, just as they occur against doctors, so every figure, letter, note, and word on a drawing should be very legible. If poor lettering is proven to be the cause of a mistake in construction on a civil engineering project, the job and future of the drafter could be insecure.

In the back of the chapter are seven tear-out lettering exercises of increasing difficulty. All of the exercises should be done by the student; specific instructions are in the learning activity package.

LEARNING ACTIVITY PACKAGE

Read Chap. 2 carefully, then check objectives a through h. If any of these objectives are not well understood, reread that part of the chapter where the objectives are explained.

Objectives read and studied ____________ (*date*).

Now take the removable Chap. 2 Quiz, remove it from the back of the chapter, and answer all the questions.

Test completed ____________ (*date*).

The exercises are to be completed in this order:

Read the chapter through the explanation of the straight line capitals *I, A, L, T, H, F, E, V, W, M, N, Z,* and *K*. Then complete the first four exercises. Take plenty of time with each individual letter. This is the way to gain perfection in lettering.

Remove each exercise before starting it. Do the exercise, using a soft lead pencil, on the exercise sheet itself, or if the instructor desires, do it on a B-size sheet of vellum.

Exercise 1 completed ____________ (*date*).

Exercise 2 completed ____________ (*date*).

Exercise 3 completed ____________ (*date*).

Exercise 4 completed ____________ (*date*).

After finishing curved and straight line combinations *O, Q, C, G, U, J, D, P, R, B, S,* and &, and after studying lowercase letters, numerals, fractions, do Exercise 5.

Exercise 5 completed ____________ (*date*).

After reading the paragraph on mechanical lettering do Exercise 6. If no mechanical lettering devices are available, do it freehand.

Exercise 6 completed ____________ (*date*).

Because lettering is so important, all students should do all six lettering exercises.

2

QUIZ

1. Notes and dimensions must be ____legible____ .
2. The lettering style for civil drafting is single-stroke uppercase commercial Gothic. (T or F) ____True____
3. Plan and profile drawings allow lower ____case____ letters.
4. Single-stroke lettering implies that each letter is made by a single stroke of the pencil. (T or F) ____False____
5. Uppercase refers to small letters. (T or F) ____false____
6. Letter width may be decreased in relation to letter height to conserve space. (T or F) ____True____
7. A letter of decreased height is said to be ____compressed____.
8. Some letters are drawn smaller at the top to increase their impression of stability. (T or F) ____True____
9. Uniform height, alignment, and inclination are generally achieved without guidelines. (T or F) ____False____
10. Guidelines may be horizontal or vertical but never inclined. (T or F) ____True____
11. Uppercase letters require just two guidelines. (T or F) ____True____
12. For uppercase letters the top guideline is called the cap line. (T or F) ____True____
13. Lowercase letters require just three guidelines. (T or F) ____false____
14. Vertical and inclined guidelines are spaced at random. (T or F) ____False____
15. Because civil drawings are usually reduced in size lettering should always be ⅛ in [3 mm] or larger. (T or F) ____True____
16. The lettering triangle is used with its ____hypotenuse____ sliding against the working edge of the T-square or other straightedge.
17. A lettering triangle is not meant for making lowercase letters as it does not provide for a dropline. (T or F) ____________
18. The standard slope for inclined lettering is an angle of ____67 1/2____ with the horizontal.
19. The ____Ames____ lettering instrument works on the same principle as the lettering triangle.
20. In the ____Ames____ lettering instrument, a circular disk is turned to give various heights to resulting capital ____________ .
21. In lettering, the forearm rests on the drawing board below the edge of the papor. (T or F) ____True____

22. Horizontal strokes are drawn from right to left. (T or F) False
23. Why is the horizontal stroke of the *T* drawn first?
vertical is drawn from the center
24. In *H, F,* and *E,* the central horizontal bar is placed slightly above the center for Stability.
25. Outside strokes of m and N are drawn first.
26. In the lowercase letters the waistline is three-fifths the distance from the baseline to the cap line. (T or F) false
27. Extensions of lowercase letters above the waistline are called ascenders.
28. All descenders extend to the dropline. (T or F) false
29. Numerals must be carefully. drawn

3 THE MUNICIPAL KEY MAP

Objectives

a. Read and understand how a design squad in a civil engineering office basically works
b. Learn the meaning of the different views
c. Learn what key maps consist of and how to draw them
d. Learn the proper way to study the text while doing the drawings

Rationale

Sets of road design plans begin with the key map, which is always the cover page for a set of plans. The student should know how to draw key maps and their essential elements. The location map is the biggest part of the key map and is always traced. Tracing is very easy, so this is a good way to begin civil engineering drafting.

This chapter also gives basic information on plan, elevation or profile, and cross-section views. Rendering Drawing No. 1, a small town in Green River County, and Drawings No. 2 and No. 3 will give the student a good introduction to the making of a municipal key map. (Note: Drawings appear on pages 49 to 51.)

The previous chapters explained the drafting tools and some of their uses and gave instructions for freehand lettering. Chapter 3 is the beginning of the highway design portion of the text. The student will first learn how to draw key maps; the following chapters will then introduce drainage maps, plan and profile sheets, drainage structures, and roadway cross sections. In addition, the student will do elementary surveying, including the layout of a city lot or a small subdivision and several piling location plans. Mastery of these topics should enable the student to work in an entry level position in the office of a consulting engineer, or a city, county, or state road department.

This chapter also gives a brief description of the various procedures used in designing highways. The student will then learn about the different types of views which are used in roadway plans and will begin drafting by drawing a key map.

The entire class should study the plan-reading information and do the drafting work in this chapter. Then, if the school has surveying equipment, the instructor can divide the class into groups; some groups can begin land development surveys, which are covered in the later chapters. The students who do land development surveys early in the course can draw the results of their surveys later in the course when they return to drafting work. Breaking the class into sections will maximize equipment usage, which is helpful if the school has a limited supply of field equipment.

HIGHWAY DESIGN PROCEDURES

First we will learn how civil drafting is done in industry, where highways and transit systems (like the one in Fig. 3–1) are often designed.

THE DESIGN SQUAD

The ideal design squad consists of two or more designers and drafters. Students, however, should work individually. This text will go through all phases of drafting

Figure 3-1
A rapid transit system designed by a civil engineering firm *(PRC Harris, Inc.).*

highway plans, and each student should do the drafting alone. In the later part of the text, the surveying projects will require group work.

The Squad Leader

In an engineering office one designer is designated as the squad leader (Fig. 3–2) and is responsible for the progress of the work. The squad leader should be a designer with considerable experience who is capable of directing the design and plans assembly with minimum supervision. Designers supervising work on municipal construction and freeway plans require more design experience than those planning rural construction.

Throughout the process of preparing the plans, the squad leader should be completely familiar with all work performed by subordinates, thus minimizing errors, discrepancies, faulty designs, and lack of standardization.

Prior to proceeding on designs for any job, the squad leader should become familiar with all data concerning the project, including the location of job, the approved typical section, the design speed, the anticipated traffic conditions, and the correspondence file. The skeleton right-of-way map should also be examined, taking into consideration the requirements of the typical section.

THE TYPICAL SECTION FOR THE JOB

The typical section (a cross-section view of the roadway, see Fig. 3–3 for an example) should be examined for compliance with current design standards. The proposed typical section is, to a great extent, established on the basis of the traffic volume forecast for 20 years in the future and on the availability of right-of-way, both of which could be subject to reappraisal.

Figure 3-2
Squad leader *(PRC Harris, Inc.)*.

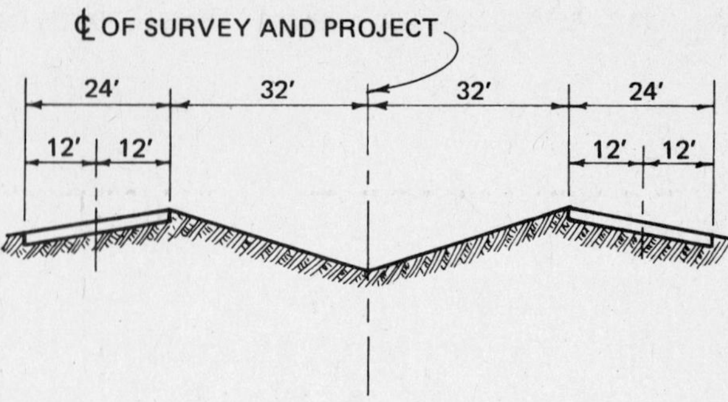

Figure 3-3
Typical road section.

THE FIELD NOTES

All the material in the field notebooks should be indexed prior to plotting any of the field notes. No erasures are permitted in field notebooks, either by the location party or by the designers. After the field notes have been indexed, bench marks and levels can be checked and reduced in this order:

Check bench marks
Check H.I. elevations
Reduce elevations at centerline, high water shots, flow lines of existing structures, rail elevations at railroads and other pertinent elevations

The proposed typical section is plotted first on a cross-section work sheet so that prints are available to all design squad members; plotting of field notes can then proceed.

VIEWS USED IN CIVIL DRAFTING

There are several basic views that are used particularly in highway designs and land planning, as well as in all other types of civil drafting plans.

Most objects have different appearances when viewed from different angles. A top view is usually quite different from a side view. Objects on road plans are shown from several different views. A drafter must be able to recognize each view and know what it means. For an example, we will study a view of a small end table.

PLAN VIEW

Figure 3–4 is a plan view of the end table. A *plan view* is a view from directly above an object, looking directly down at the object. Dashed lines indicate parts of the

Figure 3-4
Plan view of an end table.

object which *cannot be seen* from this viewpoint (in this case, the legs and table supports).

ELEVATION VIEW

In civil drafting, elevation refers to a view of an object from the side.

REMEMBER Elevation means height. In an *elevation view* one sees the height of the object being viewed.

Figure 3–5 shows two different elevation views of an end table. Elevations may be shown from the front, the rear, or from either side of the object. Notice that the front elevation shows the length of the end table.

CROSS-SECTION VIEW

A *cross-section view* shows the inside of an object as if it had been cut open. Figure 3–6 shows a cross-section view facing the side of the end table; it looks as if it were sliced in two through the center. The inside of the table top can be seen.

Figure 3-5
Two elevations of an end table.

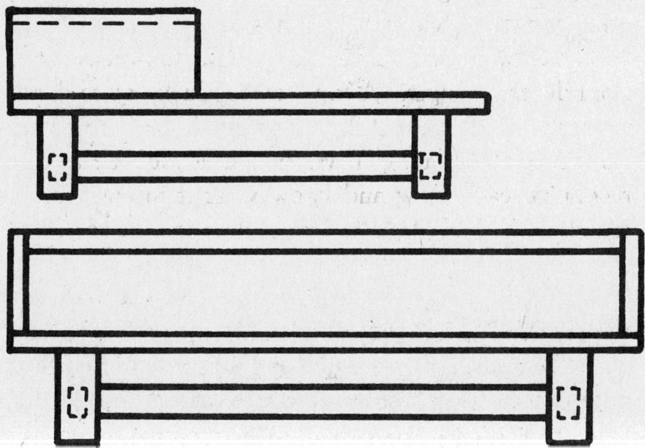

Figure 3-6
Side cross section of end table.

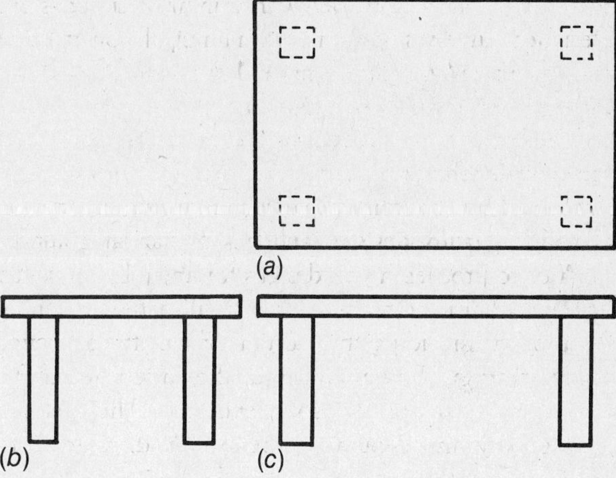

Figure 3-7
Three views of a table (*a*) plan, (*b*) side elevation, and (*c*) front elevation.

Summary of the Different Views

Sometimes different views of the same object are drawn close together, as in Fig. 3–7. In civil drafting it is often necessary to show only one view.

REMEMBER

A view from above is a *plan* view.
A view from the front, rear, or side is an *elevation* view.
An inside view, as if the object had been cut open, is a *cross-section* view.

PLAN AND PROFILE VIEWS

Figures 3–8 and 3–9 show civil drafting *plan* and *profile* views. Figure 3–8 looks directly down from above—this is a *plan*. *Profile* and *elevation* have the same meaning in civil drafting. Figure 3–9 looks at the subject from the side so it is a *profile* or an *elevation* view.

Views on Roadway Plan Sheets

There are several types of sheets found in roadway plans. Most of them show different views of things to be built—

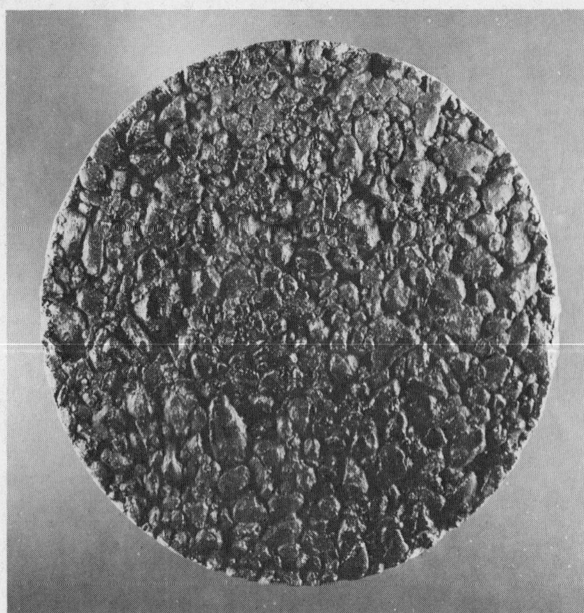

Figure 3-8
Plan view of a test sample of asphaltic concrete *(Florida Department of Transportation).*

Figure 3-9
Elevation (profile) view of a road and overpass *(Florida Department of Transportation).*

plan views, elevations, and cross sections. Some sheets also have notes or listings of materials needed. Standard symbols are used to represent various objects.

How to Use the Text

The preceding discussion of road design is a condensed version of the procedure used in industry. At this point, the student probably feels that the job is immense. Civil drafting is more complicated than other types of drafting, but this text will cover each phase of civil drafting in its simplest form, step by step. This method of instruction is similar to that used in industry when a trainee learns on the job.

The student will do a lot of tracing, which is the easiest kind of drafting. This book contains many drawings which are to be studied along with the explanations in the text. By reading each explanation and studying the drawing carefully, the student will learn civil drafting one step at a time. After becoming familiar with the drawings in this manner, the student will then render the drawing on a separate sheet of drafting paper. By reading the text while working on each drawing, the student should have very few questions for the instructor; and drawing while reading will make it easier for the student to remember what has just been learned.

KEY MAP

The key map, often called the key sheet or title sheet, is the front cover of a set of plans. Find Drawing No. 1 and compare it with Fig. 3–10. The key sheet

- ☐ *identifies* the project with a name and number
- ☐ shows the *location* of the project on the state map
- ☐ gives an *index* to all sheets in the plan set
- ☐ shows the *length* of the project

The Need for Municipal Key Maps

Cities are growing, the suburbs are expanding, even the rural areas are becoming more developed. As this happens, railroad lines and highways must be built to provide easy access to the new developments. When new airports are built in the expanded areas, they must be connected to existing areas by highways, roads, and city streets. These new roadways, as well as improvements on older roadways, require plans; the first sheet of any set of plans is the key map.

General Instructions on Key Maps

First, the student needs the general instructions for making key maps, so read these general instructions, returning to them if more information is required, while drawing the key map. A set of specific instructions will be given in the text to guide the student in drawing the map. These specific instructions give nearly line-by-line advice and discuss unusual features which will be of interest.

WHAT THE KEY MAP CONTAINS

The key map, sometimes called the title sheet, is the first sheet in a set of highway plans. The key map contains general information concerning the project and the plans themselves. It is prepared on standard printed cloth or mylar sheets and shows the information discussed in the following paragraphs.

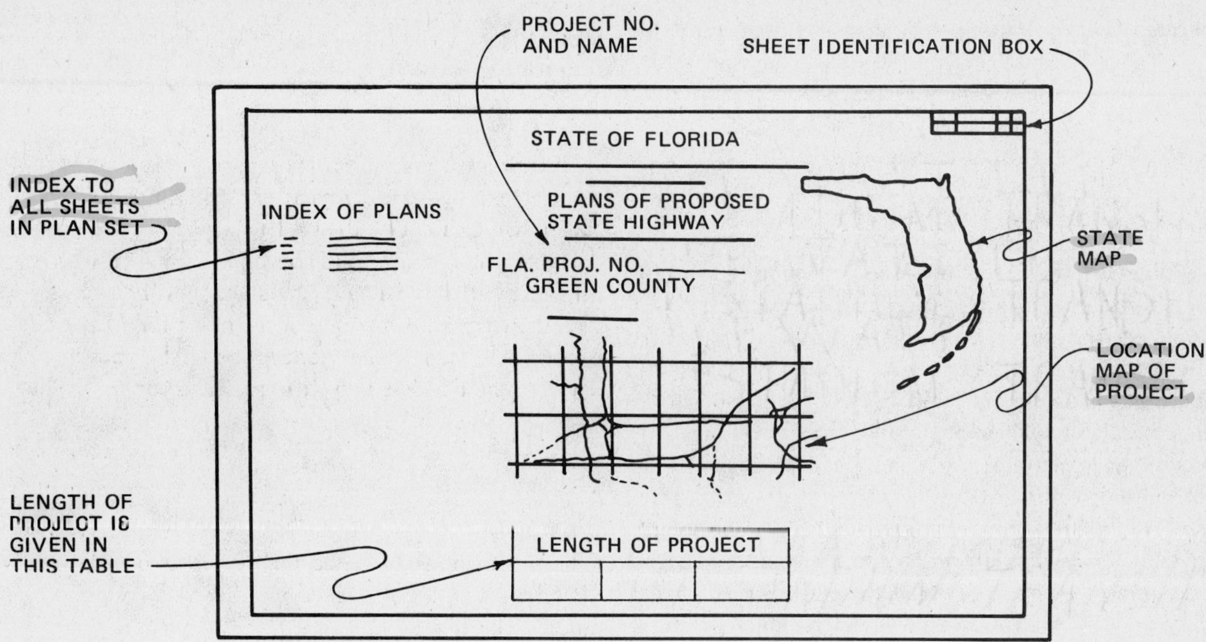

Figure 3-10
Line drawing of key map with items explained.

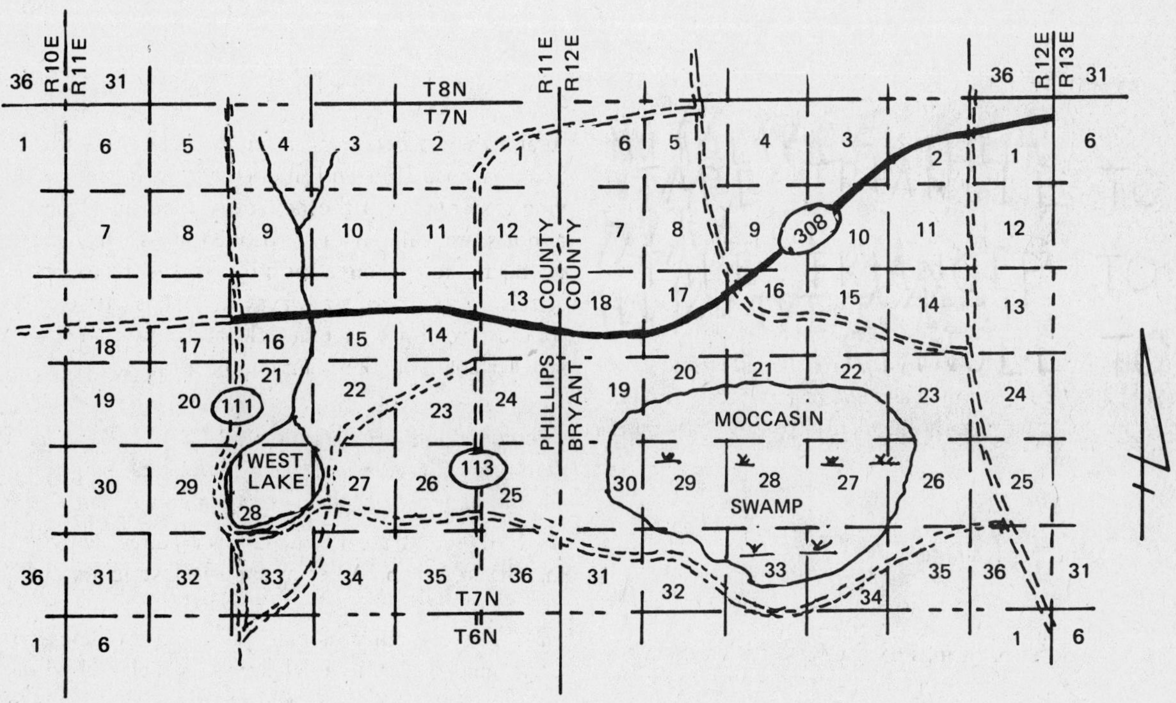

Figure 3-11
Sample location map.

Location Map

The location map is placed in the center of the sheet; it is a reproduced portion of the county map (or maps) that shows the project location. An example is shown in Fig 3–11. Key maps are usually given to the beginning drafting technician to prepare. Since the reproduction of the city or county map is a tracing job, this is an excellent way to start developing young technicians for this complicated field of drafting. City maps are used in the location maps for municipal projects. Any convenient scale may be used. The key maps are traced directly from the county or city maps on any scale that suits the paper. In general, the scale for county maps is

$$\frac{1}{2} \text{ inch [in]} = 1 \text{ mile [mi] or } 1 \text{ in} = 1 \text{ mi}$$

Features of the Location Map. Section, township, range, and county lines, together with section, township, and range numbers, should be shown on rural maps. Cities, towns, and physical features such as lakes, streams, and canals must be indicated. City limits are shown, as are urban limits, where applicable. If a city map is used, section lines are not important, but streets should be shown and named. State highways are shown by state road number and U.S. highway number, if appropriate. Arrows are put at the edge of the map pointing to the next principal cities to which these roads lead. Local roads are indicated with parallel, broken lines.

When tracing county maps, avoid copying hatched or stippled areas, cultural symbols, and other information which is not pertinent. However, the populations of incorporated towns and cities and the census year should be given; the latest federal census should be used.

Project Location

The project location is shown by a heavy, solid line of substantial width. It is sometimes advantageous to show station numbers (the station number plus two zeros gives the distance in feet from the beginning of the survey) at regular intervals, particularly with city street projects. The beginning and end of federal projects or state jobs, any station equations, exceptions, and the beginnings and endings of proposed bridges should be stationed.

When several jobs or projects are covered by the same set of plans, the beginning and end of each job or project must be indicated clearly by the job or project number and stationing.

ARRANGEMENT OF THE KEY MAP

The scale of the location map should be chosen so that it will not interfere with other features of the key map. Sometimes stationing flags are inked in advance of completion of the key map, and interference with these flags is later discovered. The flags, however, should be arranged to lie outside the body of the map whenever possible.

SPECIFIC INSTRUCTIONS FOR DRAWING A KEY MAP—DRAWING NO. 1

Times are changing: In the 1960s most of the plans for road key maps were prepared on a good type of specially

Figure 3-12
Technician preparing overlays *(Ross, Saarinen, Bolten, and Wilder, Inc., Consulting Engineers).*

printed irish linen. Now technicians (like the one in Fig. 3–12) prepare most plans on mylar. Mylar is a plastic material with a thickness of about 3/1000 to 5/1000 in [0.08 to 0.13 mm], matted on one or both sides. Mylar is easy to erase with water after inking, and it has an indefinite life.

Drawing No. 1

The student will render Drawing No. 1. This will give experience in drawing while the student learns what is required to produce a key map properly. First, we will do a map of a small city. If this work were done for a consulting engineer, or a city, county, or a state office, it would be done at a larger scale on a 22 × 34-in paper. States generally reduce all plans photographically to one-half this size so that they will be a convenient size for the contractor who constructs the job. We will work on a smaller scale; the student can learn as much at half scale as at full size. This makes it possible to use the Drawings as county and city maps. The key map vellum should be 11 × 17 in or any larger size that the instructor prefers. Any good vellum will do for the maps in this course. GAF Draftrace 280, a tracing vellum with 100 percent rag and 20-lb weight, works well. Any similar vellum preferred by the instructor may be used; it should erase well for both ink and pencil.

Working on the Location Map

Drawing No. 1 shows a small town in Green River County, Fla. The first step in making a key map is to trace a location map of the area where the work will be done. All the necessary city and county maps would be available in city, county, or state offices or in a consulting engineering firm. The drafting technician would find the one with the appropriate street or road and place it directly under the center of the linen or mylar key map sheet. In an independent engineering firm, the state may provide the printed key map blank. The outline of the state would be printed on the right edge of the blank. The student will have to use a blank sheet of vellum and trace the state map from the drawing.

Method of Drawing

In the industry the key map is almost universally done in india ink. We would prefer the student to use ink. Some schools may have the Rapidograph type of inking pens, see Figs. 3–13 and 3–14. If not, the student may be able to buy two or three of various line widths. This is very desirable, as students interviewing for jobs are frequently asked if they have had much experience in inking. Rapidograph line sizes 1, 2, and 3 should give the student full coverage. With sizes smaller than 1, it is hard to keep the ink flowing, and nothing larger than No. 3 should be needed. For schools and students without the inking equipment, mechanical lead holders can be used, although the product will not be quite as professional.

Figure 3-14
Rapidograph technical pens *(Koh-I-Noor Rapidograph Co.).*

Figure 3-13
Technical pen set *(Koh-I-Noor Rapidograph Co.).*

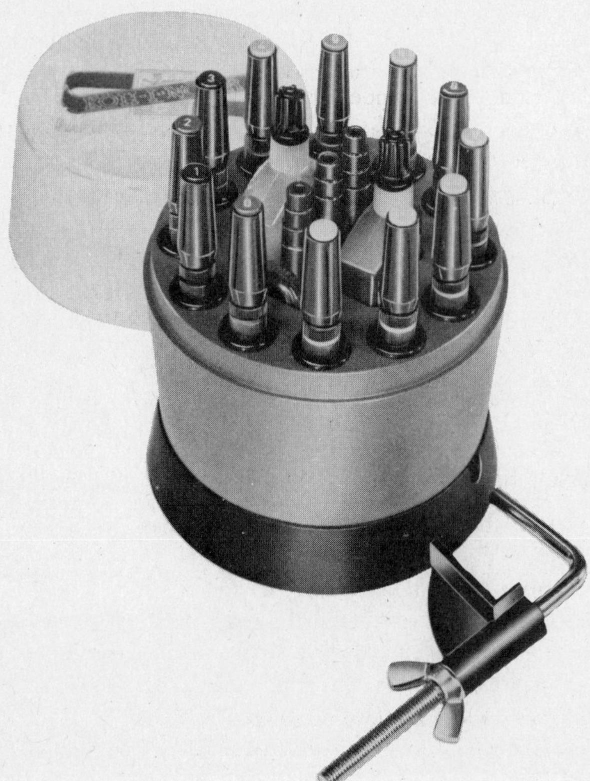

Tracing the Location Map

Now center the location map (the location map which is on Drawing No. 1) under the vellum sheet and ink the location map onto the vellum paper. This is only a matter of tracing the map underneath onto the blank vellum sheet. Since schools have no reference file of county and city maps, use Drawing No. 1 as a city map. Be sure to have centered the location map under the key map so that sufficient space remains for the *index of sheets*, which is always put at the upper left-hand corner of the sheet. Keep space for the *project title* in the center of the sheet directly above the location map. Also save space for the *length-of-project box* in the center below the location map. A common error is to trace the location map in ink and then discover that insufficient space remains for the index of sheets, project title, or length of project tabulation.

Be careful to work from the top of the page toward the bottom. This allows the ink to dry at the top, and the drafter will not be working over wet ink. If the ink is blotted, it is usually removable with an electric eraser (see Fig. 3–15). Do not use the old-fashioned hard ink erasers; they tear up the surface of the vellum and produce poor results.

If the triangles and other tools which rest flat on the vellum are not elevated in some manner, the ink may

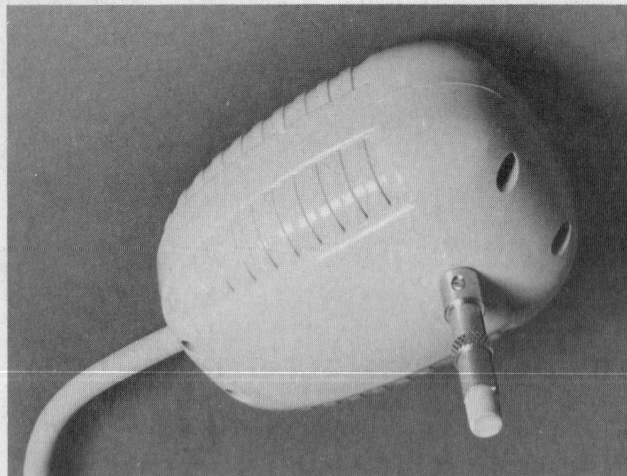

Figure 3-15
A small electric eraser good for ink removal *(Faber-Castell Corp.)*.

back under the tool and blot the paper. A method used by old-time drafters is to tape three copper cent pieces to the triangle. Tape one under each angle of the triangle with Scotch tape. Do not use drafting tape—it will get dirty immediately and smudge the paper. This method elevates the triangles enough to prevent the ink from running back under and causing blots.

Physical Features of the Location Map

The location map is part of a small city. In city maps section lines are unimportant and are never shown, but street names must be shown. The lettering used should be of a size to fit the map and still allow readability. We suggest that the lettering be ⅛ or 5/32 in [3 or 4 mm] high. Physical features of the area must be shown. Lakes, streams, and canals must be indicated. In this drawing of Dune City, the Green River is shown on the east side, and Willow Branch Creek meanders through from north to southeast. City limits are shown by hatching on the west side of the map.

Notice that State Highway 22 runs from north to south and State Highway 101 runs west to east. All state and federal highways must be called out on location maps. Notice that State Road 101 is the project road. It is much thicker and solid. Use a No. 3 or No. 4 Rapidograph pen to bring this detail to the immediate attention of the reader of the plans.

Stationing of the Project

Notice the *flags* used along Road 101. These show the start-of-project and end-of-project as well as any exceptions along the way. *The importance of stationing cannot be stressed enough*. The flags carry station numbers that indicate the distance along the project from some predetermined starting point. Most work on existing roads such as this one in Dune City involve repaving the road, widening it, or both. Many times bridges or crossing roads are not included in the contract, as shown here. Notice that at Sta. 339 + 61.22 there is a proposed 132-foot (ft) [40.2-m] bridge that is not in this contract. At Sta. 366 + 39.11 there is another exception for State Route 22, which is undoubtedly in good condition and needs no work done on it. Finally, the end-of-project is flagged at Sta. 402 + 53.33.

Explanation of Station Numbers

The *station number* plus *two zeros* gives the distance in feet from the beginning of the survey. For example, Sta. 300 + 00 would be 300 × 100 or 30,000 ft [9144.0 m] from the point where the survey began. Station 340 + 93.22 is 34,000 + 93.22 ft or 34,093.22 ft [10391.63 m] from the start of the survey. All survey work is labeled by station in this manner.

REMEMBER The station number given plus two zeros gives the stationing in feet. The number of feet beyond a station is added to this. This number is between 0 and 100 ft. (100 ft would be one more station.) The additional feet added to a station is carried to two decimal places, such as Sta. 102 + 23.75.

Physical Characteristics of the Area

Notice that the Green River is labeled and marked by waves; waves are used to indicate bodies of water. The conventional signs legend at the lower left of the key map gives most of the signs found on the map; however, the wavy lines indicating water are not included. Willow Branch Creek is located and is done freehand, as is the west bank of Green River, which is so large that only the west bank can be shown on the map. Rivers, lakes, streams, and the ocean are all done freehand on maps, and waves are shown against the banks so as to identify them.

Why is the City Population Shown?

Under Dune City's name is the population and the year the census was taken. Always use the population and the latest census year. The population is important because the contractors who will bid on the jobs need to know if there is a major source of labor in the area. The contractor who gets the job in Dune City may well be from Jacksonville, Fla., or Kansas City, Mo. When the job is far from the home base, the contractor often sends only a crew of supervisors and the road building machinery and thus needs to know if a source of labor is available. A small town such as this would discourage a contractor who is over one day's daily driving distance from the job. This contractor would have to bid high on the job since there is no local labor supply. A large town, however, would indicate a local labor supply and therefore a lower bid.

State Outline on the Key Map

An outline of the particular state where the project is located is printed on the right-hand side of the key map blank sheet. This is so that the technician who is drafting the job can put a flag pointing to the general location of the job site. This gives those who read the plans a very quick general reference to the location of the job.

Project Identification

There is always a north arrow (make it simple), and under the north arrow is the scale of the location map.

The federal aid project number and county are shown in No. 500 LeRoy guide letters and figures. The words *State Road No. 101*, the project title, are done with a No. 350 LeRoy guide. (An example of a project title is shown in Fig. 3–16.) This part of the job identification is always done with a mechanical lettering device like the one shown in Fig. 3–17. LeRoy, Doric, and Unitech are a few of the various kinds of these devices. The number 500 simply means that the letter or figure made with the lettering device will be 500/1000-in high. Number 350 makes letters and figures 350/1000-in high. (To visualize a Unitech, LeRoy, or Doric scale of 140, realize that 140 is larger than 125 by 15/1000 in. One hundred and twenty-five (125/1000) is the decimal equivalent of 1/8 in [3 mm]. So the letters produced by the 140 scale are 1/8 in [3 mm] plus the thickness of four or five human hairs.)

STATE HIGHWAY

STATE JOBS NOS. 99736-3502-01-21
AND 98863-3503-01-21
PHILLIPS & BRYANT COUNTIES
STATE ROAD NO. 308

Figure 3-16
Sample project title.

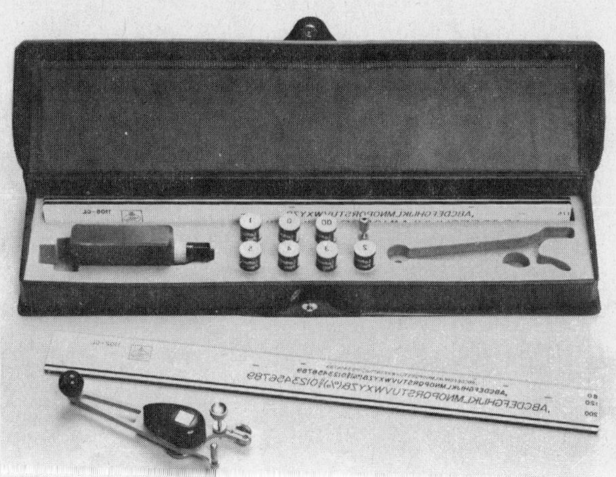

Figure 3-17
Mechanical lettering device *(Faber-Castell Corp.)*.

Index of Sheets and Length of Project

In the upper left-hand corner is the index of sheets. The index of sheets is the list of all the drawings in the set of plans; an example is shown in Fig. 3–18. Sometimes this list is quite long. Some sets of road plans drawn on mylar weigh as much as 75 to 100 lb [34 to 45 kg].

The length-of-project box is in the center of the drawing under the location map. To calculate the length of the project, take the end station distance of 402 + 53.33 and subtract the starting station of 300 + 00; this gives 102 stations plus 53.33 ft. Converting this to feet by adding two zeros to the station figure gives 10,253.33 ft [3125.22 m] as total distance. There were, however, two exceptions on the job. One was 124 ft [37.8 m] and the other was 132 ft [40.2 m]. These must be subtracted from the total length of the job to get the actual number of feet in the job, 9997.33 ft [3047.19 m]. Dividing by 5280 ft (the number of ft in one mile) gives the length in miles (1.893 mi).

Review

1. Why do we need roads? We need them for easy access to new developments.
2. What is a Drawing? Drawings are used to explain the drafting procedures. The word "Plate" was used until recent years. Plates are the same as Drawings, but in the industry the modern term "Drawing" is preferred.
3. Why are location maps traced from Drawings? The main reason is that most schools will not have a supply of city, state, and county maps available. The experience of drafting the map, even though it may be a tracing job, will help the student learn the map features and drawing procedures. In industry the location map is always traced.
4. What is a location map? It is a portion of a city or county map that includes the project and thus shows the place where the work will be performed.
5. What is a section line and how is it shown? A section is one of the primary units of measurement in the government survey system of legal descriptions of land. A section is 1 mi square and contains 640 acres [259 hectares]. Section lines are shown by a series of heavy dashes.
6. What is a township and how is it shown? A township is a square tract of land that measures 6 mi [9.7 km] on each side and includes 36 sections (formed by the

Sample Index of Sheets For Municipal Projects

Index of Sheets

Sheet No.	
1	Key Map
2-4	Drainage Map
5-11	Typical Section and Summary of Quantities
12	Mass Diagram
13	Back-of-Sidewalk Profiles
14-26	Plan and Profiles
27-37	Drainage Structures
38-42	Special Profiles along Project
43-46	Intersection Details
47-57	Intersection Profiles
58-65	Outfall Plan and Profiles
66-70	Outfall Ditch Cross Sections
71-73	Borrow Pit Soil Survey
74-77	Roadway Soil Survey
78-120	Roadway Cross Sections
Index No.	
1101-X	Miscellaneous Roadway Construction Details (2 sheets)
1307-X	Inlets (Sheet 1 of 2)
ETC	ETC
Sheet No.	
T-1 to T-5	Signalization Plans
L-1 to L-4	Highway Lighting Plans

For Index of Retaining Wall Sheets, See Retaining Wall Plans

For Index of Bridge Sheets, See Bridge Plans

Figure 3-18
Sample index of sheets for a municipal project *(Florida Department of Transportation).*

crossing of range and township lines). A township is 36 square miles (sq mi) [93 sq. km] in area. Township lines are shown by a heavy long dash, three short dashes, then another heavy long dash.

7. How are the various symbols used on the key map identified? They are in the lower left-hand corner of all key maps under the heading *Conventional signs*.
8. Why is stationing used? It tells the reader of the plans where to start and finish the job and where exceptions occur. Stationing also tells the length of the job.
9. What is the purpose of a key map? It gives general information concerning the project and the plans themselves. It also contains the index to all the sheets in the plan.
10. Where do civil engineering drafting technicians work? There are many places for civil drafting technicians to work: city engineering offices, county engineering offices, or state departments of transportation. There are, in addition, many consulting engineering offices in every city. These engineers do more road design than all the city, county, and state offices combined. In the southern part of the United States, where there is limited manufacturing, about 60 percent of all the people trained in drafting do civil engineering drafting.
11. What is a Rapidograph pen? It is a brand name for a type of inking pen that always gives a line of a selected width. They are numbered for line size, with smaller numbers indicating a smaller line size. A No. 00 would give a very thin line while a No. 4 would give a thick line. Old devices used to give variable line widths due to wearing of the instrument and varying pressure by the drafter. The use of these pens and the advent of mylar, a plastic type of paper, have revolutionized the civil drafting field. Most engineering offices now use mylar and ink for clarity, especially if the drawings are to be microfilmed for storage.
12. Why is it important to elevate the triangles above the work surface when inking? It keeps the ink from being attracted to the triangle edge and running under the triangle consequently causing a blot on the paper surface.
13. What is a flag? A flag is a large arrow that points to a particular feature that the designer wants called out.
14. What is a station? It is a position on the centerline of the project at some exact distance from the beginning of the survey. This distance (in feet) is always the station number plus two zeros.
15. What is P.O.B.? It is an abbreviation for point of beginning.

PROBLEMS

1. Remove Drawing No. 2 from the end of Chap. 3. Insert the drawing under a B-size (11 × 17 in) sheet of vellum drafting paper. Put the location map roughly under the center of the vellum sheet. Remember that Drawing No. 1 has all the items encountered on any municipal key map. Drawing No. 1 should always be used as a guide when making key maps.
   (a) Trace the outline of the state map with the location-of-project flag.
   (b) Trace the north arrow and scale.
   (c) Trace the location map, flags, and street names.
   (d) At the upper left corner of the vellum add an index of sheets. List only Sheet No. 1, the key map, as this is the only sheet in the set of plans at this time.
   (e) Trace the length-of-project box and add in the following required items:

	Linear Feet	Miles
Roadway	1550.0	0.293
Bridges	000.0	0.000
Net length of project	1550.0	0.293
Exceptions	00.000	0.000
Gross length of project	1550.0	0.293

   (f) At the location map fill in the begin- and end-project flags:

BEGIN PROJECT—STA. 10 + 00.00
END PROJECT—STA. 25 + 50.00

   (g) Fill in the little box in the far right upper corner with the state [Florida (FLA.)], the year (1970), and the sheet number (NO. 1).
   (h) The title for Drawing No. 2 will be:

Plans of Proposed State Highway
STATE JOB NO. 87505-3603-02-44
DADE COUNTY
W. FLAGLER ST.

   Sign your name as the drafter above *Drawing No. 2*.
   (i) Check your drawing against Drawing No. 1 in the text to see if anything is missing.

   Note: Notice two things:

   1. The scale is not correct. This is due to reduction of sheet size in printing.

2. The population of the city of Miami seems small. Notice that the census year for this job is 1960; this was the population at that time.

2. Key Map Stationing: A size
   (a) Use a B-size (11 × 17 in) sheet of vellum.
   (b) Place Drawing No. 3, location map, approximately under the center of the B-size vellum and trace the location map. Add the location-of-project arrow and point it to Montgomery, Ala.
   (c) Add the stationing to the map:

BEGIN PROJECT—STA. 10 + 00

The new paving is not to go over SW FIRST AVENUE. It is in good condition and is an exception to the job, so flags are needed:

BEGIN EXCEPTION—STA. 17 + 50

END EXCEPTION—STA. 18 + 00.

There is a bridge across Mad River, so flag the start and end of the proposed bridge:

BEGIN BRIDGE—STA. 25 + 20

The proposed bridge is 145 ft [44.2 m] long. To obtain the end bridge station, add 145 ft (1 station plus 45 ft):

Start bridge at	25 + 20
Bridge length	1 + 45
	26 + 65

So the end of the bridge is Sta. 26 + 65; add an appropriate flag to the map.

The job ends at Sta. 33 + 45.

   (d) Add the north arrow and the index of sheets.

3. This is partially a county and partially a city problem; there will be some sections on the location map even though it is a city job. This problem will review the features of key maps.
   (a) Use a sheet of B-size vellum.
   (b) Place the location map (Drawing No. 4) in a central position under the drafting vellum. Trace the location map.
   (c) Add the stationing:

CYPRESS AVENUE	BEGIN—STA. 10 + 16.5
CYPRESS AVENUE	END—STA. 16 + 73.88
COCONUT DRIVE	STA. 40 + 20 to STA. 43 + 40
CACTUS DRIVE	STA. 30 + 20 to STA. 35 + 70

   (d) Add the index of sheets and the headings.
   (e) Draw the location-of-project map and flag the location.
   (f) Put in the north arrow and the scale. Sign the sheet just above the drawing number.
4. Drawing No. 5 is a location map of the islands of Nassau and Paradise in the Commonwealth of the Bahamas. The student should design a project and use this location map to set up a key map for the project.
5. The city of Montreal, Quebec, Canada, was founded in the very early 1600s. Therefore the streets have very unusual shapes. For this reason we have selected three problems for this city. They will give the student excellent drafting practice.
   (a) As in the other problems, the student must set up the work with a B-size sheet of vellum and trace the location map in the center of the sheet. Use Drawing No. 6 for the location map.
   (b) Select a title for the project.
   (c) Put in an index-of-sheets column.
   (d) Show the beginning and end stationing as well as the north arrow and the scale.
6. Trace the location map (Drawing No. 7) on B-size sheet of vellum. Add a title, stationing, a north arrow, an index of sheets, and a length-of-project box.
7. Follow the instructions in Problem No. 6. Use Drawing No. 8 for the location map.

LEARNING ACTIVITY PACKAGE

Read Chap. 3 carefully.

Chapter 3 read ____________ (*date*).

Drawing No. 1 should be rendered while reading the explanation in the chapter.

Drawing No. 1 completed ____________ (*date*).

If the student has read Chap. 3 but has not understood any of the objectives (a) through (d), the paragraphs discussing these objectives should be reread.

Objectives read and studied ____________ (*date*).

Read the chapter review.

Take the quiz on Chap. 3. Remove the quiz from the back of the chapter and answer all the questions.

Chapter 3 quiz completed ____________ (*date*).

Now work the problems of Chap. 3.

The student should understand that not all students will necessarily be asked to work all the problems. The text was designed to have ample problems for average-speed students who attend class a total of 540 hours per year. While some vocational and technical schools may have this many hours per year, most junior colleges have less than 540 hours. Depending on the student's ability and speed, and the length of the class, the instructor will assign certain select problems from each chapter.

Remember that *speed is not everything*. Attention to the quality and detail of the linework and the production of good lettering should count much more than speed. Work carefully and try to learn from every problem.

Remember to keep all the drawings. These can be used to create a portfolio for future job interviews.

All students should do Problem No. 1 (Drawing No. 2); completed ____________ (*date*).

Problem No. 2 (Drawing No. 3) completed ____________ (*date*).

Problem No. 3 (Drawing No. 4) completed ____________ (*date*).

Problem No. 4 (Drawing No. 5) completed ____________ (*date*).

Problem No. 5 (Drawing No. 6) completed ____________ (*date*).

Problem No. 6 (Drawing No. 7) completed ____________ (*date*).

Problem No. 7 (Drawing No. 8) completed ____________ (*date*).

Remember to work on the specific problems assigned by the instructor.

3

QUIZ

1. Give another name for a key map. cover page
2. What scale is often used for the location map in county work?
   1/2" = 1mile
3. What type of location map requires section, township, and range lines?
   rural maps
4. What do the arrows on the roads leading off the edge of the location map point to? the next closest city
5. What method is used to show the project location on a location map?
   station numbers
6. Are station numbers shown at regular intervals on city streets?
   yes
7. What items are stationed with flags on the project line?
   beginning and end
8. Should stationing flags be outside the boundaries of the location map?
   yes
9. Why are the populations of towns given?
   So that the contractor knows to bid high or low do to the labor ability
10. What is a good method for erasing ink from mylar?
    erase with water after inking
11. The drawing sheets used in engineering offices are 22 × 34 in. (T or F)
    True
12. Why do state transportation departments reduce plans to one-half the drafted size?
    will be convenient size for the contractor who constructs the job
13. The preferred method of drafting in industry uses india ink on mylar. (T or F) True
14. What type of line would a Rapidograph pen of size 4 give? thick
15. Why should the triangle be elevated above the paper surface for inking?
    so it does not smear
16. What is generally a good height for lettering? 1/8 inch

17. Give the actual footage in this job:
Begin Project Sta. 101 + 00.00
Exception Sta. 109 + 50.00 to Sta. 110 + 50.00
End Project Sta. 132 + 00.00.
3,000

18. What is added to the station number to get the actual distance in feet?
plus two numbers

19. Waves are freehanded. What does this really mean?
indicated bodies of water.

20. Why do most contractors like jobs in larger towns?
a local labor supply

10,100
13,200
10,100
3,100

110,50
10950
100

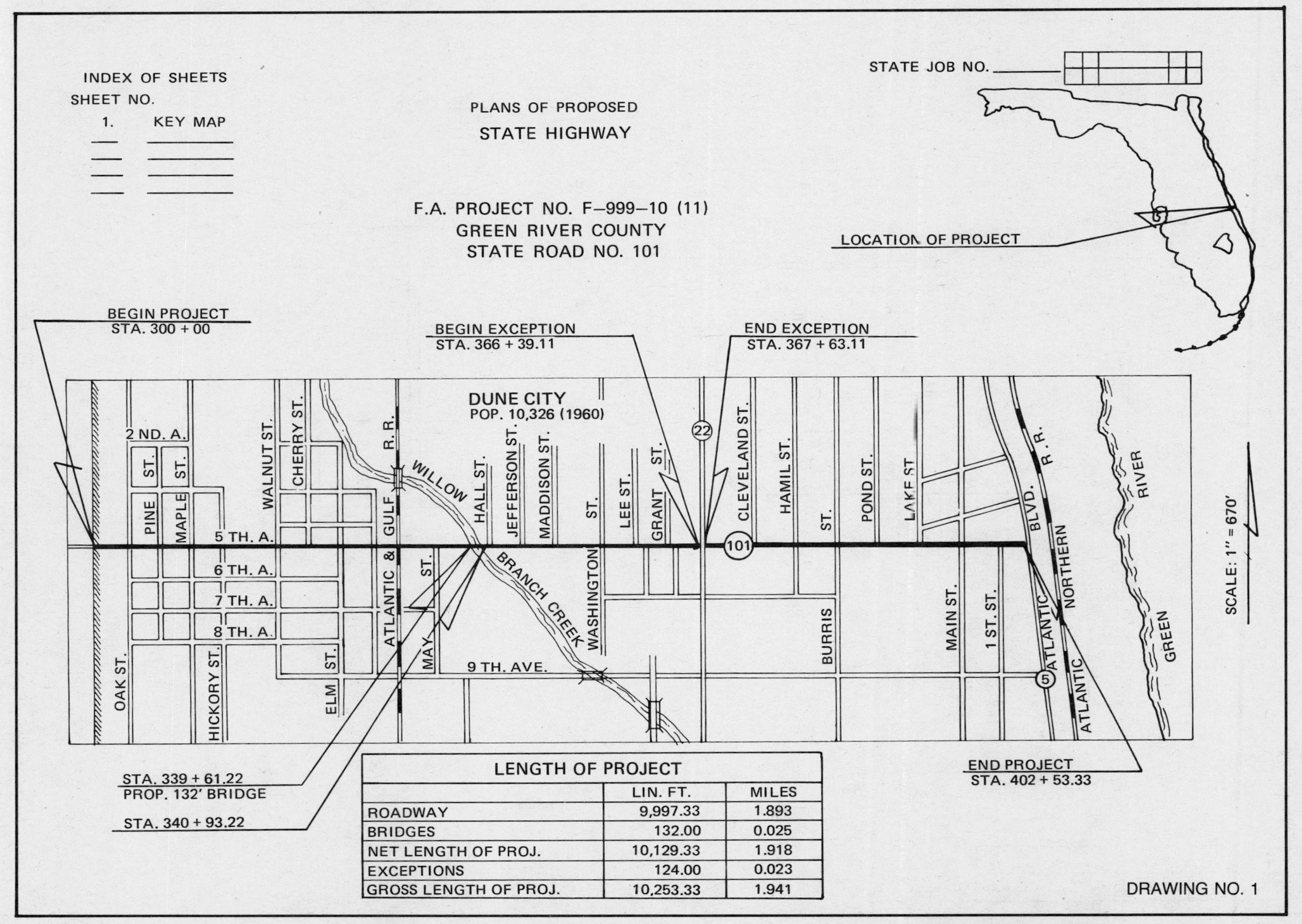

LENGTH OF PROJECT

	LIN. FT.	MILES
ROADWAY	9,997.33	1.893
BRIDGES	132.00	0.025
NET LENGTH OF PROJ.	10,129.33	1.918
EXCEPTIONS	124.00	0.023
GROSS LENGTH OF PROJ.	10,253.33	1.941

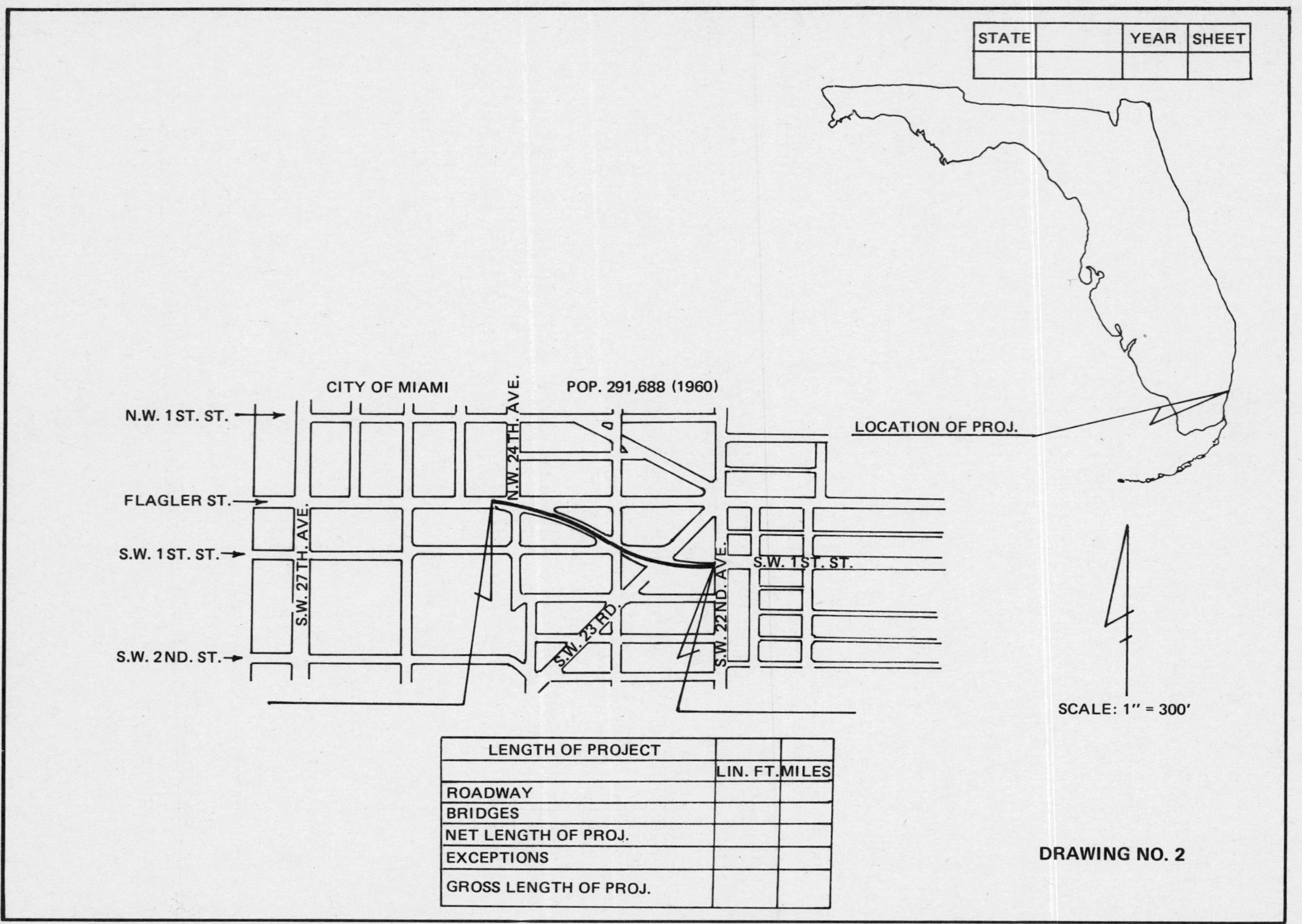
STATE
YEAR
SHEET
CITY OF MIAMI
POP. 291,688 (1960)
N.W. 1ST. ST.
FLAGLER ST.
S.W. 1ST. ST.
S.W. 2ND. ST.
S.W. 27TH. AVE.
N.W. 24TH. AVE.
S.W. 23 RD.
S.W. 22ND. AVE.
S.W. 1ST. ST.
LOCATION OF PROJ.
SCALE: 1" = 300'
LENGTH OF PROJECT
LIN. FT.
MILES
ROADWAY
BRIDGES
NET LENGTH OF PROJ.
EXCEPTIONS
GROSS LENGTH OF PROJ.
DRAWING NO. 2

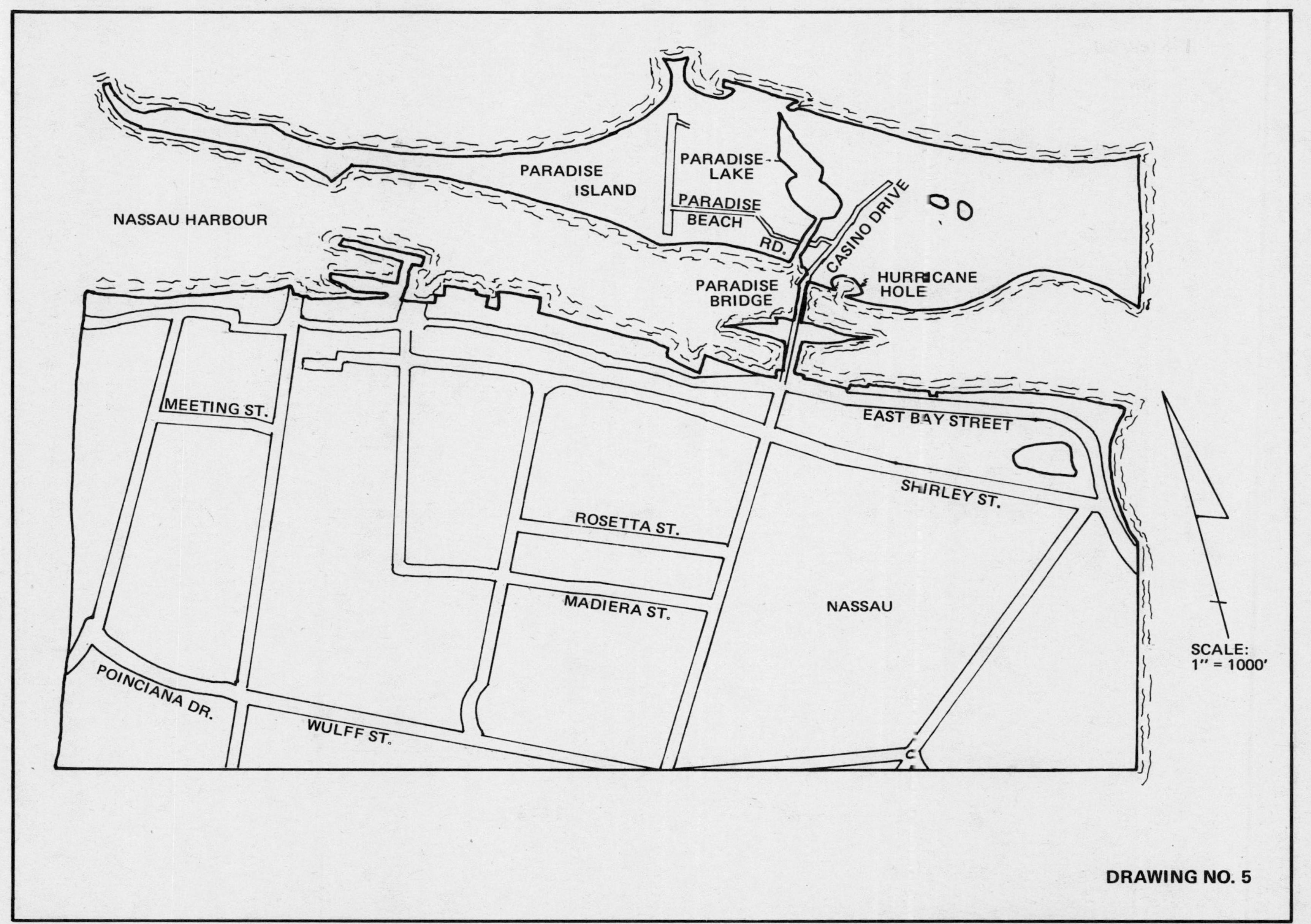
PARADISE ISLAND
PARADISE LAKE
PARADISE BEACH RD.
CASINO DRIVE
NASSAU HARBOUR
PARADISE BRIDGE
HURRICANE HOLE
MEETING ST.
EAST BAY STREET
SHIRLEY ST.
ROSETTA ST.
MADIERA ST.
NASSAU
SCALE:
1" = 1000'
POINCIANA DR.
WULFF ST.
DRAWING NO. 5

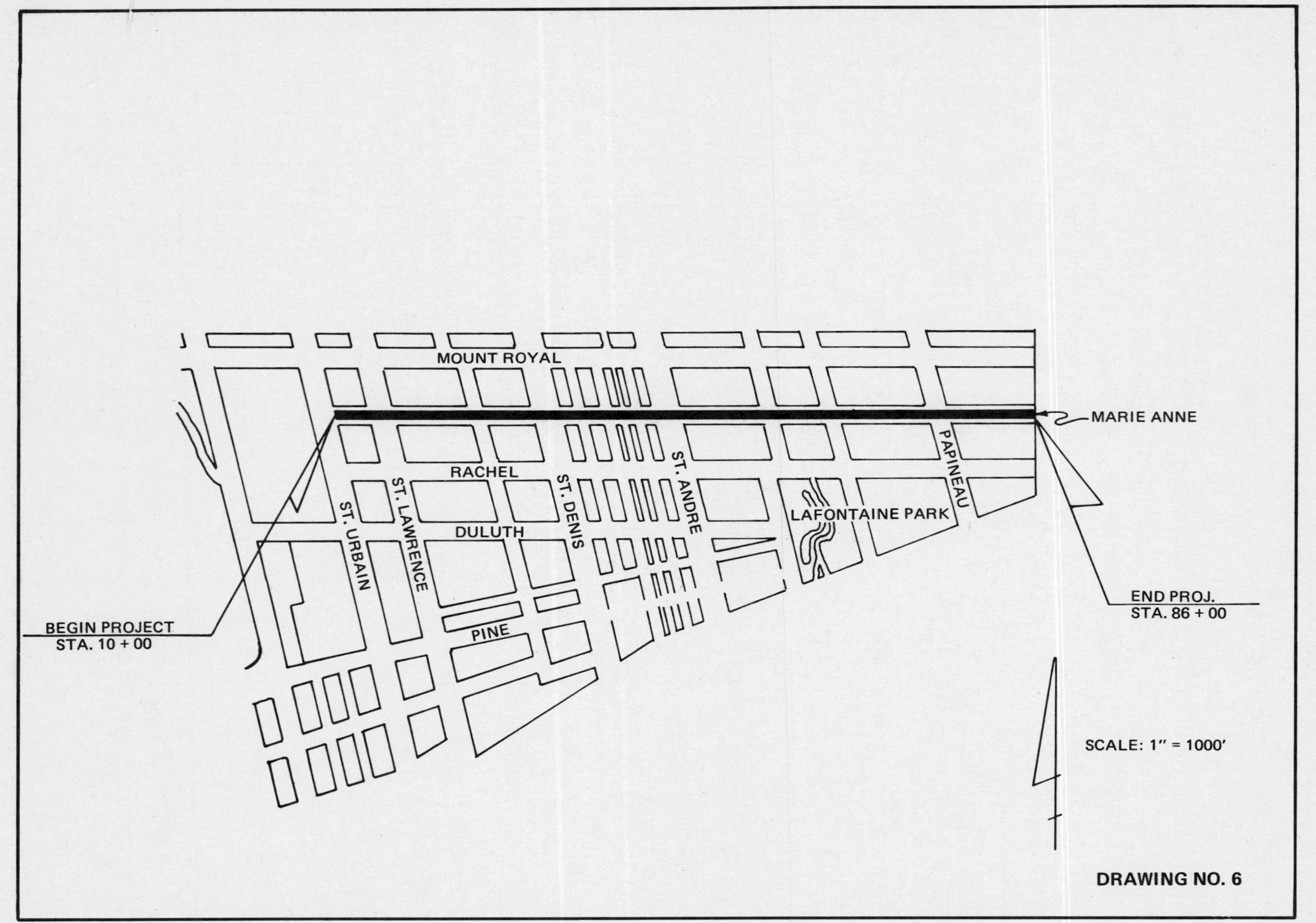
MOUNT ROYAL
MARIE ANNE
RACHEL
ST. ANDRE
PAPINEAU
ST. LAWRENCE
ST. DENIS
LAFONTAINE PARK
ST. URBAIN
DULUTH
END PROJ.
STA. 86 + 00
BEGIN PROJECT
STA. 10 + 00
PINE
SCALE: 1" = 1000'
DRAWING NO. 6

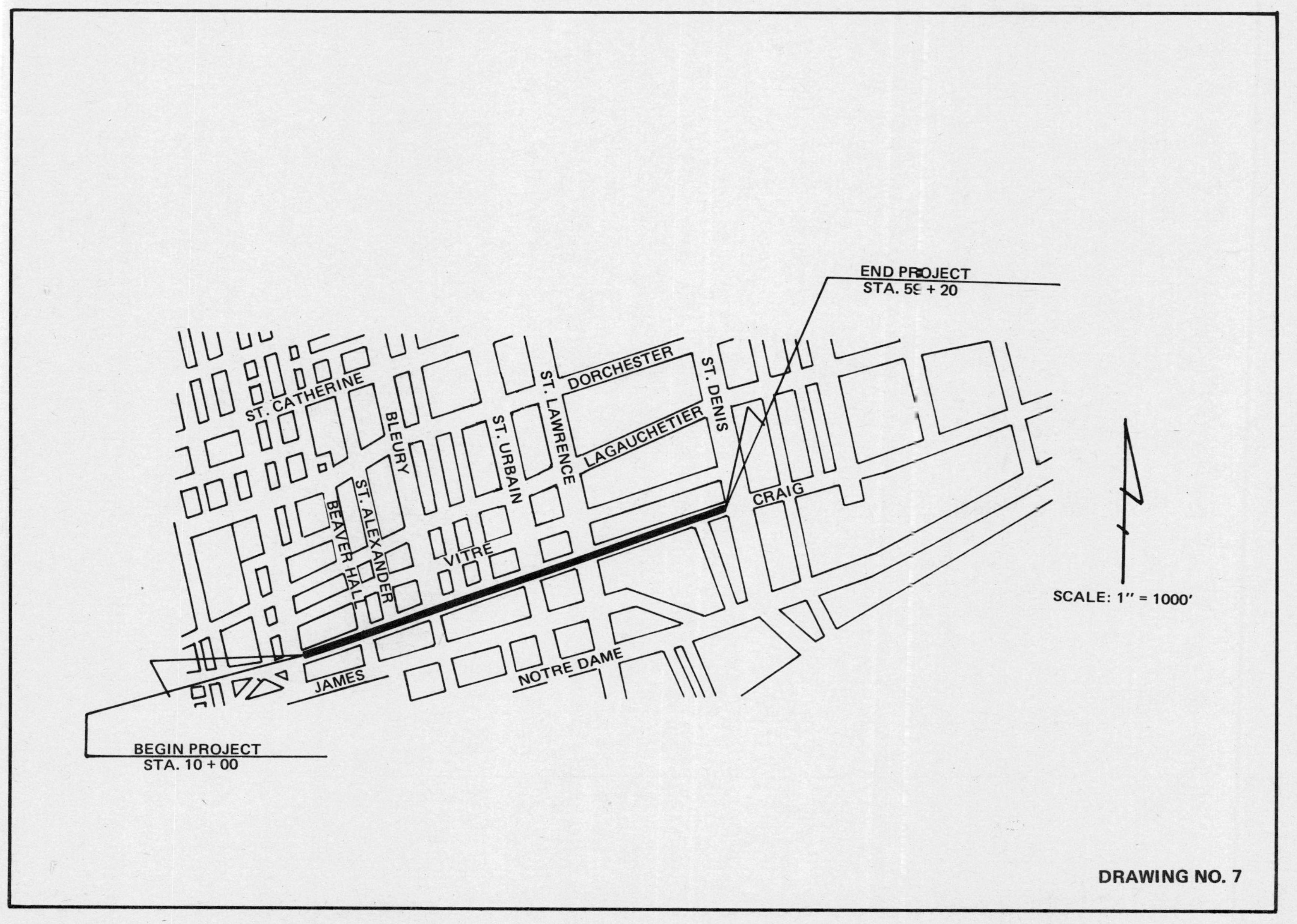
END PROJECT
STA. 59 + 20
ST. CATHERINE
BLEURY
ST. URBAIN
ST. LAWRENCE
DORCHESTER
LAGAUCHETIER
ST. DENIS
CRAIG
ST. ALEXANDER
BEAVER HALL
VITRE
JAMES
NOTRE DAME
SCALE: 1" = 1000'
BEGIN PROJECT
STA. 10 + 00
DRAWING NO. 7

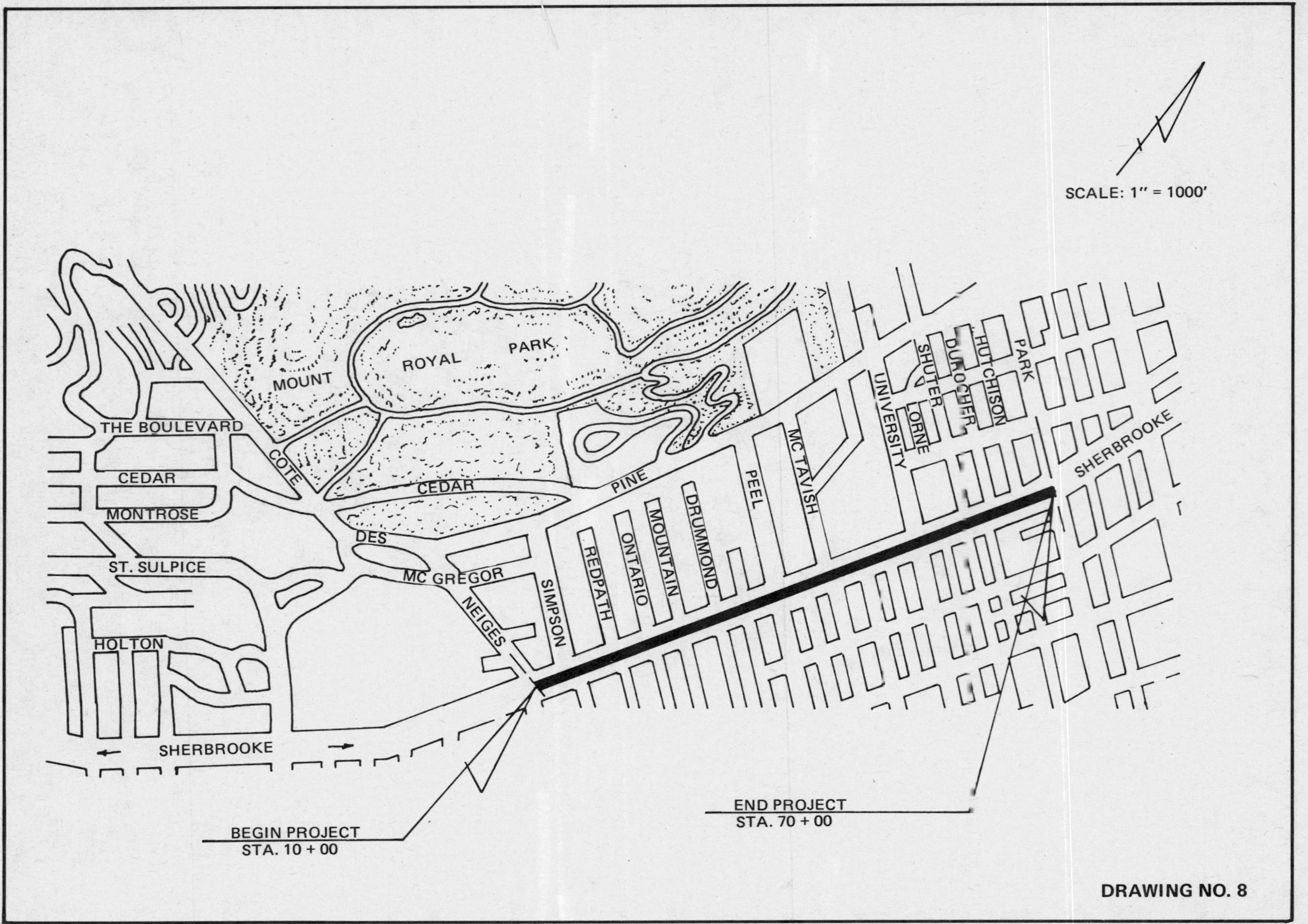
SCALE: 1" = 1000'
MOUNT
ROYAL
PARK
THE BOULEVARD
COTE
CEDAR
CEDAR
MONTROSE
DES
ST. SULPICE
MC GREGOR
NEIGES
HOLTON
SHERBROOKE
SIMPSON
REDPATH
ONTARIO
MOUNTAIN
DRUMMOND
PINE
PEEL
MC TAVISH
UNIVERSITY
SHUTER
LORNE
DUROCHER
HUTCHISON
PARK
SHERBROOKE
BEGIN PROJECT
STA. 10 + 00
END PROJECT
STA. 70 + 00
DRAWING NO. 8

4 RURAL KEY MAPS

Objectives

a. Learn about section, township, range, and county lines
b. Learn to develop the location map and to do flagging
c. Be able to ascertain the dominant physical features of an area and be able to show them on the location map
d. Learn about new and old work and how to show them on the map
e. Understand how to determine the length of the project
f. Understand the symbols for range and township lines
g. Study the units of measurement

Rationale

There are two types of key maps. There are city key maps, which were discussed in Chapter 3, and there are county key maps for projects such as the rural highway shown in Fig. 4–1. Now the student must learn what constitutes a county key map and practice drawing some.

GENERAL FEATURES OF KEY MAPS FOR COUNTY JOBS

County key maps are quite different from city key maps in that street stationing is not required. City streets and their names are replaced by range, township, and section lines. A county map scale is also quite different from that of a city map.

Drawing No. 9 is a typical county job. It is a state road running 10.549 miles (mi) [16.976 km] through two counties in Florida. There are 3.971 mi [6.391 km] in Phillips County and 6.578 mi [10.586 km] in Bryant County. This project thus requires two job numbers.

This rural job will introduce *section, township, range,* and *county lines* (see Fig. 4–2), as well as *section numbers* and highway *arrows* to the next towns. Notice that the scale on this drawing is 1 inch (in) = 1 mi. This is a normal scale for county work. However, due to photographic reduction, the actual scale is now about 0.4375 in = 1

Figure 4-1
A rural highway approaching a city. Notice an entrance lead-in and guardrail because a canal is nearby. The normal road is two lanes in each direction *(Florida Department of Transportation).*

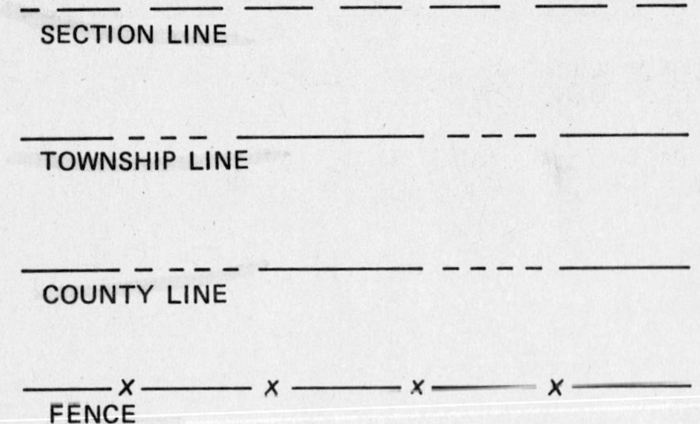

Figure 4-2
Lines often encountered on key maps.

mi; that is, every 7/16 in [11 mm] on the plate is approximately 1 mi.

JOB LOCATION

The location of the job is flagged by an arrow on the state outline printed on the key map blank, see Fig. 4–3. The flag is placed by the drafting technician at a point close to the area of the job. This catches the eye of the reader immediately and shows the general location.

INDEX OF SHEETS

The index of sheets is a very important item on the key map; an example is shown in Fig. 4–5. It locates every map used in the set of plans. At this time the student will not work on the index of sheets because we have only a key map and have not developed the rest of the set of plans.

Figure 4-3
A state map with a flag to indicate the job location.

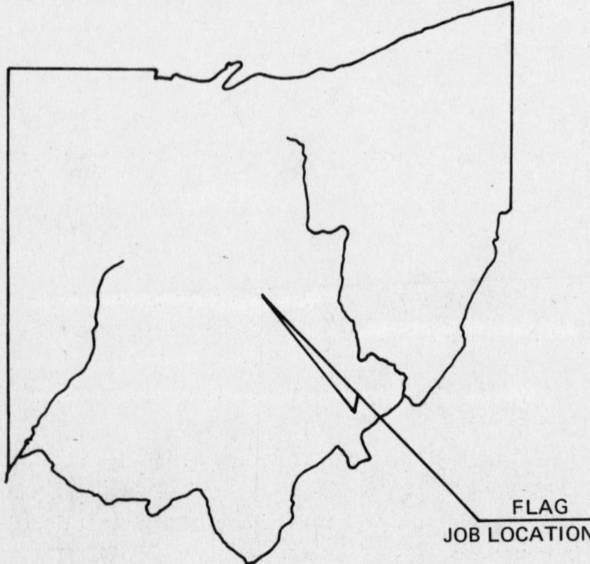

DEVELOPING THE LOCATION MAP

The first step is to develop the location map. Place Drawing No. 9, which serves the same purpose as a county map in industry, under the key map blank sheet of vellum. Center Drawing No. 9 under the vellum and prepare to trace the location map. Any convenient scale may be used for rural projects. The scale for this map is determined by the drawing. The location map is usually traced directly from a county map on a scale of ½ in = 1 mi, or 1 in = 1 mi, depending on the size required. In our case, due to the small size of the drafting paper and location map, the actual scale is about 7/16 in = 1 mi; this odd scale is caused by photographic reduction of the drawing.

Dominant Physical Features

Trace the location map on the vellum. Notice that Moccasin Swamp is clearly outlined on the map. This is a dominant physical feature of Bryant County; physical features must be shown. In Phillips County, Ford Creek and West Lake are dominant physical features. In Moccasin Swamp, notice the marsh symbol from the conventional signs (refer to Fig. 5–25 for common drainage symbols, p. 89). A location map showing typical symbols is shown in Fig. 4–4.

Figure 4-4
Part of a location map illustrating linework and symbols

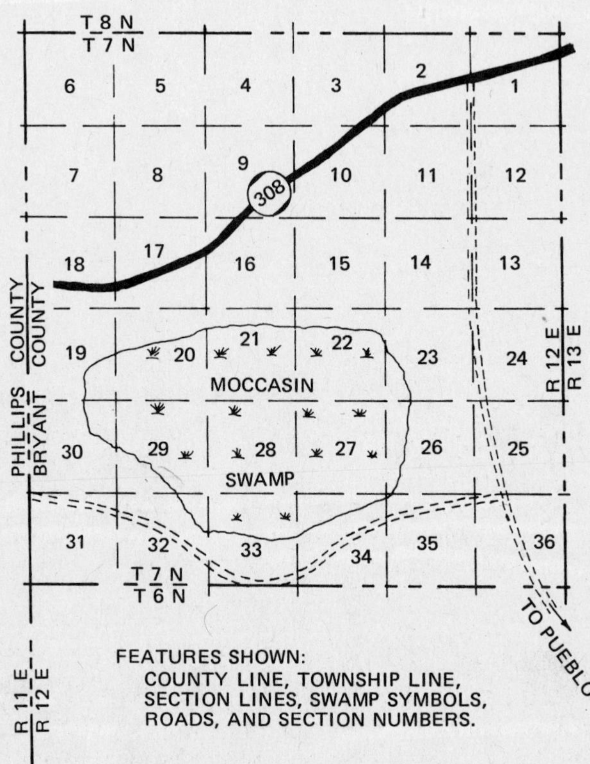

Sample Index of Sheets For Rural Projects

Index of Sheets

Sheet No.	
1	Key Map
2-3	Drainage Map
4-6	Typical Section and Summary of Quantities
7	Mass Diagram
8-14	Plan and Profiles
15-21	Drainage Structures
22-31	Intersection Details
32-35	Lateral Ditch Plan and Profiles
36-45	Lateral Ditch Cross Sections
46-49	Borrow Pit Soil Survey
50-57	Roadway Soil Survey
58-100	Roadway Cross Sections
Index No.	
1101-X	Miscellaneous Roadway Construction Details (2 sheets)
2300-X	Guardrail (4 sheets)
ETC	ETC

For Index of Bridge Sheets, See Bridge Plans

For Index of Signing Sheets, See Signing Plans

Figure 4-5
Sample index of sheets for a rural project.

At the edges of the map note that all existing roads have an arrow and the next prominent town is named, such as "TO MANSVILLE."

LINEWORK

Figure 4–4 also shows examples of linework. The road which will be worked on, called the *project location,* is shown by a line of substantial width. Existing roads are shown by broken lines. New work to be done will always show as solid lines. This is a good rule in civil drafting:

solid lines = new work; broken lines = existing work

State Roads 111 and 113 should be indicated as well as State Road 308, which is the project road. Be sure to flag the beginning and end of the first and second jobs. In county jobs all the sections must be shown.

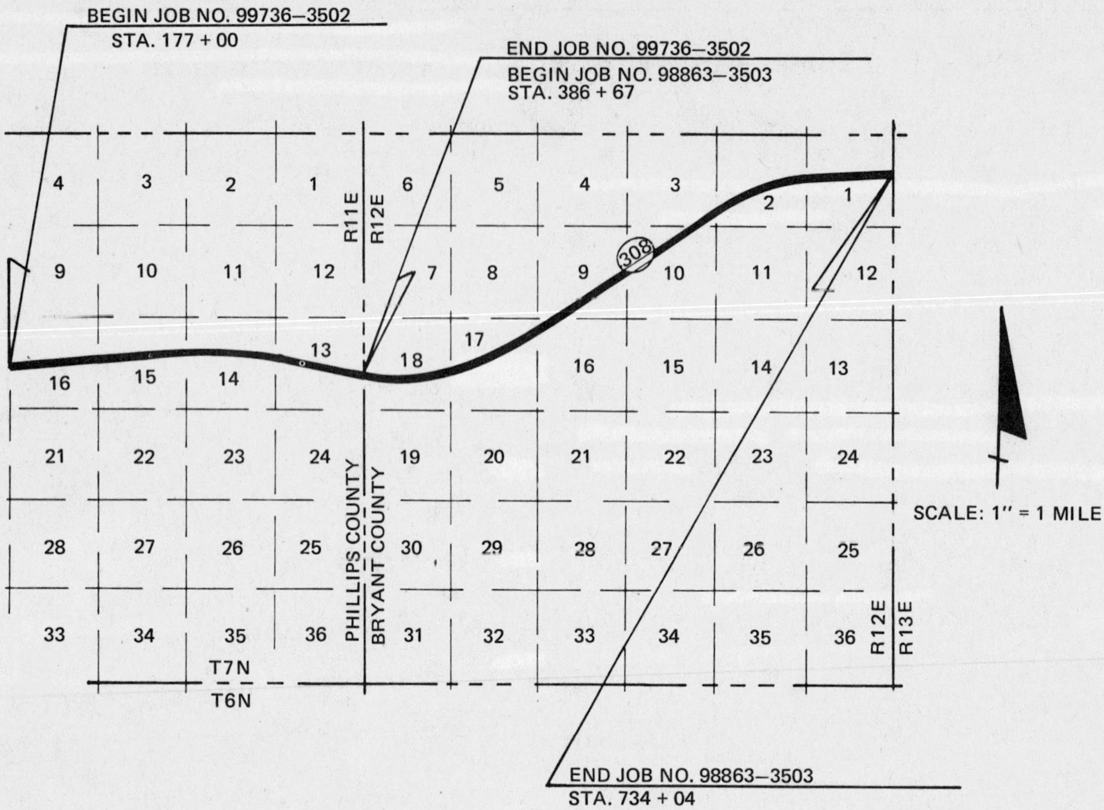

Figure 4-6
Illustrations of flagging and north arrow.

The north point is placed on one side of the location map, preferably to the right. The map scale is shown along with the north point. The map should always be oriented so that the north point will be located either toward the top of the sheet or to the right. Examples of flagging and a north point are shown in Fig. 4–6.

The student need not put an *index of sheets* such as the one shown in Fig. 4–5 on this map. This would only be done if there were other drawings in the set to index.

PROJECT OR JOB NUMBER, COUNTY, AND ROAD NUMBER

These are in the form of a title, and large, heavy letters are used; they are placed above the location map. The student should remember that in industry D-size sheets of about 22 × 34 in are used. Unreduced letter size will be ½ in [13 mm] on the state job numbers and 0.350 in [9 mm] on the state road number. These drawings are photographically reduced to approximately 11 × 17-in size, which allows the set of plans to be more easily handled in the field. Because of the size reduction, letter size is very important. Lettering which is legible at full size may well be illegible at a reduced size.

The student may use any mechanical type lettering device available for the project or job number, county, and road number. If none are available, the numbers from the drawing should be traced with a large-width pen. If a lettering device is available, the student may measure the height of the letters on Drawing No. 9; remember that on lettering devices the scale is in thousandths of an inch. If the reading is 140 on a civil engineer's scale or on any scale that is graduated in tenths of an inch, this means $^{140}/_{1000}$ in, so the 140 scale on the lettering device should be used. If the letters measure 0.2 in [5 mm], as they do on Drawing No. 9, then the 200 scale on the lettering set should be used.

Only the project numbers, county numbers, and state road numbers need be in mechanical lettering. All of the remaining lettering on the key map may be rendered freehand.

LENGTH OF PROJECT

Lengths of roadway, bridges, and exceptions and net and gross lengths are shown in a box at the center of the sheet below the location map. Show the length of the job in linear feet and miles.

REMEMBER To get miles from linear feet just divide the number of linear feet by the number of feet in 1 mi.

RANGE LINES AND TOWNSHIP LINES

Range lines contain a long dash followed by three short dashes, repeated over and over. A township line is shown exactly the same way. Dashed lines are used between sections. Range and township lines must be called out, such as R 10 E over R 11 E, and T 7 N over T 6 N. Figure 4–7 and the following paragraph give an explanation of range and township lines.

Township lines on a state map run *east* and *west*; they are 6 mi [9.7 km] apart on the ground. *Range lines* run *north* and *south* and are also located 6 mi [9.7 km] apart on the ground. The area between range and township lines is divided into 1-mi [1.6-km] spaces. Thus, within one 6-mi township and one 6-mi range area are 6 × 6 or 36 squares. Each of these 36 squares is 1 sq mi [2.59 sq km] in area. These square mile areas are called *sections*, and they are all numbered within each 36-square-mile township. Numbers start at the upper right-hand corner with section 1, go west to section 6, then south to section 7, east to section 12, and so forth. This unusual numbering system follows the path surveyors would take as they walked through the township; it is the most economical way to measure ground.

UNITS OF MEASUREMENT

The following units of measurement should be learned:

Township: a square which is 6 mi [9.7 km] on each side (6 miles square, not 6 square miles). Townships are 6 × 6 or 36 sq mi [93.2 sq km] in area.

Section: a square which is 1 mi [1.6 km] on each side and is thus 1 × 1 or 1 sq mi [2.59 sq km] in area; there are 640 acres [259 hectares] in a section.

Mile: 5280 ft. The determination was made by Queen Elizabeth the First. This was the exact distance between Buckingham Palace and a summer palace.

Acre: 43,560 sq ft (remember this figure).

640 acres per 1 square mile

Figure 4-7
Land section.

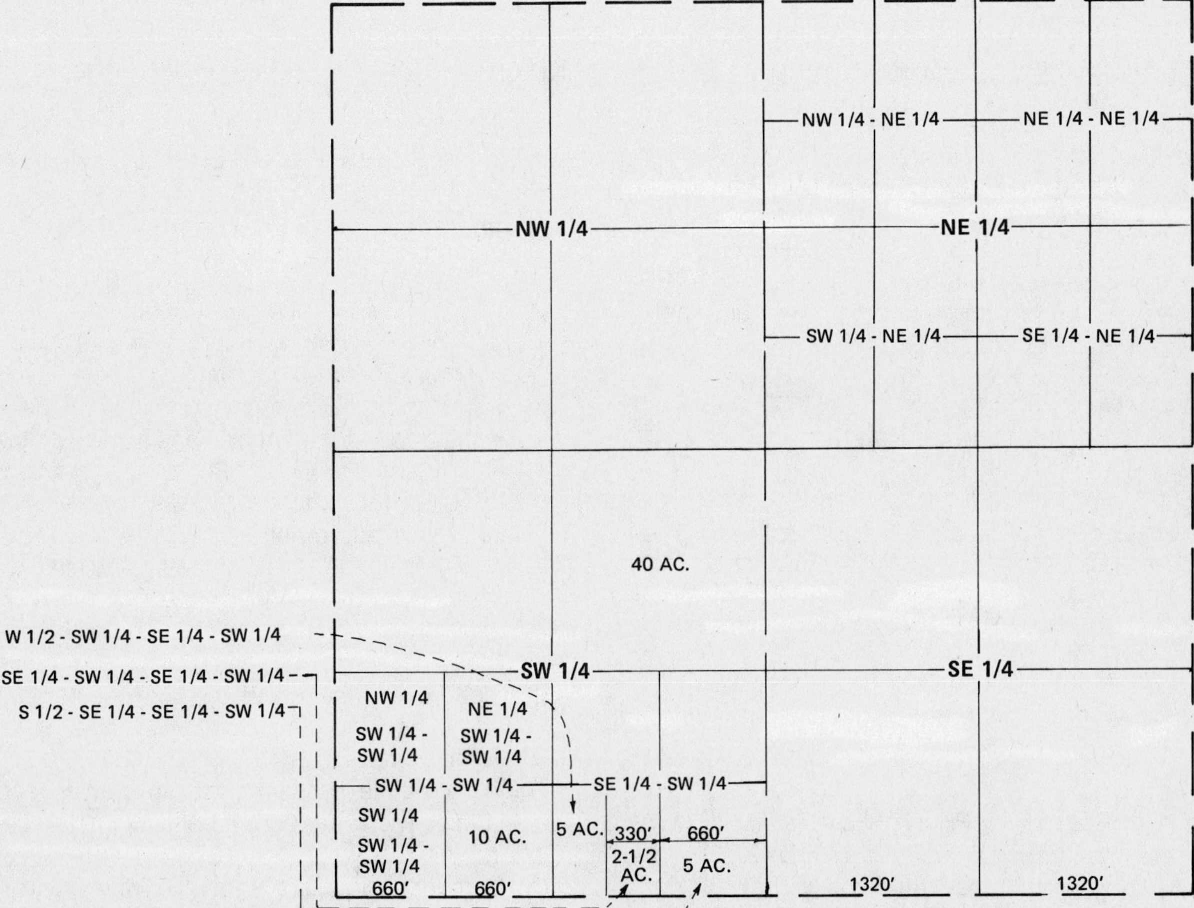

PROBLEMS

1. Remove Drawing No. 10 from the back of the Chapter. Insert Drawing No. 10 under a B-size (11 × 17 in) sheet of vellum drafting paper. Put the location map roughly under the center of the vellum.
   (a) Trace the location map on the vellum.
   (b) Move the vellum around on top of Drawing No. 10 to properly locatc thc additional items to be traced. (The state map may be in too far toward the center of the drawing and likewise the index of sheets may be too close to the center. The length-of-project box can be moved closer to the bottom of the drawing.) The book is 8¼ × 11 in, but the vellum sheets are 11 × 17 in, so there is extra room on the sheet. Use the extra room to produce a satisfactory drawing. The location maps of the states and Canadian provinces have all been produced at the proper size for tracing directly from the drawings onto the 11 × 17 in sheets.
   (c) Trace the north point and the scale.
   (d) Put in the following stations:

BEGIN PROJECT—STA. 11 + 88
END PROJECT—STA. 497 + 11

Also put in the stations for the beginning and end of the bridge.

   (e) In the upper left corner of sheet will be the index of sheets. Put in No. 1—KEY MAP.
   (f) Trace the length-of-project box and letter in the following:

	Linear Feet	Miles
Roadway	48,418.00	9.170
Bridges	105.00	0.019
Net length of project	48,523.00	9.189
Exceptions	0.00	0.000
Gross length of project	48,523.00	9.189

   (g) At the top center of the sheet letter the following (use a mechanical lettering device if one is available):

PLANS OF PROPOSED STATE HIGHWAY
F.A. PROJECT NO. S-427(2)
COLLIER COUNTY
STATE ROAD NO. S-846

Note: Use Drawing No. 9 as a guide when rendering rural key maps. It has all the essential items of a rural key map.

Suggestion Once the Drawings and quizzes have been removed from the text and completed, put three holes in each sheet and bind them all in a three-ring binder for future reference. It will be helpful to refer back to these items later in this course or when working in industry.

2. This problem will give experience in both drafting and in calculating road distance and exceptions. The student will have to fill in the distance chart.
   (a) Center the location map (Drawing No. 11) under a B-size (11 × 17 in) sheet of vellum drafting paper. Trace the location map with begin- and end-project flags and bridge exception stationing.
   (b) Move the vellum to get a good location for the Length-of-Project Box and trace it. Do the appropriate calculations to fill in all the blanks. The stationing is as follows:

BEGIN PROJECT—STA. 10 + 00
START BRIDGE EXCEPTION— STA. 114 + 80
END BRIDGE EXCEPTION—STA. 116 + 40
START SECOND BRIDGE EXCEPTION—STA. 220 + 80
END SECOND BRIDGE EXCEPTION—STA. 221 + 60
END PROJECT—STA. 274 + 00

Fill in End of Project. (Whenever *Begin-* and *End-Project* are given without any station figures, the stationing must be calculated from information in the problem.)

   (c) Adjust the vellum to put the map of Indiana in the upper right corner; trace it and add the words "LOCATION OF PROJECT" to this flag.
   (d) Readjust vellum to put "INDEX OF SHEETS" in the top left corner.
   (e) Now write in the project heading and title with a mechanical lettering device, if one is available; if not, letter this in freehand with thick lines.
   (f) Sign your name above the drawing number after checking against Drawing No. 9 for completeness.
3. This is a simple problem, both in drafting and arithmetic. There are no exceptions, just an uninterrupted roadway.
   (a) Center the location map (Drawing No. 12) under a B-size sheet of vellum drafting pa-

per. Trace the location map and begin- and end-project flags.

(b) Move the vellum to get a good location in top right corner of the sheet for the map of the state of Oklahoma. Trace the map and add the location-of-project flag and the north point.

(c) Move the vellum to get a good top left location for the index of sheets and trace this on the vellum.

(d) Move the vellum to give a good low-center location for the length-of-project box. Trace it and figure the linear feet and miles from the stationing, which is as follows (letter this information on the flags):

BEGIN PROJECT—STA. 10 + 00
END PROJECT—STA. 379 + 60

Notice that the job is exactly 7 mi [11.3 km] long (5280 feet per mile). Also note that the project begins at station 10 + 00, which is 1000 ft [304.8 m] from the point of beginning of the survey.

Take Sta. 379 + 60, subtract Sta. 10 + 00 to give a length of 369 + 60 stations. Multiply 369 + 60 by 100 ft per station: 369 stations × 100 + 60 ft = 36,960 ft [11,265 m]. This is the total number of linear feet.

(e) Put the subject heading and project number on the key map in the center top location. Use a mechanical lettering device if possible.

OKLAHOMA
ROAD DEPARTMENT
PROJECT NO. 32620-7201
HIGH PLAINS COUNTY
WICHITA ROAD

(f) Check over the map to see if anything seems to be missing, then sign your name above the drawing number.

4. Use Drawing No. 13 for the location map, and proceed as in the previous problems. Using a B-size vellum, center and trace the location map, then move the vellum and trace the length-of-project box, the north point, the North Dakota state location-of-project map, and the index of sheets.

Put the title and project in the top center of the sheet.

Work out the length of the project in linear feet and miles. The stationing is:

BEGIN PROJECT—STA. 10 + 00
START BRIDGE EXCEPTION—STA. 220 + 40
END BRIDGE EXCEPTION—STA. 222 + 00
END PROJECT—STA. 274 + 00

Sign above the drawing number.

5. This is a simple problem in the province of New Brunswick, Canada. Center the location map (Drawing No. 14) as in previous problems under a B-size vellum; then move the vellum to trace the location of project, province map, and index of sheets.

Draw in the length-of-project box and figure all lengths from the stationing on the drawing.

LEARNING ACTIVITY PACKAGE

Read Chap. 4 carefully.

Chapter 4 read ____________ (*date*).

Drawing No. 9 will be completed while reading the chapter.

Drawing No. 9 completed ____________ (*date*).

Read the list of objectives at the beginning of the chapter again. If any of the objectives (a) through (g) are not understood, the material in the appropriate paragraphs of the chapter should be reread.

Objectives read and studied ____________ (*date*).

Remove the Chap. 4 quiz from the back of the chapter and answer all the questions.

Chapter 4 quiz completed ____________ (*date*).

All students should do Problem No. 1 (Drawing No. 10); completed ____________ (*date*).

Problem No. 2 (Drawing No. 11) completed

____________ (*date*).

All students should do Problem No. 3 (Drawing No. 12); completed ____________ (*date*).

Problem No. 4 (Drawing No. 13) completed ____________ (*date*)

Problem No. 5 (Drawing No. 14) completed ____________ (*date*).

Do only the problems which the instructor assigns.

4

QUIZ

1. Street stationing is Never required on county key maps.
2. Range, township, and section lines replace the city street names on rural key maps. (T or F) True
3. City and county key maps are the same in one respect: The scales are the same for both. (T or F) False
4. Separate counties do not require separate job numbers. (T or F) False
5. The job location flag is placed by the drafting technician to point to the area in which the job lies. (T or F) True
6. An index of sheets is found on both rural and urban key maps. (T or F) True
7. The index of sheets saves the reader of the plans time, as it serves the same function as a book index. (T or F) True
8. The first item to draft on the vellum is always the index of sheets. (T or F) False
9. The scale for location maps is determined by the scale of the drawing used for the location map model. (T or F) True
10. Location maps are not traced in industry. There an entire new map is developed for each key sheet. (T or F) False
11. All dominant physical features in an area must be clearly shown on the rural key map. (T or F) True
12. At the location map edges, roads leading away from the map are labeled with the name of the next prominent town on that road. (T or F) True
13. The road which will be worked on, called the project location, is shown by a double dotted line. (T or F) False
14. Existing roads are shown by broken lines. (T or F) True
15. New work is shown by solid (unbroken) lines. (T or F) True
16. If there are two jobs on one key map, are the beginning and end of both jobs flagged? (*yes* or *no*) yes
17. Project or job number, county, and road number form a Title for the key map.
18. Large, heavy letters are used for project or job number, county, and road number. (T or F) True
19. The title always goes above the location map. (T or F) True

20. Letters 0.2 in [5 mm] high will be No. 200 on a mechanical lettering device. (T or F) True

21. All lettering on a key map must be done with a mechanical lettering device. (T or F) False

22. To reduce linear feet to miles, divide the linear feet by 5280. (T or F) True

23. Range and township lines must be called out on rural key maps. (T or F) True

24. Township lines are lines on a state map running north and south. (T or F) False

25. Township lines are 6 mi [9.7 km] apart on the ground. (T or F) True

26. There are 36 sq mi within one township. section (T or F) false

27. An area of one square mile within a range or township is called a section. (T or F) True

28. How many square feet are in one acre? 43,560 sq ft

29. How many acres are in one square mile? ______

30. How many linear feet are in one mile? 5280 ft

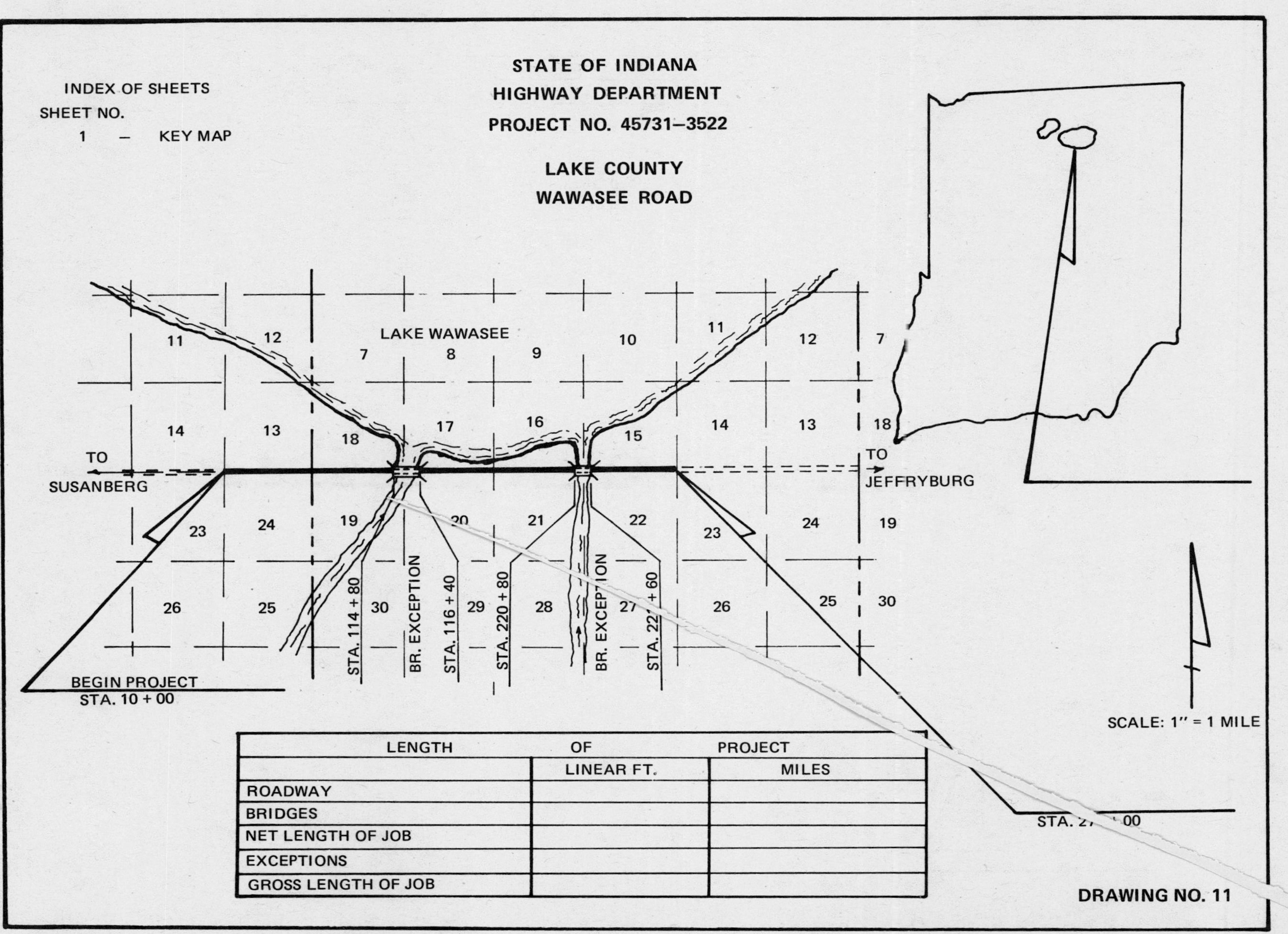
STATE OF INDIANA
HIGHWAY DEPARTMENT
PROJECT NO. 45731–3522
LAKE COUNTY
WAWASEE ROAD
INDEX OF SHEETS
SHEET NO.
1 – KEY MAP
LAKE WAWASEE
TO SUSANBERG
TO JEFFRYBURG
BEGIN PROJECT
STA. 10 + 00
STA. 114 + 80
BR. EXCEPTION
STA. 116 + 40
STA. 220 + 80
BR. EXCEPTION
SCALE: 1" = 1 MILE
DRAWING NO. 11
LENGTH OF PROJECT
LINEAR FT.
MILES
ROADWAY
BRIDGES
NET LENGTH OF JOB
EXCEPTIONS
GROSS LENGTH OF JOB

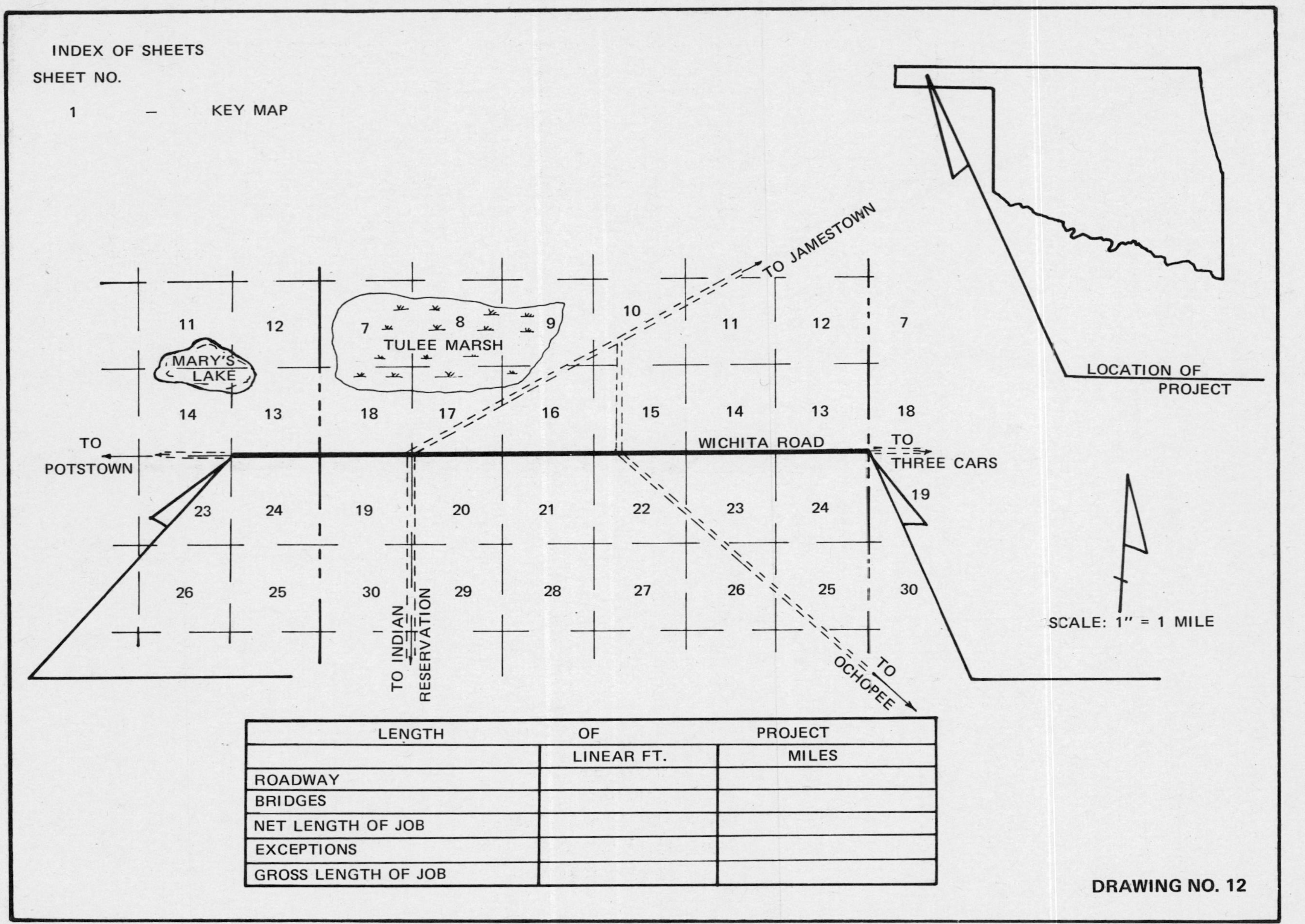
INDEX OF SHEETS
SHEET NO.
1 — KEY MAP
MARY'S LAKE
TULEE MARSH
TO JAMESTOWN
LOCATION OF PROJECT
TO POTSTOWN
WICHITA ROAD
TO THREE CARS
TO INDIAN RESERVATION
TO OCHOPEE
SCALE: 1" = 1 MILE
11
12
7
8
9
10
11
12
7
14
13
18
17
16
15
14
13
18
23
24
19
20
21
22
23
24
19
26
25
30
29
28
27
26
25
30
LENGTH OF PROJECT
LINEAR FT.
MILES
ROADWAY
BRIDGES
NET LENGTH OF JOB
EXCEPTIONS
GROSS LENGTH OF JOB
DRAWING NO. 12

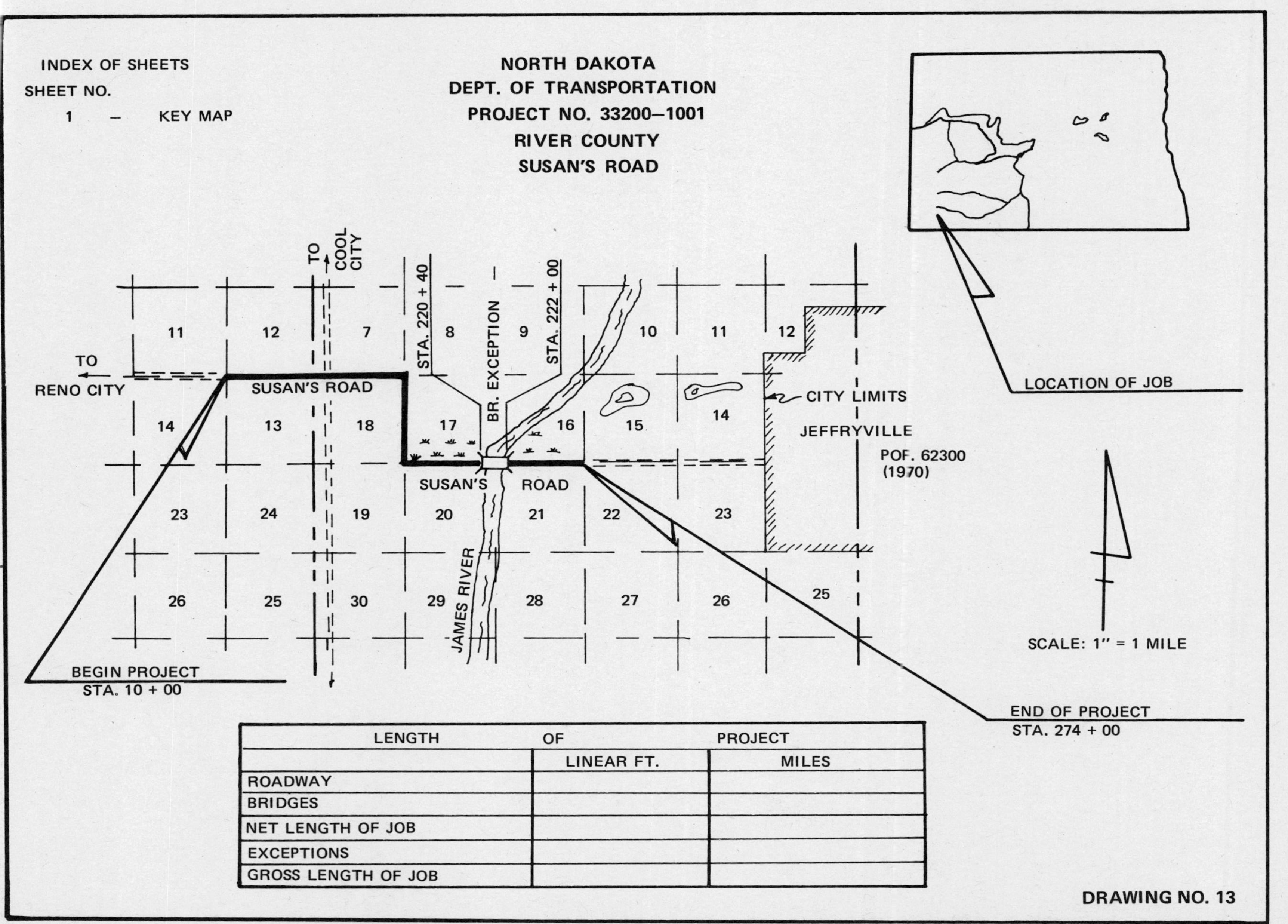
INDEX OF SHEETS
SHEET NO.
1 – KEY MAP
NORTH DAKOTA
DEPT. OF TRANSPORTATION
PROJECT NO. 33200–1001
RIVER COUNTY
SUSAN'S ROAD
LOCATION OF JOB
TO COOL CITY
TO RENO CITY
SUSAN'S ROAD
STA. 220 + 40
BR. EXCEPTION
STA. 222 + 00
SUSAN'S ROAD
JAMES RIVER
CITY LIMITS
JEFFRYVILLE
POF. 62300 (1970)
11 12 7 8 9 10 11 12
14 13 18 17 16 15 14
23 24 19 20 21 22 23
26 25 30 29 28 27 26 25
BEGIN PROJECT
STA. 10 + 00
END OF PROJECT
STA. 274 + 00
SCALE: 1″ = 1 MILE
LENGTH OF PROJECT
LINEAR FT.
MILES
ROADWAY
BRIDGES
NET LENGTH OF JOB
EXCEPTIONS
GROSS LENGTH OF JOB
DRAWING NO. 13

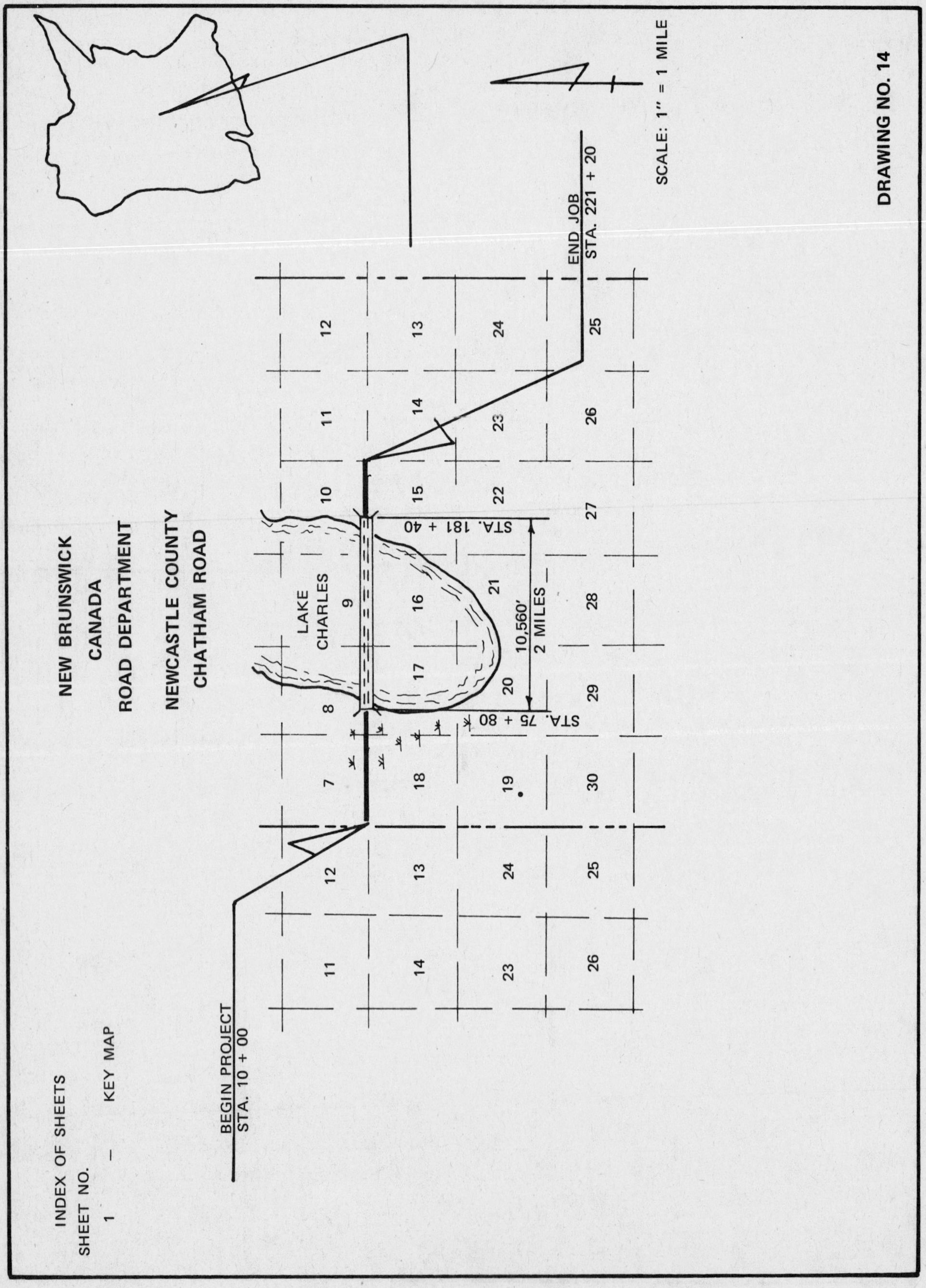
NEW BRUNSWICK
CANADA
ROAD DEPARTMENT
NEWCASTLE COUNTY
CHATHAM ROAD
INDEX OF SHEETS
SHEET NO.
1 — KEY MAP
BEGIN PROJECT
STA. 10 + 00
END JOB
STA. 221 + 20
LAKE
CHARLES
STA. 75 + 80
STA. 181 + 40
10,560'
2 MILES
11
12
13
14
23
24
25
26
7
8
9
10
18
17
16
15
19
20
21
22
30
29
28
27
SCALE: 1" = 1 MILE
DRAWING NO. 14

5 DRAINAGE BASICS

Objectives

a. Learn the basics of drainage
b. Learn about channel changes and pipe culverts
c. Study manholes and box culverts
d. Understand how the direction of water flow is indicated on the drainage map
e. Understand the significance of the physical features shown on the drainage map
f. Learn how existing drainage structures are indicated

Rationale

Drainage is basic to the design of good highways and must be understood thoroughly. The student must learn about the natural flow of water in various areas. Drainage systems serve to control storm waters and direct them to appropriate places. The use of side slopes to protect the roads from erosion and the use of roadway ditches to conduct water and drain it to the proper place must also be understood.

A major concern in highway construction is water drainage; a typical drainage situation is shown in Fig. 5–1. Water must be kept from standing on or washing over the road, and the side slopes must be protected from erosion. To handle these drainage problems, the natural flow of water in the area is studied and a drainage system of slopes, ditches, pipes, and culverts is devised. These are shown on plan and profile sheets, typical section sheets, drainage structure sheets, and roadway cross-section sheets.

DITCHES AND CHANNELS

Roadway ditches are formed along roadways in cut sections and in the median strips of divided roadways. They collect and drain water from back slopes and cross slopes.

Figure 5-1
A drainage situation. Notice the ditch on the left that handles rainfall from roadway and all adjacent fields *(Florida Department of Transportation).*

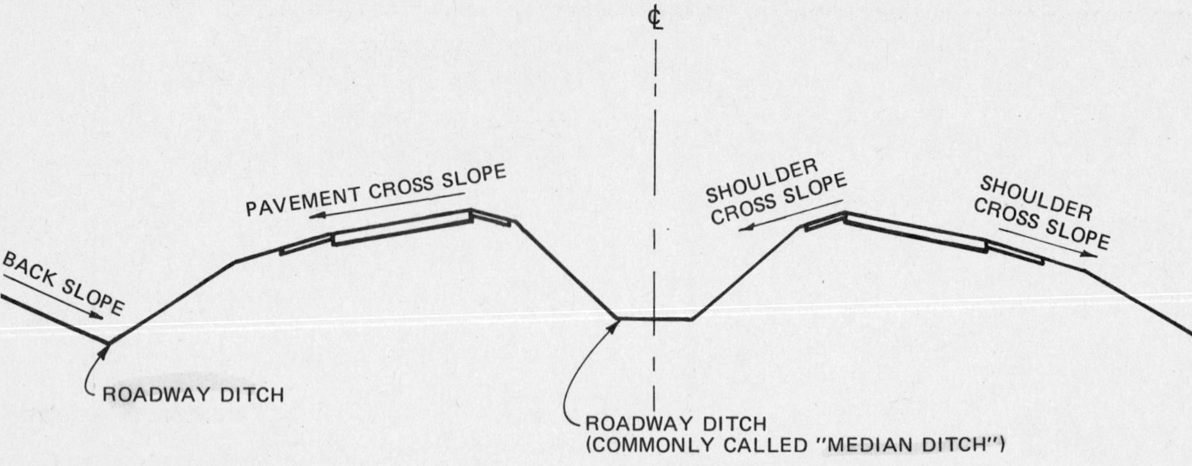

Figure 5-2
Typical section of roadway ditches.

Figure 5-3
An oceanside erosion problem *(Florida Department of Transportation).*

Figure 5-4
Erosion and some erosion control methods *(Florida Department of Transportation).*

An example is shown in Fig. 5–2 of a typical road cross section where there are back slopes, cross slopes, and a roadway ditch in the center of the cross section (this is called a median ditch). Roadway ditches often are sodded or paved to prevent erosion. Examples of erosion problems are shown in Figs. 5–3 and 5–4.

Details of Ditch Requirements

Several types of drawings are used to present the necessary information on roadway ditch requirements:

- ☐ *Summary-of-quantities* sheets show station locations and sodding and paving requirements.
- ☐ *Typical section* sheets give general details of width, height, side slopes, and thickness of sodding or paving.
- ☐ *Plan and profile* sheets show the lengths of ditches and their location relative to the roadway.
- ☐ *Roadway cross-section* sheets contain specific details of width and height.

Special Ditches

Special ditches are different from roadway ditches in grade, elevation, or location. Special ditches usually are labeled and described on plan and profile sheets; any sodding or paving requirements are found on summary of quantities sheets.

Turn to Fig. 5–5, which is Sheet 15 of Project 54001–3402, and find the special paved ditch between Sta. 275 + 00 and 278 + 12. The ditch can be seen in the profile view. The profile view is the lower portion of the drawing, which is drawn over a grid. There are two profiles for the region between Sta. 275 + 00 and 278 + 12. One is the profile grade line, the other is the ditch grade line.

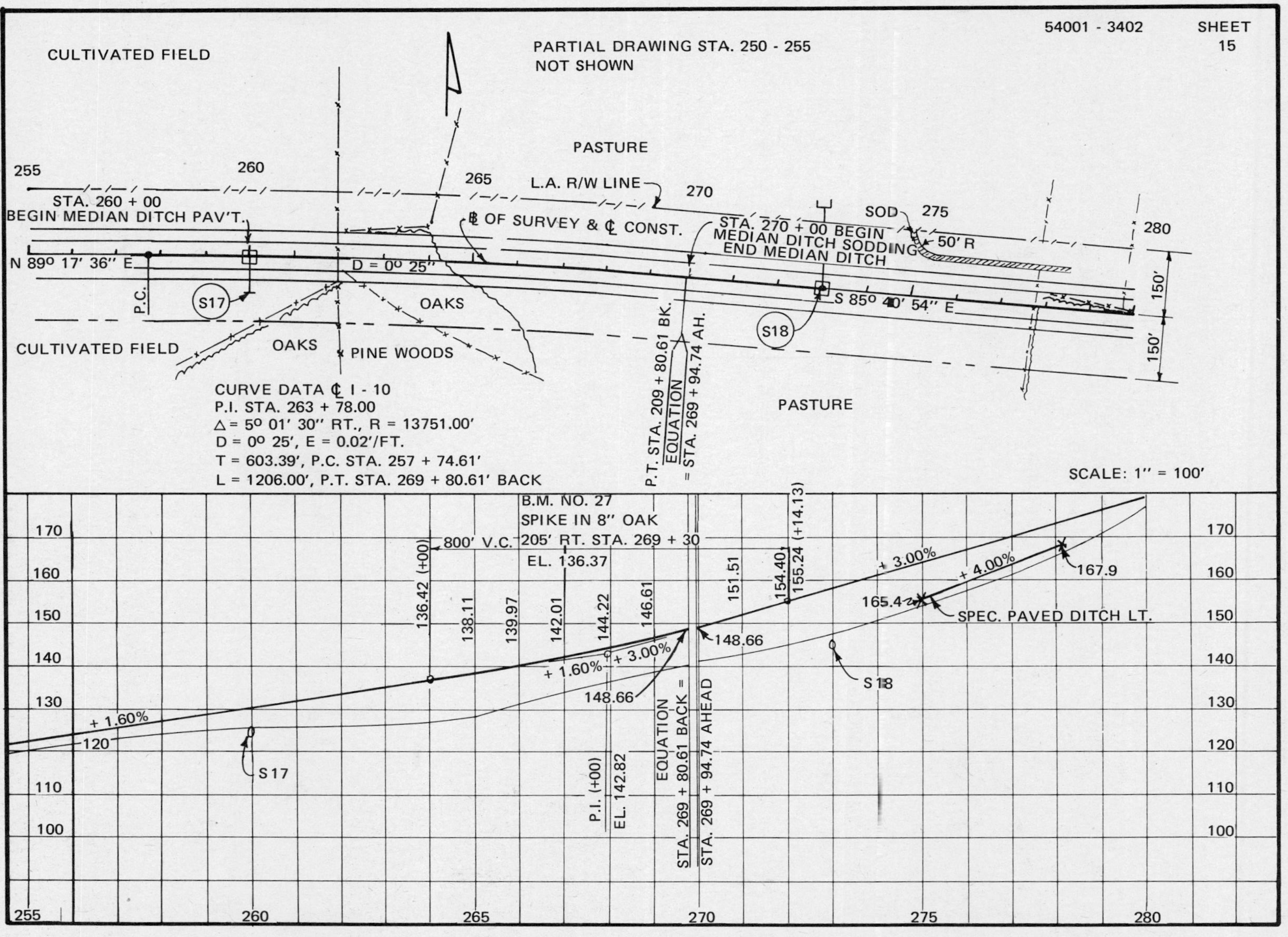

Figure 5-5
Partial drawing of State Project 54001-3402 between Stations 255 and 280.

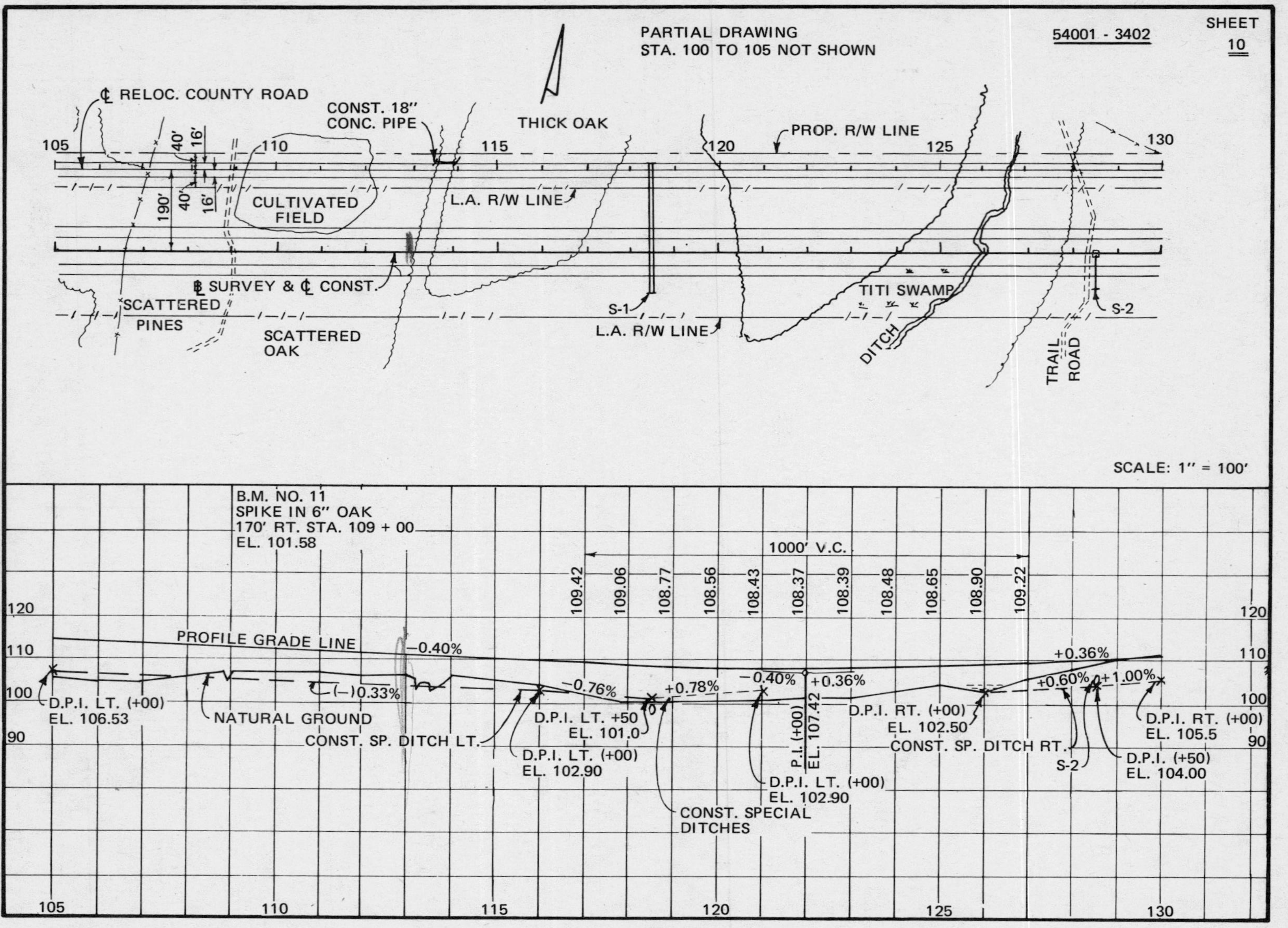

Figure 5-6
Partial drawing of State Project 54001-3402 between Stations 105 and 130.

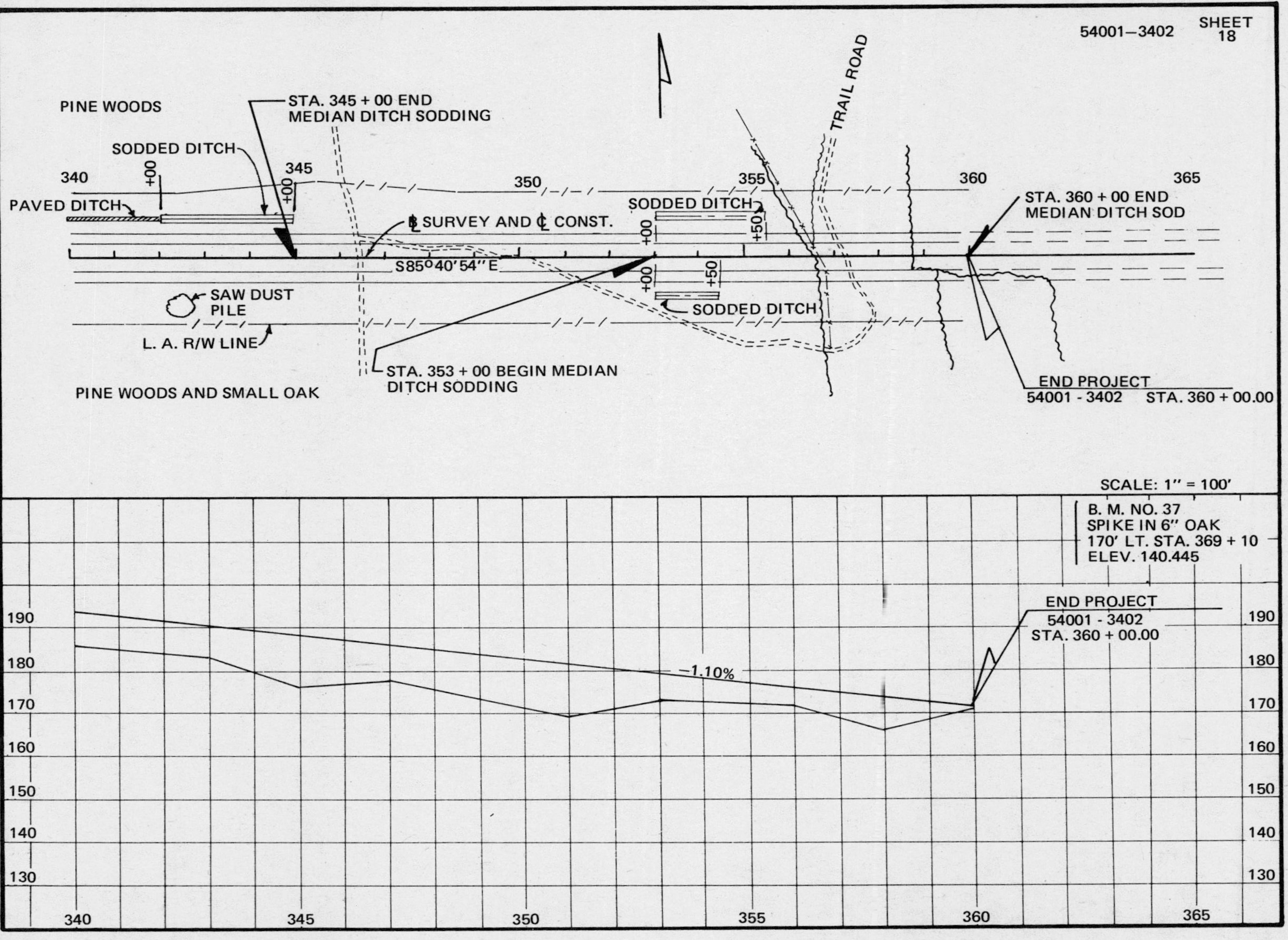

Figure 5-7
Several special ditches at the end of State Project 54001-3402.

QUIZ

Refer to Project 54001–3402 Sheets 10 (Fig. 5–6) and 18 (Fig. 5–7) (they will be easily found in the text—it is good if the student practices looking up work by the job numbers) and answer the following questions:

Should the median between Sta. 345 + 00 and 353 + 00 be sodded? NO

What is the length of the sodded ditch to the left of the roadway beginning at Sta. 353 + 00?

250'

Is the special ditch at Sta. 113 + 00 right or left of the centerline? left

What is the percent of grade of the roadway profile at Sta. 113 + 00? -.4%

What is the percent of grade of the special ditch profile at Sta. 113 + 00 -.33

D.P.I. means __________.

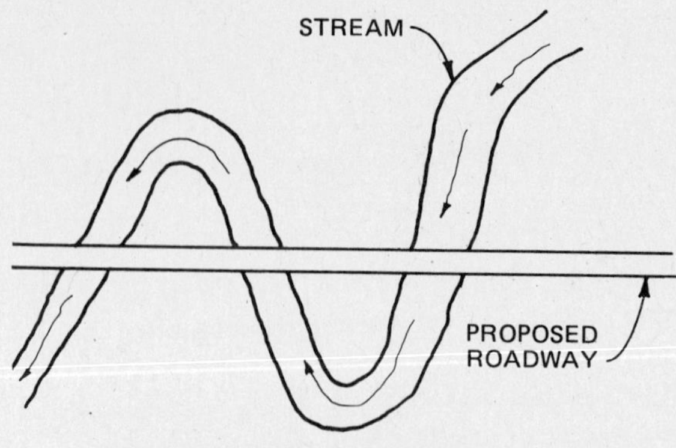

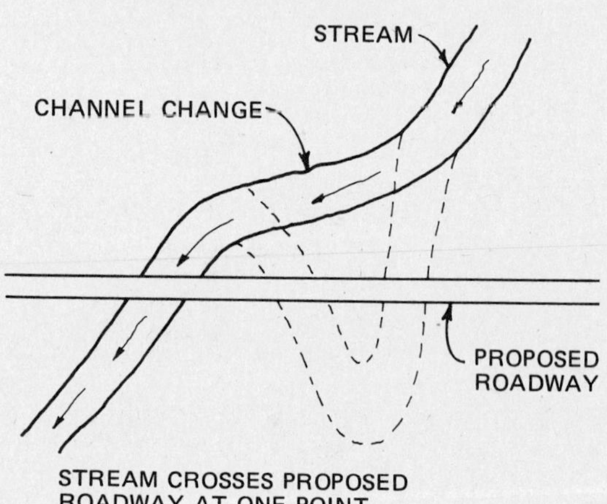

Figure 5-8
Channel changes.

CHANNEL CHANGES

Channels sometimes are changed to straighten stream alignments. Study the channel-change situation in Fig. 5–8. Notice how a proposed roadway may intersect a meandering stream several times. In these cases it is sometimes less expensive to construct a new channel than to construct the several drainage structures that would be necessary if the stream crossed the roadway several times. Scour protection for the channel walls may be called for in the plans.

PIPE CULVERTS

A culvert is a structure which provides an opening under the roadway. When an opening under the roadway is provided with a pipe, the pipe is called a pipe culvert. A pipe culvert can be a corrugated metal pipe (C.M.P.) or a concrete pipe. Pipe culverts may have several different shapes.

QUIZ

End views of two of the more common pipes are shown in Fig. 5–9. What do the letters represent?

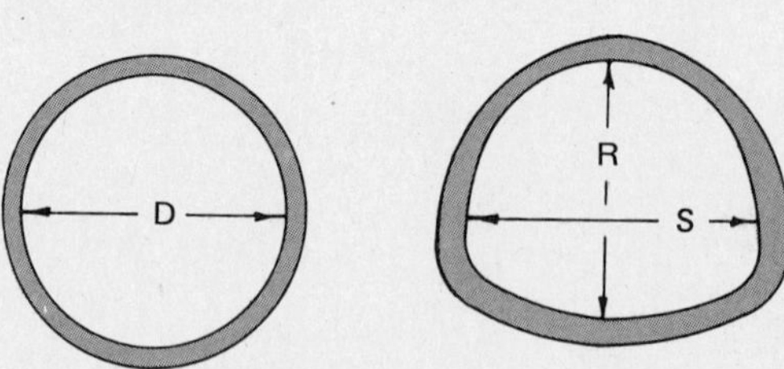

Figure 5-9
End views of common pipes.

D = diameter

S = __________

R = __________

Construction details of drainage structures such as pipe culverts are shown on drainage structure sheets, where they are referred to by structure number. Fig. 5–10 shows how pipe culverts appear on plan and profile views.

Another example is shown on Plan and Profile Sheet 14 of Project 54001–3402 (Fig. 9–6 in Chap. 9). Locate

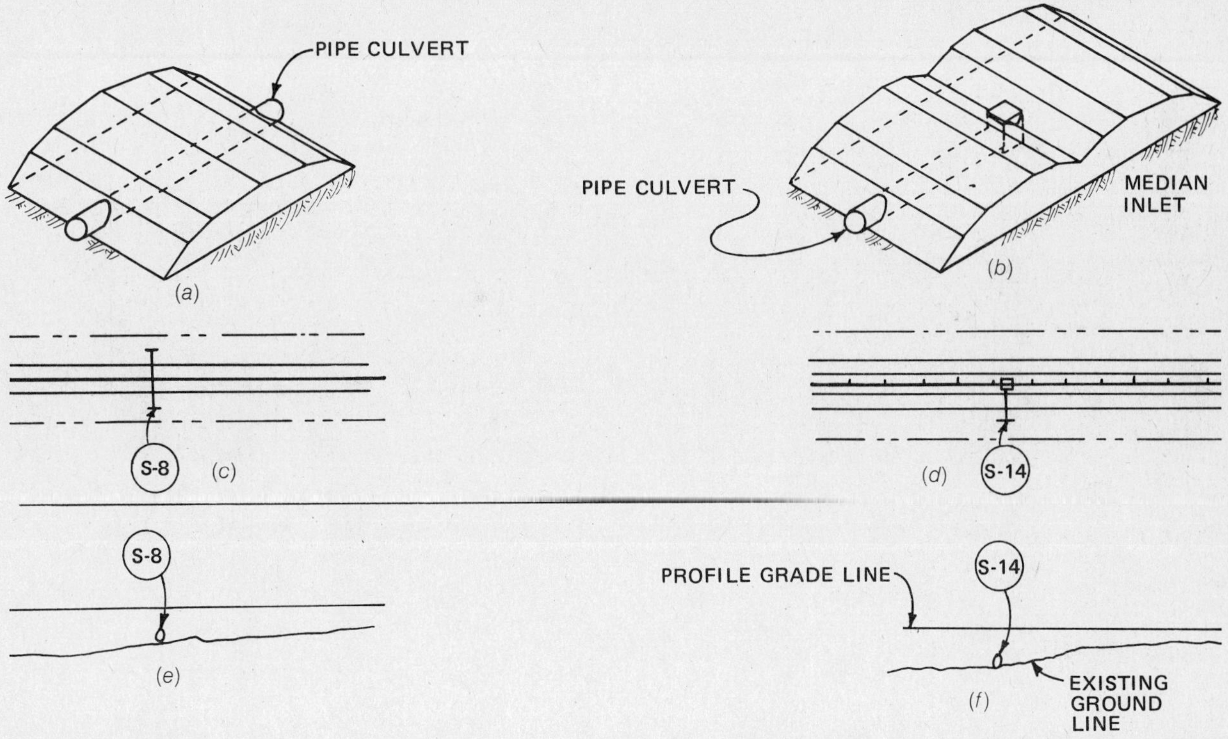

Figure 5-10
Pipe culverts may go under an entire roadway (*a*) or under only one roadway, with an inlet from the median (*b*). Views (*c*) and (*d*) show how these two types of culverts appear in plan views; (*e*) and (*f*) show the profile views.

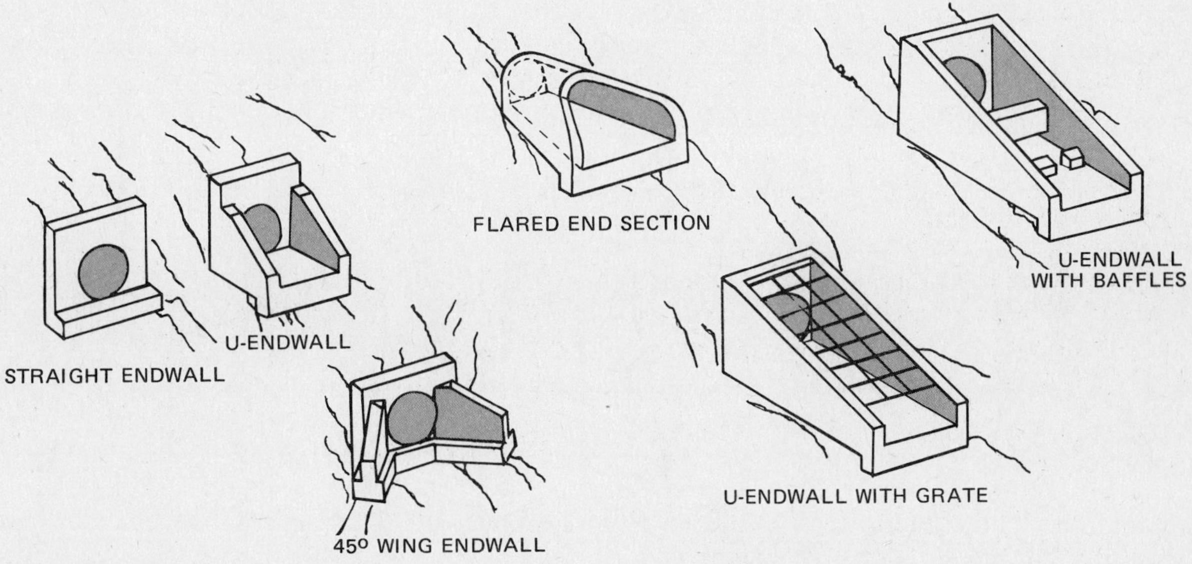

Figure 5-11
Endwalls

the pipe culvert under the left roadway at Sta. 233 + 00. The structure number, S–15, is shown on both the plan view and the profile view. The drainage sheet on this project would show that S–15 is 82 feet (ft) [25 m] of 18-inch (in) [46-cm] pipe with a suitable inlet and endwall.

END TREATMENT

Endwalls or other end treatments help prevent erosion of surrounding embankments. Endwalls increase efficiency of water flow (see Fig. 5–11). Standard drawings give details of endwalls; the drawing numbers are given on the appropriate structures sheet.

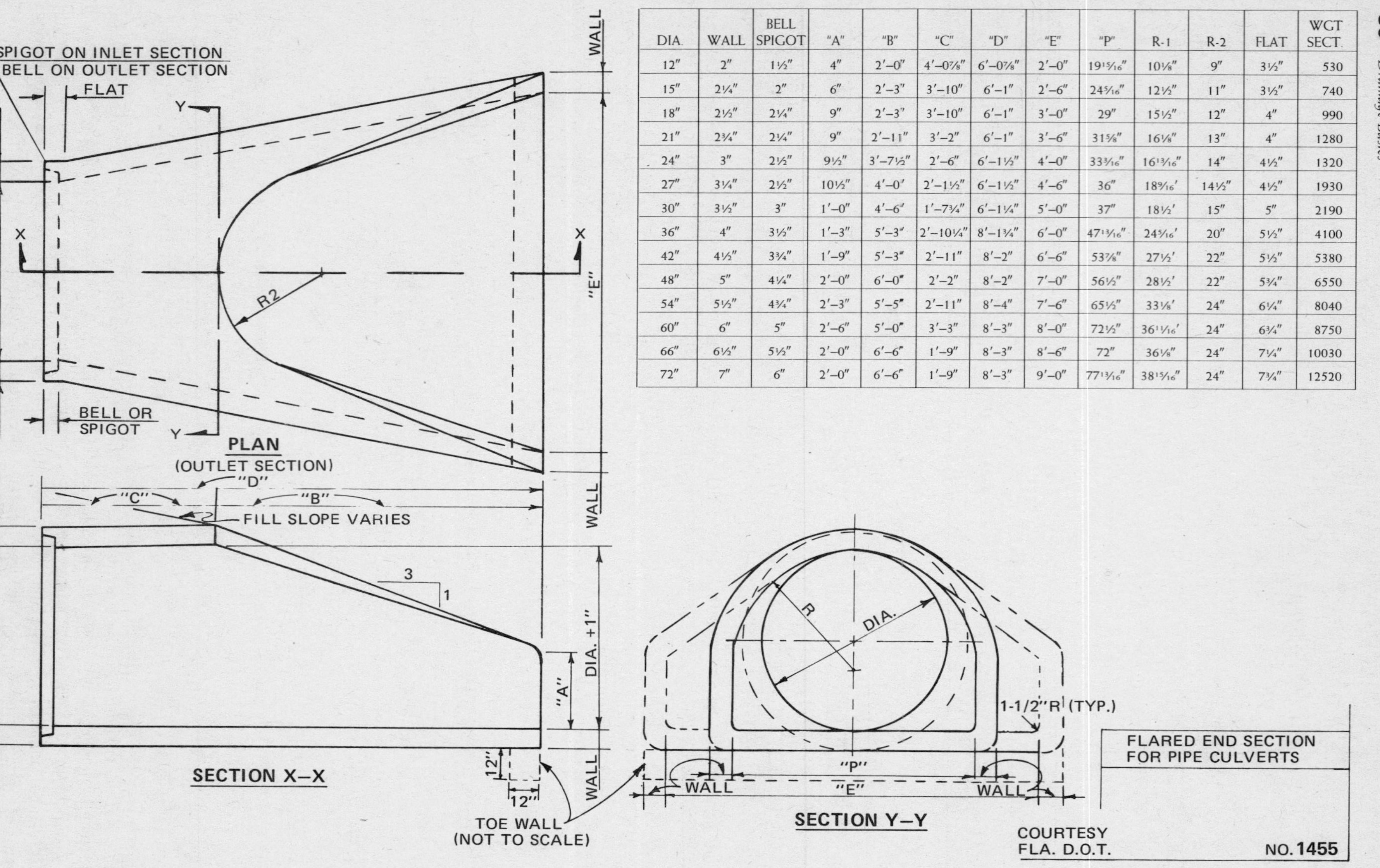

DIA.	WALL	BELL SPIGOT	"A"	"B"	"C"	"D"	"E"	"P"	R-1	R-2	FLAT	WGT SECT.
12″	2″	1½″	4″	2′–0″	4′–0⅞″	6′–0⅞″	2′–0″	19¹⁵⁄₁₆″	10⅛″	9″	3½″	530
15″	2¼″	2″	6″	2′–3″	3′–10″	6′–1″	2′–6″	24⁵⁄₁₆″	12½″	11″	3½″	740
18″	2½″	2¼″	9″	2′–3″	3′–10″	6′–1″	3′–0″	29″	15½″	12″	4″	990
21″	2¾″	2¼″	9″	2′–11″	3′–2″	6′–1″	3′–6″	31⅝″	16⅛″	13″	4″	1280
24″	3″	2½″	9½″	3′–7½″	2′–6″	6′–1½″	4′–0″	33³⁄₁₆″	16¹³⁄₁₆″	14″	4½″	1320
27″	3¼″	2½″	10½″	4′–0′	2′–1½″	6′–1½″	4′–6″	36″	18⁹⁄₁₆′	14½″	4½″	1930
30″	3½″	3″	1′–0″	4′–6′	1′–7¾″	6′–1¼″	5′–0″	37″	18½′	15″	5″	2190
36″	4″	3½″	1′–3″	5′–3″	2′–10¼″	8′–1¾″	6′–0″	47¹³⁄₁₆″	24⁵⁄₁₆′	20″	5½″	4100
42″	4½″	3¾″	1′–9″	5′–3″	2′–11″	8′–2″	6′–6″	53⅞″	27½′	22″	5½″	5380
48″	5″	4¼″	2′–0″	6′–0″	2′–2″	8′–2″	7′–0″	56½″	28½′	22″	5¾″	6550
54″	5½″	4¾″	2′–3″	5′–5″	2′–11″	8′–4″	7′–6″	65½″	33⅛′	24″	6¼″	8040
60″	6″	5″	2′–6″	5′–0″	3′–3″	8′–3″	8′–0″	72½″	36¹¹⁄₁₆′	24″	6¾″	8750
66″	6½″	5½″	2′–0″	6′–6″	1′–9″	8′–3″	8′–6″	72″	36⅛″	24″	7¼″	10030
72″	7″	6″	2′–0″	6′–6″	1′–9″	8′–3″	9′–0″	77¹³⁄₁₆″	38¹⁵⁄₁₆″	24″	7¾″	12520

Figure 5-12
Standardized drawing of flared end sections for pipe culverts *(Florida Department of Transportation).*

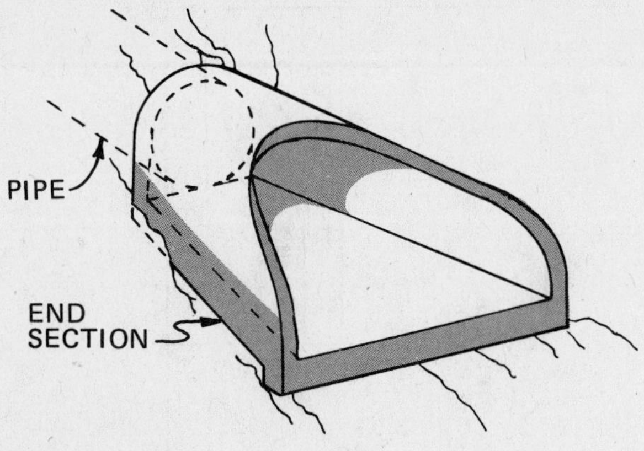

Figure 5-13
Flared-end pipe culvert.

Look at Standard Drawing 1455 (Fig. 5–12). It shows the details of construction of a flared-end section for pipe culverts like the one shown in Fig. 5–13. The dimensions of endwalls are shown on standard drawings as letters. Usually the letters are related to each other in such a way that if the diameter of the pipe culvert is known, all the dimensions of the structure can be calculated or found in a table.

FLOW LINE

In any drainage structure, the lowest line along which water can flow is called the *flow line* (F.L.).

QUIZ

The inside dimension representing the longest vertical distance across the end of a pipe arch is called the ____________.

The inside dimension representing the longest horizontal distance across the end of a pipe arch is called the ____________.

Refer to Project 54001–3402 Sheet 14 (Fig. 9–6 in Chap. 9) and locate the pipe culvert at Sta. 233 + 00.

Which roadway does it lie under? left side

What is its structure number? S15

What is the approximate length of the pipe (measure it)? ____________

Skew Angles

Look at the pipe culvert at Sta. 223 + 90, Fig. 9–6. This culvert does not cross the road at 90°, but the crossing angle, or skew angle, is 35° right.

The skew of a culvert is measured in degrees turning to the right or left of a normal crossing (study Fig. 5–14).

Figure 5-14
Skew angles of pipes crossing a roadway—the skew angle is measured from normal crossing to the end of the culvert ahead.

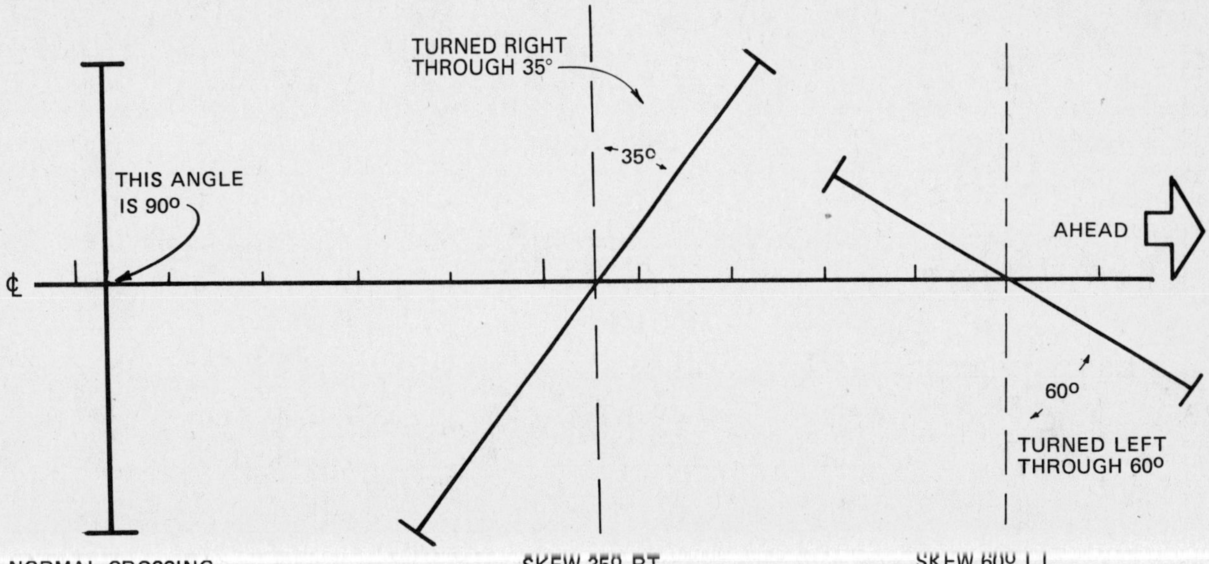

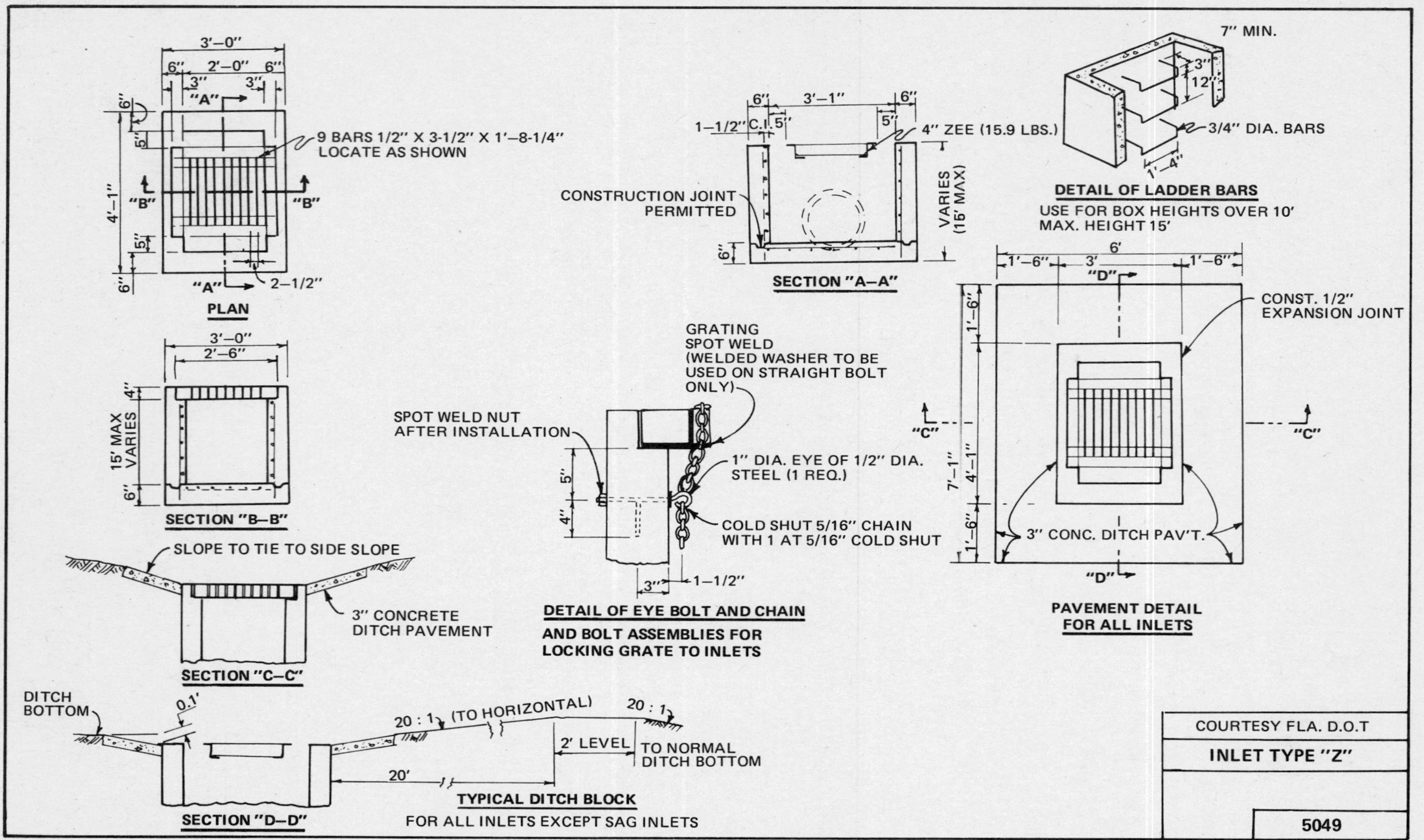

Figure 5-16
Standardized drawings like this one are always submitted with a set of road plans. This is inlet type Z.

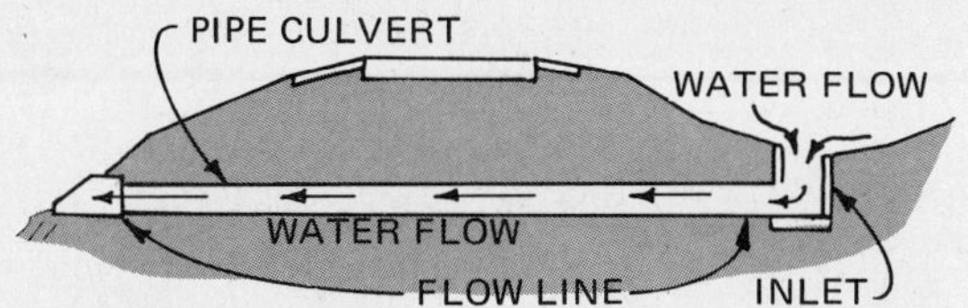

Figure 5-15
Cross section of a roadway showing an inlet flowing to a culvert.

INLETS

Inlets often are used in conjunction with pipe culverts. Inlets permit surface water to fall into culverts or other underground pipes, Fig. 5–15.

Locate structure S–15 of Project 54001–3402. It is at Sta. 233 + 00. The drainage structure sheet indicates that an inlet, type Z, is required and that details of the construction of this inlet are on Standard Drawing 5049. Turn to that standard drawing (Fig. 5–16) now.

Inlet Type Z

Standard Drawing 5049 (Fig. 5–16) shows various views and details of inlet type Z. Study the drawing and Fig. 5–17 carefully.

NOTICE

- ☐ The cross-section views on Standard Drawing 5049 (more detail can be shown using such views)
- ☐ The reinforcing bars placed in the concrete to add strength

QUIZ

Refer to Standard Drawing 5049 (Inlet Type Z), Fig. 5–16.

Figure 5-17
Inlet type Z.

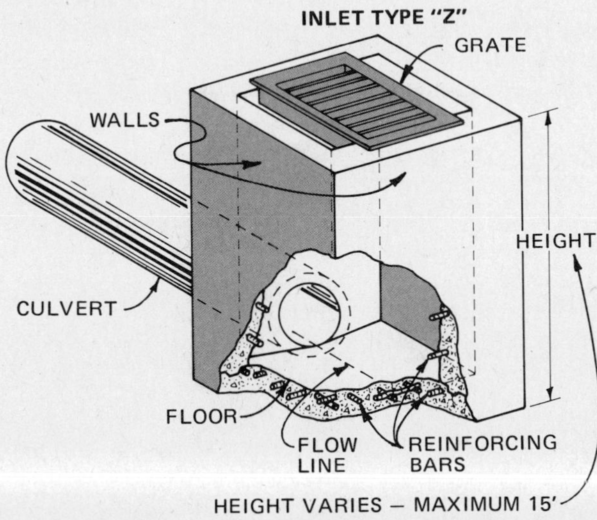

How thick is the ditch pavement surrounding the inlet? 3″ CONC

If the box is over 10′ ft, a ladder is installed.

The ladder bars are 3/4″ in diameter.

How many bars form the grating? 9

What are the dimensions of the grating bars?
1/2″ × 3 1/2″ × 1′ 8 1/4″

How thick is the inlet floor? 6″

The flow line is the lowest line along which water can flow through a drainage structure.

MANHOLES

Manholes (see Fig. 5–18) usually are found in urban projects. Manholes are brick or concrete shafts situated

Figure 5-18
Detail of manhole.

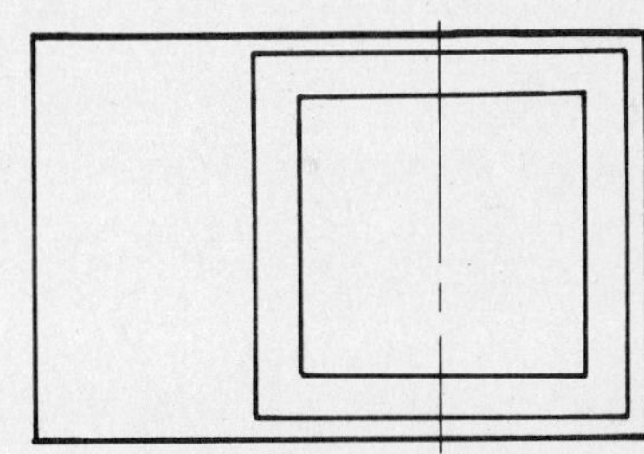

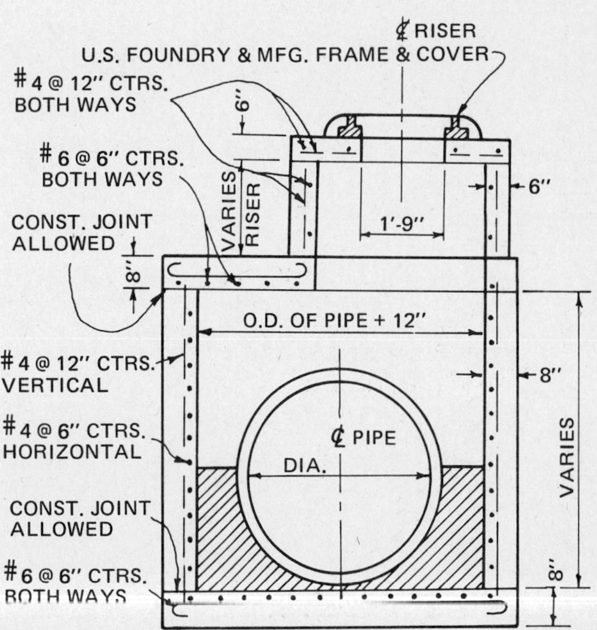

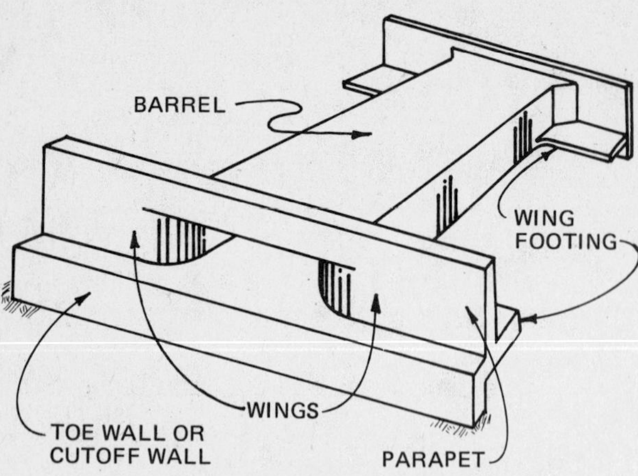

Figure 5-19
Box culvert shown in perspective to make identification of parts easier.

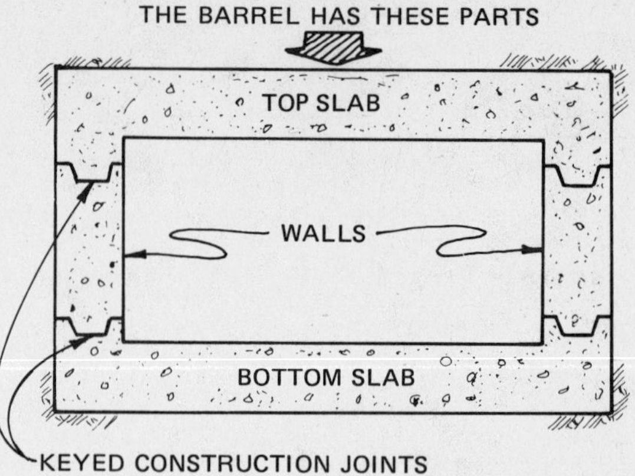

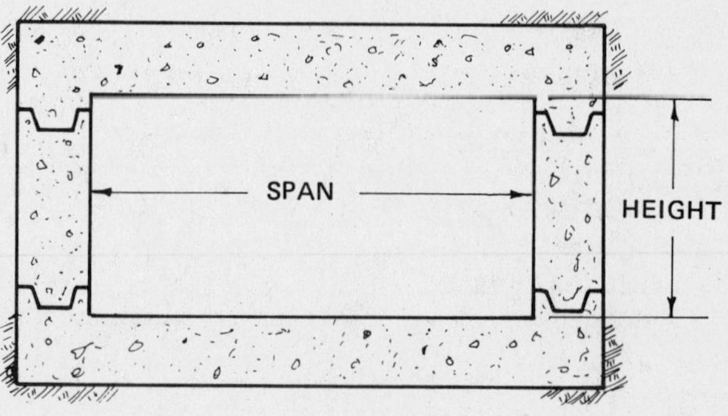

Figure 5-20
Barrel culvert terminology. Notice how the dimensions are measured.

to allow maintenance and inspection personnel access to culverts, storm sewers, and other underground structures.

BOX CULVERTS

Box-shaped culverts are called box culverts. They are constructed with reinforced concrete. Before reading box culvert plans, the student needs to become familiar with some terms.

Terminology

A box culvert is shown in Fig. 5–19—study the names of its parts.

Dimensions of box culverts often are written as 8 × 4 ft [2.4 × 1.2 m], 10 × 8 ft [3.0 × 2.4 m], and so forth. The first number always refers to the span, and the second number always refers to the height. A barrel culvert is shown in Fig. 5–20.

QUIZ

The major part of the culvert, the part between the two ends, is called the Barrel.

The part which projects above the top slab is called a parapet.

The part which "hangs down" from the end of the barrel is called a toe wall.

The top and the bottom of the culvert barrel are referred to as slab.

The distance from the inside of one wall to the inside of the other wall is the span.

The height is the distance between the inside surfaces of the walls.

DRAINAGE

This is one of the most important considerations in road design. An improperly drained road will wash away in a very short time. Some jobs show just a plan view of the road and drainage area; others show both plan and profile views. Remember that a *plan* view of an object is a view from above looking down. A *profile* view of an object is a view looking at it from the side.

Turn to Standard Drawing 1455. Notice that the plan view has marks like those shown in Fig. 5–21*a*. Alongside such a plan view is a view labeled "Section X—X." This is a cross-section view. Marks like those in Fig. 5–21*a* show where the figure was sliced to give the cross section labeled Section X—X. The arrows show the direction in which Section X—X is viewed. Examine Figs.

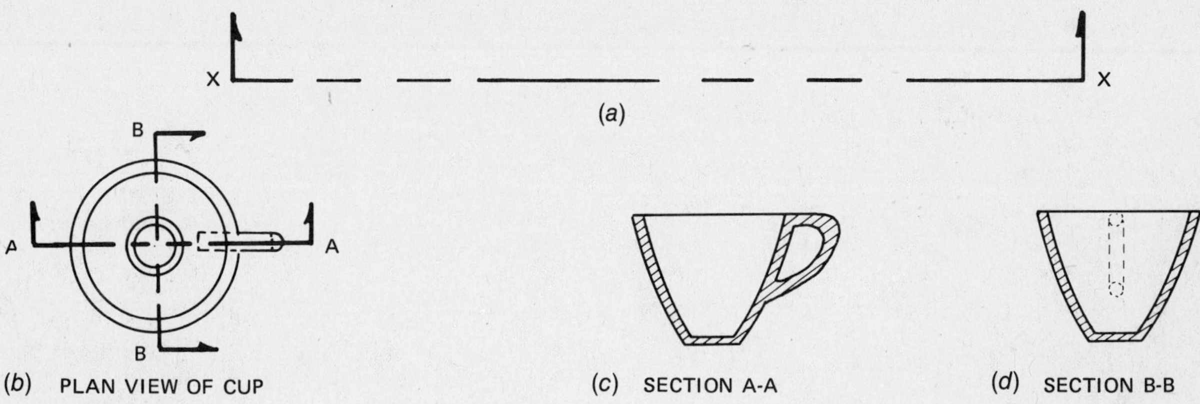

Figure 5-21
Section views.

5–21*b*, *c*, and *d*. These are drawings of a cup. The first one is a plan view (Fig. 5–21*b*). The second view (Fig. 5–21*c*) is Section A—A, the view of the cup sliced along the line indicated in the plan view. Section B—B (Fig. 5–21*d*) is a cross-section view of the cup sliced along a different line. These cross-section views are common on detail sheets and standard drawings.

Most road designs come with a plan and profile view of the drainage area. We will show only a plan view, since the profile is more difficult and probably should not be approached until after the student has had a lot of drafting practice. In addition, this text is directed toward civil drafting, not designing. Designing takes many years of drafting experience (Fig. 5–22).

Figure 5-22
The head of the drafting department in a large consulting engineering office doubles as drainage engineer for many projects *(Ross, Saarinen, Bolten. and Wilder Inc.).*

Drainage Map Survey

A drainage survey is first made by a survey crew. A survey crew usually consists of a crew chief and four other workers. They usually have a carryall-type vehicle with four-wheel drive capable of negotiating any difficult terrain. This survey should furnish all necessary information to make a complete and adequate drainage system design for the proposed highway improvement. The following information is provided by the drainage survey:

1. Drainage areas
2. Elevations (would show only on a profile view)
3. Culture
   a. Roads and trails
   b. Orchards, citrus groves, forests, and farm lands
   c. Rivers, streams, lakes, ponds, canals, ditches, borrow pits, and swamps
   d. Existing inlets, culverts, bridges, and drainage pipes
   e. Miscellaneous structures (pumps, control gates, dams, and dikes)
4. Normal and storm water elevations

PREPARATION OF DRAINAGE MAPS

The student will prepare a drainage map from Drawing No. 15 and will thus learn the nomenclature and become familiar with the method of drafting the maps.

In the industry a drainage map is normally drawn on a plain vellum sheet of size 22 × 34 or 36 in. We will obtain the same results by drawing at the reduced size of 11 × 17 in; that is the size to which industrial drainage maps would eventually be reduced by photography. The drainage map is not normally inked when produced on vellum. It should be drawn with a fairly hard pencil. The student should use 2H lead in the mechanical lead holder. In industry the old wooden pencil is seldom used, so the student should begin to use the more modern tools right now.

Scale of Map

The scale for a rural drainage map would be 1 in = 300 ft, or 1 in = 500 ft. The student should disregard the scale on Drawing No. 15 because of a reduction of the map scale during printing. To know the actual scale of the drawing, measure the distance between station 170 and 180. This is ten stations; every station is 100 feet, so ten stations is 1000 ft. For instance, suppose the distance between station 170 and 180 is 27⁄32 in (in decimals 27 divided by 32 equals 0.843 in). Then the true scale of the drawing would be 1 in = 1186 ft (1000 ft divided by 0.843).

Drawing the Rural Drainage Map

Insert Drawing No. 15 under a plain vellum sheet of a size near 11 × 17 in. It is important to trace the rural drainage map while reading the text material for the map. Do not try to be the fastest student in the class. The way to learn this subject is to do each line after reading what the line signifies. Students who race through the plates will have a little tracing experience, but they will learn little or nothing about civil drafting.

Centerline and Stationing

The general features of our map have been discussed, now we begin to deal with the specific features of this rural plan view drainage map.

Refer to the Following Statements as You Draw. The centerline of the project should be shown, along with the beginning and end stations of the job and station equations and exceptions. Stationing should be shown at regular intervals. Show the job starting at Sta. 120 + 00.00 and ending at Sta. 186 + 73.12. Notice the beginning and ending of the first 160-ft [48.8-m] bridge. Show flags for BEGIN BRIDGE at Sta. 145 + 60.00 and END BRIDGE at Sta. 147 + 20.00. This 160-ft [48.8-m] bridge will have to be constructed. The note "Construct 160-ft bridge" instructs the contractor to estimate the cost and include it in the plans. The contractor must be prepared to build the small bridge over the 18-ft [5.5-m] wide road that now exists in the area.

Direction of Water Flow

The existing 18-ft [5.5-m] road has swales, or ditches, on both its sides. These swales serve to drain the water from the area to the northwest and from 70 acres [28 hectares] to the southwest. The water in the 83 acres [34 hectares] to the east runs to Spring Creek, from which it runs north to Lake Mead. There is also another small bridge to be constructed over Spring Creek. It is 77 ft [23.5 m] long and must also be called out and stationed.

The "squiggle" arrows are one of the most important features of a drainage map, as they show the direction the water will flow. They are made freehand.

Physical Features

Physical features affecting drainage, such as lakes, streams, swamps, and so forth, must be shown; high water elevations are also noted.

1. Notice the swamp in the vicinity of Sta. 130; swamp or marsh symbols are used there. When it drains, the swamp sends water south toward the old 18-ft [5.5-m] road which has swales on each side. The water will be carried in these swales and will eventually discharge into Spring Creek, where it flows onward to Lake Mead.
2. Spring Creek, Feeder Creek, and Swamp are shown along with their destination, Lake Mead.
3. On Lake Mead the high water elevation is shown. Usually the date on which high water occurred is also given. Notice the wave symbols for Lake Mead.

Roads existing in the area are shown by double-line dashes. (Remember the rule: Existing, dashed—new, solid.) The county line road on the Rand county and Stowe county boundary line, the 18-ft [5.5-m] grade road near Lake Mead, and the 18-ft [5.5-m] RBST road are shown. Swales on each side of the 18-ft [5.5-m] RBST road are an important feature of this drainage area, as these swales carry water toward Spring Creek.

Ground Cover

Scattered pine designates the type of ground cover. This is very important on drainage maps because the type of ground cover greatly influences the water runoff rate.

Look at Fig. 5–23, which shows runoff velocities. It will show the difference between wooded high-storage (such as a Northern forest) and wooded low-storage, the condition here. From Fig. 5–23 note that a 6 percent slope gives a forest runoff of 39 ft/min [11.9 m/min]. The runoff at 6 percent in this scattered pine woods is 47.2 ft/min [14.4 m/min]. Drafting technicians are not required to do these calculations. A drainage engineer will compute the data for the drafter to put on the plans.

Existing Drainage Structures

Every drainage structure, large or small, must be indicated. Near Lake Mead is an 18-in [46-cm] concrete pipe. The survey team found that its flow line at the north was at elevation 87.22 ft [26.58 m] above sea level and the south flow line was 87.30 ft [26.61 m] above sea level. Since the north end of the pipe is lower, water flows through this pipe from south to north.

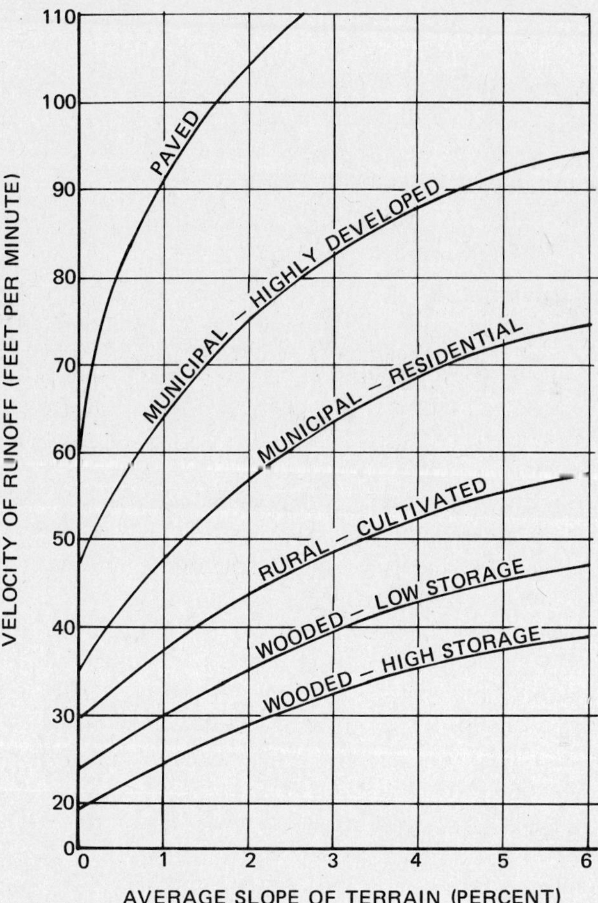

Figure 5-23
Chart No. 1—runoff velocity.

At the wooden bridge on the 18-ft [5.5-m] grade road in the northern portion of the map, note that the high water on October 7, 1959, was 90.10 ft [27.46 m]. Facts like this must be shown to allow the drainage engineer to assess the entire situation and give the proper design height for prospective roads in the area.

Final Details of the Drainage Map

The students should look over their maps and check the following:

North point and scale must be shown.
Marsh symbols should be placed in the swamp area.
Stationing—note that in this job no road is built, just two small bridges over a road and a creek.
All drainage structures are to be shown.
Squiggle arrows indicate water flow. (The drainage engineer would carefully check the arrows shown on the drainage map by going to the area after a heavy rain to see if the water was actually running in the direction shown by all the arrows on the map.)

A DRAINAGE MAP OF A FAMILIAR AREA

This exercise should familiarize the student with the symbols and procedures used to draft a rural drainage map. The faster students are encouraged to design their own rural drainage map of an area that they know rather well. Although memory of the area may not be exact, it will still be a good learning exercise. Plot the physical features of this area, then it will be possible to ascertain the direction in which the water would drain.

Figure 5–23 gives students some idea of how the drainage engineer must develop a design by using the runoff velocity of various surfaces. The wooded area in rural land has by far the slowest runoff. Paved surfaces have a very fast runoff.

The rainfall intensity chart, Fig. 5–24, shows how rainfall decreases dramatically with time. It rains very hard at the start of a shower and decreases rapidly as time goes on.

MUNICIPAL DRAINAGE MAP

Municipal drainage maps are quite different from rural maps. For one thing, the rural map covers much more area so the scale is a lot smaller. On municipal maps, all

Figure 5-24
Chart No. 2—rainfall intensity.

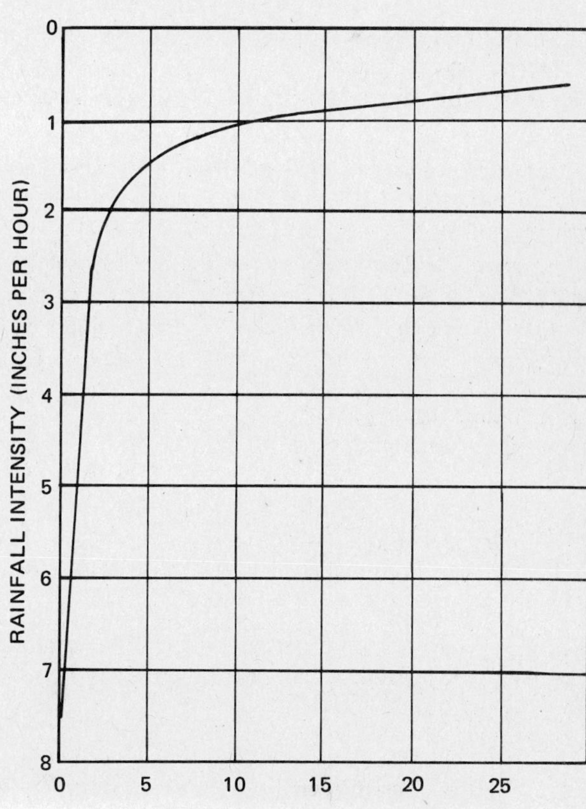

street elevations are posted at 100-ft [30.5-m] intervals, and station ticks are used.

General Information

Draw to the largest scale possible, consistent with the amount of information to be shown and the length of the job. In general, a scale smaller than 1 in = 300 ft is too small, since the drainage areas, also being small, would be quite hard to distinguish in some cases.

Show street *dedications* (not pavement). A street profile should have been run on each cross street and parallel street within the scope of the drainage area by the survey party. These profile elevations should be shown on the plan every 100 ft [30.5 m] starting 100 ft [30.5 m] from the job. These profiles are the principal information used to determine the drainage areas. Since we are simplifying the drainage maps by showing just the plan view, the student will not be showing the profile that the survey team determined. This is the domain of the drainage engineer, who will determine the flow using these profile grades. The drafting technician will make the maps showing the flow directions determined by the drainage engineer.

All existing drainage structures within the scope of the map should be shown with the size and average flow line or channel bottom indicated. Streams, ditches, ponds, canals, lakes, and so forth, should be shown topographically. (In other words, topography pertaining to drainage is desirable.)

The items listed above are necessary to determine the proposed drainage. When the drainage system is determined, it should be plotted on the plan, using appropriate symbols for inlets and manholes and indicating the proposed pipe size. Outfall ditches or pipes should also be shown.

Again, the student will *not* draw the profile view. It will be enough at this time to become familiar with the plan view of the drainage, which is the responsibility of the drainage engineer. If this book were to cover every detail, it would become very long and the student might get lost in minute details, which can be learned rapidly in industry.

DRAWING THE MUNICIPAL DRAINAGE MAP

The student should place Drawing No. 16 under an 11 × 17 in blank sheet of vellum. Follow the text very carefully and trace the map while reading the various explanations. The explanations, not just the tracing practice, are necessary.

Centerline of Construction

Draw the centerline of construction. Note the small "ticks" on the centerline of construction. These ticks are at 100-ft [30.5-m] intervals and serve the same purpose as stationing on a rural map. City maps generally do not contain more than 600 ft [183 m] on each page. In this case, put the first tick 90.00 ft beyond the project start, since the job starts at Sta. 82 + 10.00. This tick would then be stationed as 83 + 00.00. Continue putting ticks every 100 ft [30.5 m].

Flagging

Flag the beginning of the job at Sta. 82 + 10.00 and the end of job at Sta. 112 + 79.60. Flag the exception on Howard Street, too.

Drawing in City Streets

Draw in the city streets, using double lines for streets, and note that on this map existing streets are not dashed but solid. (This is one of the exceptions that proves the rule, as the old saying goes.) On a drainage map the drainage is all-important; notice that the catch basins and storm sewer (new design) are shown in single line dash-dot-dash symbols. Also note that the existing discharge line on Wilbur Street is dotted, as is existing 15-in [38-cm] T.C.P. (Terra Cotta Pipe) on John Street.

Street names need to be put on city maps. Without the street names, the plan reader would be hopelessly lost when viewing the city map. Remember that on a rural map the scale is much smaller and areas such as swamps, lakes, and so forth, are easier to distinguish than city streets.

Additional Symbols

Note that all manholes (shown round), gutter drains, and catch basins are shown with the size of pipe connecting them.

Show the north arrow and the scale.

Now, freehand dashes with larger and darker lines should be used to enclose the drainage areas. Inside these areas, note the acreage of each and indicate the water flow with arrows.

As each map is completed, check carefully to see that everything is included and reread the text to see that everything on the map is well understood.

Figure 5–25 summarizes common drainage symbols.

Review

1. Drainage arrows indicate the flow of water down a street or road in the city. In the country the arrows indicate the direction water flows over the ground.
2. Heavy, dashed freehand lines indicate the extent of certain drainage areas.
3. Manholes are shown by circles on the plan view.
4. Catch basins are square in the plan view.

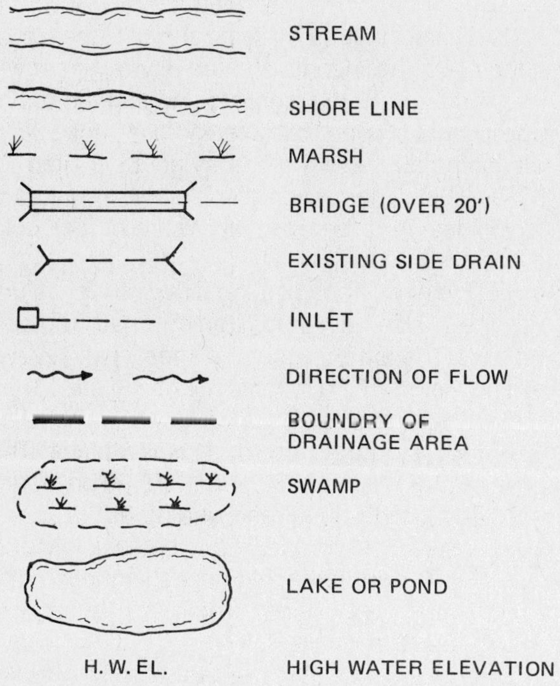

Figure 5-25
Symbols used on drainage maps.

5. Pipe sizes are shown in inches with arrows pointing to the pipe.
6. Stationing on a city map is shown by ticks, which are small lines about 1/16 to 1/8 in [1.6 to 3.2 mm] in height, drawn perpendicular to the centerline of the project and attached at their lower end to the centerline. These ticks are always 100 ft [30.5 m] apart. They serve to orient the viewer to the area of the job.
7. Physical features of the area are of supreme importance. It is the physical characteristics of the terrain that make the water flow the way it does.
8. Show all bridges, culverts, and pipes on drainage maps.
9. High water marks with the year of occurrence are very important.
10. Stationing, as usual, must show on the drainage map.

PROBLEMS

1. This problem will illustrate the importance of drainage structures; there are 15 on the plan.

Remove Drawing No. 17 from the end of the chapter and tape it under a B-size (11 × 17 in) sheet of vellum. This will be a tracing job, so tape the two sheets together and slant the vellum, with Drawing No. 17 taped to it, at any angle that is comfortable for tracing. Be sure to center the drainage map horizontally and vertically to make a good-looking drawing.

First, put in the centerline of survey. Flag the beginning of the project at Sta. 278 + 00. Notice that the project does not have an ending station. This is very unusual, as nearly all projects show an end station. However, this is an actual job taken from Florida Department of Transportation files; since it does not have an ending, we will not put one on.

Take note that on State Route 135 there are many existing concrete pipes going under the road. At about Sta. 285 there is an existing 30-in [76-cm] pipe which equalizes the water in the 57 acre [23 hectare] drainage tract at the start of the job. At approximately Sta. 300 there is an existing 24-in [61-cm] pipe equalizing water in the 685 acre [277 hectare] tract; there are other similar structures farther down State Road 135. Canal C–13 crosses the road through a triple 24-in [61-cm] pipe.

Those structures under S.R. 135 are all existing structures, but on the centerline of survey there are drainage structures that are not called out as existing. This means that the drainage engineer has told the technician the location of the new structures needed to control the drainage. The technician draws them in as shown. However, the new structures are not yet called out on the map. Do this (as the technician would) to complete the drainage map.

After tracing the entire map (ink is preferable, but a soft-lead pencil is allowable), make the following notes (these structures are on the centerline of survey):

Near the start of project:

Construct three 24-in concrete pipes, one each at Sta. 288 + 00, 293 + 50, 301 + 00.
(Show leader with arrows to the three pipes from the notes.)

At Sta. 333 + 00:
Construct triple 30-in concrete pipes
Sta. 333 + 00

At Sta. 367 + 70:
Construct 24-in concrete pipe
Sta. 367 + 70

At Sta. 379 + 00:
Construct 30-in concrete pipe
Sta. 379 + 00

At Sta. 405 + 00:
Construct double 36-in concrete pipes
Sta. 405 + 00, each side of centerline survey

Check the drawing to make sure it is complete.

2. This is an interesting problem in adding *inlets*. Trace Drawing No. 18 (after removing it from the end of the chapter) on a B-size (11 × 17 in) sheet of vellum

   We start with the main outfall line located on North Miami Avenue. The size of the pipe in the outfall line is given, but only two inlets are shown. The student will establish new inlets that will feed into this outfall line. Since the outfall line starts at 42 in [1.07 m] (which is quite large), it is obvious even before looking at the map that much water feeds into the system. This outfall will handle all the storm water the new inlets can feed it and lots more.

   Notice the three-digit figures located on the streets that run into North Miami Avenue. These figures are elevations above sea level measured by the survey crew. On Northeast Eighty-second Street, going from west to east, the elevations are 4.90, 5.25, and 6.00 ft [1.49, 1.60, and 1.83 m]; 6.00 ft [1.83 m] is the highest of these elevations. Water always runs downhill to the lowest elevation, so it flows from 6.00 to 5.25 to 4.90 ft [1.83 to 1.60 to 1.49 m], or from east to west on Northeast Eighty-second Street. Thus an inlet placed at the edge of Northeast Eighty-second Street and North Miami Avenue will catch all the water draining down this street and that caught between streets also.

   Put all the new inlets at the edge of the right-of-way line on North Miami Avenue, as is shown on Drawing No. 18 for the new inlets on North Miami Avenue near Northeast Seventy-ninth Street.

   REMEMBER *Circles* on storm lines are *manholes*. *Inlets* show as little *squares*.

   On main lines the pipe can change size only at manholes. Reducers and increasers are used only on pipes as small as 8 in [20 cm] or smaller. Manholes are always required at intervals of 500 ft [152.4 m] or less; they serve as inspection stations so that the storm sewer can be entered and serviced.

   There is no perfect answer to this problem—the important points are to trace the map well and to provide drainage for each of the blocked-out drainage areas. If pencil was used for this work be sure to go over the linework to make it heavier so that it prints well.

3. This is only a small drainage job, but it looks like a lot of drawing to solve a small problem. Remember though that every detail must be on the plans to get the job done completely. The engineer and the drafting technicians must show every required item, since the contractors will bid on and construct only those items shown in the plans. If the plans are incomplete, the city engineer will check the finished job only to find that the drainage problem is not completely fixed; for example, some pocket of water may not be picked up by an inlet. Thus, even a minor job requires a major design to be absolutely sure of including all details.

   Notice now, when placing Drawing No. 19 under the B-size vellum for tracing, that Frontage Road (at the lower part of the sheet) has several existing inlets and a manhole. Existing structures are dotted; new construction is put in solid so that it will stand out on the finished plans. The new job, beginning at Sta. 90 + 78.90 on Northwest Thirty-sixth Street and ending at Sta. 98 + 00, consists only of installing two new inlets and the 15-in [38-cm] pipe that connects them to the existing drainage system, which exits at an endwall in the Miami Canal.

   Evidently the corner of Northwest Thirty-sixth Street and Royal Poinciana Boulevard was standing in water after rains and needed to be fixed. Thus, the additional two inlets are designed into the system; in this problem the job is to show them on a drainage map so they can be built. The drafter would also be required to draw plans of the inlets on *proposed drainage structure* sheets which will be studied later in the course.

   On Royal Poinciana Boulevard and Northwest Forty-second Avenue, there are a number of existing (dotted) structures. The improvement here adds one new inlet and the 15-in [38-cm] pipe to connect it to the existing system, which runs north on Northwest Forty-second Avenue and exits into the Miami Canal. This is a good problem to show drainage in the city (including the water *flow direction*) and give good tracing practice.

4. Remove Drawing No. 20 from the end of the chapter. Center it under a B-size (11 × 17 in) sheet of vellum. We will trace this small city in Arizona on the vellum.

   This is the center of the town of Stinking Springs. In the past there has been flooding at the two cul-de-sacs on Susan Avenue. There has also been three inches of water standing on the main street (Andree Avenue) near the James River.

   Recently a miner was buried in the local cemetery, and in the bottom of his grave, copper was found. This gave a new industry to Stinking Springs, which before only had the bad-tasting and -smelling spring water for export. Now, with copper mining, new money has come into the city coffers, and the city is able to fix its drainage. The city engineer, who is also city manager and mayor, designed this system of inlets and outfalls to dry up the center of the town.

This job will introduce changes in pipe sizes. Note how the pipes become larger as more inlets are added and more pipe diameter is required to carry the storm water.

5. Remove Drawing No. 21 from the end of the chapter. Tape it under the center of a B-sized sheet of vellum. Trace the drainage map on the vellum.

   Notice the contours shown on the map. Contour lines are continuations of the elevations noted on the lines. The survey crew found that at about Sta. 230 + 35 the elevation was 5 ft [1.5 m] above mean sea level. Following this line around in an oval shape, every point on this line has an elevation of 5 ft [1.5 m]. At Sta. 230 + 05 the elevation has risen to 6 ft [1.8 m] above sea level. Each line rises 1 ft [0.3 m] in elevation until an elevation of 11 ft [3.3 m] is reached. This is the top of the hill. Of course the railroad track has been graded so that it is a steady 8 ft [2.4 m] above mean sea level. At Sta. 250 + 60 another small hill rises to the east and crosses the railroad tracks.

   Note that Upland Pond and Wolf Lake both have normal water elevations of 4.2 ft [1.3 m] above sea level. These levels would not be the same unless the waters in the lake and pond had free movement toward each other.

   At present, there is no connection, and since the railroad has a constant elevation of +8 feet above sea level, these two bodies of water cannot normalize.

   The task in this problem is to normalize them. "Jack"[1] a double 30-in [76-cm] pipe under the railroad track in the spot where it will work best.

   Draw in the 30-in [76-cm] pipes and call them out by note. Be sure to call out the stationing of the pipes, and put the flow line elevation of the bottom of the pipes in the note. A hint: The flow line should be 3.5 ft [1.1 m] above sea level, or thereabouts.

6. Remove Drawing No. 22 from the end of the chapter. Tape a B-size sheet of vellum over the center of the drawing. This problem is for drafting practice and to learn a little about areas enclosed for drainage. Notice that the map covers much territory. Originally scaled at 1 in = 1000 ft, it is photographically reduced to a scale of 1 in = approximately 3000 ft. The number of sections indicates that it is a large area. (A section is 1 mi [1.6 km] on each side or 640 acres [259 hectares].) The three areas enclosed for drainage are 184, 119, and 340 acres [74, 48, and 138 hectares]. Rural drainage jobs are often sizable.

   Notice the elevation lines with the elevation written into them. Also notice many "spot" elevations, each with an *X* and the elevation marked beside it. This area is a swampy one, although this is not a really low sea level for Florida. Elevations range from 30 to 35 ft [9.1 to 10.7 m] above mean sea level.

   Just trace this map and think about the drainage divides to help learn the art.

[1]"Jack" means forcing a pipe under the railroad track by means of water or air under pressure.

LEARNING ACTIVITY PACKAGE

Read Chap. 5 carefully. Drawing No. 15 will be drawn while reading the instructions in the chapter.

Drawing No. 15 completed ____________ (*date*).

Drawing No. 16 will also be drawn while reading Chap. 5.

Drawing No. 16 completed ____________ (*date*).

After reading Chap. 5, go over the objectives (a) through (f). If there are some which are not understood, go back and reread the paragraphs which explain these objectives.

Objectives read and understood ____________ (*date*).

Study the chapter review.

Review studied ____________ (*date*).

Now take the Chap. 5 quiz. Remove the quiz from the text and answer all the questions.

Quiz completed ____________ (*date*).

All students should do Problem No. 1 (Drawing No.17).

Problem 1 (Drawing No.17) completed ________ (*date*).

Problem 2 (Drawing No. 18) completed ________ (*date*).

Problem 3 (Drawing No. 19) completed ________ (*date*).

Problem 4 (Drawing No. 20) completed ________ (*date*).

Problem 5 (Drawing No. 21) completed ________ (*date*).

Problem 6 (Drawing No. 22) completed ________ (*date*).

Do all problems assigned by the instructor for this chapter.

____

5

QUIZ

1. What is the major concern in highway construction? water drainage ____________

2. Side slopes of ditches must be protected from erosion. (T or F) True

3. Slopes, ditches, pipes, and culverts are shown on ~~plan and profile, typical section~~, drainage structure, and roadway cross-section sheets. (T or F) True

4. A roadway ditch which is in the center of the typical section is called a median ditch.

5. Roadway ditches can be sodded or paved to prevent erosion. (T or F) True

6. Information on roadway ditches is found on four different types of drawings. (T or F) true

7. What does D.P.I. mean? ____________

8. It is often less expensive to construct a new channel than to construct several drainage structures for a meandering stream. (T or F) True

9. A culvert is a structure which provides an opening under the roadway.

10. If an opening under a roadway is provided with a pipe, it is called a pipe culvert. (T or F) True

11. Construction details of drainage structures such as pipe culverts are shown on drainage structure sheets.

12. Drainage structures are shown on both the plan and profile view in plan and profile sheets. (T or F) True

13. In a drainage structure, the lowest line along which water can flow is called the flow line.

14. Inlets permit surface water to fall into culverts or other underground pipes. (T or F) True

15. Manholes are not used for inspection of storm sewers. (T or F) false

16. An improperly drained road will wash away. (T or F) true

17. A profile view of anything is a view looking at the object from the side.

18. Why do survey crews need carryall vehicles with four-wheel drive? capable of negotiating any difficult terrain

19. A good scale for a rural drainage map is 1 in = 300 ft.
20. The centerline of the project is usually the last item drawn in after topography has been drawn on the map. (T or F) false
21. Flags are shown at the beginning and end of a project but never for bridges or exceptions to the job. (T or F) false
22. Squiggle arrows point out the direction of water flow. (T or F) True
23. High water elevations are unimportant on a drainage map. (T or F) false
24. New features are always shown as dashed lines on a drainage map. (T or F) false
25. Drainage structures of any type must be shown on a drainage map. (T or F) true
26. Drainage engineers often return to the area to see if the water really runs in the directions shown on the drainage map. (T or F) True
27. Water runoff from wooded areas is quite rapid compared to that from paved surfaces. (T or F) false
28. Station ticks are shown on municipal maps. (T or F) True
29. A scale smaller than 1 in = 300 ft is too small for a municipal drainage map. (T or F) True
30. Topography pertaining to drainage is shown on the municipal drainage map. (T or F) True
31. City maps usually show 500 ft [152 m] of the project on each page. (T or F) false
32. Ticks are put at every 100 ft interval for the length of the job on municipal maps.
33. City streets are drawn with double lines. (T or F) True
34. City streets must be named on drainage maps. (T or F) True
35. The size of pipes between manholes and inlets is unimportant and need not be shown. (T or F) false
36. The drainage area is enclosed by dark, freehand dashes. (T or F) false
37. Manholes are shown as squares on the plan view. (T or F) False
38. The physical characteristics of the terrain make the water flow as it does. (T or F) true
39. Stationing is not necessary on drainage maps. (T or F) false
40. The year of the occurrence of high water is unimportant; the important thing is the elevation. (T or F) false

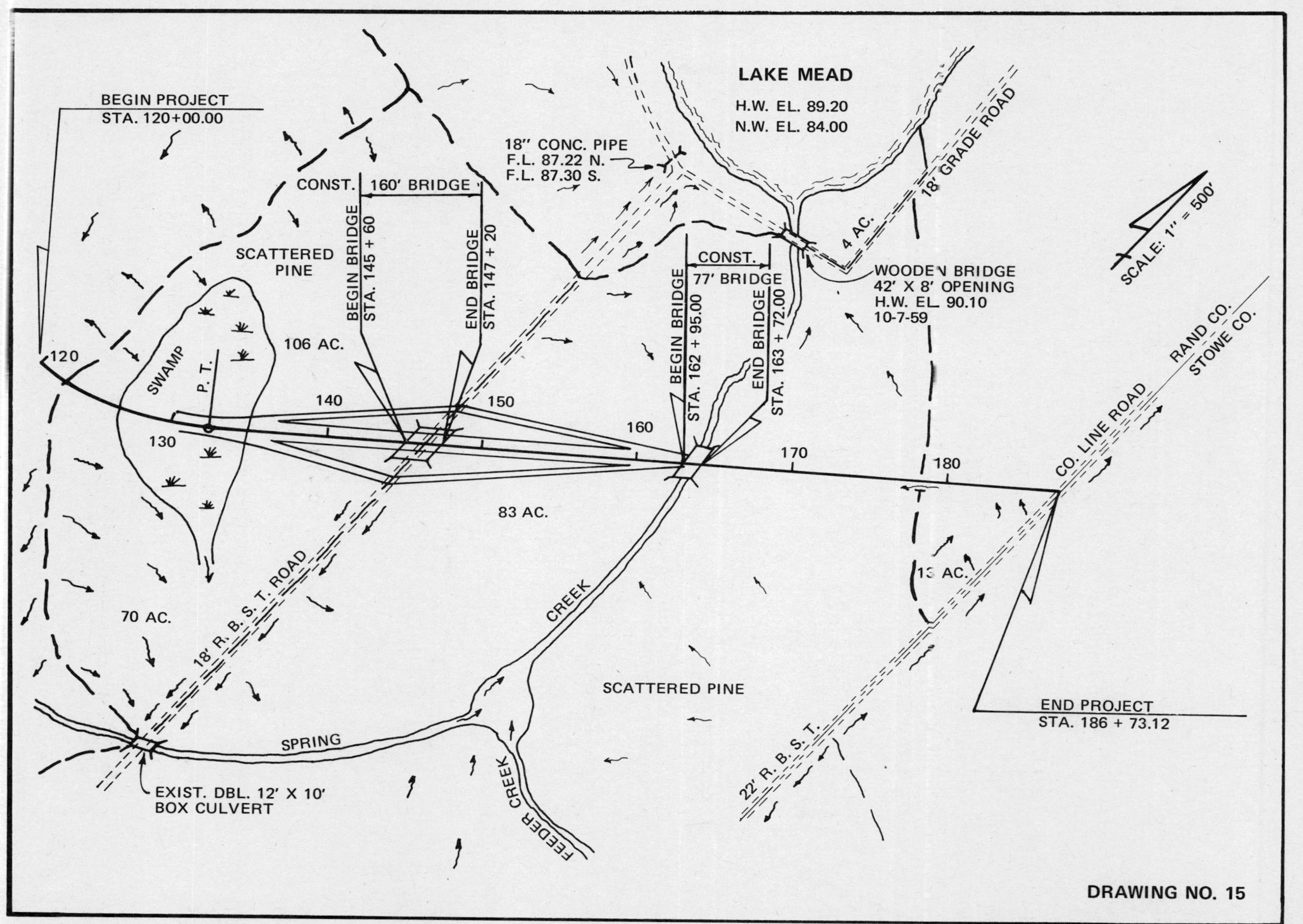
BEGIN PROJECT
STA. 120+00.00
CONST.
160' BRIDGE
BEGIN BRIDGE
STA. 145 + 60
END BRIDGE
STA. 147 + 20
18" CONC. PIPE
F.L. 87.22 N.
F.L. 87.30 S.
LAKE MEAD
H.W. EL. 89.20
N.W. EL. 84.00
18' GRADE ROAD
4 AC.
CONST.
77' BRIDGE
BEGIN BRIDGE
STA. 162 + 95.00
END BRIDGE
STA. 163 + 72.00
WOODEN BRIDGE
42' X 8' OPENING
H.W. EL 90.10
10-7-59
SCALE: 1" = 500'
SCATTERED PINE
106 AC.
SWAMP
P. T.
120
130
140
150
160
170
180
83 AC.
70 AC.
13 AC.
18' R. B. S. T. ROAD
CREEK
SCATTERED PINE
RAND CO.
STOWE CO.
CO. LINE ROAD
SPRING
FEEDER CREEK
22' R. B. S. T.
EXIST. DBL. 12' X 10'
BOX CULVERT
END PROJECT
STA. 186 + 73.12
DRAWING NO. 15

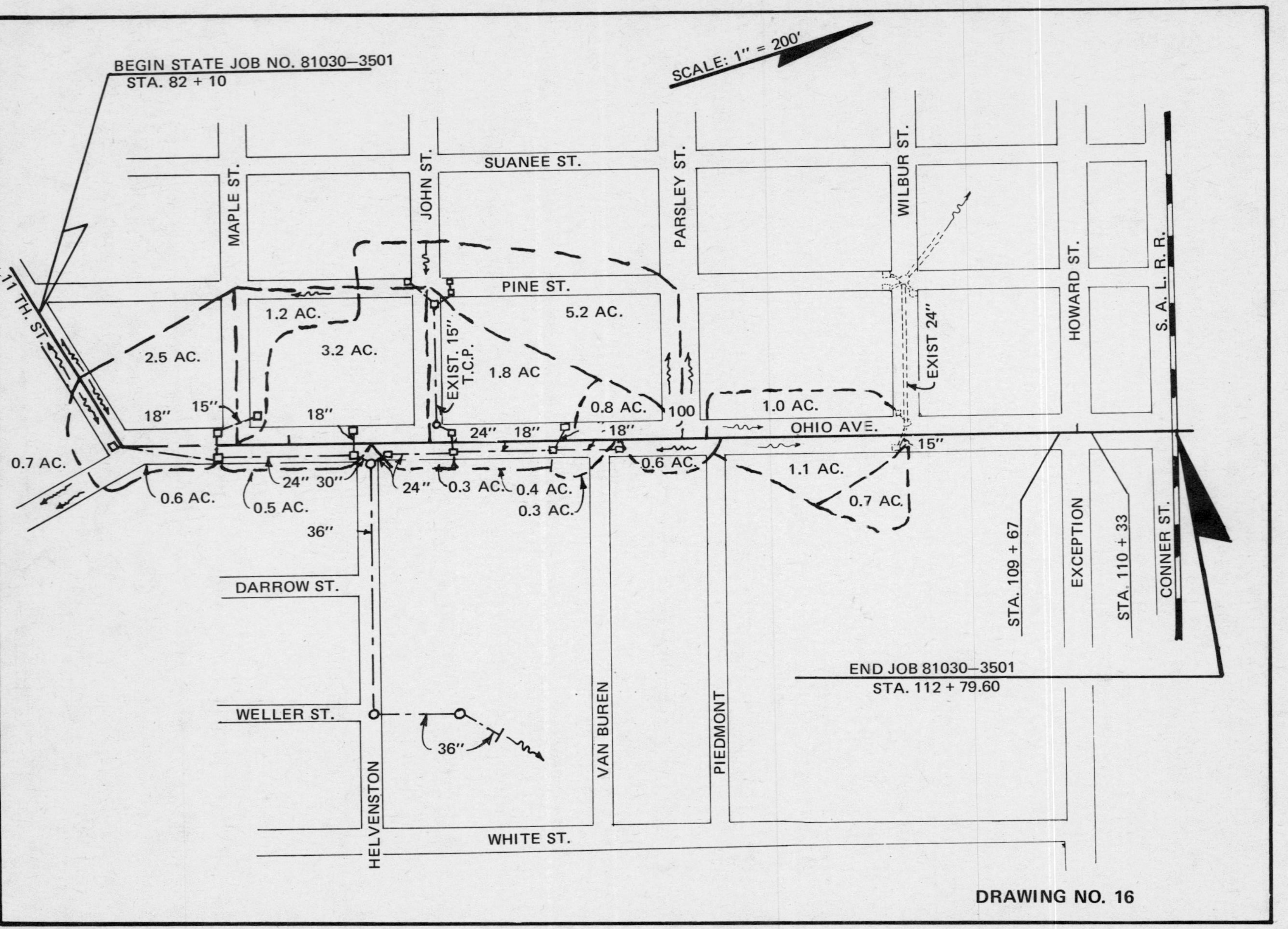
BEGIN STATE JOB NO. 81030—3501
STA. 82 + 10
SCALE: 1" = 200'
SUANEE ST.
MAPLE ST.
JOHN ST.
PARSLEY ST.
WILBUR ST.
HOWARD ST.
S. A. L. R. R.
PINE ST.
11 TH. ST.
1.2 AC.
3.2 AC.
2.5 AC.
5.2 AC.
1.8 AC
EXIST. 15"
T.C.P.
EXIST 24"
0.8 AC.
100
1.0 AC.
OHIO AVE.
15"
18"
15"
18"
24"
18"
18"
0.7 AC.
0.6 AC.
24" 30"
0.5 AC.
24"
0.3 AC.
0.4 AC.
0.3 AC.
0.6 AC.
1.1 AC.
0.7 AC.
36"
STA. 109 + 67
EXCEPTION
STA. 110 + 33
CONNER ST.
DARROW ST.
END JOB 81030—3501
STA. 112 + 79.60
WELLER ST.
36"
VAN BUREN
PIEDMONT
HELVENSTON
WHITE ST.
DRAWING NO. 16

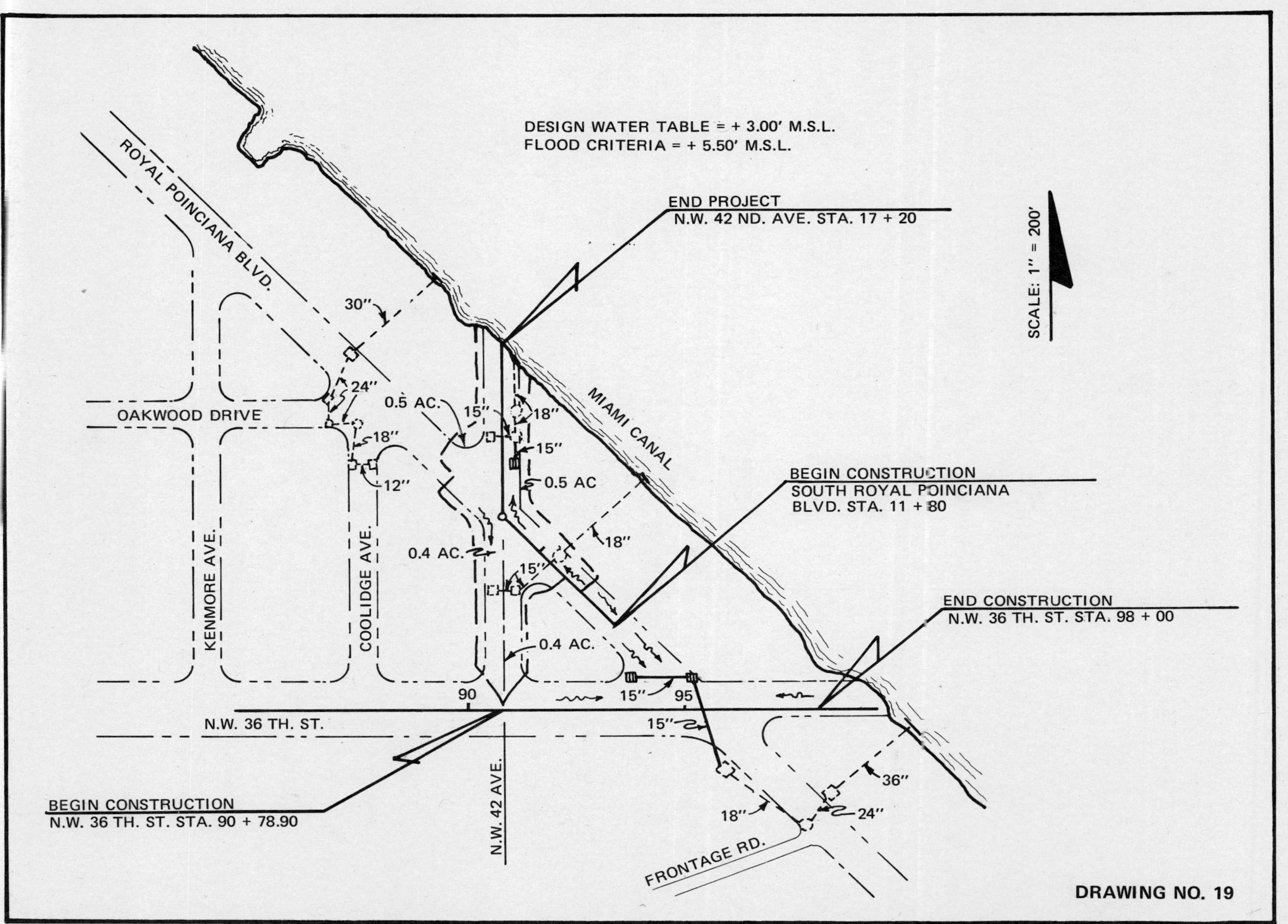
DESIGN WATER TABLE = + 3.00' M.S.L.
FLOOD CRITERIA = + 5.50' M.S.L.
END PROJECT
N.W. 42 ND. AVE. STA. 17 + 20
SCALE: 1" = 200'
ROYAL POINCIANA BLVD.
30"
24"
0.5 AC.
15"
18"
OAKWOOD DRIVE
MIAMI CANAL
18"
15"
12"
0.5 AC
BEGIN CONSTRUCTION
SOUTH ROYAL POINCIANA
BLVD. STA. 11 + 80
KENMORE AVE.
COOLIDGE AVE.
0.4 AC.
15"
18"
0.4 AC.
END CONSTRUCTION
N.W. 36 TH. ST. STA. 98 + 00
90
15"
95
N.W. 36 TH. ST.
15"
36"
BEGIN CONSTRUCTION
N.W. 36 TH. ST. STA. 90 + 78.90
N.W. 42 AVE.
18"
24"
FRONTAGE RD.
DRAWING NO. 19

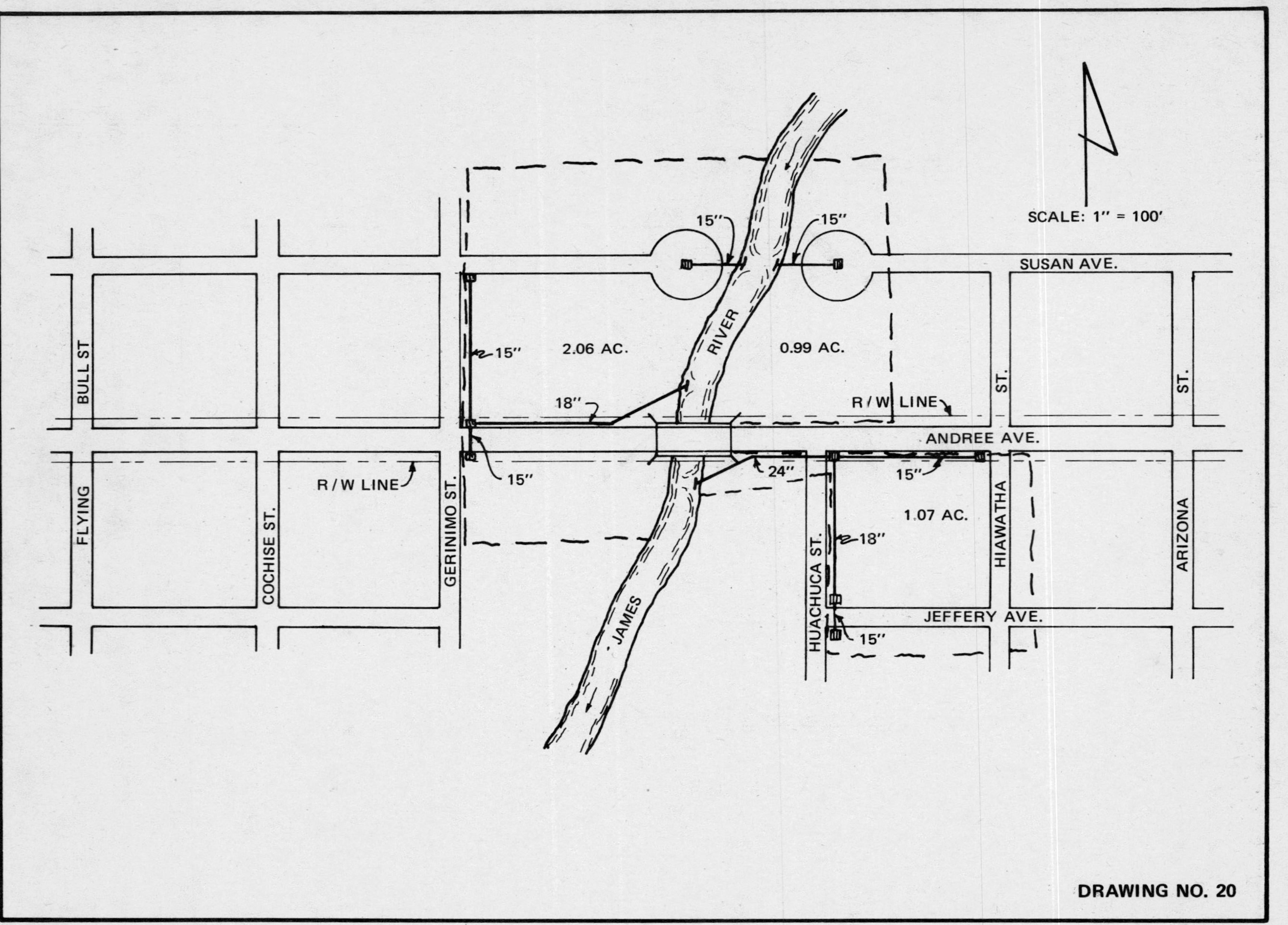
SCALE: 1" = 100'
15"
15"
SUSAN AVE.
BULL ST
15"
2.06 AC.
RIVER
0.99 AC.
ST.
ST.
18"
R/W LINE
ANDREE AVE.
15"
24"
15"
R/W LINE
FLYING
COCHISE ST.
GERINIMO ST.
1.07 AC.
HUACHUCA ST.
18"
HIAWATHA
ARIZONA
JEFFERY AVE.
JAMES
15"
DRAWING NO. 20

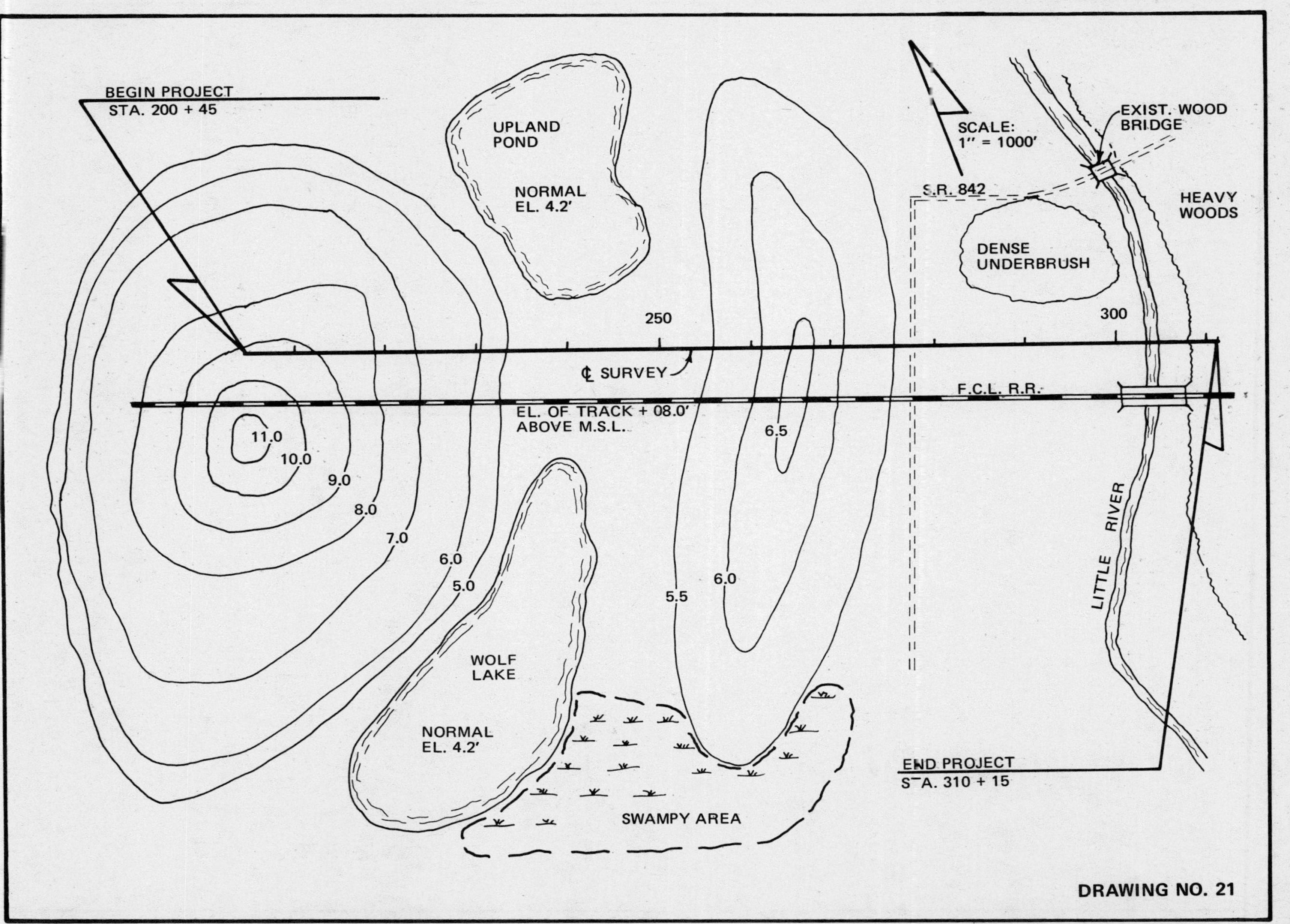
BEGIN PROJECT
STA. 200 + 45
UPLAND POND
NORMAL EL. 4.2'
SCALE: 1" = 1000'
EXIST. WOOD BRIDGE
S.R. 842
HEAVY WOODS
DENSE UNDERBRUSH
250
300
℄ SURVEY
F.C.L. R.R.
EL. OF TRACK + 08.0' ABOVE M.S.L.
6.5
11.0
10.0
9.0
8.0
7.0
6.0
5.0
5.5
6.0
LITTLE RIVER
WOLF LAKE
NORMAL EL. 4.2'
END PROJECT
S‾A. 310 + 15
SWAMPY AREA
DRAWING NO. 21

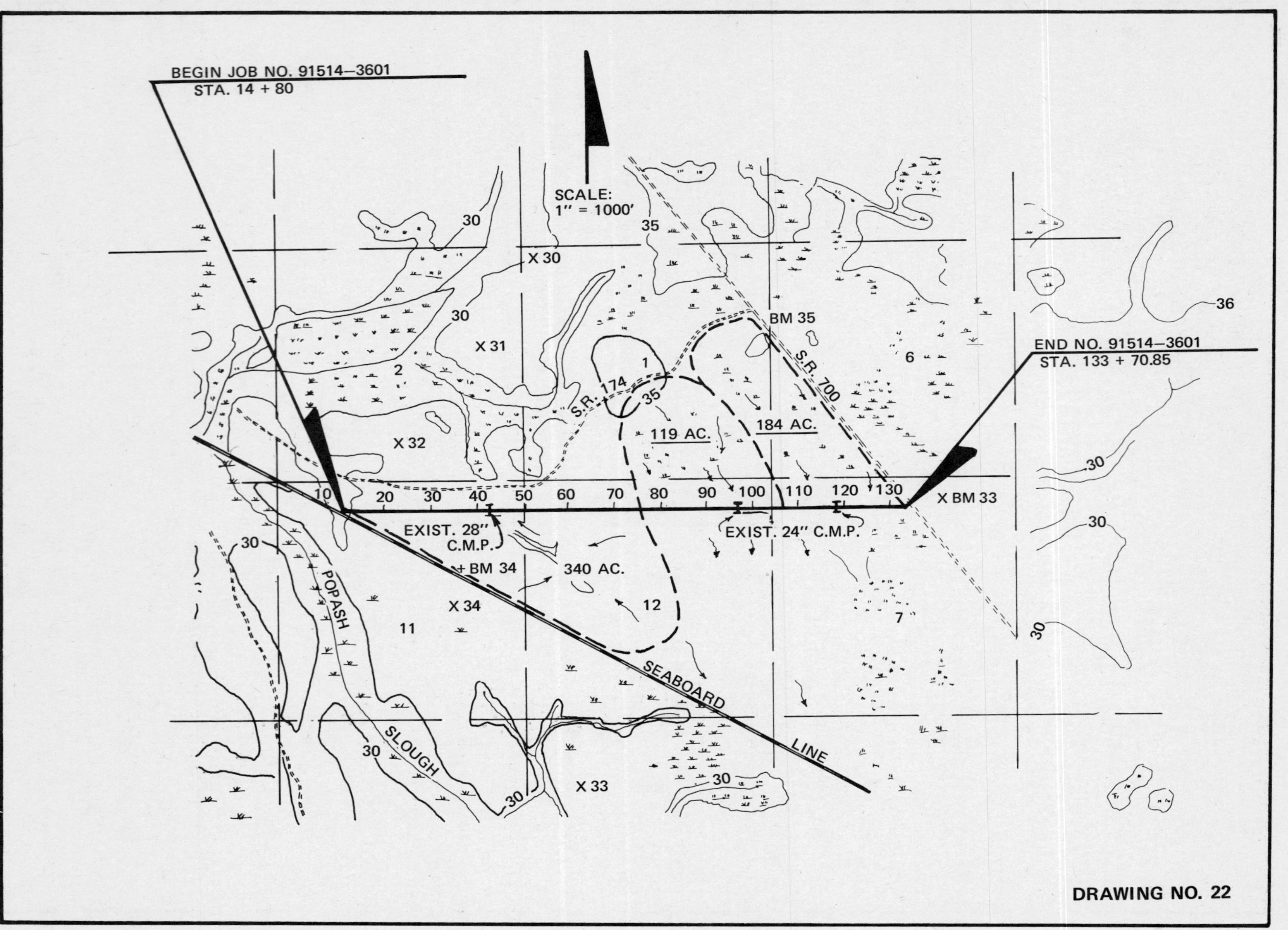
BEGIN JOB NO. 91514–3601
STA. 14 + 80
SCALE:
1" = 1000'
END NO. 91514–3601
STA. 133 + 70.85
S.R. 700
S.R. 174
BM 35
X BM 33
+ BM 34
184 AC.
119 AC.
340 AC.
EXIST. 28"
C.M.P.
EXIST. 24" C.M.P.
SEABOARD
LINE
POPASH
SLOUGH
X 30
X 31
X 32
X 33
X 34
10
20
30
40
50
60
70
80
90
100
110
120
130
DRAWING NO. 22

6 ESSENTIAL ITEMS ON PLAN VIEWS

Objectives

a. Understand the use of bearings
b. Be able to write bearings on the drawings properly
c. Learn stationing as used by the civil engineer in surveying
d. Be able to figure stations on the centerline of maps
e. Understand the terms *line back* and *line ahead*
f. Understand the equations used on lines of survey
g. Have an elementary understanding of how a survey team finds the elevations of hills
h. Understand grades
i. Study slope ratios
j. Study the use of cross slopes on highway surfaces carefully

Rationale

The drafter must know the fundamentals of reading bearings, stationing survey lines, and working out station equations in plan view drawings. Drafters must also know how to measure grades, slopes, and cross slopes. This chapter will better the student's understanding of these basic elements before going on to drawings which employ them.

BEARINGS

The directions of surveyed lines are described by *bearings*. Bearings are just like compass readings, showing whether the lines are going north, south, east or west. (Look at an ordinary pocket compass.) However, bearings are much more accurate than the ordinary compass. Bearings are described in terms of degrees (°), minutes (′), and seconds (″) in relation to north or south.

There are 360° of angle in a circle, so each quadrant, or quarter circle (see Fig. 6-1), must have 90°. Also, there are 60 minutes in a degree and 60 seconds in a minute:

1° (degree) = 60′ (minutes)
1′ (minute) = 60″ (seconds)

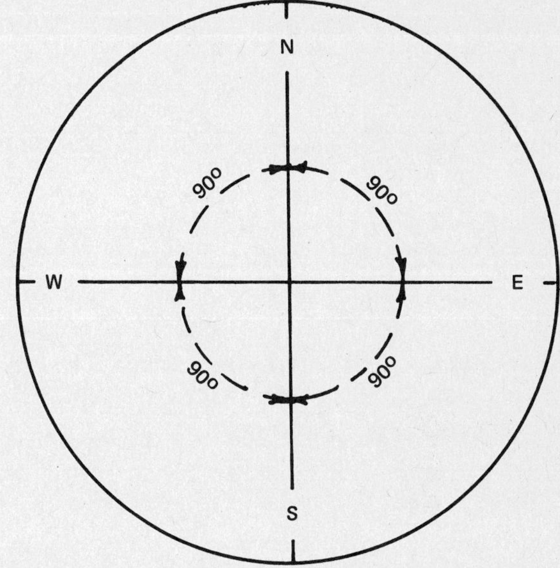

Figure 6-1
Quadrants of a circle.

How a bearing tells direction
A bearing might look like this example (see Fig. 6-2):

N84°30′00″E

The bearing tells what to do; follow it in the order it is written:

1. First, face north (N).
2. Second, turn an angle of 84°30′00″ to the east.
3. You are now looking along a bearing of N84°30′00″E. The solid line in Fig. 6-2 is the direction of the surveyed line.

The same procedure is used for all bearings; see Fig. 6-3 for more examples.

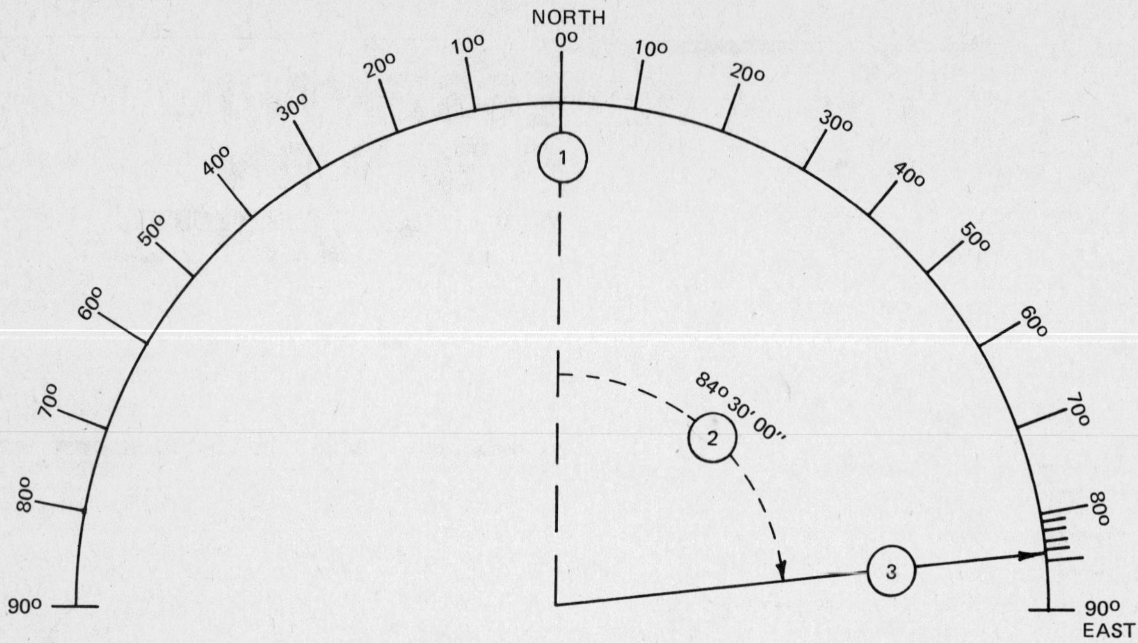

Figure 6-2
Example of a bearing.

Figure 6-3
Bearings.

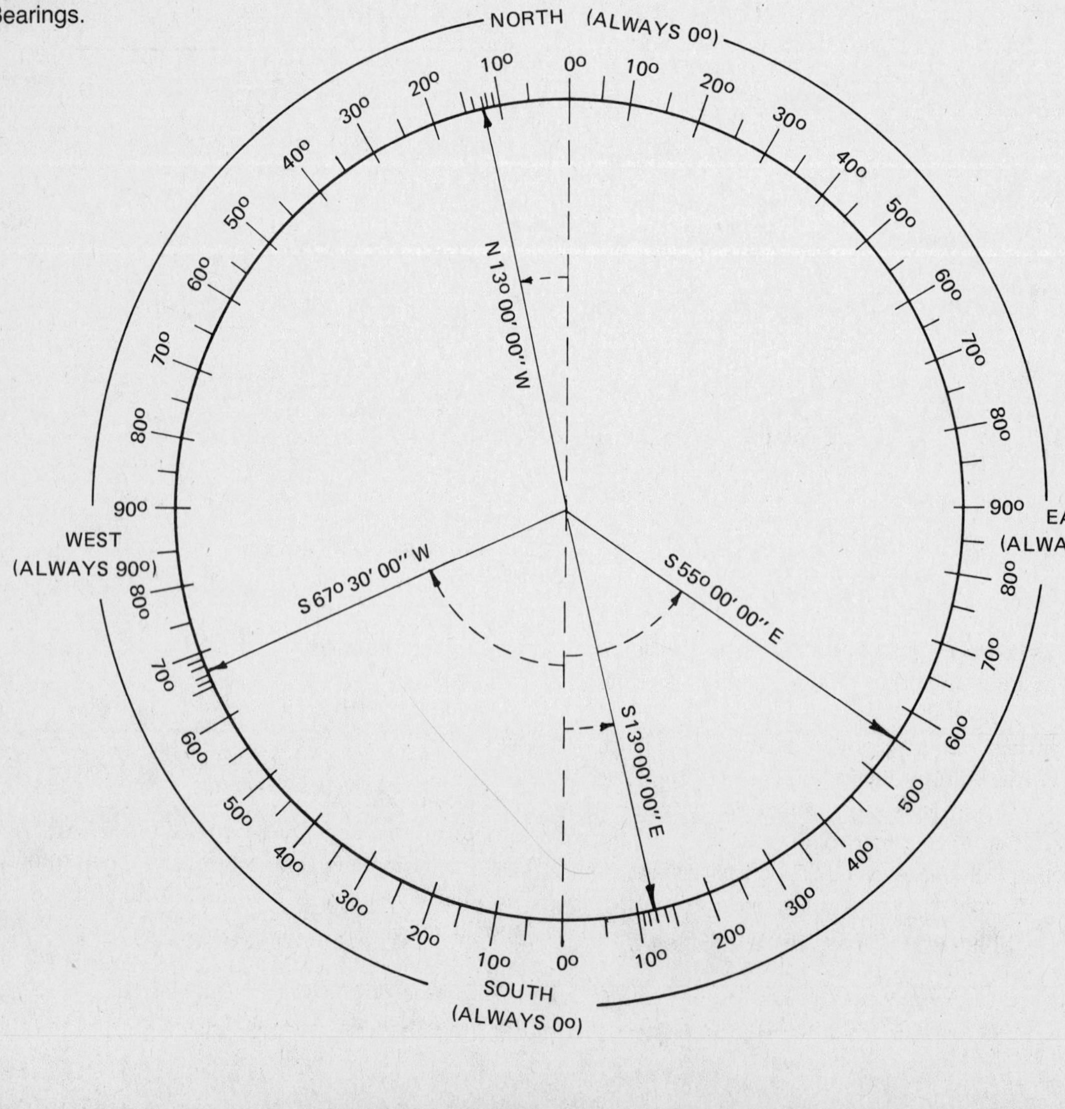

QUIZ

Refer to the Fig. 6-4 and fill in the blanks to show how the bearings would be written for each of the four lines.

A ___N 28° 14' 30" E___

B ___S 78° 12' 00" E___

C ___S 42° 50' 45" W___

D ___N 60° 00' 00" W___

(Be careful of D—it is tricky.)

STATIONS

Stations were mentioned in an earlier chapter. They will now be explained more fully. On nearly all plan sheets there are references to stations. This is a term used for measuring distances and identifying points on the ground along a surveyed line. In surveying, a *station* represents 100 feet (ft) [30.5 m] of distance. Think of it like this:

1 ft = 12 inches (in)
1 station = 100 ft

Surveyors also use stations to identify points along a surveyed line. For example, if the beginning of a line is Station 0 (Sta. 0) a point 500 ft [152 m] from Sta. 0 is Sta. 5, and Sta. 12 represents a point 1200 ft [366 m] from Sta. 0. Another example: Station 37 is 8 stations (800 ft [244 m]) ahead of Sta. 29. The word *station* is used in two ways: 25 stations is a distance of 2500 ft [762 m] and Sta. 25 is a point 2500 ft [762 m] from Sta. 0. [Projects, however, rarely begin at Sta. 0. For example, the location map on the key map for State Road 101, Green River County (Drawing No. 1) has the note "Begin Project Sta. 300 + 00."]

Plan sheets show stationing on the centerlines of proposed projects, as illustrated by Fig. 6-5. When a specific

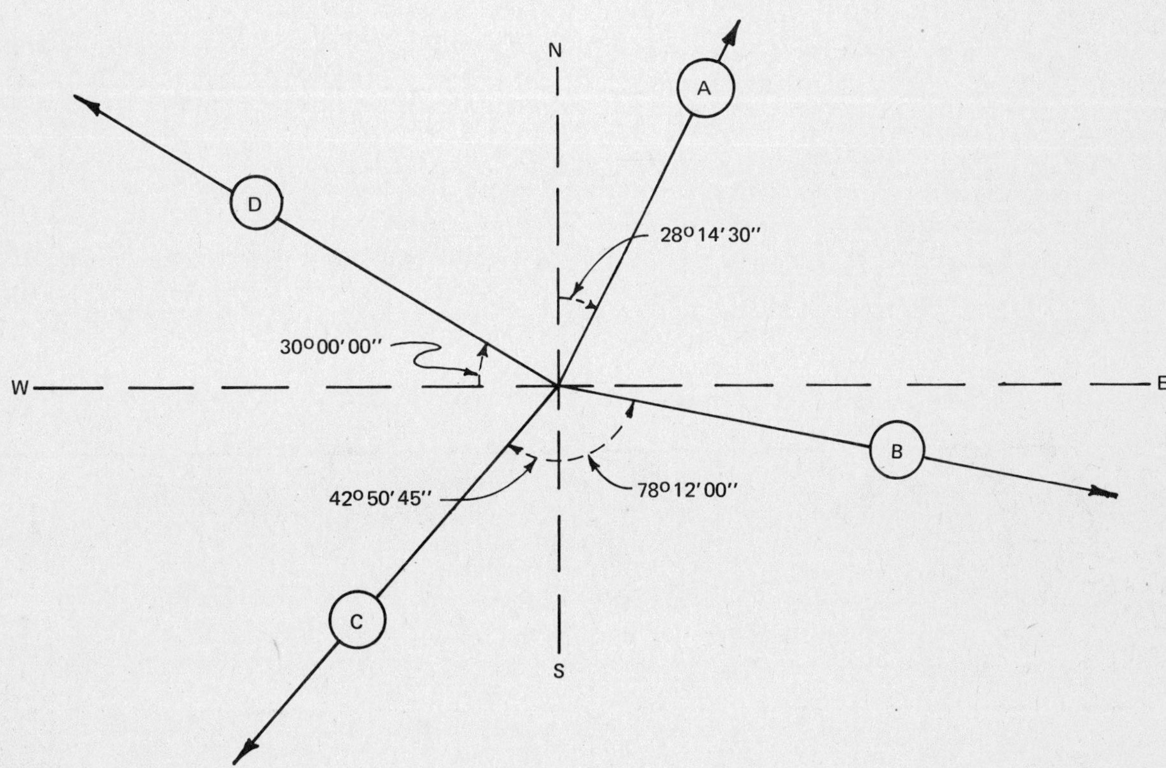

Figure 6-4
Quiz bearings.

Figure 6-5
Stationing on the centerline of proposed projects.

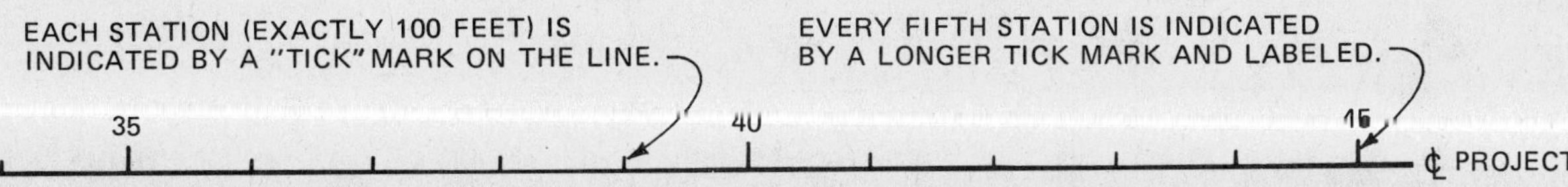

construction item is described in the plans, the exact location is described by a station number. If the item is exactly on a station "+ 00" is written after the number. A point halfway between two stations would be shown with "+ 50" after the lower station number. The location of any point is always shown as a positive (+) distance in feet beyond the last station. For example, Sta. 345 + 67 is a point 67 ft beyond Sta. 345 + 00; Sta. 98 + 76.54 is a point 76.54 ft beyond Sta. 98 + 00.

QUIZ

Fill in the blanks below with the letters that best describe the stationing shown in Fig. 6-6.

Station 91 + 00 ___A___

Station 98 + 50 ___H___

Station 93 + 25 ___C___

Station 97 + 15 ___F___

Station 91 + 50 ___B___

Station 96 + 75 ___E___

Station 93 + 90 ___D___

Line Ahead and Line Back

Generally, station numbers get larger going from west to east ➡ or south to north ⬆.

Station numbers usually get larger in this direction: ➡ Looking in this direction is looking at the *line ahead* (Fig. 6-7).

Station numbers usually get smaller looking in this direction: ⬅ Looking in that direction is looking at the *line back* (Fig. 6-8).

Distances Between Stations

To find the distance between two points along a centerline, subtract the lower station number from the higher station number. Ignore the plus sign when calculating the answer.

EXAMPLE Find the distance between Sta. 20 + 60 and 12 + 80.

Ignore the plus sign.	2060
Subtract smaller station	− 1280
Answer	780 ft [238 m]

Here is a way to check the answer of the preceding problem:

The distance from Sta. 12 + 80 to Sta. 13 + 00 is	20
The distance from Sta. 13 + 00 to Sta. 20 + 00 is	700
The distance from Sta. 20 + 00 to Sta. 20 + 60 is	60
Add—the total distance is	780 ft

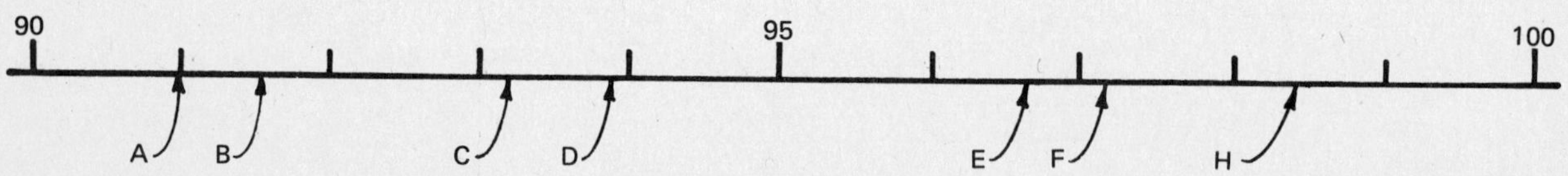

Figure 6-6
Quiz stationing.

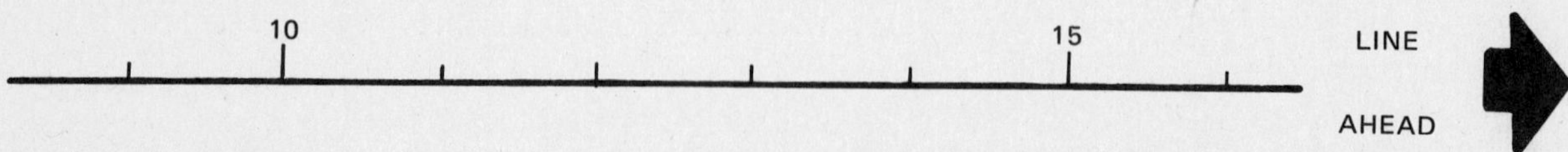

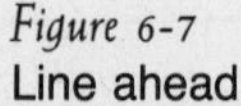

Figure 6-7
Line ahead.

Figure 6-8
Line back.

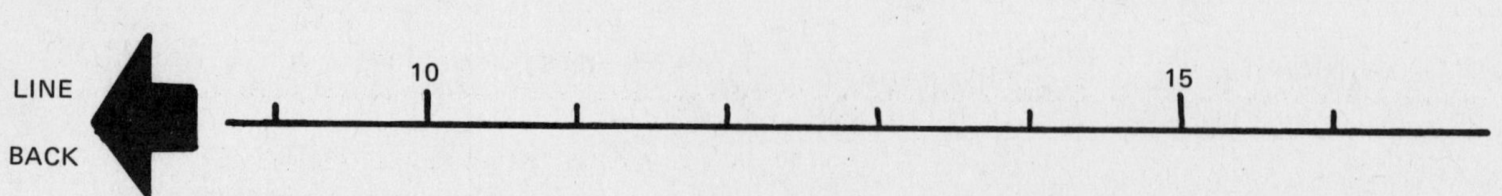

QUIZ

Find the distances between these stations:

Stations 29 + 10 and 34 + 30 ___520 ft___

Stations 93 + 40 and 116 + 20 ___2280 ft___

Stations 450 + 00 and 455 + 10 ___510 ft___

Stations 23 + 28 and 245 + 50 ___22222 ft___

Some measurements shown on the plans need to be more exact than others. The stations and distances previously talked about were shown to the nearest foot. In Florida and many other states, stations are normally written to the nearest one-hundredth of a foot, such as Sta. 148 + 35.08.

EQUATIONS

We just learned that the distance between two stations is found by subtracting the smaller station from the larger station. *This is not always the case!*

Suppose the stationing on an old road looks like that shown in Fig. 6-9. Then suppose a new road is built partly over the old road as shown in Fig. 6-10. Station 9 + 00 on the new road is the same point as Sta. 7 + 00 on the old road. Check to see that this is true. The stationing on the new road does not have to be continuous. A lot of time can be saved by using the old road stationing for the new road.

All we have to be concerned about is *where* the stationing for the new road *changes*. The point where the stationing changes is Sta. 9 + 00 on the new road or Sta. 7 + 00 on the old road—both stations represent the same point. Since they are the *same* point, we can say that Sta. 9 + 00 = Sta. 7 + 00. That is, Sta. 9 + 00 on the line *back* of station-change point equals Sta. 7 + 00 on the line *ahead* of the station-change point. In abbreviated form,

Sta. 9 + 00 Bk = Sta. 7 + 00 Ah

In this form, it is an *equation*. An equation thus indicates that the station numbering has changed. The point of the equation has two station numbers, one that is correct when measuring on the line *back* of the equation, and another that is correct when measuring *ahead* of the equation.

Now we see why the distance between two stations sometimes cannot be determined by subtracting the smaller station number from the larger station number. Refer to Fig. 6-10. On the new road, look at the distance between Sta. 5 + 00 and 10 + 00. It is more than 500 ft [152 m]—it is 700 ft [213 m]! This is tricky; subtracting Sta. 5 + 00 from Sta. 10 + 00 does not give the actual distance. Another procedure must be followed:

First, substract Sta. 5 + 00 from Sta. 10 + 00.

$$\begin{array}{r} 1000 \text{ ft} \\ -\ \underline{500 \text{ ft}} \\ 500 \text{ ft} \end{array}$$

This is only the *apparent length*, not the actual length.

Then, find the difference between the station numbers at the equation.

$$\begin{array}{r} 900 \text{ ft} \\ -\underline{700 \text{ ft}} \\ 200 \text{ ft} \end{array}$$

This is the *equation length*.

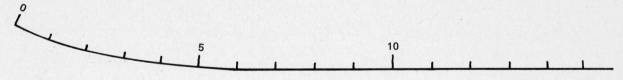

Figure 6-9
Old road stationing.

Figure 6-10
Old and new road stationing.

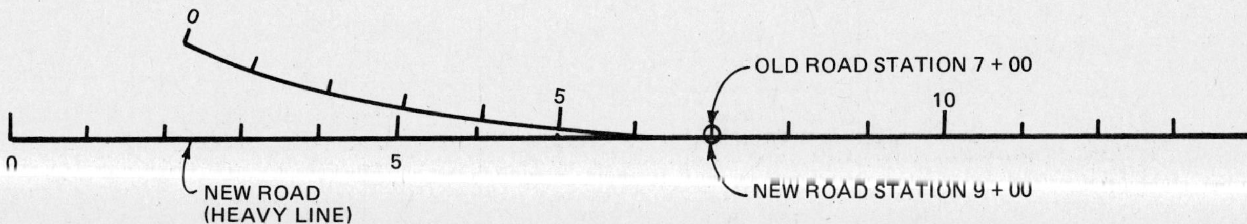

If the back station number in the equation is larger than the ahead station number, add the *equation length* to the *apparent length* to find the *actual length.*

$$\begin{array}{r} 500 \text{ ft} \\ +200 \text{ ft} \\ \hline 700 \text{ ft} \end{array}$$

This is the *actual length.*

REMEMBER If the back station number in the equation is larger than the ahead station number, add the equation length to the apparent length to find the actual length.

What if the back station number is smaller? Let us do that now. Suppose a new road is built over an old road as shown in Fig. 6-11. In this case, the equation looks like this:

Sta. 4 + 00 Bk. = Sta. 7 + 00 Ah.

On the new road, the length between Stations 0 + 00 and 10 + 00 appears to be 1000 ft, [305 m] but it's not. The actual length is 700 ft [213 m]. Here is the method of finding the actual length: Since the back station number in the equation is smaller than the ahead station number, subtract the equation length from the apparent length to find actual length.

First, find the apparent length.

$$\begin{array}{r} 1000 \text{ ft} \\ -000 \text{ ft} \\ \hline 1000 \text{ ft} \end{array}$$

Then find the equation length.

$$\begin{array}{r} 700 \text{ ft} \\ -400 \text{ ft} \\ \hline 300 \text{ ft} \end{array}$$

Figure 6-11
Stations back and ahead.

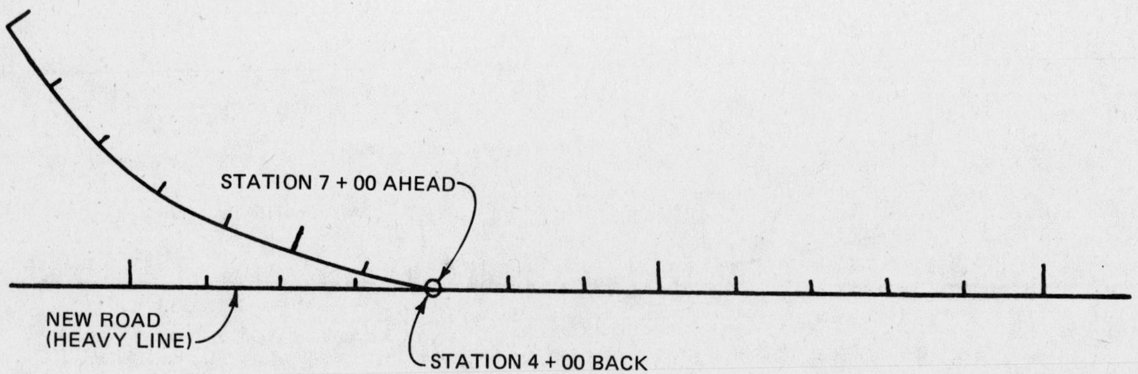

Subtract the equation length from the apparent length.

$$\begin{array}{r} 1000 \text{ ft} \\ -300 \text{ ft} \\ \hline 700 \text{ ft} \end{array}$$

This is the actual length.

REMEMBER When you want to know the actual distance between any two stations, and there is an equation between them,

- ☐ *add the equation length to the apparent length* if the back station is *larger.*
- ☐ *Subtract the equation length from the apparent length* if the back station is *smaller.*

This method will always give the correct answer.

Equations are easy to find on the plans. They are shown on

- ☐ the location map on the key sheet
- ☐ plan views of plan and profile sheets

Equation notes like those in Fig. 6-12 show the location of equations.

QUIZ

Can you determine the actual distance between two stations by subtracting the smaller station from the larger station?

If there is no equation between them.__________

If there is an equation between them.__________

Does the stationing of a project have to be continuous? __________

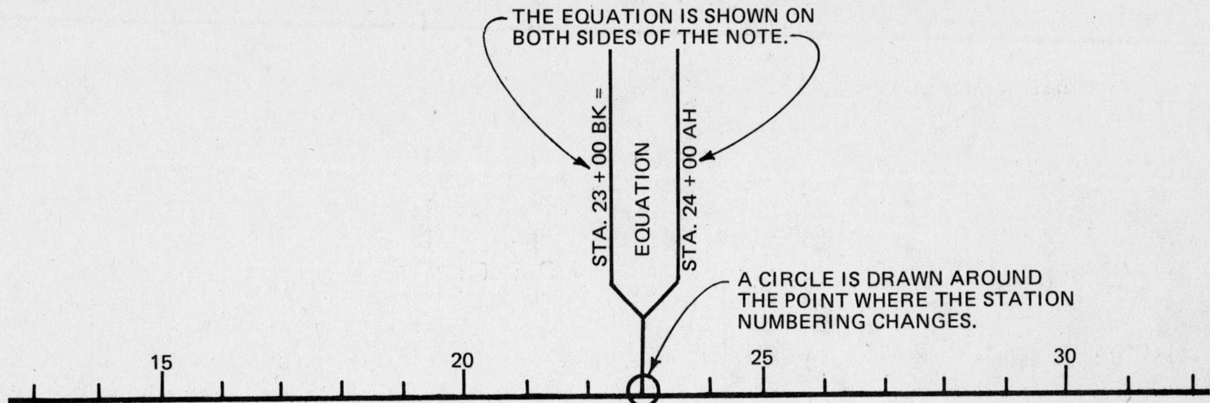

Figure 6-12
Stationing equation.

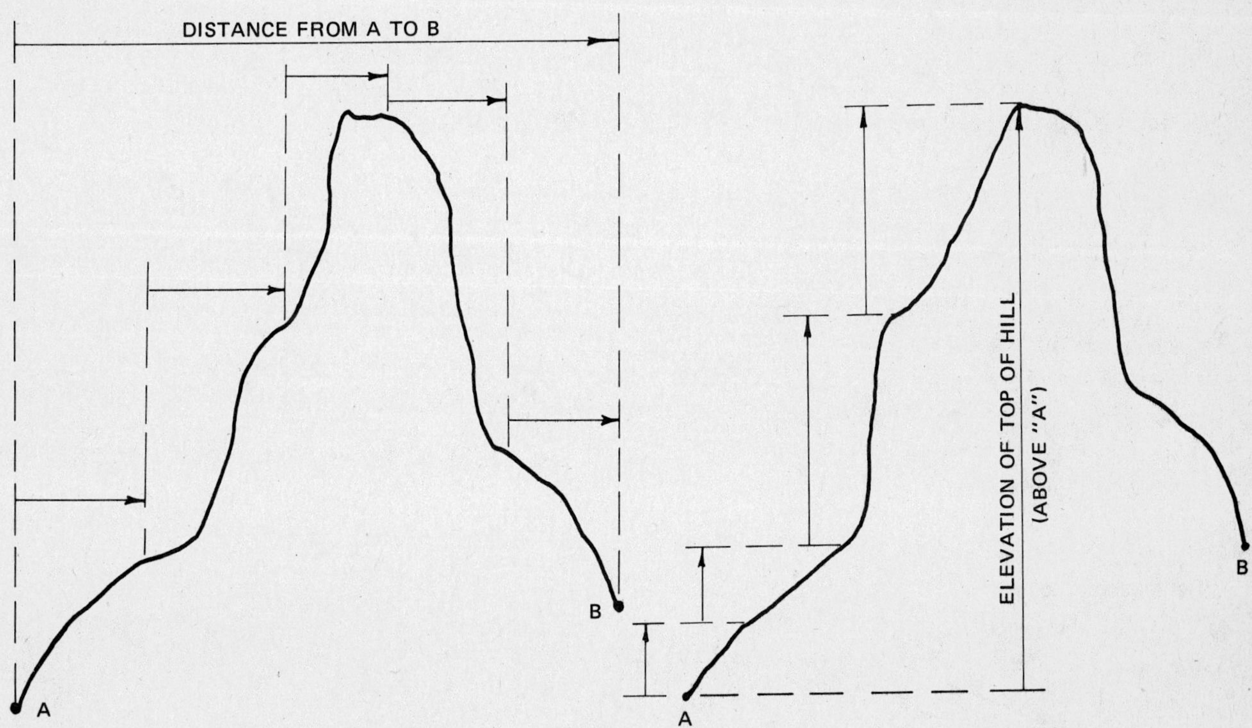

Figure 6-13
Surveying method of making horizontal and vertical measurements.

At the point where the stationing of a project changes, there is an ____________.

Distances on Plans

There is one more point to remember about distances shown on the plans: They always are measured either *horizontally* or *vertically*, never along the slope of the ground. The profile views in Fig. 6-13 show how the surveyor makes a series of short level measurements to find the total distance from *A* to *B* and several vertical measurements to find the elevation of the top of the hill.

QUIZ

Refer to Fig. 6-14 when answering the following questions.

What are the apparent lengths between these stations?

5 + 00 and 10 + 00 ___500___

10 + 00 and 15 + 00 ___500___

15 + 00 and 20 + 00 ___500___

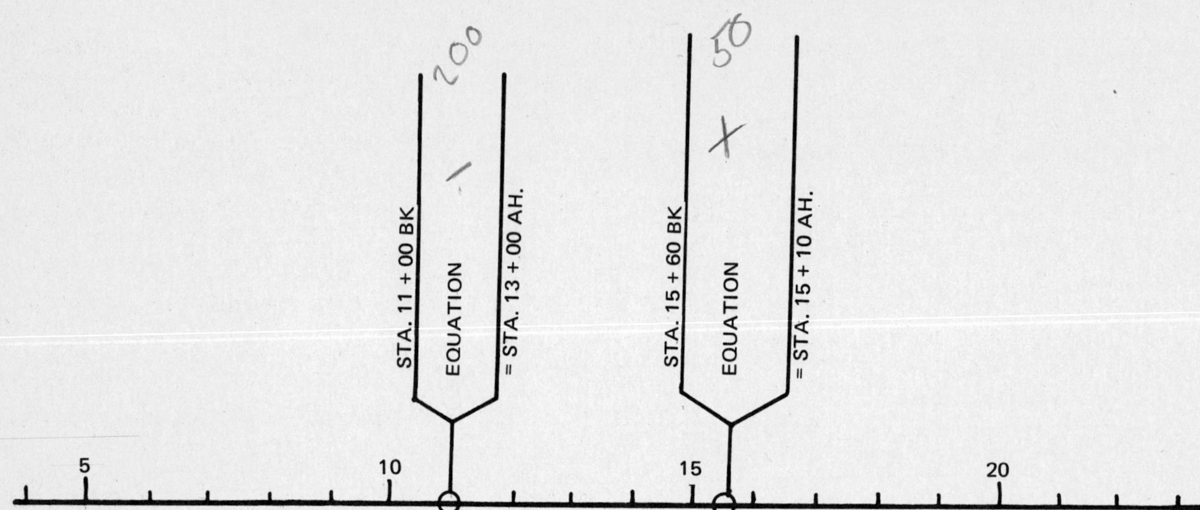

Figure 6-14
Quiz stationing.

What are the actual lengths between these stations?

5 + 00 and 10 + 00__________

10 + 00 and 15 + 00__________

15 + 00 and 20 + 00__________

5 + 00 and 20 + 00__________

REMEMBER *Add* the equation length if the back station is *larger.*
Subtract the equation length if the back station is *smaller.*

MEASURING GRADES, SLOPES, AND CROSS SLOPES

If distances are always measured vertically or horizontally, how is the rise and fall of the ground expressed? It is expressed in one of three ways—as a *grade*, a *slope* or a *cross slope*.

Grades

Grades are written as a percent of vertical rise or fall, based on horizontal distance (see Figs. 6-15 and 6-16). Figure 6-15 shows how grades are computed. The three heavy lines represent profiles of proposed roads.

Figure 6-15
Computing grades.

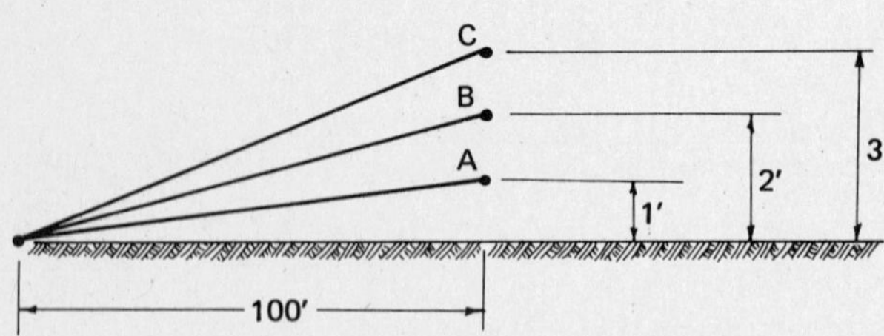

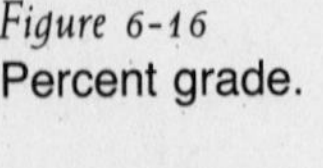

Figure 6-16
Percent grade.

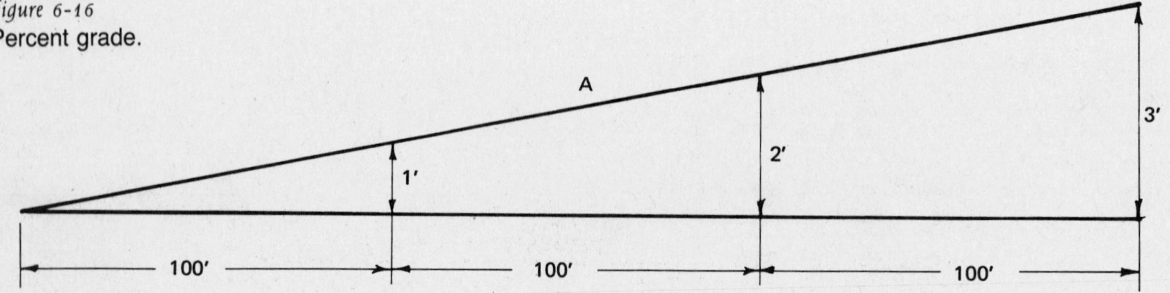

Line A rises 1 ft [0.305 m] vertically in 100 ft [30.5 m] of horizontal distance. The grade is 1⁄100 [0.305/30.5] or 0.01 or 1 percent. (Look at line A extended out farther. No matter how far you go, the percent of rise to distance is always the same.)

Line B rises 2 ft [0.610 m] vertically in 100 ft [30.5 m] of horizontal distance. The grade is 2⁄100 [0.610/30.5] or 0.02 or 2 percent.

The line C rises 3 ft [0.914 m] vertically in 100 ft [30.5 m] of horizontal distance. The grade is 3⁄100 [0.914/30.5] or 0.03 or 3 percent.

A single formula that can be used to determine percent of grade is:

$$\%\ \text{Grade} = \frac{\text{vertical distance}}{\text{horizontal distance}} \times 100$$

We can apply this formula to lines A, B, and C:

$$\%\ \text{Grade} = \frac{1\ \text{ft}}{100\ \text{ft}} \left[\frac{0.305\ \text{m}}{30.5\ \text{m}}\right] = 0.01 \times 100 = 1\%$$

$$\%\ \text{Grade} = \frac{2\ \text{ft}}{100\ \text{ft}} \left[\frac{0.610\ \text{m}}{30.5\ \text{m}}\right] = 0.02 \times 100 = 2\%$$

$$\%\ \text{Grade} = \frac{3\ \text{ft}}{100\ \text{ft}} \left[\frac{0.914\ \text{m}}{30.5\ \text{m}}\right] = 0.03 \times 100 = 3\%$$

Grades not only go up, they also go down, and the computation is made the same way. The plans show a plus sign (+) in front of the percentage for an up grade (rising grade) and minus sign (−) in front of the percentage for a down grade (falling grade). If a grade does not go up or down, it is a level grade and is shown without a plus or minus sign. A level grade is always 0.00 percent. The three types of grades are illustrated by Fig. 6-17. Notice that for the rising grade the roadway rises 3 ft [0.91 m] in 100 ft [30.5 m] of horizontal travel; the grade is +3.00 percent. For the falling grade, the roadway falls 3 ft [0.91 m] in 100 ft [30.5 m] of horizontal travel; the grade is −3.00 percent. For the level grade, the roadway does not rise or fall; it is level, and the grade is 0.00 percent.

QUIZ

Fill in the blanks to show the percentage of grade for the changes of elevation shown below:

Horizontal Distance (ft)	Elevation Change (ft)	% Grade
100	5.00 rise	5/100 + 5%
100	6.50 fall	−6.5%
200	4.00 rise	+ 2%
300	7.50 rise	+ 2.5%
400	2.00 fall	−0.5%
500	1.25 fall	−0.25%
700	0.00	0.00%

Figure 6-17
Rising and falling grades.

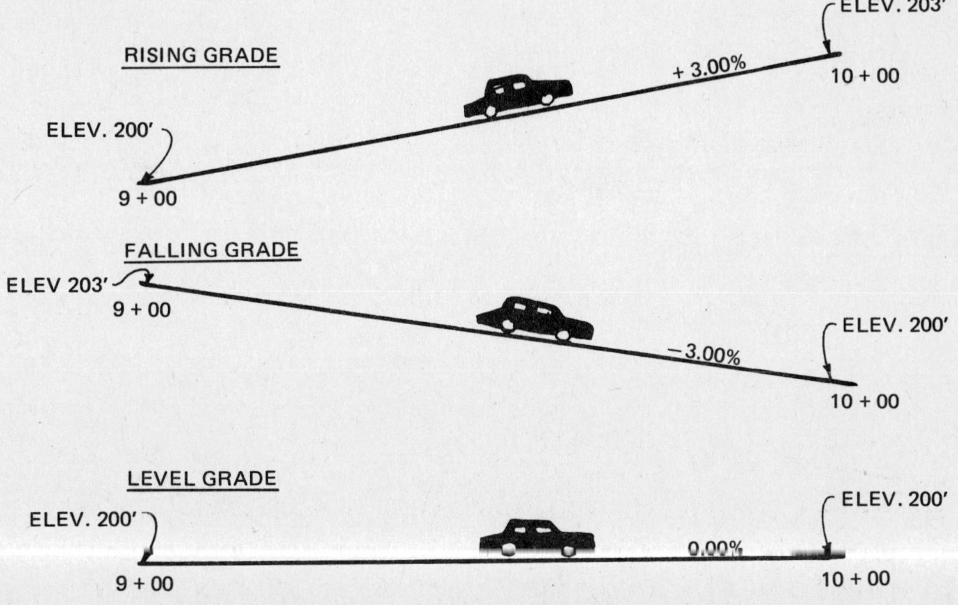

Try it another way. For each distance and grade that is given, compute the elevation change:

Horizontal Distance (ft)	% Grade	Elevation Change (ft)
100	+ 2.50%	______
150	− 4.00%	______
225	+ 3.00%	______
450	+ 0.50%	______
200	0.00%	______
1000	+ 1.42%	______

Slopes

Slopes are written as a *ratio* between horizontal and vertical distance. When the plans describe such things as the slopes of embankments and slopes of excavation, they are expressed as ratios, not percentages. For example, look at the typical section-view of a roadside ditch in Fig. 6-18. What does the 4:1 (read this as 4 to 1) slope mean? It means that for every 4 ft [1.2 m] of horizontal distance away from the road, the elevation falls 1 ft [0.3 m]. Look at the diagram in Fig. 6-19.

The same method is used for the 3:1 slope shown in Fig. 6-20; this time, for every 3 ft [0.9 m] of horizontal distance the slope rises 1 ft [0.3 m].

Notice that when slope ratios are given, the horizontal distance is always given first, and the second figure—vertical distance—is always 1. This gives a measure of steepness. The first number is large for flat slopes and small for steep slopes.

Figure 6-21 shows some examples of how slope ratio measurements are used. What is the vertical distance A from the shoulder edge to the bottom of the ditch? The 4:1 slope goes down 1 ft [0.3 m] for every 4 ft [1.2 m] horizontally. Since the bottom of the ditch is 12.0 ft [3.6 m] from the shoulder, it will be 3.0 ft [0.9 m] (12.0 ft divided by 4.0 ft [3.6 m divided by 1.2 m]) below the shoulder.

What is the horizontal distance B from the bottom of the ditch to the top of the backslope? For each 1 ft [0.3 m] of rise, the slope goes out horizontally 3 ft [0.9 m]. Therefore, for the slope to rise 2.5 ft [0.76 m] the horizontal distance will have to be 7.5 ft [2.3 m] (3 ft × 2.5 ft [(0.9 m/0.3 m) × 0.76 m]). This result can be calculated from the formula:

$$\text{Slope ratio} = \frac{\text{horizontal distance}}{\text{vertical distance}}$$

QUIZ

See Fig. 6-22.

Cross Slopes

Cross slopes of highway surfaces are shown differently. Figure 6-23 shows the slopes of the pavement away from the centerline, the pavement cross slopes, to be 0.02 feet per foot [0.02 meters per meter]. Cross slopes allow water to drain from the pavement surface.

A cross slope of 0.02 feet per foot [0.02 meters per meter] means that the pavement elevation drops 0.02 ft vertically for each foot [0.02 m for each meter] horizontally away from the centerline. If the outside edge of the pavement is 20.0 ft [6.1 m] from the centerline, it would be 0.4 ft [0.12 m] (0.02 × 20.0 = 0.4 [0.02 × 6.1 m = 0.12 m]) below the centerline elevation.

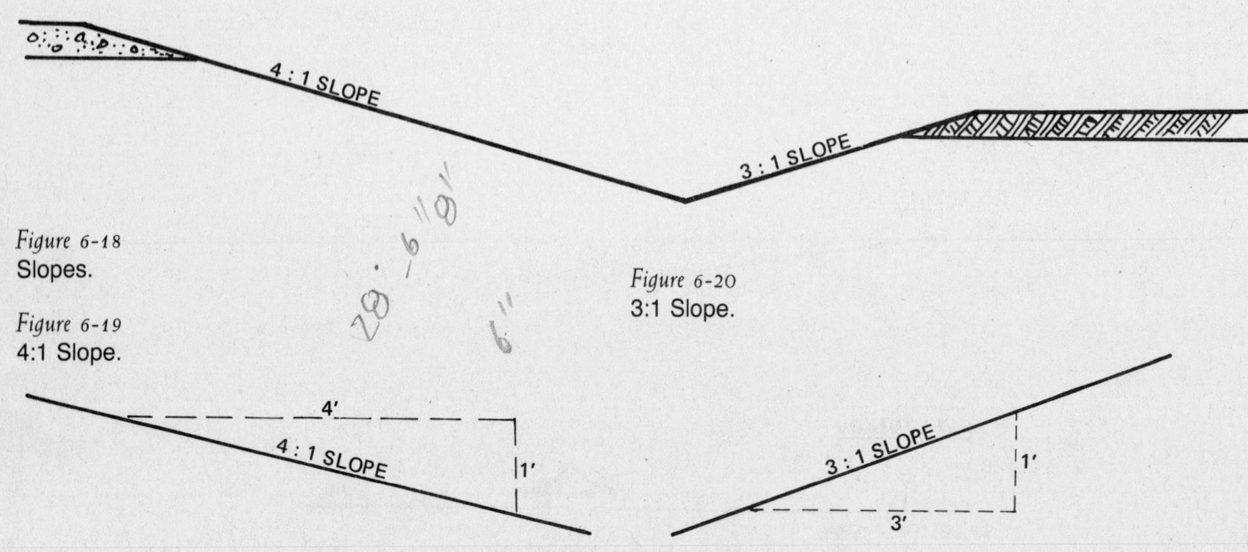

Figure 6-18 Slopes.

Figure 6-19 4:1 Slope.

Figure 6-20 3:1 Slope.

12.0′
SHOULDER EDGE
B
4 : 1 SLOPE
A
3 : 1 SLOPE
2.5′
BOTTOM OF DITCH

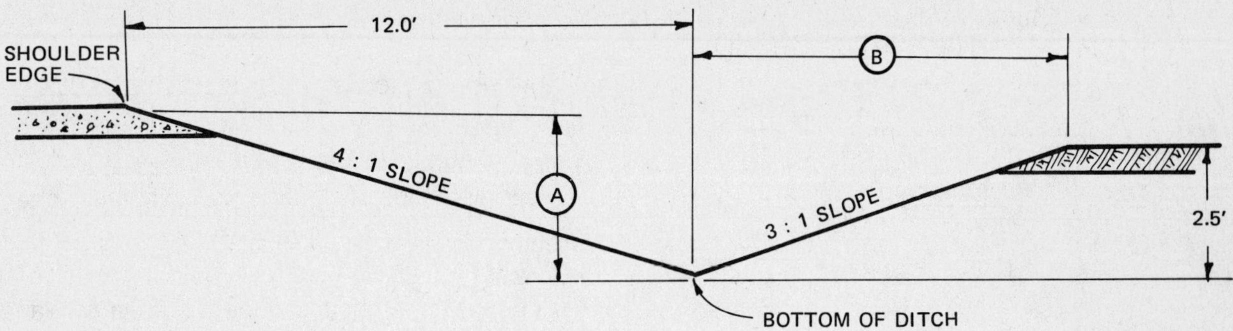

Figure 6-21
Slope ratio measurements.

HORIZONTAL DISTANCE	VERTICAL DISTANCE	SLOPE
4.0′	2.0′	___
6.0′	___	3 : 1
___	3.0′	5 : 1
45.0′	30.0′	___
20.0′	___	10 : 1
___	4.0′	4 : 1

Figure 6-22
Slope quiz.

Figure 6-23
Pavement cross slopes.

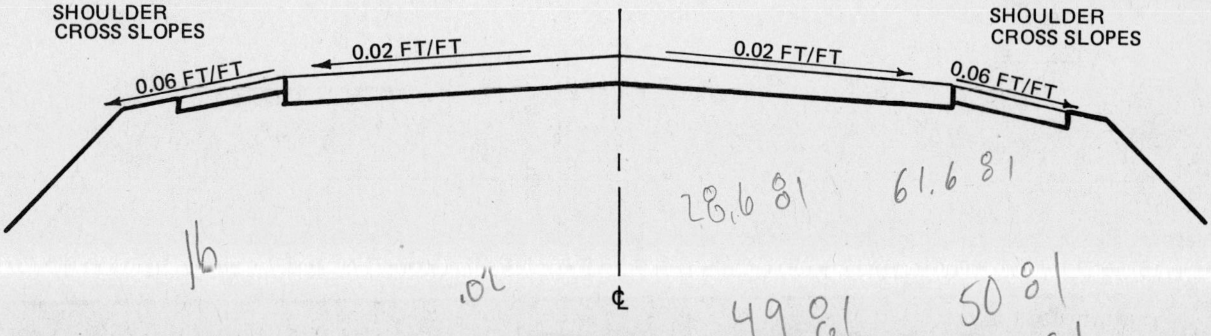

SHOULDER CROSS SLOPES
0.06 FT/FT
0.02 FT/FT
0.02 FT/FT
SHOULDER CROSS SLOPES
0.06 FT/FT
℄

Another way of seeing this relationship is by solving the problem using the cross-slope rate formula:

$$\text{Cross-slope rate} = \frac{\text{vertical distance}}{\text{horizontal distance}}$$

$$\frac{0.02\text{ ft}}{1.00\text{ ft}} = \frac{\text{vertical distance}}{20\text{ ft}}$$

$$\text{Vertical distance} = 20\text{ ft} \times 0.02$$

$$\text{Vertical distance} = 0.4\text{ ft}$$

When working with cross slopes, the formula used for determining the slope is reversed. While slope ratios are expressed in horizontal distance to vertical distance, cross slope rates are expressed as vertical distance to horizontal distance.

QUIZ

Fill in the blank spaces.

Cross Slope (ft/ft)	Horizontal Distance (ft)	Vertical Distance
0.02	24.0	.48
0.02	36.0	.72
0.03	48.0	1.44
0.06	10.0	.60
0.045	50.0	2.25
0.01	15.0	.15

.02 = x / 24.0

An additional review:

A view from the top is a plan view.

A view from the front or side is an profile view. An inside view, as if the object had been cut open, is a section view.

An index to the sheets included in a set of plans will be found on the ________ sheet.

What is the percentage grade of a line which falls 5.00 ft [1.52 m] in a horizontal distance of 100 ft [30.4 m]? − 5%

If the grade of a line is + 2.50 percent, what is the elevation change of the line in a horizontal distance of 100 ft [30.4 m]? 2.5 rise

If the slope of a line is 0.02 feet per foot [0.02 meters per meter], what is the vertical distance between the beginning and the end of a line 48.0 ft [14.6 m] long? 2,400

What is the percentage grade of a roadway which neither rises nor falls? 0.00%

A distance of 18.5 stations is equal to 1850 ft.

What is the actual length of the project in Fig. 6-24*a*? 2734 ft.

What do the symbols and abbreviations in Fig. 6-24*b* mean? Write the correct answer on the line next to the symbol or abbreviation. Look them up if necessary—do not guess.

.02 = 48 / X   X .02 = 48

Figure 6-24a
Length of project.

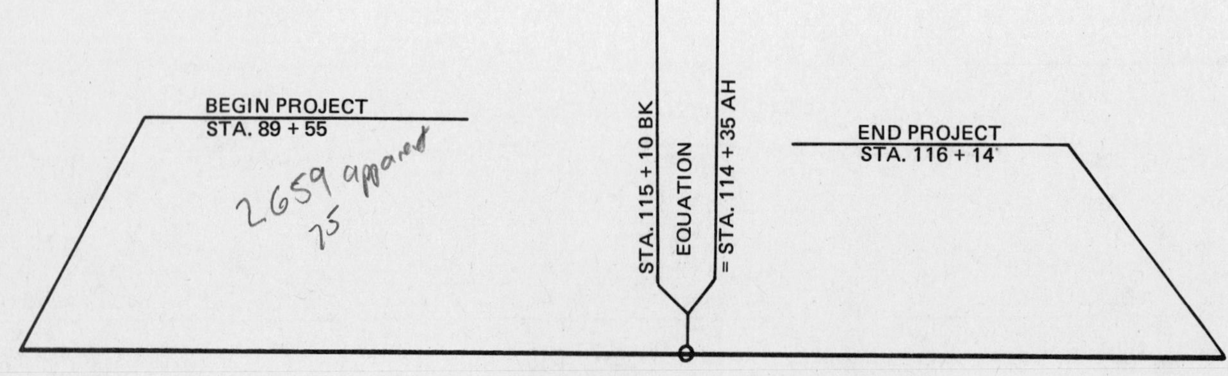

R.R.	Railroad
RT.	right
STA.	Station
—x——x———	fence
— —10" WM- — — —	
P̶L	
℄	Centerline

Figure 6-24b
Symbols and abbreviations quiz.

LEARNING ACTIVITY PACKAGE

Read Chap. 6 carefully.

Chapter 6 read ____________ (date).

If after reading Chap. 6 some of the objectives from (a) through (j) are not understood reread the paragraphs containing the appropriate information.

This chapter is an explanatory chapter and there will be no drawing problems. Since there are no problems, it would be wise to study the objectives carefully as these topics will all occur very soon in the drawings. Gaining a good understanding of the fundamentals explained in this chapter now will help immensely on the more complicated drawings in later chapters.

Objectives read and understood ____________ (date).

Now take the removable quiz on Chap. 6. Remove it from the end of the chapter and answer all the questions.

Quiz completed on ____________ (date).

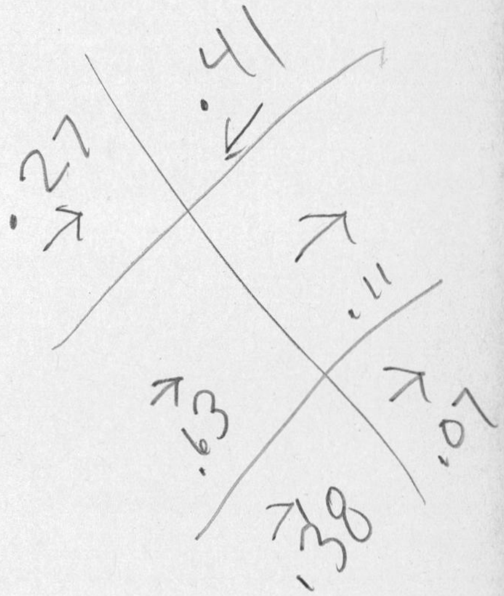

6

QUIZ

1. Directions of surveyed lines are described by bearings.
2. Bearings show whether lines are going north, south, east, or west. (T or F) True
3. Bearings always have a relationship to north or south. (T or F) True
4. There are five quadrants in a circle, each having 72°. (T or F) false
5. How many seconds are in one minute? 60"
6. For a bearing of N60°30′00″W, the steps to follow to find that direction are: Face north; turn an angle of 60°30′00″ west; you are now looking at the line with the bearing N60°30′00″W. (T or F) True
7. One station equals 100 ft.
8. How far is Sta. 12 + 50 from the point of beginning? 1,250'
9. Projects usually begin at Sta. 0 (zero). (T or F) false
10. Stations are given with a plus distance in feet beyond the last station. (T or F) True
11. How far (in feet) is station 80 + 67.51 from the point of beginning? 8,067.51'
12. Generally station numbers get larger going from east to west or north to south. (T or F) false
13. Station numbers get smaller looking ahead. (T or F) False
14. To find the distance between two points along a centerline, subtract the lower station number from the higher one. (T or F) True
15. Stationing is usually written to thousandths of a foot. (T or F) false
16. Are old road stationings ever used when making new plans? (*yes* or *no*) yes
17. The point where the stationing for a new road changes is an *equal point.* (T or F) false.
18. The abbreviated form, Sta. 10 + 00 Bk = Sta. 6 + 00 Ah, is called a station equation. (T or F) True
19. If the back station number in an equation is larger than the ahead station number, subtract the equation length from the apparent length to find the actual length. (T or F) false

20. What two places always show station equations? location map and plan views

21. Plan distance is always measured along the slope of the ground.
    (T or F) false

22. What are three ways of expressing the rise and fall of the ground?
    (1) grade, (2) slope, and (3) cross slope

23. A grade is a percent of vertical rise or fall based on horizontal distance.
    (T or F) True

24. If line *B* rises 2 ft [0.61 m] vertically in 100 ft [30.5 m] of horizontal distance, what is the percentage grade? 2%

25. We use + or − signs to indicate whether a grade is rising or falling.
    (T or F) True

26. How is a level grade shown? 0.00%

27. Slopes are written as a ratio between horizontal and vertical distance.
    (T or F) True

28. How much does a 3:1 slope rise in 3 ft [0.9 m] of horizontal distance?
    1 foot

29. In slope ratios the first number is small for flat slopes.
    (T or F) false

30. Cross slopes allow water to drain from pavement surfaces.
    (T or F) True

7 FUNDAMENTALS FOR USE IN PLAN AND PROFILE DRAWINGS

Objectives

a. Learn a little about drawing scales
b. Understand bench marks
c. Read about horizontal alignment
d. Understand points of beginning and ending
e. Study the method of showing a direction change for a roadway
f. Study the computation of bearings for changes in direction
g. Understand a little about degree of curvature
h. Learn the other curve elements
i. Study elevations of roadways
j. Understand vertical curves

Rationale

This is the second chapter to present fundamental ideas that are essential in drafting. It introduces the scale of drawings and systems of marking survey locations, such as bench marks. Roadway alignment is also discussed, along with bearings, distances, and changes of direction. The computation of bearings and control and reference points are discussed. (Even an ordinary suburban street like the one in Fig. 7-1 requires plans that include many or all of these items.) Finally, some pertinent abbreviations and definitions are presented in this chapter, just before they will be encountered in the drawings.

We discussed the tools of the civil drafting trade in Chap. 1. Chapter 2 was concerned with lettering, a very important subject. In Chaps. 3 and 4 we started drafting by doing a few key maps. These maps are primarily a tracing job and can be done with minimal explanation of the fundamental features of roadway design. In Chap. 5 we progressed a little further in drafting by working on drainage maps.

Chapters 6 and 7 contain the principal features of road design. These chapters are arranged so that the student can study the text and then take a short quiz on the subject matter. This self-study method is designed to make the work easier for both the student and the instructor. Chapter 7 will have many of the features necessary for proper reading of plan and profile drawings. The student will not be required to design highways, but the methods used in vertical and horizontal curves, bearings, and profile grade calculations should be understood. Just as memory is not accurate enough in industry, the student should not try to memorize the material in Chaps. 6 and 7 but should refer back to these chapters for the methods of doing these calculations.

Figure 7-1
A civil engineering project—a street in the suburbs. *(Florida Department of Transportation).*

SCALES OF DRAWINGS

Many things on plan sheets are drawn according to *Scales.* This means that lines on the plans are drawn an exact length so as to represent a real distance on the ground or the dimension of a real object.

If a line on a drawing is measured and the scale is known, the real length of the line could be computed, but many plan sheets are reduced by state transportation departments to approximately *half* their original size. This means that a line which is exactly 1 inch (in) [25 mm] long on a full-size original will be approximately ½ in [13 mm] long on a reduced sheet. For this reason, *avoid* trying to measure distances on plan sheets with a ruler. Look for a written dimension, or calculate distances from written figures.

The scale of a drawing is often noted in the lower right corner of the sheet, along with the sheet name. The words "Scale 1 in = 2000 ft" mean that every inch on the plan view represents 2000 ft on the ground (2 in represents 4000 ft, 5 in represents 10,000 ft, and ½ in is 1000 ft).

QUIZ

Fill in the blanks:

Scale	Map Distance	Ground Distance
1 in = 1000 ft	½ in	______
1 in = 100 ft	3 in	______
1 in = 100 ft	4¾ in	______
1 in = 200 ft	½ in	______
1 in = 200 ft	2½ in	______
1 in = 10 ft	½ in	______
1 in = 4000 ft	2¼ in	______

Scales of Plan and Profile Sheets

Plan Views. Plan views on plan and profile sheets usually are shown with a 1 in = 100 ft scale. Sometimes plan views are drawn larger to show more detail. For example, in urban or other congested areas, plan views are often drawn to a scale of 1 in = 20 ft.

Profile Views. Two scales are used for each profile view. Usually, the scales are as follows:

- ☐ Horizontal 1 in = 100 ft
- ☐ Vertical 1 in = 10 ft

The horizontal scales are the same as those used on plan views, but the vertical scales are much larger—1 in equals only 10 ft. This is done in order to exaggerate small differences in elevation so that they can be seen more clearly. Though the drawings on the profile view look out of proportion, don't let this fool you. A vertical distance of 100 ft will look 10 times larger than a horizontal distance of 100 ft.

Figure 7-2 shows one section of the grid for a profile drawing. Notice that the vertical scale for measuring elevation is 1 in = 10 ft of elevation. This is a scale exaggerated 10 times compared to the horizontal scale of 1 in = 100 ft along the highway. If the map were not made in this way, the small differences in the profile grade of the highway would never be seen.

QUIZ

Look at the example of a profile grid, Fig. 7-3, and use the grid lines to read the distances and elevations:

Point D is ______ ft ahead of point E.

Point E is ______ ft above point C.

Point A is ______ ft above point C.

Point B is ______ ft back of point A, at an elevation of ____ ft.

Point C is ______ ft below point E, at an elevation of ____ ft.

Point D is ____ ft ____ of point C, at an elevation of ____ ft.

LAND SURVEY DATA—BENCH MARKS

Much of the information shown on the plan sheets is based on surveys made in the field. Learning a little about land survey data will help make this information clear.

A bench mark (B.M.) is an elevation marker, such as a spike in a tree or a concrete monument. Bench-mark elevations usually are referenced from mean sea level.

Most surveys start from permanent United States Coast and Geodetic Survey (USC&GS) bench marks, which are usually concrete monuments. During the surveys, additional bench marks are established and recorded by the department of transportation or the consulting engineers who are making the surveys. They are used during construction to establish accurate elevations. Bench marks often are established by placing spikes in trees or by marking walls or bridges. (The student may wonder why a spike in a tree would serve as an elevation mark, expecting that the spike would tend to rise from the ground as the tree grows. This isn't so; a tree grows out as it gets older and branches grow out from the top, but the elevation where the spike was driven into the tree stays the same until the tree dies.) Bench marks are estalished about every 1000 ft [305 m] along the project.

The importance of a bench mark is to give a point of known elevation and the known location of that point. Bench-mark notes are shown along the top of profile

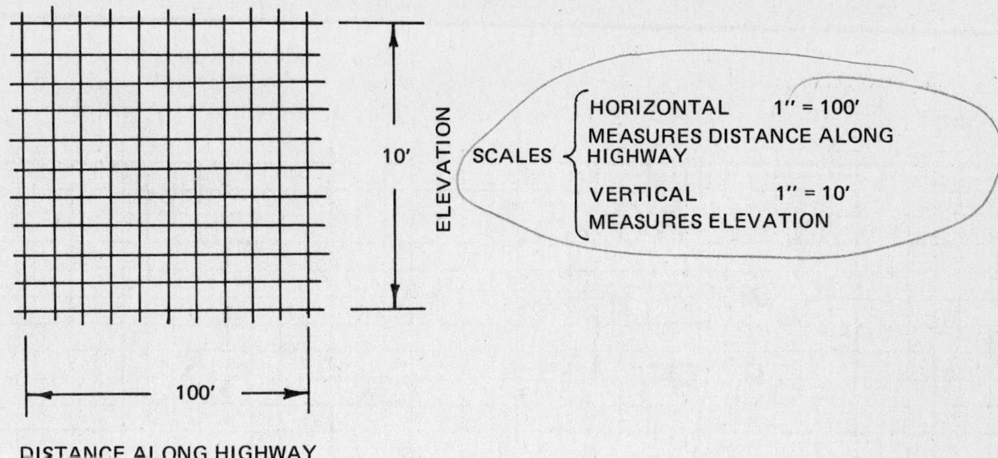

Figure 7-2
Grid for a profile drawing.

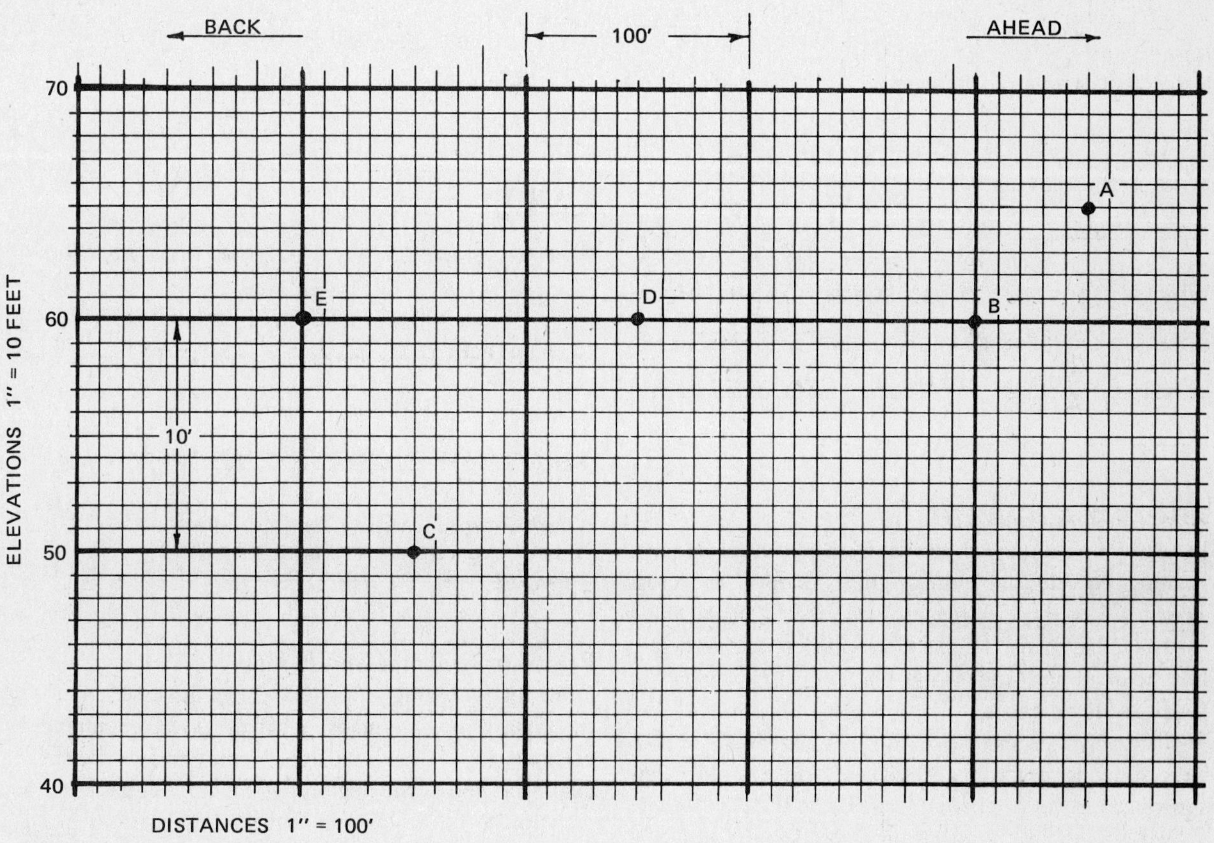

Figure 7-3
Grid quiz.

views on plan and profile sheets (see Fig. 7-4 for an example). A bench-mark number is given first, then the description of the bench mark. The location of the bench mark is shown next, and finally the elevation of the bench mark (this is the important item). The purpose of the mark is to give an accurate elevation at that particular place.

QUIZ

Bench marks give precise elevations.

Bench-mark notes are found in the top views of plan and profile sheets.

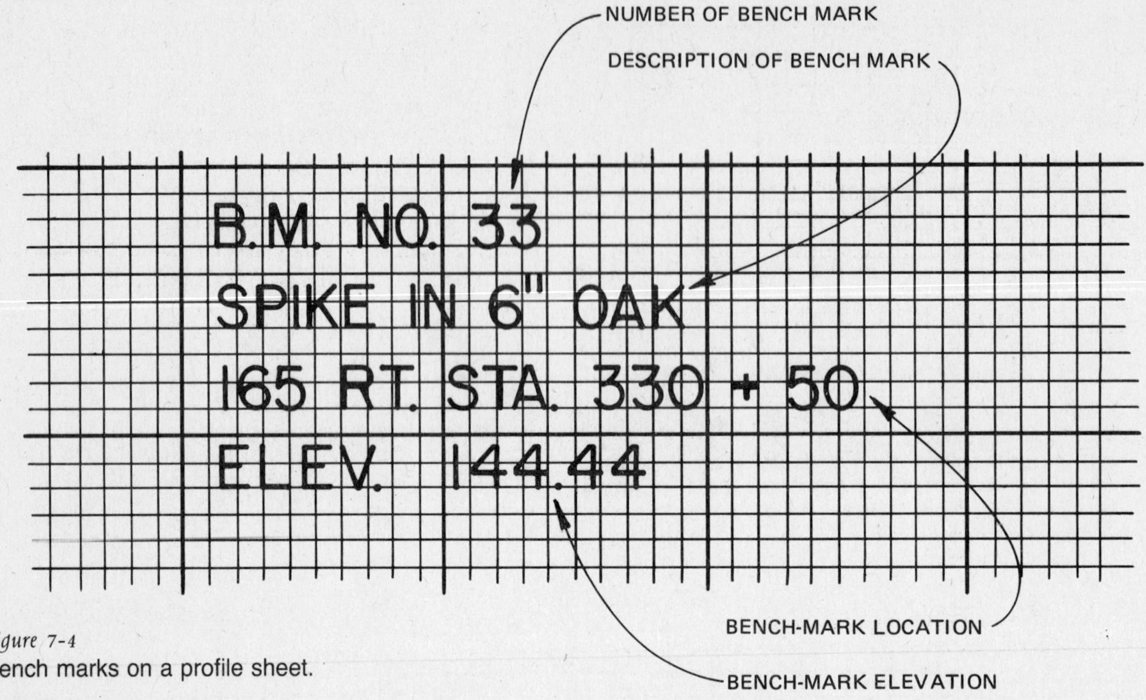

Figure 7-4
Bench marks on a profile sheet.

What is the elevation of B.M. 33 in Fig 7-4?
144.44.

Why is it possible to use spikes in trees to give accurate elevation points? trees grow outward, the spike stay the same elevation

ROADWAY ALIGNMENT

In Chap. 6 we discussed horizontal distances, elevations, stations, equations, bearings, grades, slopes, and cross slopes. All of these things are important when defining roadway alignment. This section will describe, in detail, how to read and understand plan and profile views of roadway alignment.

Plans of roads show two views of alignment—a plan view showing horizontal alignment and a profile view showing vertical alignment. Normally these views are shown one above the other on plan and profile sheets; this is done so that the roadway can be better visualized. Occasionally a plan view is shown on one sheet while the elevation view is shown on another.

HORIZONTAL ALIGNMENT

The horizontal alignment of the proposed road is found in the top half of plan and profile sheets. The alignment is shown in relation to buildings, utility poles, fences, trees, property lines, and other topographical features.

QUIZ

What two views usually are shown on plan and profile sheets? a plan view showing horizontal alignment + profile showing vertical

Normally, the top half of a plan and profile sheet shows a horizontal alignment view.

Which view shows horizontal alignment?
top half of plan + profile

Points of Beginning and Ending

Points of beginning and ending were discussed briefly in the chapter on key maps (Chap. 3). The beginning of each project is shown on the first plan and profile sheet. Figure 7-5 shows the beginning of a job that has a station equation in its stationing. Notice the equations in Fig. 7-5. In this case, in order to simplify station numbering, they are set up between the end of a previous project and the beginning of this project.

The note on the plan sheet shows exactly where the project starts. The end of the project is shown with a similar note on the last plan and profile sheet.

Bearings and Distances

Chapter 6 discussed how bearings measure direction in relation to north or south. It also explained how dis-

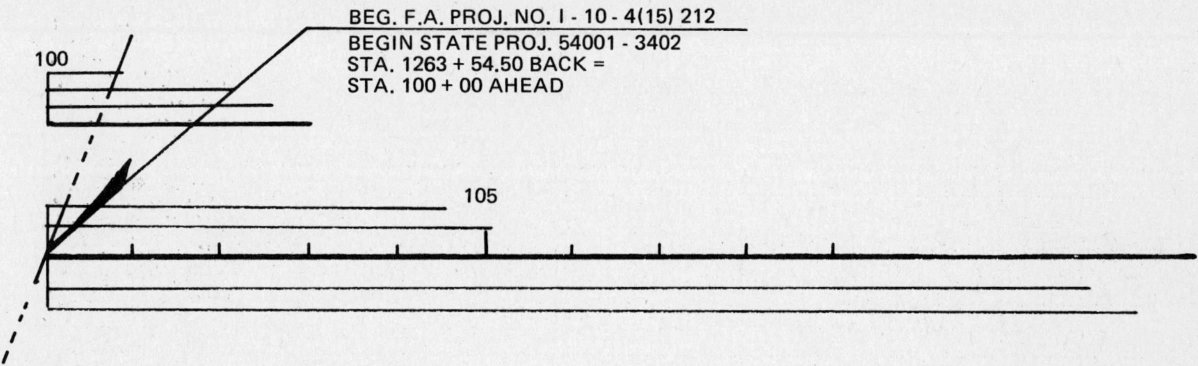

Figure 7-5
A station equation used to set up a job.

Figure 7-6
A point of intersection.

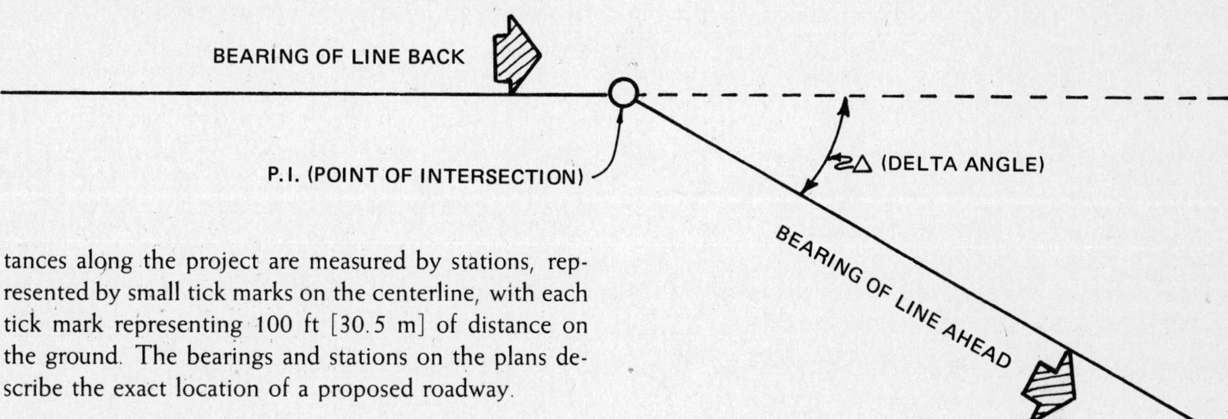

tances along the project are measured by stations, represented by small tick marks on the centerline, with each tick mark representing 100 ft [30.5 m] of distance on the ground. The bearings and stations on the plans describe the exact location of a proposed roadway.

Changes of Direction

What happens when the roadway changes direction? The surveyor simply drives a stake in the ground, turns the transit in the direction the roadway should go, and measures the angle of the change. This angle is called the *delta angle* and is identified with the symbol Δ. The point where the stake is driven is called the *point of intersection* (PI) because the line back and the line ahead intersect at this point. Figure 7-6 shows this relationship.

QUIZ

What does Δ represent delta angle

____

The point at which Δ occurs (the point where the stake is driven) is called the point of intersection, which has the abbreviation PI.

⌒ This is the symbol for angle.

Computing Bearings

The bearings for the line ahead can be computed if the following are known: (1) the bearing of the line back; (2) the delta angle; and (3) whether the delta angle turns left or right. See the examples in Figs. 7-7 to 7-11.

In Fig. 7-11, because the angle is in excess of 90°, the bearing is closer to south than to north; it can be changed to a bearing from the south by subtracting it from 180°. In order to simplify the subtraction, change 180° to 179°60′00″.

	179°60′00″
subtract	110°45′00″
	69°15′00″

Bearing ahead = S69°15′00″E

NOTE: Bearing equations, which are similar to the stationing equations we discussed earlier, are occasionally used to adjust inconsistencies in bearing data.

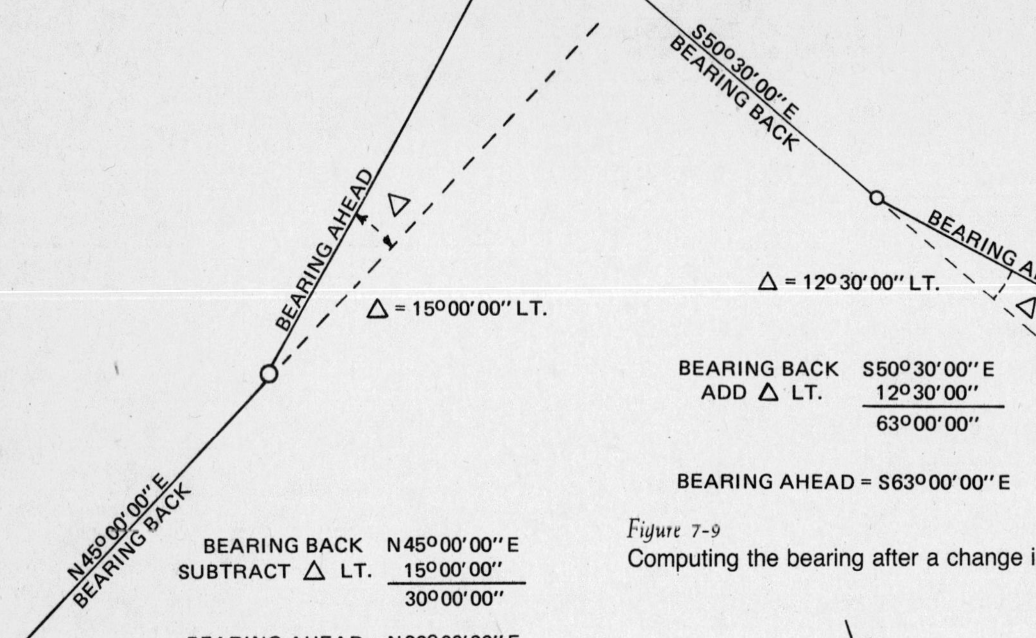

Figure 7-9
Computing the bearing after a change in direction.

Figure 7-7
Computing the bearing after a change in direction.

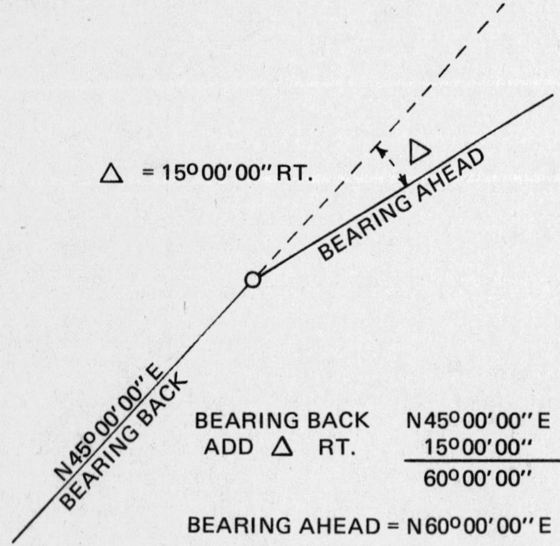

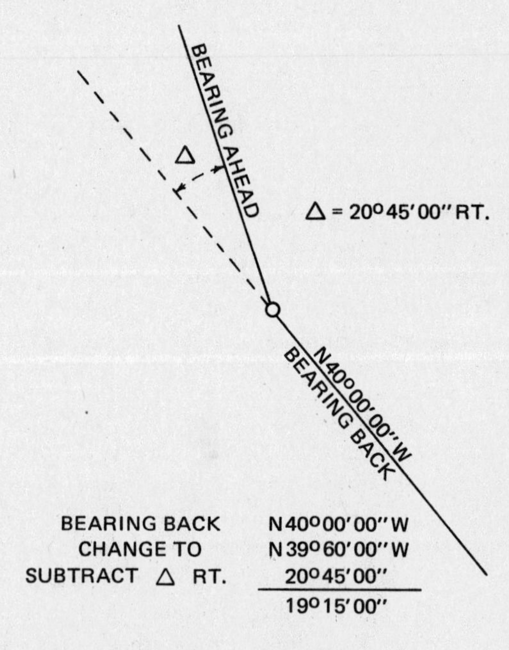

Figure 7-8
Computing the bearing after a change in direction.

Figure 7-10
Computing the bearing after a change in direction. In order to subtract 20°45′00″ from 40°00′00″, 40°00′00″ was changed to 39°60′00″ (the same angle).

Figure 7-11
Computing the bearing after a change in direction.

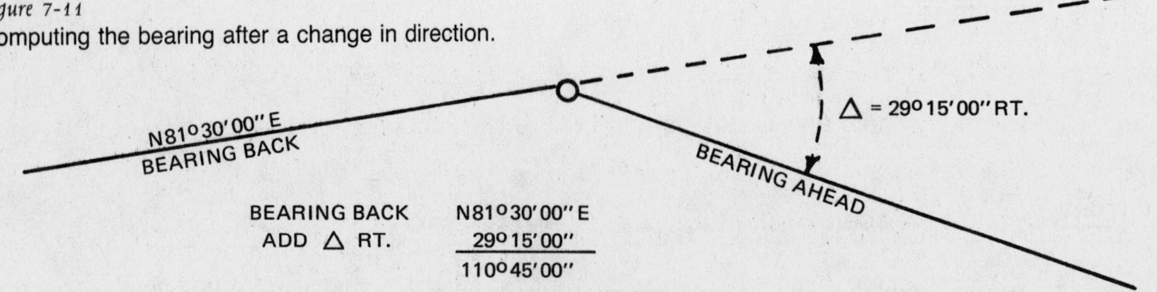

QUIZ

Bearing of Line Back	Delta Angle Δ	Bearing of Line Ahead
N60°00′00″E	15°00′00″ RT	______
N60°00′00″E	15°00′00″ LT	______
S32°10′00″W	12°05′00″ RT	______
S52°45′30″E	5°30′00″ RT	______
N18°20′15″W	8°25′15″ LT	______
N85°30′00″E	25°30′00″ RT	______

To adjust inconsistencies in bearing data, bearing ______ are used.

Be sure you understand *bearings* and *delta angles*.

HORIZONTAL CURVES

A series of straight lines can describe the horizontal alignment of a road, but the road cannot be built that way. Since cars cannot make a sharp turn at a PI, a horizontal curve is surveyed between the straight lines to permit the cars to change direction easily. Let us look at some of the elements of horizontal curves.

Degrees of Curvature

If the road is for high-speed traffic, the curve must be "flat" and extend a considerable distance on each side of the PI. For low-speed design, the curves may be sharper. The plans tell how sharp the curve is by identifying the *degree of curvature* (D). The degree of curvature is measured by the angle at the center of a circle made by two radii extending to points 100 ft [30.5 m] apart on the circumference of a circle. Figure 7-12 shows that small D values represent flat curves with large radii and large D values represent sharp curves with small radii.

REMEMBER that the letter D is always used to identify degrees of curvature.

QUIZ

If two radii extend to points 100 ft [30.5 m] apart on the circumference of a circle, the angle at the center represents the ______.

D is the abbreviation for ______.

Do large D values represent sharp curves?

______

The degree of curvature is the directional change along ______ ft of a curve.

Additional Curve Elements

Several other parts of a curve are identified by symbols and abbreviations. Some of these are: Point of curvature (*PC*), point of tangency (*PT*), tangent length (*T*), curve length (*L*), and Radius (*R*). They are shown in Fig. 7-13.

Figure 7-12
Degree of curvature.

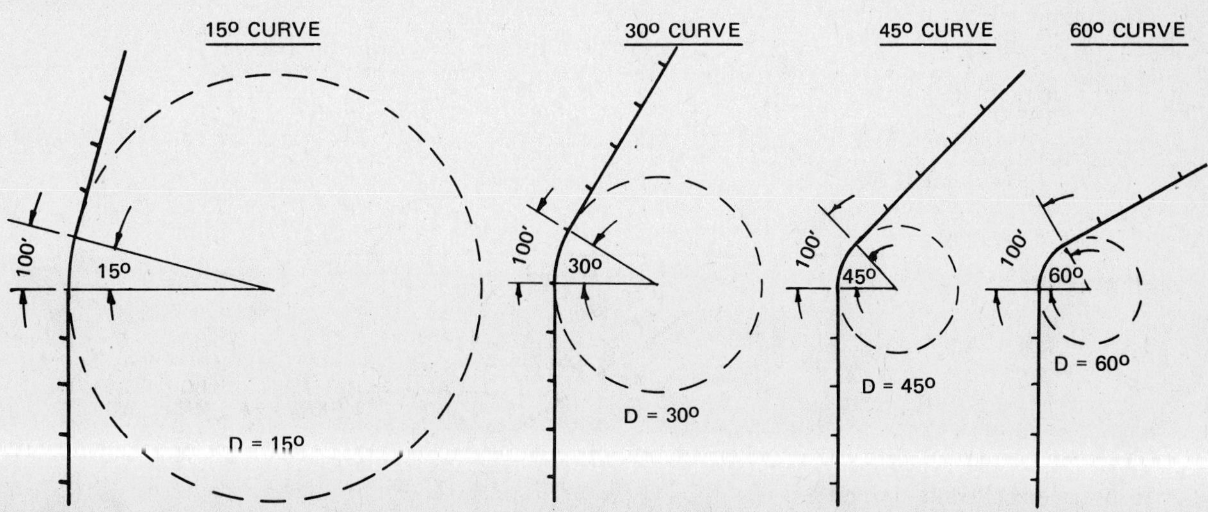

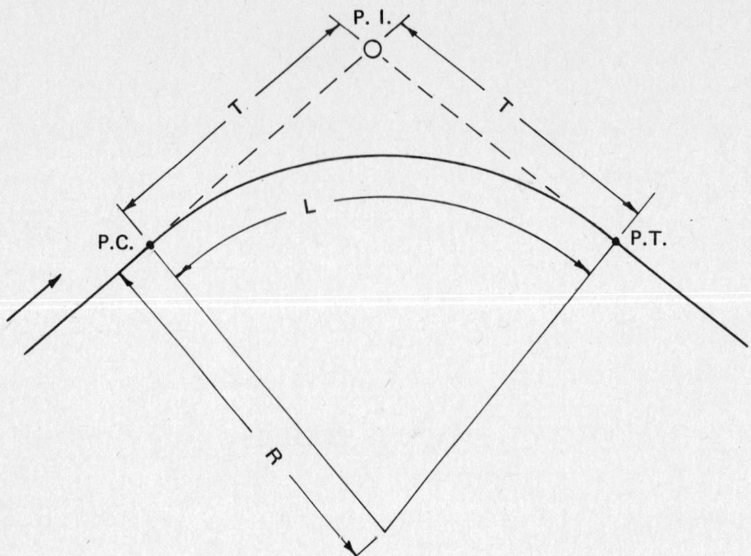

Figure 7-13
Curve elements.

The point of curvature (PC) is the point where the horizontal curve begins.

Point of tangency (PT) is where the horizontal curve ends.

Curve length (*L*) is the distance measured along the curve from the point of curvature to the point of tangency.

Tangent length (*T*) represents the equal distances from the point of curvature to the point of intersection and from the point of intersection to the point of tangency.

Radius (*R*) of the curve represents the distance from the center of the imaginary circle, used to draw the curve, to the edge of the circle.

The radius (*R*) is always perpendicular (at a 90° angle) to the tangent (*T*).

Plan views on plan and profile sheets list horizontal curve elements with their values. These data are located near the curve to which they apply.

Control Points and Reference Points

Points on curves and points on tangents are control points to help assure that the roadway is constructed exactly where it is supposed to be. The location of each control point is identified by reference points (see Fig. 7-14). In Fig. 7-14, the point on tangent is the control point. The markers and trees are reference points that can be used to establish the exact location of the point on tangent. Note that all plan and profile sheets will have several control or reference points on each sheet.

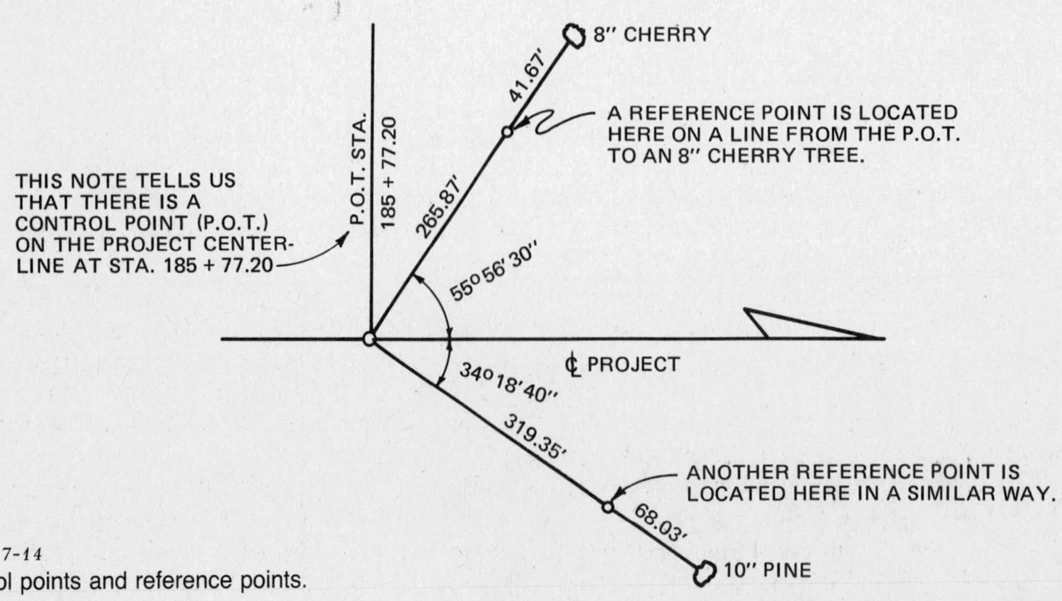

Figure 7-14
Control points and reference points.

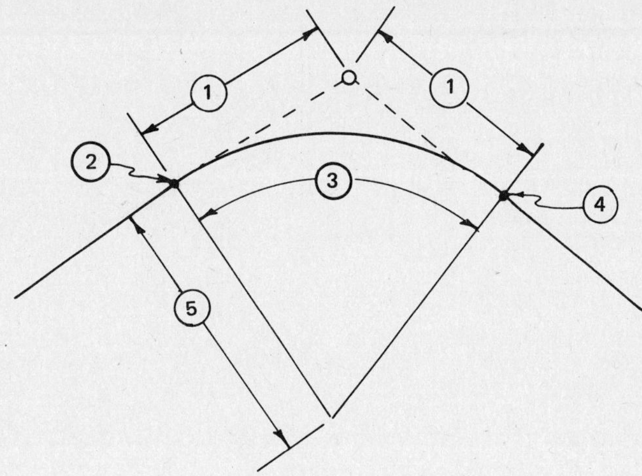

Figure 7-15
Quiz.

QUIZ

Name the curve elements shown in Fig. 7-15.

1. T tagent length
2. P.C. point of curvature
3. L curve length
4. P.T point of tagency
5. R radus

D represents degree of curvature.

Δ represents delta angle.

QUIZ

What is the bearing ahead for the line in Fig. 7-16?

S 70° 00' 00" E

T = tangent length

L = curve length

R = radius

PI = point of intersection

PC = point of curvature

PT = point of tangency

VERTICAL ALIGNMENT

Vertical alignment is the relationship of roadway elevations along the project. A roadway changes elevations at various points along the way; it rises or falls.

Vertical-alignment control points are defined by stations and elevations. Stations and elevations form a grid for measuring and plotting vertical alignment. Vertical alignment data are shown in profile views on plan and profile sheets.

Turn to sheet 14 of Project 54001-3402 (Fig. 9-6). First, notice the difference between the top and bottom halves of the sheet. The top half shows a plan view; the bottom half shows a profile view.

(Profile views are not always shown together with plan views; sometimes they are shown on different sheets.)

Elevations of the Proposed Roadway

The elevation of the proposed roadway is represented by the *profile grade line* shown on profile views. The profile view (or profile) shows both the natural ground line and the profile grade line, see Fig. 7-17. Each line is plotted on a profile grid according to elevations and stations. The natural ground line usually is an irregular line. It represents a profile view of the original ground (before construction). The profile grade line is a smooth, continuous line. It represents a profile view of the proposed roadway.

Elevations of the profile grade line serve as control points for construction of the proposed roadway. Many elements of the roadway are based on (or constructed in relation to) profile grade elevations.

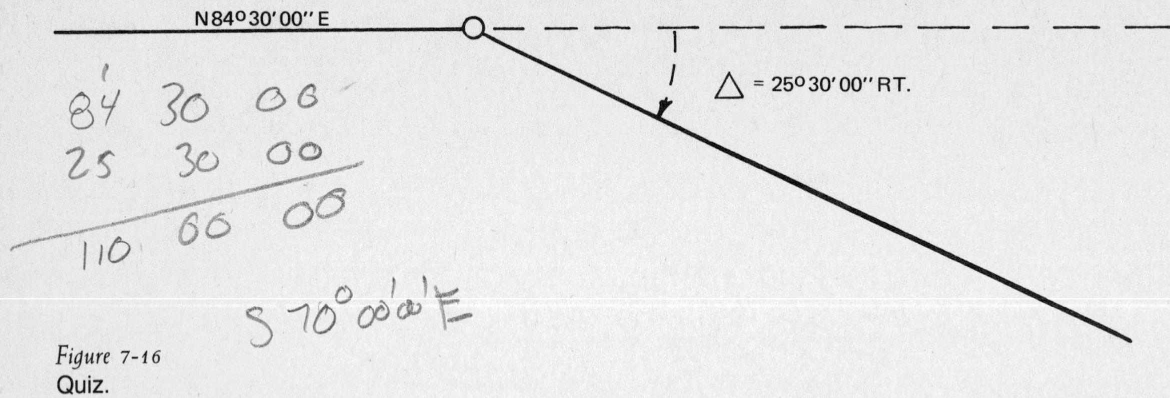

Figure 7-16
Quiz.

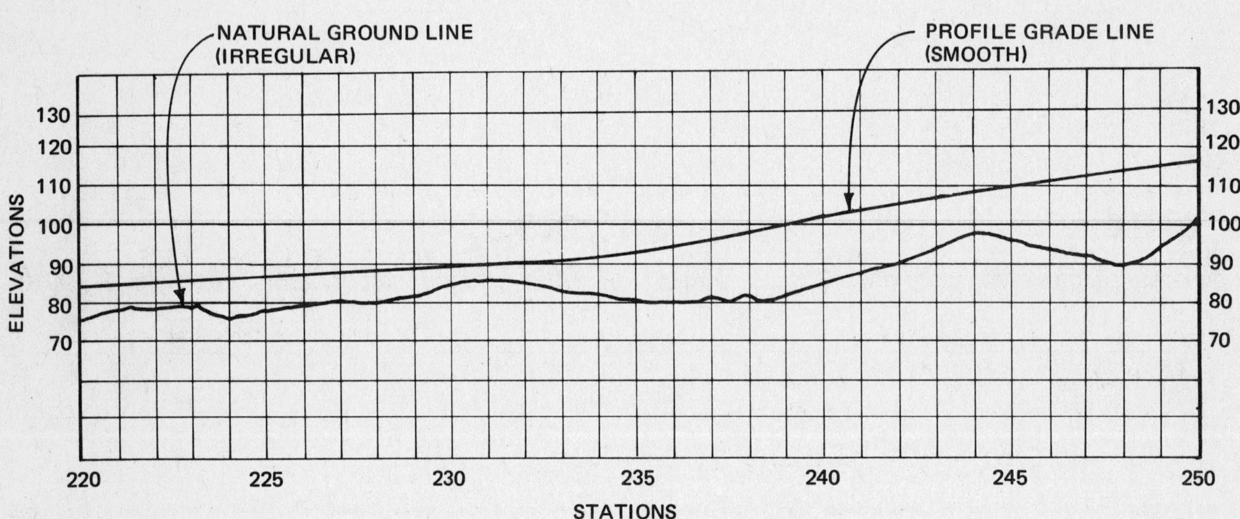

Figure 7-17
Profile grade and natural ground lines. Stations are marked along the bottom of the grid.

Refer again to sheet 14 of Project 54001-3402, Fig. 9-6. Vertical lines are drawn every 10 ft to provide horizontal reference points. Also, horizontal lines every foot provide vertical reference points. On the left and right sides of the profile grid are the elevations of the project in feet. Along the bottom of the grid are station numbers. Station numbers and elevations are identified like this on all profile views. Elevation lines and station-number lines thus form grids upon which profile views are shown.

Notice particularly the difference between the horizontal and vertical scales. On the reduced sheets, 100 ft [30.5 m] of horizontal distance (one station) equals approximately 5⁄16 in. However, only 10 ft [3.0 m] of vertical distance (elevation) equals approximtely 5⁄16 in on the sheet. The vertical scale is ten times larger than the horizontal scale. Changes of grades can thus be seen easily by looking at the profiles, since the changes are exaggerated ten times.

QUIZ

The vertical alignment of a roadway is based on elevations and stations.

The bottom half of most plan and profile sheets shows profile views of the proposed highway.

Are roadway elevations represented by the profile grade line? ______________

Profile grade elevations serve as control points for highway construction.

The irregular line in the profile view is the natural ground line.

Refer to sheet 14 of Project 54001–3402, Fig. 9-6.

What is the approximate elevation of the natural ground line at Sta. 231 + 00? 89

What is the approximate elevation of the natural ground line at Sta. 228 + 00? 85

What is the approximate difference in elevation between the natural ground line and the profile grade line at Sta. 237 + 00? 4

What is the approximate profile grade elevation at Sta. 245 + 00? 105

What is the approximate profile grade elevation at Sta. 229 + 80? 91

At Sta. 244 + 00, is the natural ground higher or lower than the profile grade line? lower

VERTICAL CURVES

Vertical curves are the curved portions on the profile, as shown in Fig. 7-18. Vertical curves form "transitions" between two different profile tangents. Without vertical curves to provide smooth grade changes, there would be sharp breaks in the profile.

Grades change in the same way that bearings change. In other words, roads go uphill and downhill as well as left and right. For each grade change, there is a point of intersection (PI), just as there are points of intersection for changes in horizontal direction. The length of a vertical curve is the *horizontal* distance between the beginning and the end of the curve.

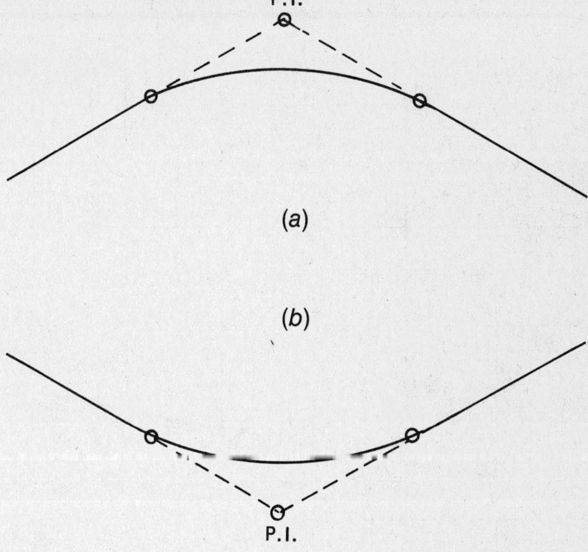

Figure 7-19
(*a*) Crest and (*b*) sag vertical curves.

When a road goes over a hill or mountain, it may curve over the top. The term *crest* describes the vertical curve shown in Fig. 7-19(*a*). When a roadway goes down in a valley or other depression, it may "sag" as in Fig. 7-19(*b*).

Vertical Curve Data

For each vertical curve, the station and elevation of the point of intersection are written on the profile. The vertical curve length also is shown (see Fig. 7-20).

Stations and elevations of vertical curve points usually are written vertically. Vertical curve lengths are written horizontally between the beginning and the end of the curve. In the example, Fig. 7-20, "800 ft V.C." means "800-ft vertical curve." In other words, the vertical curve is 800 ft long, measured *horizontally*.

Figure 7-18
a. Crest vertical curve; *b*. Sag vertical curve.

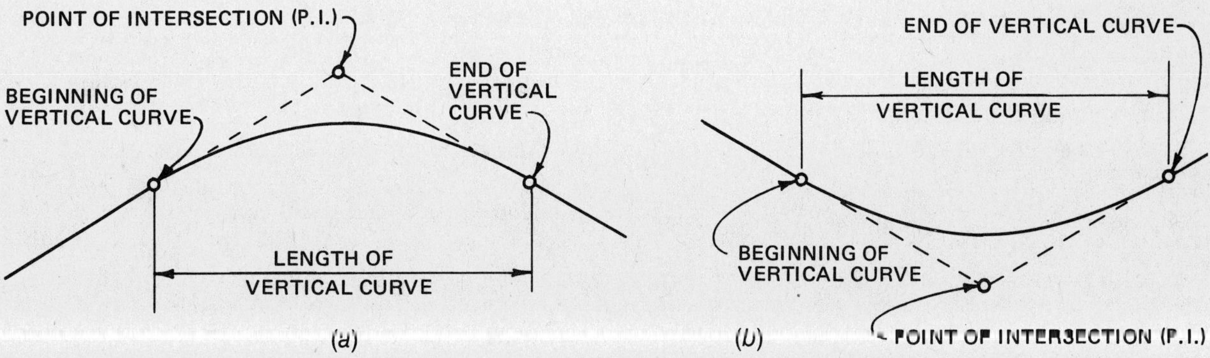

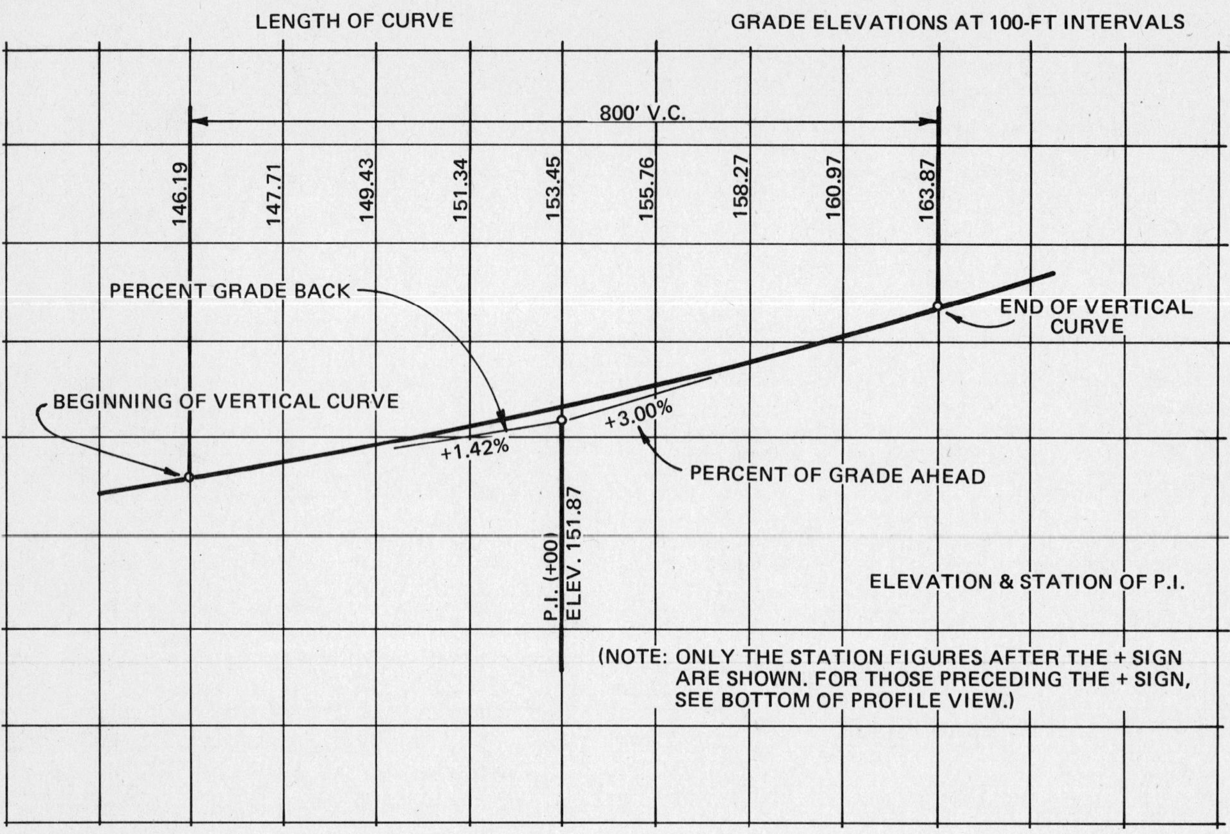

Figure 7-20
Vertical curve data on a profile view.

QUIZ

Refer to page 18 of Project 54001–3402 and answer these questions about the vertical curve beginning at Sta. 340 + 00:

The PI elevation is 151.87.

The PI station is +00.

The length of the vertical curve is 806′ V.C..

The percentage grade preceding the curve is +1.42%

The percentage grade ahead of the curve is +3.00%.

What is the profile grade elevation at Sta. 358 + 00? ____________

REMEMBER There is *no* relationship between a horizontal curve (as shown on the plan) and a vertical curve (as shown on the profile). A road may have a horizontal curve where there is a vertical curve, or it may not.

ABBREVIATIONS AND DEFINITIONS

abandoned	abd
acre	ac
afternoon	PM
alternate	alt
angle	angle
area	*A*
asphalt	asph
avenue	Ave
backsight	bs
barrel	bbl
bearing	brg
bench mark	B.M.
bituminous coated corrugated metal pipe culvert	BCCMP
bituminous coated and paved corrugated metal pipe culvert	BCPMP
bituminous coated pipe arch culvert	BCPA
bituminous coated and paved pipe arch culvert	BCPPA
bottom	bot

boulevard	Blvd	inch	in
brook	brook	incorporated	Inc
building	bldg	iron pipe	I.P.
cast iron	C.I.	junction	jt
cast iron pipe	C.I.P.	junction box	J.B.
concrete	conc	lake	lake
concrete pipe	C.P.	latitude	lat
cement	cem	left	lt
centerline	C.L.	length	lgth
center	ctr	length of curve	*L*
chain	ch	length of tangent	*T*
channel	channel	linear	lin
corner	cor	longitude	long.
corrugated iron	Corr. I.	manhole	M.H.
corrugated metal	C.M.	maximum	max
corrugated metal pipe	C.M.P.	mean sea level	MSL
creek	Cr	meridian	mer
cubic yard	C.Y.	mile	mile
culvert	culv	miles per hour	mph
degree	deg	minimum	min
degree of curvature	*D*	minute	min
delta	delta	national	natl
diameter	*D* or diam	negative	neg
dimension	dim.	north	N
drawing	dwg	northeast	NE
east	E	northwest	NW
elevation (above sea level)	El	number	No.
elevation (view)	elev	on centers	oc
engineer	Engr	opposite	opp
engineering	engg	ounce	oz
equation	eq	outside diameter	od
excavation	exc	page	p
extra	extra	pages	pp
federal	Fed.	parallel	par
Federal Aid	FA	plane	pl
Federal Aid Primary	FAP	plate	pl
Federal Aid Secondary	FAS	point	pt
feet per minute	fpm	point of compund curvature	PCC
feet per second	fps	point of curvature	PC
figure	Fig.	point of intersection	PI
fire hydrant	F.H.	point of reverse curve	PRC
floor	fl	point of tangency	PT
foot	ft	point on tangent	POT
forenoon	AM	pound, pounds	lb
foresight	fs	power	pwr
gage	ga	power pole	P.P.
gallon	gal	primary	pri
gallons per second	gps	principal meridian	prin mer
gallons per minute	gpm	project	Proj.
galvanized iron	G.I.	radius	*R* or rad
ground	grd	railroad	RR
high water	H.W.	railway	Ry
horizontal	horiz	range	R
hour	hr	reference	ref
house	hse or h	reinforcement	reinf

reinforcing	reinf
right	rt
right-of-way	R/W
river	R
road	rd
route	Rte.
sanitary sewer	San. S.
second	sec
service	serv
south	S
southeast	SE
southwest	SW
square mile	sq mile
square yard	sq yd
station	sta
State	State
storm sewer	S.S.
street	St
survey	surv
tangent	tan.
telephone	telp
telephone pole	T.P.
thousand	M
township	Twp
typical	typ
underground	ug
U.S. Geological Survey	USGS
U.S. Coast & Geodetic Survey	USC&GS
variable	var
vertical	vert
vertical curve	V.C.
volume	vol
weight	wt
west	W
yard	yd
year	yr

DEFINITIONS:

At-grade intersection: An intersection where all roadways join or cross at the same level.

Bus: A self-propelled motor vehicle designed for the transportation of more than eight persons.

Cul-de-sac street: A local street open at one end only and with special provision for turning around.

Dead-end street: A local street open at one end only without special provision for turning around.

Dedication: The setting apart by the owner and acceptance by the public of property for highway use, in accordance with statutory or common law provisions.

Design speed: A speed determined for design and correlation of the physical highway features that influence vehicle operation. It is the maximum safe speed that can be maintained over a specified section of highway when conditions are such that the design features of the highway govern.

Divided highway: A highway with separated roadways for traffic in opposite directions.

Drainage easement: An easement for directing the flow of water.

Easement: A right acquired by public authority to use or control property for a designated highway purpose.

Expressway: A divided arterial highway for through traffic with full or partial control of access and generally with grade separations at intersections.

Frontage street or frontage road: A local street or road auxiliary to and located on the side of an arterial highway for service to abutting property and adjacent areas and for control of access.

Grade separation: A crossing of two highways, or a highway and a railroad, at different levels.

Highway, street or road: A general term denoting a public way for purposes of vehicular travel, including the entire area within the right-of-way (Recommended usage: in urban areas, highway or street; in rural areas, highway or road).

Intersection: The general area where two or more highways join or cross, within which are included the roadway and roadside facilities for traffic movements in that area.

Intersection Angle: The angle between two intersection legs.

Local street or local road: A street or road primarily for access to residence, business, or other abutting property.

Median: The portion of a divided highway separating the traveled ways for traffic in opposite directions.

Median opening: A gap in a median provided for crossing and turning traffic.

Overpass: A grade separation where the subject highway passes over an intersecting highway or railroad (also called overcrossing).

Passenger car: A motor vehicle designed for the transportation of not more than eight persons. The term includes taxicabs, limousines, and station wagons.

Railroad crossing angle: The angle of 90° or less where a railroad and a highway intersect.

Railroad grade crossing: The general area where a highway and a railroad cross at the same level, within which are included the railroad, roadway, and roadside facilities for traffic traversing that area.

Right of access: The right of ingress to a highway from abutting land and egress from a highway to abutting land.

Right-of-way: A general term denoting land, property, or interest therein, usually in a strip, acquired for or devoted to a highway.

Roadway: (General): The portion of a highway, including shoulders, for vehicular use. A divided highway has two or more roadways.

Shoulder: The portion of the roadway contiguous with the traveled way for accommodation of stopped vehicles, for emergency use, and for lateral support of base and surface courses.

Slope easement: An easement for cuts or fills.

Skew angle: The complement of the acute angle between two centerlines which cross.

Speed: The rate of movement of a vehicle, generally expressed in miles per hour.

Traffic sign: A traffic control device mounted on a support above the level of the roadway. A traffic sign conveys a specific message by means of unchanging words or symbols.

Traffic signal: A power-operated traffic control device by which traffic is regulated, warned, or alternately directed to take specific actions.

Traveled way: The portion of the roadway for the movement of vehicles, exclusive of shoulders and auxiliary lanes.

Underpass: A grade separation where the subject highway passes under an intersecting highway or railroad (also called undercrossing).

Volume: The number of vehicles passing a given point during a specified period of time.

LEARNING ACTIVITY PACKAGE

Read Chap. 7 carefully. It contains no drafting problems. For this reason, extra time should be spent on the fundamentals, in order to maximize the student's understanding of the items on the Drawings, which will be reproduced on the student's drawings.

Chapter 7 read ____________ (*date*).

Chapters 6 and 7 contain a great deal of information. If some of the objectives are not understood now, the student can come back to these two chapters to reread this basic material when drawing the maps.

Objectives read ____________ (*date*).

Now take the removable quiz. Remove the quiz from the text and answer all the questions.

Test completed ____________ (*date*).

7

QUIZ

1. Drafting students should be able to design a highway upon completion of this course. (T or F) false
2. Should workers rely on their memory for formulas when solving problems? NO
3. Scales represent real distances on the ground or a dimension of real objects. (T or F) true
4. Dimensions can be determined by measuring drawings, since drawings are to scale. (T or F) false
5. If a drawing scale says 1 in = 2000 ft, then 1 in represents nearly ½ mile on the actual ground surface. (T or F) True
6. A scale of 1 in = 20 ft would be common in an urban area.
7. In the profile view, the horizontal scale is usually 1 in = 100 ft. (T or F) True
8. Vertical scales are made larger to exaggerate small differences of elevation so that they can be seen more clearly.
9. Bench-mark elevations usually are referenced from mean sea level.
10. USC&GS means United States Coast and Geodetic Survey. (T or F) True
11. Bence marks are never spikes in trees, as upward growth would change the elevation of the bench mark. (T or F) False
12. Bench marks are established about every 100 ft [30.5 m] along a project. (T or F) false 1000'
13. A bench mark is a point of known elevation and location. (T or F) True
14. Bench marks are shown at the ~~bottom~~ top of the profile views on plan and profile sheets. (T or F) false
15. The plan view shows vertical alignment. (T or F) false
16. Flags are used with station equations, where necessary, to give starting locations of project. (T or F) ________
17. There is a space of 100 ft [30.5 m] between tick marks on the centerline of construction. (T or F) True
18. PI means positive intercept. (T or F) point of intercection
19. Horizontal curves permit autos to change direction easily. (T or F) True

20. For low speed curves the degree of curvature must be a low degree value. (T or F) false
21. The letter *D* identifies the degree of curvature. (T or F) True
22. PC is the end of a horizontal curve. (T or F) false
23. Locations of each control point are identified by reference points. (T or F) True
24. The point of tangency is the control point. The markers and trees are reference points that can be used to establish the exact location of the point of tangency. (T or F) True
25. A roadway never changes elevation along its course. (T or F) false
26. Elevations of the proposed roadway are represented by the profile grade line shown on profile views. (T or F) True
27 *Natural ground line* is usually a smooth line. (T or F) false
28. A profile grade line is an irregular line representing the original ground. (T or F) false
29. The length of a vertical curve is the horizontal distance between the beginning and the end of the curve. (T or F) True
30. Stations and elevations of vertical curve points usually are written horizontally. (T or F) false

8 ROADWAY PLAN AND PROFILE SHEETS

Objectives

a. Understand the scales used in both plan and profile views
b. Become accustomed to drawing the centerline of survey, and stationing and ticking it
c. Learn to draw existing topography
d. Understand bearings and the north arrow
e. Understand reference points and how to represent them
f. Understand flagging of project limits, bridges, and so forth
g. Become familiar with right-of-way lines and learn how to draw them on the maps
h. Understand the vertical elevation data in the profile view
i. Understand how to put in the existing ground line
j. Understand bench marks
k. Understand how the profile grade line is drawn
l. Understand a little about vertical curves and percentage of grade

Rationale

We studied basic information on roadway design in Chaps. 6 and 7. This chapter contains general information on how to draw plan and profile views. Plan and profile views are probably the most important sheets in a set of roadway plans. They present a picture of conditions along the proposed job as they exist and as they will be when the proposed work is completed.

To draw plan and profile sheets, the student will use scales, centerline of survey, points of curve, tangents, bearings, reference points, flagging, stationing, existing topography, and much of the basic material learned in the two previous chapters.

Chapters 6 and 7 discussed essential elements for both reading and drawing plan and profile views. Now we are ready to work on plan and profile sheets. These are some of the most important drawings in a set of roadway plans.

The information in this chapter may be very hard to grasp unless the student draws while reading the directions. At the end of the chapter are many exercises which should be drawn in order to understand the general principles. The various items in this chapter should not be memorized, but should be referred to when items in the exercises are unclear.

ALIGNMENT

The plan and profile sheets present a picture of conditions along the proposed job as they exist now and as they will be when the job is completed. It should be quite obvious that the picture of the completed work is the picture which should stand out on the plans. This is done by varying the type and relative weight of lines and by using appropriate symbols. Features which exist today but which will be removed or changed during construction should be made as transparent and ghostlike as possible by using light, relatively open lines. The heavier and more nearly solid lines are assigned to items which represent the finished picture. The use of standard symbols and lines of various weights is an important part of the preparation of highway plans.

STANDARD SHEET SIZE

In industry the roadway plans and profiles are prepared on standard 22 × 36 in plan and profile sheets. The top half of the sheet is blank for the plan portion, and the bottom portion contains a grid having 10 × 10 units per square inch.

All the following directions assume that a 22 × 36 in sheet is used and are given with this scale in mind. However, our drawings are produced at contractor size, which means that all the scales are reduced by half. This was necessary in order to provide maps and other items to trace at a suitable scale in the textbook. Consequently, our drawings are smaller and the tick marks specified as 0.2 inch (in) [5 mm] on our drawings are actually 0.1 in [2.5 mm] high.

SCALE

Standard scales for rural construction maps are 1 in = 100 feet (ft) horizontally for plans and profiles and 1 in = 10 ft vertically for profiles. Scales for municipal maps usually are 1 in = 20 ft horizontally and 1 in = 2 ft vertically.

It is advantageous at times to use scales other than those mentioned. The most common variation is a scale combination of 1 in = 50 ft horizontally and 1 in = 5 ft vertically. Such a combination of scales is useful when a large amount of existing topography would result in difficulty using a 1 in = 100 ft scale and in cases where it is desirable to show the profile to greater accuracy than is possible with the usual 1 in = 100 ft horizontal and 1 in = 10 ft vertical combination.

PLAN VIEWS FOR RURAL ROADWAY CONSTRUCTION

A plan view is a view looking directly down. Look at the highway in Fig. 8-1 and try to imagine what the plan view for this highway would look like.

We know now that highway plans are made for both municipal and rural work. Since the rural plan is a little simpler, we will take the general instructions for rural construction first.

REMEMBER that the general instructions are to be read first, then if there are difficulties in understanding the specific instructions for a project, the general instructions should be reread.

Centerline of Survey

The centerline of survey (see Fig. 8-2) is most important. It is usually the first thing drawn on the sheet. It is abbreviated by a capital *C* with a capital *L* slanted through the center. The survey centerline is approximately centered in the plan portion of the sheet, with the stationing running from left to right. When horizontal curves are involved, the centerline is located on the sheet in a way that avoids breaks or match lines whenever possible.

Each sheet contains 30 stations when the horizontal scale is 1 in = 100 ft. For 30 stations per sheet, each sheet should begin and end on an even station. A tick mark perpendicular to the centerline and on its upper side is placed at every station. When there are 15 or 30 stations to the sheet, tick marks on the stations with numbers evenly divisible by five (Sta. 5, 10, 15, and so forth) are made approximately 0.2 in [5 mm] long, and the station numbers are shown above the tick marks. For the remaining stations, the tick marks are approximately 0.1 in [2.5 mm] long and no station number is shown.

Figure 8-1
View of highway overpasses looking down from an airplane. Views looking directly down are plan views. This picture is not a true plan view, since it was taken at an angle *(Florida Department of Transportation)*.

CENTERLINE OF SURVEY IS MOST IMPORTANT. IT IS USUALLY THE FIRST THING DRAWN ON THE SHEET. ABBREVIATION USED: CAPITAL "C" WITH CAPITAL "L" SLANTED THROUGH CENTER: ℄

Figure 8-2
Centerline of survey.

CAUTION To make the ticks 0.1 in [2.5 mm] long, the student must use the civil engineer's scale which is divided into tenths of an inch, not the architect's scale, which is divided into 1/16 and 1/8 in spaces. The civil engineer's scale (see Fig. 8-3) is easier to use than the architect's scale.

When a 1 in = 100 ft scale is used, the station numbers are placed outside the right-of-way line, and when 1 in = 50 ft scales are used, the station numbers should be placed near the tick marks.

The centerline and station ticks, station numbers, and stationing information are inked. The remaining work usually is in pencil.

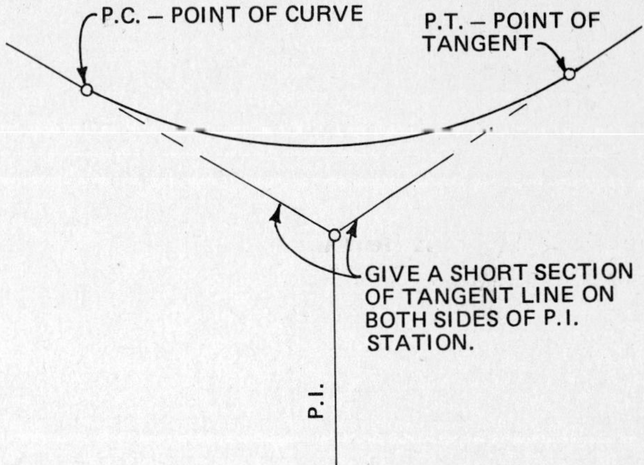

Figure 8-4
Points of curvature, tangency, and intersection.

Points of Curve and Tangent

The points of curvature (PC) and points of tangency (PT) of horizontal curves are indicated by small circles, as shown in Fig. 8-4. Always use a circle template to make these circles, a compass is too cumbersome. Short radial lines are drawn from the point of curvature and the point of tangency with the station of the points (PC and PT) shown above these lines. Points of intersection (PI) are plotted using a small circle with a short section tangent on either side. Complete curve data are tabulated for each horizontal curve.

Figure 8-3
Technician using an engineer's scale at a consulting engineer's office *(Ross, Saarinen, Bolten and Wilder, Inc.)*.

Construction Centerline

In cases where the construction centerline does not coincide with the survey centerline, the construction centerline is to be indicated with complete alignment data and ties to the survey centerline (see Figure 8-5). There is an exception to this: The construction centerline need not be shown when it is offset uniformly from the survey centerline for the entire length of the job. In Fig. 8-5 note that the line where the road is to be built (the centerline of construction) lies uniformly 35 ft [10.7 m] south of the line which was run by the survey crew. Such a situation is rather common.

Figure 8-5
Baseline of survey and centerline of construction.

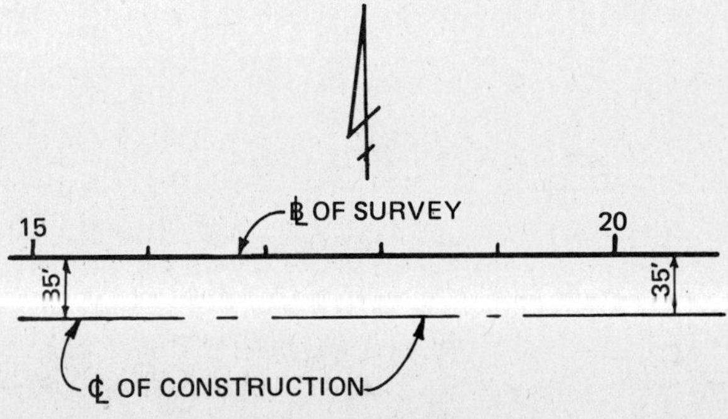

Equations

All station equations must be included, both equations occurring on the survey centerline and those equating survey and construction centerlines.

Topography

All existing topography is shown. Topographic symbols are shown in Fig. 8-6. Of particular importance are existing roads, streets, drives, buildings, power and telephone lines, both aboveground and underground, underground pipes and cables of all kinds, inlets and manholes, retaining walls, curbs, sidewalks, fences, railroads, bridges and culverts. Streams, lakes, swamps, wooded areas and other physical features also must be included, and the type of vegetation must be indicated.

There is one exception for interstate highway projects: It is presumed that all buildings will be removed prior to taking bids, so buildings within the right-of-way need not be plotted.

Existing Pavement

Existing pavement edges, pipes, culverts, sidewalks, and so forth, are plotted using a light broken line. The type of existing pavement must be noted.

Bearings and North Arrow

Bearings are indicated for all tangents. A north point (Fig. 8-7) is placed on every plan sheet and should be

Figure 8-7
North arrow. Place the north arrow in a clear area. The letter *N* need not be indicated.

Figure 8-6
Conventional topographic symbols.

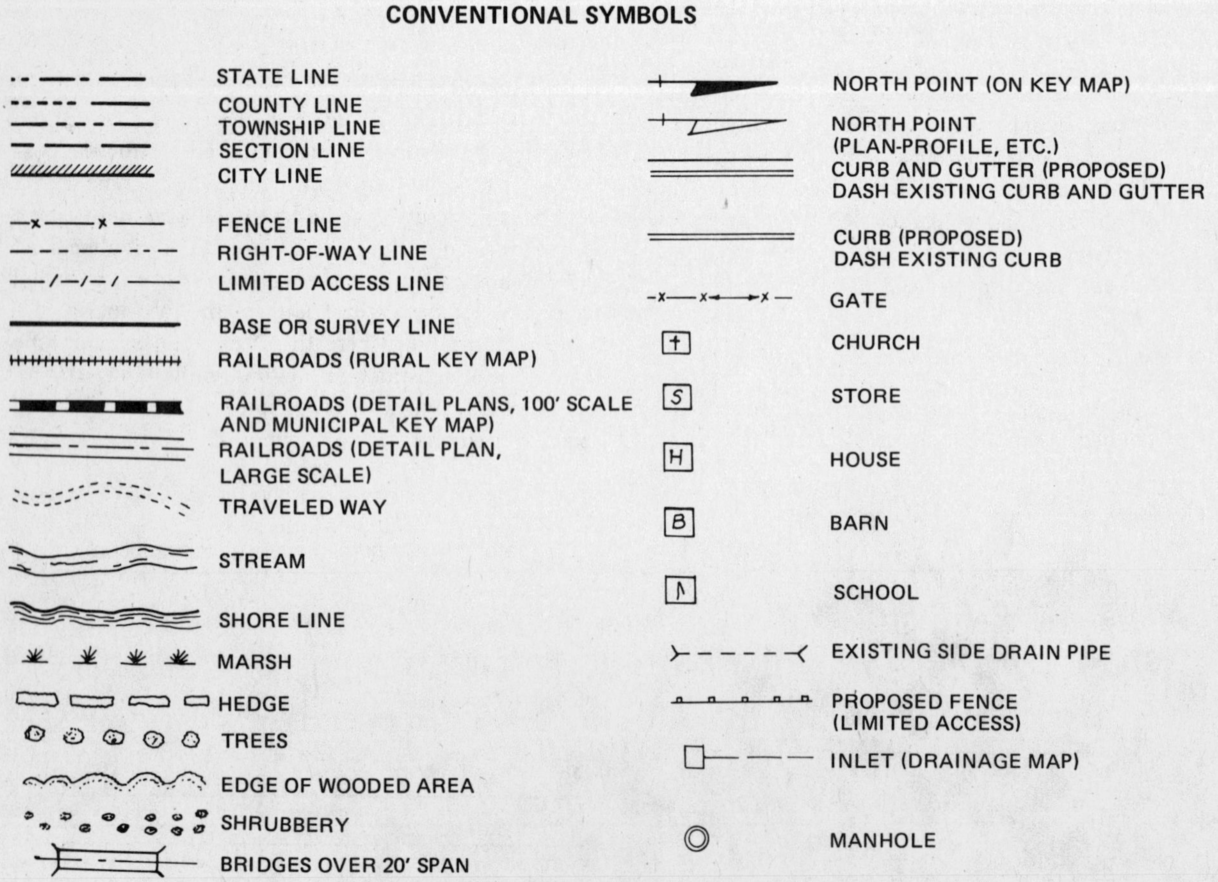

CONVENTIONAL SYMBOLS

STATE LINE
COUNTY LINE
TOWNSHIP LINE
SECTION LINE
CITY LINE
FENCE LINE
RIGHT-OF-WAY LINE
LIMITED ACCESS LINE
BASE OR SURVEY LINE
RAILROADS (RURAL KEY MAP)
RAILROADS (DETAIL PLANS, 100' SCALE AND MUNICIPAL KEY MAP)
RAILROADS (DETAIL PLAN, LARGE SCALE)
TRAVELED WAY
STREAM
SHORE LINE
MARSH
HEDGE
TREES
EDGE OF WOODED AREA
SHRUBBERY
BRIDGES OVER 20' SPAN
NORTH POINT (ON KEY MAP)
NORTH POINT (PLAN-PROFILE, ETC.)
CURB AND GUTTER (PROPOSED) DASH EXISTING CURB AND GUTTER
CURB (PROPOSED) DASH EXISTING CURB
GATE
S CHURCH
S STORE
H HOUSE
B BARN
SCHOOL
EXISTING SIDE DRAIN PIPE
PROPOSED FENCE (LIMITED ACCESS)
INLET (DRAINAGE MAP)
MANHOLE

located in a clear area near the center of the sheet or in the right-hand portion of the sheet. This north point need not be large but should be of such weight as to be easily located. Never make the north point ornate.

Side Roads

Where side roads and streets intersect the project, the station of and angle between the intersecting centerlines are noted.

Reference Points

All reference points (see Fig. 8-8) are indicated by sketches or diagrams. The sketches should be located at places removed from the centerline of the project. They should give the station and the intersecting angle.

City Limits

County, city, and urban limits are included and tied to the centerline by station and angle. The proposed construction limits for rural projects are indicated in the plans.

Flagging Project Limits

A *flag* is a large one-sided arrow (see Fig. 8-9) used to indicate the beginning and end of construction in cases where construction limits are outside the job or project limits. If one set of plans covers more than one job or project, the limits of each must be shown clearly by job or project number and stationing.

The limits of job and project breakdown necessary for separation of length and quantities on federal-aid projects must be flagged.

Figure 8-8
Reference points.

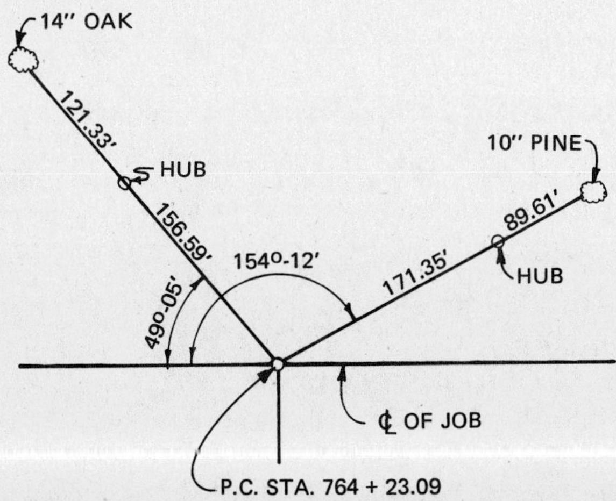

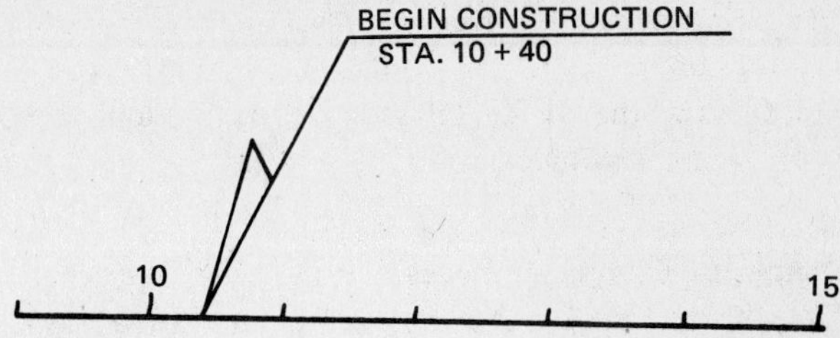

Figure 8-9
Flagging.

The limits of each type of construction classification must be flagged where more than one type is involved, such as urban, rural, federal aid (FA) nonparticipating, and so forth.

OTHER FLAGGED FEATURES

In addition to the previously mentioned flagging points, there are many more features that either must be flagged with a larger pointer (called a flag) or stationed. These are discussed in the following paragraphs.

Cross Drains and Culverts

For rural projects, cross drain pipes and small culverts are indicated in the plan by plotted symbol only. Culverts having a clear span (between inside faces) of 20 ft [6.1 m] or more are designated as bridge culverts. On the plan, bridge culverts are indicated by noting the beginning and ending stations (outside wall to outside wall) along the centerline.

Stationing of Bridges

Proposed bridges and approach slabs are plotted by simple outline. The beginning and ending stations of the bridges are noted. Notes given for the approach slabs include the lengths and index numbers.

Lateral Ditch Details

Lateral ditch details usually are shown on plan-profile sheets separate from the roadway details. A short section of lateral ditch centerline is plotted on the roadway plan-profile sheet together with a note referring to the proper lateral ditch sheet. When very short lateral ditches are to be constructed, the ditch details may be included on the roadway plan-profile sheets. If it is necessary, however, in a particular assembly of plans to have separate sheets for some lateral ditches, all lateral ditch details should be shown in that portion of the plans.

Pavement Edges

Proposed pavement edges are not ordinarily plotted on plan sheets for rural construction. Exceptions are in the case of intersections, pavement transitions, and median openings on four-lane projects. Pavement edges here are indicated only within the limits of the intersection, transition, or median opening.

Nontypical Pavement Edges

Where the proposed roadway construction is in accordance with the typical section, it is not necessary to plot the edges of pavement on rural construction plan sheets. The pavement edges should be plotted only at nontypical locations such as intersections, pavement transition, median openings, and so forth. At these locations, only sufficient details to outline the limits of the nontypical design are required. Notes are given referring to standard design sheets or special designs shown in the plans.

Right-of-Way Lines

Right-of-way lines are made with one long dash, two short dashes, and another long dash (see Fig. 8-10). They are dimensioned from the survey centerline or baseline. All breaks in the right-of-way are shown by station, dimension, and angle. Dimensions are shown at both ends of the sheet and must always be placed outside the beginning and ending station for each sheet.

PLAN VIEWS FOR MUNICIPAL ROADWAY CONSTRUCTION

The necessary features of rural construction plan views have just been given. Now the general layout of plans for municipal construction will be discussed.

Centerline of Project

The centerline is laid out on a scale of 1 in = 20 ft, and exactly six stations are placed on each sheet. Each sheet should begin and end with an even-numbered station. Each station is marked by a tick mark 0.2 in [5 mm] long, and the station number is placed near this mark. Ticks 0.1 in [2.5 mm] long are placed at every 20-ft [6.1-m] point between stations, but no intermediate (plus) station numbers are shown.

Figure 8-10
Right-of-way (R/W) lines.

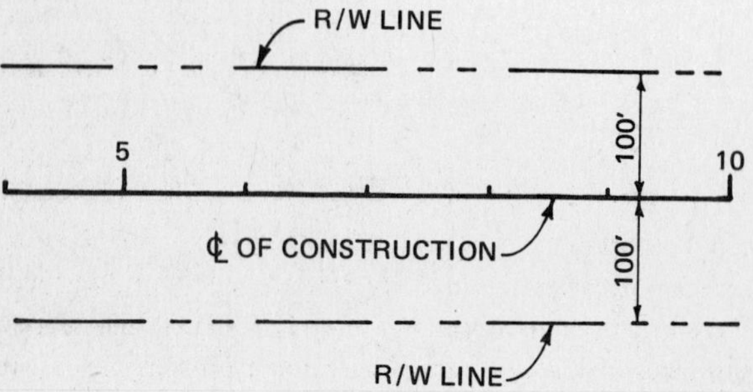

Existing Topography

Existing topography is plotted. Alignment data, reference points, north point, bearings, job and project limits, and so forth, are shown as they are on plan views for rural construction.

Features of Municipal Construction Plans

The following items must be included on municipal plan views:

1. Pavement edges, curbs and gutters, median curbs, barrier curbs, traffic separators, sidewalks, retaining walls, steps, bridges, approach slabs, and so forth.
2. Station of return points, with grade elevations of gutters or pavement edges at these points.
3. Station of radius points of traffic separators or median curbs at median openings.
4. Station of ends of curbs and gutters at side street intersections (when the end is not at a return point), with proposed gutter grade elevations at these points. No station need be shown when the curb and gutter on returns is terminated 3 ft [0.9 m] back of the right-of-way line, as the point of termination is set by the right-of-way width.
5. Limits of pavement and grading at side street intersections. The limits of stabilizing and clearing and grubbing may be shown on the plan sheets or by special details.
6. Control radii for traffic turns when these set median nose locations.
7. Proposed drainage. The storm sewer system is indicated by plotting the storm sewer centerline and the outline of inlets, manholes, and junction boxes. Storm sewer pipes are noted by size and length. Proposed inlets, manholes, junction boxes, and special structures are noted only by station and type.
8. Construction limits, when outside of the right-of-way line, are indicated by a broken line and so noted, except in the case of pavement areas such as filling station drives, parking areas, and so forth, where construction limits cannot be determined accurately by the designer. In such cases, the limit of construction line should be omitted through the limits of the paved areas.

PROFILE VIEWS FOR RURAL ROADWAY CONSTRUCTION

We have progressed through the plan portion, which is drawn on the top half of a plan and profile drawing, for both rural and municipal construction. Now we will discuss the profile portion, which occupies the lower half of this type of drawing.

Stationing and Scales

The horizontal scale is the same as that used in the plan portion on the top of this sheet. The station limits of the profile must correspond exactly to those of the plan portion of each sheet. Station numbers are placed across the bottom of the sheet just above the border. Full station numbers are used for stations with numbers divisible by 10, and single digit numbers are used for the remainder.

For horizontal scale of 1 in = 100 ft, a vertical scale of 1 in = 10 ft is normally used, and for a horizontal scale of 1 in = 50 ft, a vertical scale of 1 in = 5 ft generally is suitable.

Vertical Elevation Datum

The range of vertical elevations to be shown is selected with due regard for the extremes of elevation which will occur on each sheet. The profile should not crowd either the upper or lower limits of the profile portion of the sheet.

Elevation data are indicated on both the right and left sides of the sheet and should be placed so that even 10-ft [3.0 m] elevations will be on the inch lines for a 1 in = 10 ft vertical scale, and even 5-ft [1.5 m] elevations will be on the inch line for a 1 in = 5 ft vertical scale. Existing groundline elevations on the survey or baseline are lettered vertically just above the station numbers.

Breaks in Stationing

All even and "plus" station elevations should be given and plotted in the profile. Where breaks in the profile are so numerous that there is not sufficient room to show all of the elevations, breaks should be plotted in the profile, but only significant elevations, such as drainage structure flow lines, pavement edges, tops of rails, and so forth, need be given.

Figure 8-11
Undesirable materials shown on a profile view.

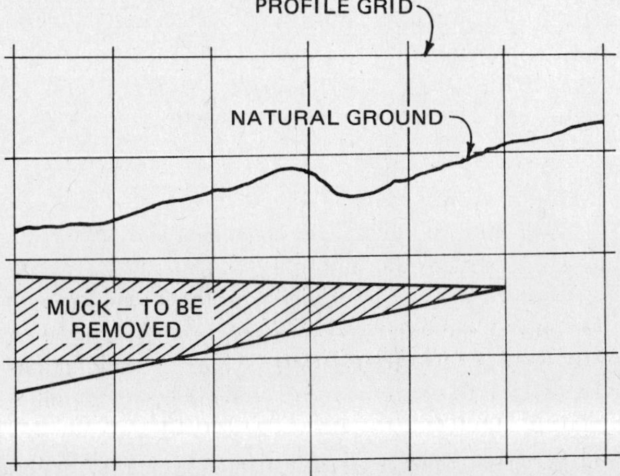

Existing Ground Line Profile

The existing ground line profile is plotted and inked, using a light, solid line. When an existing two-lane facility is being expanded to a multilane highway by construction of a parallel roadway, the plotted profile may be that of the existing pavement edge adjacent to the proposed median. This facilitates establishing matching grades, especially at the location of superelevated curves.

When the survey follows an existing road, it is sometimes advantageous to approximte and plot the original ground line profile, using a light, broken line.

Undesirable Materials

Muck or any other undesirable material is plotted on the profile grid by its strata limits, as shown in Fig. 8-11. Cross hatch the layer of undesirable material and call for its removal. In cases where no soil profile is included in the plans, strata boundaries for other unsuitable materials are also plotted in the profiles and labeled.

High Water

High water conditions are shown by the use of a light, broken line (long dashes) at the high water elevation. The elevation is indicated numerically and the year of the indicated high water is given. If high water is to be lowered, the design high water elevation must be given.

Bench Marks

Bench mark data are normally given just below the upper margin of the profile strip, or they may be placed in the plan portion just above the upper profile margin.

Profile Grade Lines and Vertical Curves

The proposed profile grade is shown by a heavy, solid line. Vertical curve PC's, PT's and PI's are indicated by small circles. The grade line is plotted around the vertical curve, and sections of tangent are drawn from the PI on either side using a light, solid line. Vertical lines are extended from the PC's and PT's, and a dimension line is placed between these lines to indicate the length of the vertical curve.

For vertical curves, the profile grade elevations are given every 50 ft [15.2 m] (on even stations and half stations) and are placed between the dimension line and the grade line. The length dimension and the profile grade elevations are placed above the grade line for sag vertical curves and below the grade line for crest vertical curves. The dimensions and elevations should be placed reasonably near the grade line whenever possible.

The PI elevation is lettered vertically above the PI circle for crest curves and below for sag curves. When the PI does not fall on an even station, the plus station is given.

The profile grade elevation of the beginning and ending station of each sheet is lettered vertically just above the grade line, except when the beginning or ending station is on the vertical curve. In cases where the beginning or ending station of the sheet is on the vertical curve, and the PI falls within the sheet, the percentage of grade of the tangent extending from the adjacent sheet is indicated.

Grades are indicated in percents for each tangent on every sheet.

Station Equations

Station equations and exceptions are shown.

Special Ditches

Special ditches are indicated in profile by a heavy, broken line (long dashes), the grade (in percent) and a beginning or ending (ditch PI) elevation should be given. In plans for four-lane projects, three special ditch grades (right and left roadway ditches and median ditch) sometimes occur at the same location. In this case, it may be necessary to plot the median ditch against separate elevation data for clarity.

Ditches of Uniform but Nonstandard Depth

When ditches of uniform but other than standard depth are used, the limits of such ditches are indicated by a dimension line and an appropriate note in the lower portion of the profile strip.

Culverts and Cross Drain Pipes

Proposed cross drain pipes and culverts are plotted in section with a solid, heavy line. The section should be at the proposed location and grade of the structure where it crosses the centerline of construction. Bridges and bridge culverts are noted as such, and their beginning and ending stations are given. Construction notes for cross drain pipes and culverts include station, size, flow lines, and skew angle. Length and index numbers are not given.

Job and Project Limits

The job and project limits on applicable sheets are given in the same manner as on the plan portion of the sheet.

General Notes

General notes for the project are placed in the upper left-hand portion of the profile strip of the first plan and profile sheet. These notes include those concerning bench mark elevation data, and placement of information signs and any special notes concerning the specific project.

PROFILE VIEWS FOR MUNICIPAL ROADWAY CONSTRUCTION

We have studied the methods of drawing the rural plan and profile sheets; we will now go on to discuss municipal profile sheets.

Scales

The profile portion of plan and profile sheets for municipal construction is prepared in a manner very similar to that for rural construction. The standard scales are 1 in = 20 ft horizontally and 1 in = 2 ft vertically, although a vertical scale of 1 in = 5 ft can be used satisfactorily for some jobs in hilly terrain.

Marking the Vertical Elevations

When a 1 in = 2 ft vertical scale is used, the vertical elevation data should be placed so that numerically even elevations fall on the inch lines; only the elevations for the even 2-ft [0.6 m] intervals are shown. When a 1 in = 5 ft scale is used, only even 5-ft [1.5 m] and 10-ft [3.0 m] elevations are shown, and these are placed on the inch lines.

General Requirements

Existing ground line profiles and elevations, proposed profile grade lines, vertical curve elevations, high water elevations, station equations, exceptions, reference points, bench mark notes, job project limits, and general notes are indicated exactly the same way as in plans for rural construction.

Underground Utilities

All water and gas mains and all sanitary sewers and ducts are plotted using light, broken lines. Small service lines for these utilities need not be plotted in the profile; however, the elevations should be shown in the plan at locations where the elevations were taken.

Clarity of Utility Lines

When a number of utility lines of various kinds are present and overlap each other in profile, it is sometimes advantageous for clarity to use different colors of ink for each type and to differentiate by use of different lengths or combinations of dashes. Different colors are helpful during design stages (Fig. 8-12) by making identification of the lines easier.

Figure 8-12
Technician working on road problem *(Ross, Saarinen, Bolten, and Wilder, Inc.).*

Gutter Profile Grades

For normal construction, proposed gutter line profiles are not necessary. However, when a warped section is used, or when gutters are not at normal grade due to proposed superelevation, the gutter profile grades should be indicated.

Gutter Grades at Street Intersections

When the plans do not include separate sheets of profile grades and sections for street intersections, prolongations of gutter profile grades across street intersections should be included.

Storm Sewer Drains

Bridges, cross drain pipes, and culverts are plotted as in rural construction. The storm sewer system including main, stub, inlets, and manholes is shown. Pipes are noted by size, and inlets and manholes by station and type for all proposed construction. Proposed flow line grades are indicated. Proposed drainage structures are plotted with a medium heavy line.

EXERCISES

EXERCISE 8-1. RURAL ROADS

Remove Exercise 8-1 from the textbook. Center and tape it under a B-size sheet of vellum. Trace the baseline of survey and centerline of construction of Road 8-A, as well as the roads themselves and the station numbering. Also trace the north point and the exercise number to identify the sheet.

The scale used on this sheet before reduction was 1 in = 100 ft so the station numbers are placed outside the right-of-way lines.

CAUTION Look at the R/W Line notes. They should be written in all capital letters. It has become common practice in the industry to use all capital letters. The lettering is called Reinhardt lettering and is usually used in civil drafting. Different types of lettering should never be mixed on one sheet. The student should avoid making this error.

Road 8-B Only the baseline of survey is shown here with a drainage structure skewed at 30° to the highway. Draw the roads as Road 8-A was drawn. Do the ticking (station numbers) and put in the drainage structure and R/W lines. Call the drainage structure out by note as follows:

30-in [76 cm] CORRUGATED IRON PIPE
SKEWED 30° RIGHT

Road 8-C Draw the north arrow, the centerline of construction, and all items found on Road 8-A. Notice that now there is a *bearing* added to the centerline of construction, a few terrain features, and a new large drainage structure at Sta. 105.

Check the exercise for completeness. The plan view has been traced once and the road drawn in three times, including the tracing. Each time a little more detail has been incorporated.

EXERCISE 8-2. RURAL PLAN VIEW WITH REFERENCE POINTS

Remove Exercise 8-2 from the text and tape it under the center of a B-size sheet of vellum. Trace the plan view of a road starting at Sta. 310 and ending at Sta. 340. Be sure to put in everything. All the linework and notes are required. Notice that the plan is getting more complicated. Physical features are included which were not in the earlier exercise.

There are several points to note while doing this exercise:

1. Stationing is put outside the right-of-way lines.
2. A *bearing* appears on the centerline of survey.
3. Drainage structures are called out by number.
4. Notes are everywhere telling the type of terrain at various locations.
5. Notice how fences are placed just 6 in [15 cm] inside the R/W lines. They must be built within the state-,

city-, or county-owned right-of-way and still protect as much of the government-owned property as possible.

6. *Reference point* (also called a point on tangent station) is located.

At Sta. 321 + 86.12 on the centerline of the survey, several "shots" were taken by the survey crew with a transit. In this case, to locate this exact point on the survey line a 140° 28′ angle is turned. A reference point is located on this line 189.87 ft away. Continuing along this line, 43.90 ft farther is a 10-in [25-cm] pine tree. A second reference point is located by turning 73° 27′ and measuring out 167.55 ft to a reference point and then 17.90 ft farther to a 10-in [25-cm] pine tree.

On the lower half of the sheet where a centerline of construction is drawn in and Sta. 310 and 340 are called out, draw (do not trace) the same (identical) plan view of road A; call it road B. From now on we will be doing more drawing and less tracing. When this exercise is completed, two identical plan views will have been drawn; road A will have been traced, and road B will have been drawn by the student but will be identical to road A.

EXERCISE 8-3. TRACING AND REPRODUCING A PLAN VIEW

Tape a B-size sheet of vellum over Exercise 8-3 after removing it from the text. Trace the items on Exercise 8-3, noting city limit stationing, beginning and end of the bridge, and the job exception at S.R. 870. On the bottom part of the sheet, on the two lines already started, reproduce the traced drawing, but *do not trace the second plan view.*

EXERCISE 8-4. PROFILE VIEW

This is the first problem involving the profile view of a plan and profile drawing. The first three exercises contained items from the plan view. A very important item shown on the profile view is the *natural ground line.* This is the way the undisturbed natural ground appears on the area covered by the map.

Tear Exercise 8-4 from the text. Cover it with a B-size sheet of vellum centered over the exercise. Trace everything on this sheet except the information on drainage structures, which is located in the center of the sheet. It will be necessary to trace the grid located on the bottom half of the sheet; profile views are always shown on a grid. Make the grid with a 2H or 3H pencil lead, if using pencil. If using ink, a No. 0 or a No. 1 technical pen will be best. To measure the distances between grid lines, which represent 10 ft, find a scale which nearly fits ten units into one of grid space (which represents ten 1-ft units). The scale which will probably fit most closely is the 40 scale on the engineer's scale. This scale can thus be used to approximate the distances between the 10-ft grid marks.

Trace all the station numbers and elevations for good practice in lettering and figures, then start plotting all the station elevations on the grid at the bottom of the sheet. When all the points are on the grid, take any type straightedge and connect all successive points. A small triangle will make a good straightedge.

Show the drainage pipes in the profile view in the same way the one at Sta. 260 is shown.

EXERCISE 8-5. PROFILE VIEW WITH BENCH MARKS

This is a similar exercise to 8-4, although some items are different. Instead of drainage structures, this problem has bench marks lettered into the grid. Trace all the station numbers and elevations as shown on Exercise 8-5. Do not trace the instructions in the center of the sheet on bench marks, but be sure to trace the grid with either 2H or 3H lead or No. 0 or No. 1 technical inking pen.

EXERCISE 8-6. VERTICAL CURVE

Trace everything on Exercise 8-6. New items include a profile grade line at −0.40%, a 1000-ft [305-m] vertical curve with elevations every 100 ft [30.5 m], and a reference point. After tracing all these items, the student should mark all the elevations shown at the proper stations. Then connect successive points to produce a natural ground line.

EXERCISE 8-7. PLAN AND PROFILE VIEW

Remove Exercise No. 8-7 from the text and tape a B-size sheet of vellum over its center. Notice that we are finally bringing the plan and profile views together.

Trace everything from Exercise 8-7 onto the vellum. Notice B.M. 12½. We put this in to show an error: B.M.'s are always even numbers, never fractions. Now add the ticking to the baseline of survey. Add the note "R/W line" on both right-of-way lines on each side of the 24-ft [7.3-m] wide road.

The road runs directly east and west so it has a bearing of N90°00′00″E. Put this bearing under the baseline of survey and add a note calling out the baseline of survey with an arrow pointing to the baseline.

EXERCISE 8-8. PLAN AND PROFILE VIEW

Trace all the items on Exercise 8-8 on a B-size sheet of vellum.

Add the following items:

C size
1"=200'
1"=20'

1. B.M. No. 23
   Spike in 8-in [20-cm] Pine
   96 ft [29.3 m] Lt. Sta. 123 + 00
   El. 100.00 ft [30.5 m]
2. Two right-of-way lines at 50 ft [15.2 m] out each side of the baseline of survey, making a 100-ft [30.5-m] right-of-way.
3. Call out the baseline of survey.
4. Add the bearing N90°00′00″E to the baseline of survey.
5. Dimension the 50-ft [15.2-m] R/W lines.
6. Add a 24-ft [7.3-m] wide road (12 ft [3.7 m] on each side of the baseline of survey), similar to the road in exercise 8-7.

LEARNING ACTIVITY PACKAGE

Read Chap. 8 carefully. Do not try to memorize all the material in it. Just refer back to the chapter as needed when working on the exercises.

Chapter 8 read ____________ (*date*).

Read the list of objectives and make sure they are all well understood. If some are not, reread the appropriate sections of the chapter.

Objectives understood ____________ (*date*).

Now take the removable quiz on Chap. 8. Remove the quiz from the text and answer all the questions.

Quiz completed on ____________ (*date*).

Start working on the exercises on Chap. 8, referring back to the chapter for explanation if the work in the exercises becomes unclear.

Do the exercises assigned by the instructor. All students should do Exercises 8-2 and 8-4.

Exercise 8-1 completed ____________ (*date*).

Exercise 8-2 completed ____________ (*date*).

Exercise 8-3 completed ____________ (*date*).

Exercise 8-4 completed ____________ (*date*).

Exercise 8-5 completed ____________ (*date*).

Exercise 8-6 completed ____________ (*date*).

Exercise 8-7 completed ____________ (*date*).

Exercise 8-8 completed ____________ (*date*).

3,000′ = 2400

8 QUIZ

1. Plan and Profile sheets present a picture of conditions along the proposed job as they ____________ and as they will be when the proposed improvement is complete.
2. The picture of the completed work should stand out on the plans. (T or F) ____________
3. Heavier, more nearly solid lines are assigned to items which represent the finished picture. (T or F) ____________
4. The weight and type of lines on plan and profile drawings are unimportant. (T or F) ____________
5. Standard symbols are used in plan and profile drawings. (T or F) ____________
6. Students will use the B-size sheets used for drawing the key maps in Chap. 3. (T or F) ____________
7. The profile portion of plan and profile drawings is drawn on a grid on the lower half of the sheet. (T or F) ____________
8. Scales for rural maps are
   1 in = ____________ horizontally 1 in = ____________ vertically
9. Scales for municipal plans are
   1 in = ____________ horizontally 1 in = ____________ vertically
10. Specific instructions for a drawing should be read first, then the general instructions. (T or F) ____________
11. Stationing runs from right to left on the survey centerline. (T or F) ____________
12. Sheets begin and end with even station numbers. (T or F) ____________
13. Engineer's scales are divided into ____________ inch spaces.
14. Architect's scales are divided in sixteenths of an inch. (T or F) ____________
15. The PC and PT of a horizontal curve are indicated by small circles. (T or F) ____________
16. Complete curve data are tabulated for each horizontal curve. (T or F) ____________
17. The survey centerline and the construction centerline must coincide. (T or F) ____________
18. Do station equations need to be included on plan and profile sheets? (*yes* or *no*) ____________

19. Buildings within the right-of-way on interstate projects need not be plotted. (T or F) True
20. Types of vegetation need not be indicated. (T or F) false
21. The North arrow should be ornate so that it will draw the viewer's attention. (T or F) false
22. Angles between the intersecting centerlines of streets are not required. (T or F) false
23. Reference point sketches should give the station and the intersecting angle.
24. If one set of plans covers more than one job or project, the limits of each must be shown clearly by job or project number and stationing. (T or F) True
25. Bridge culverts need not be stationed. (T or F) false
26. If proposed roadway construction is in accordance with the typical section, it is not necessary to plot the edges of the pavement on the plan sheets for rural construction. (T or F) True
27. Right-of-way lines are shown and dimensioned from the survey centerline or baseline.
28. The centerline with station ticks, station numbers, and stationing information are shown.
29. The existing ground line profile is plotted and inked, using a light, solid line. (T or F) True
30. Station numbers are placed across the top of the bottom half (profile grid) on a plan and profile sheet. (T or F) false
31. Undesirable materials are plotted by their Strata limits.
32. Undesirable materials are crosshatched on the profile view. (T or F) True
33. The year of high water as well as its elevation is given. (T or F) True
34. Bench-mark data are normally given just below the upper margin of the profile strip, or they may be placed in the plan just above the upper profile margin. (T or F) True
35. The proposed profile grade is shown by a dashed line. (T or F) false
36. For vertical curves, the profile grade elevations are given every 50 ft [15 m]. (T or F) True
37. When the PI does not fall on an even station, the plus station is given.
38. Grades (in percent) are indicated for each tangent on every sheet. (T or F) True
39. Proposed cross drain pipes and culverts are plotted in section with a solid, heavy line. (T or F) True

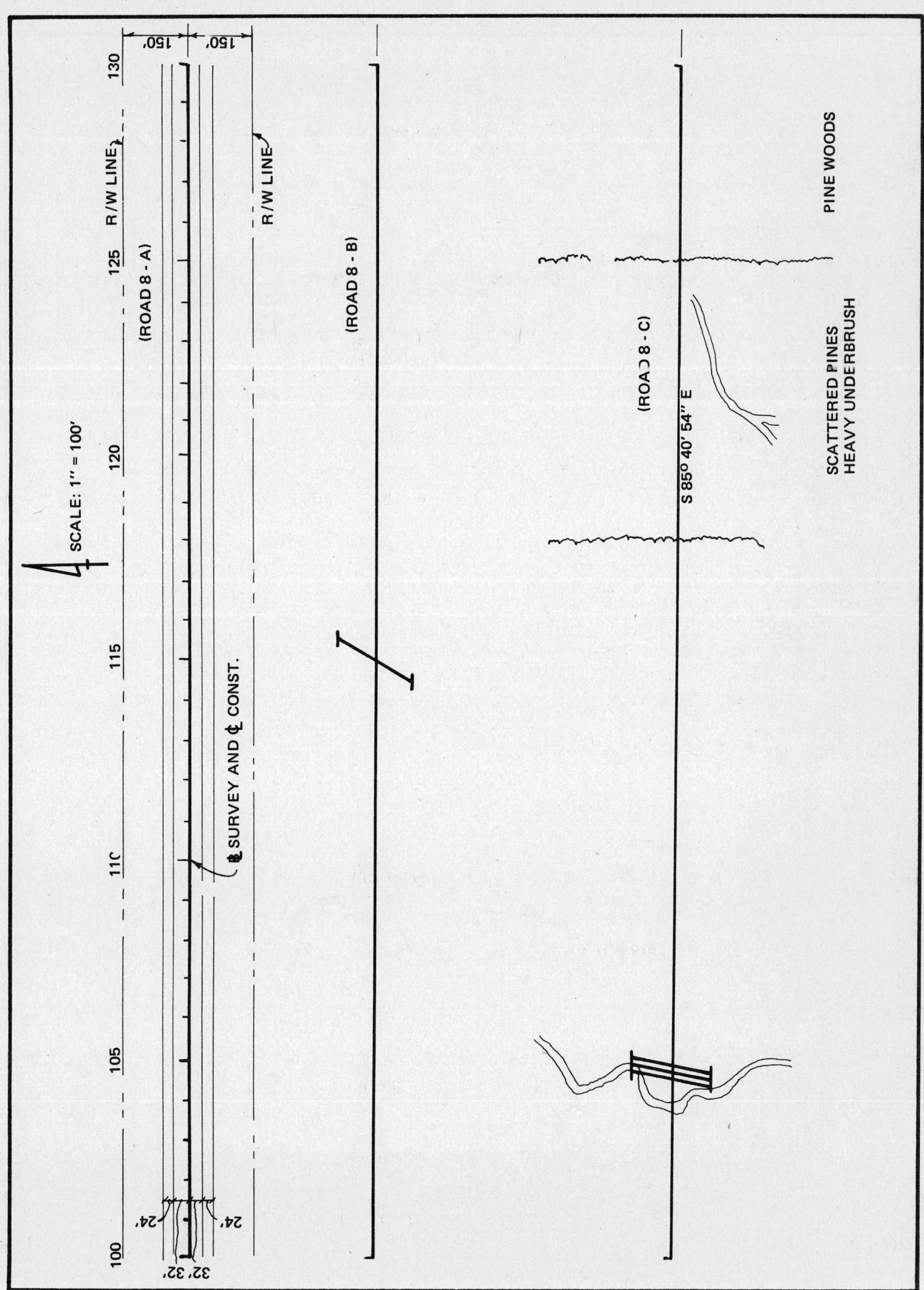

150'
150'
130
R/W LINE
R/W LINE
125
(ROAD 8 - A)
(ROAD 8 - B)
(ROAD 8 - C)
PINE WOODS
SCATTERED PINES
HEAVY UNDERBRUSH
S 85° 40' 54" E
120
SCALE: 1" = 100'
115
℄ SURVEY AND ℄ CONST.
110
105
24'
24'
100
32' 32'

Exercise 8-1

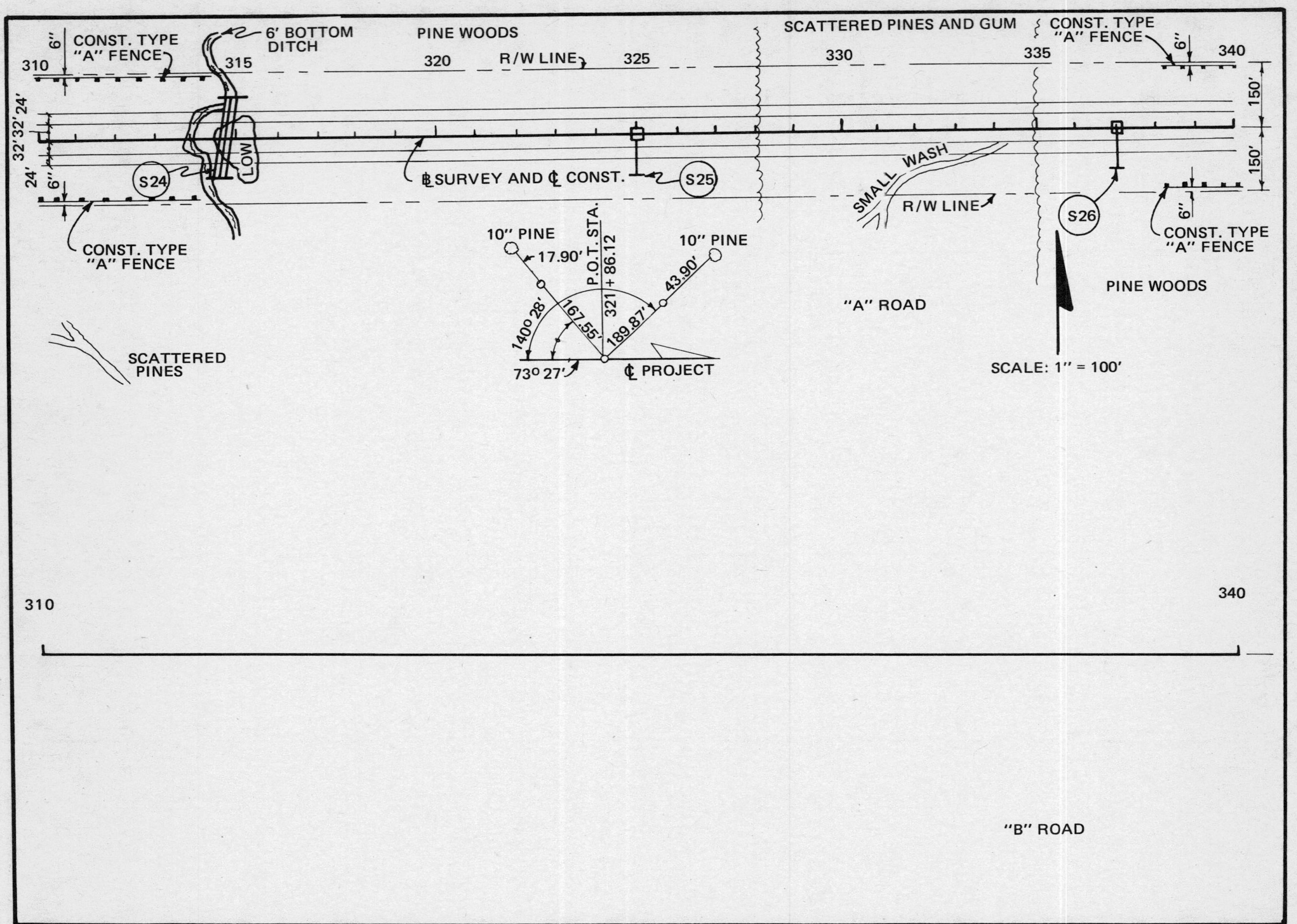

CONST. TYPE "A" FENCE
6' BOTTOM DITCH
PINE WOODS
R/W LINE
SCATTERED PINES AND GUM
CONST. TYPE "A" FENCE
310
315
320
325
330
335
340
6"
24'
32'
32'
24'
150'
150'
LOW
S24
℄ SURVEY AND ℄ CONST.
S25
SMALL WASH
R/W LINE
S26
CONST. TYPE "A" FENCE
CONST. TYPE "A" FENCE
10" PINE
17.90'
P.O.T. STA.
321 + 86.12
10" PINE
43.90'
140° 28'
167.55'
189.87'
73° 27'
℄ PROJECT
SCATTERED PINES
"A" ROAD
PINE WOODS
SCALE: 1" = 100'
310
340
"B" ROAD

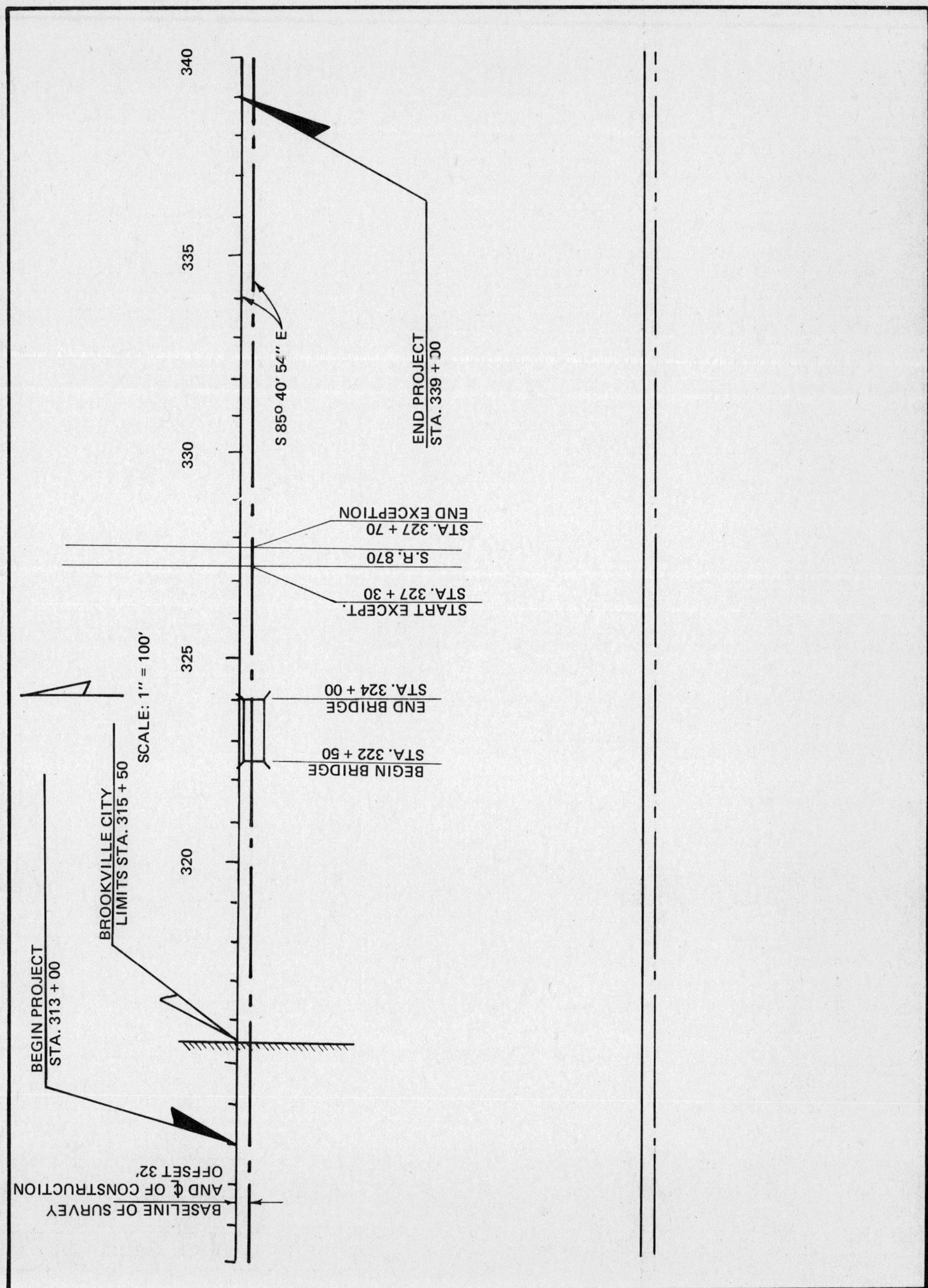
BEGIN PROJECT
STA. 313 + 00
BROOKVILLE CITY
LIMITS STA. 315 + 50
SCALE: 1" = 100'
320
325
330
335
340
BASELINE OF SURVEY
AND ℄ OF CONSTRUCTION
OFFSET 32'
BEGIN BRIDGE
STA. 322 + 50
END BRIDGE
STA. 324 + 00
START EXCEPT.
STA. 327 + 30
S.R. 870
END EXCEPTION
STA. 327 + 70
S 85° 40' 54" E
END PROJECT
STA. 339 + 00

Exercise 8-3

PLOT THE NATURAL GROUND LINE FOR THE FOLLOWING STATIONS:

STA. NO.	ELEVATION	STA. NO.	ELEVATION	STA. NO.	ELEVATION
250	103	261	126	272	144
251	108	262	126	273	147
252	113	263	126	274	150
253	115	264	127	275	154
254	118	265	128	276	158
255	120	266	130	277	162
256	122	267	133	278	166
257	123	268	136	279	172
258	124	269	138	280	177
259	125	270	140		
260	126	271	142		

NOTICE THE 24" DRAINAGE STRUCTURE AT STA. 260 WITH FLOW LINE ELEV. AT 123'?
STUDENT SHOULD DRAW IN SIMILAR 24" PIPES AT THE FOLLOWING STATIONS:
STA. 255 – F.L. EL. = 117; STA. 270 – F.L. EL. = 137 AND STA. 280 – F.L. EL. = 173
COMPLETE THE EXERCISE BY DRAWING IN THE NATURAL GROUND LINE.

170 160 150 140 130 120 110 100

250 255 260 265 270 275 280

PLOT THE NATURAL GROUND LINE FOR THE FOLLOWING STATIONS:

STA. NO.	ELEVATION	STA. NO.	ELEVATION	STA. NO.	ELEVATION
250	120	261	123	272	132
251	118	262	121	273	135
252	116	263	120	274	139
253	115	264	119	275	139
254	118	265	118	276	143
255	120	266	118	277	147
256	122	267	121	278	151
257	123	268	125	279	153
258	124	269	127	280	157
259	125	270	128		
260	126	271	129		

NOTICE BENCH MARK NO. 11 – 170' RT. STA. 253 + 00 – IN A SIMILAR STYLE LOCATING THE B.M. INFORMATION NEAR ITS STATION – RECORD THE FOLLOWING:
B.M. NO. 12 – SPIKE IN 6" PINE – 185' LT. STA. 261 + 00 – ELEV. 123.53'
B.M. NO. 13 – SPIKE IN 8" OAK – 182' LT. STA. 275 + 00 – ELEV. 138.75'

B.M. NO. 11
SPIKE IN 6" OAK
170' RT. STA. 253 + 00
EL. 115.05'

160
150
140
130
120
110
100

250 255 260 265 270 275 280

PLOT THE NATURAL GROUND LINE FOR THE FOLLOWING STATIONS:

STA. NO.	ELEVATION	STA. NO.	ELEVATION	STA. NO.	ELEVATION
100	109	111	107	122	100
101	106	112	105	123	101
102	107	113	105	124	102
103	107	114	103	125	103
104	106	115	102	126	104
105	105	116	104	127	104
106	104	117	103	128	105
107	103	118	102	129	106
108	105	119	101	130	107
109	106	120	100		
110	107	121	100		

Exercise 8-6

9 PRODUCING A PLAN AND PROFILE SHEET

Objectives

a. Learn how to set up a plan and profile sheet, drawing the grid and all necessary features
b. Understand the use of the engineer's scale
c. Learn about the centerline of survey and ticking
d. Learn how to lay out a proposed highway
e. Learn how to show the bearing of the centerline by note
f. Become acquainted with right-of-way lines and their symbol and the station numbers
g. Get experience in putting existing topography on the map
h. Learn about reference points and how they are placed on the plan part of the plan and profile sheet
i. Learn about bench marks and how they are noted on the drawing
j. Learn how to put natural ground on the grid from a chart
k. Learn how to draw in the highway profile as directed by the engineer on the project

Rationale

It is now time to begin drawing from scratch. We will reproduce a plan and profile sheet from the text exactly as shown, but at a larger scale.

The previous chapter gave general plans and directions on how to draw plan and profile sheets. Now we will give specific directions on what must be done to reproduce a standard rural plan and profile sheet.

We will reproduce sheet 14 of State Project 54001–3402 (Drawing No. 23). This is an uncluttered, simple project which is a good one to start on. Every line is mentioned in Chap. 9 and, by reading, then drawing, and then reading again, we can reproduce the same drawing at a larger scale. Now we are really getting into civil engineering drafting. It is not hard. Concentrate on the text book and try to make the drawings neat and legible. Put the completed drawings in a portfolio to take to job interviews.

SETUP PROCEDURE

It would be easier for the student if standard 22 × 34-in plan and profile blank sheets were available, but in most schools they would not be easily obtained. Assuming this will be the case, we will give the instructions for doing the job without them. We will draw a profile grid as well as plan and profile views.

By producing the grid, the student will see the relationship between the plan view (the upper half of the sheet) and the profile (the lower half of the sheet). Often the relationship between the two views is lost on the drafter when the grid is already on the sheet. If the student projects the tick marks down from the centerline of construction of the job in the plan view, it will become clear that the profile view is directly under its corresponding view in the top half of the drawing. This fact cannot be overemphasized. When reading a plan and profile, look immediately under the plan view to see how the roadway looks in profile. The only exception to this will be when projecting a horizontal curve from the plan to the profile view.

Starting the Drawing

Remove the drawing for Project 54001–3402, sheet 14 (Drawing No. 23 in the back of the chapter), and place it on the sideboard or near the drawing table. Refer to it for every line. The text will explain how to draw every line in the drawing. This way the student will realize the meaning of all the lines put on the drawing. We will do this only once on each different type of drawing. Do the drawing that is carefully explained in the text first. Later, do as many other drawings as possible for practice.

Drawing Sheet Size

Use a C-size sheet of vellum. Remember that a C-sheet is 17 × 22 in. Some schools will have 17½ × 22½-in or 18 × 24 in sheets; these are all called C-sheets, and the difference in size will complicate the drawing of the profile grid. We will overcome this difficulty by standardizing the horizontal size of the grid. This will make the grid blocks the proper size.

Place the C-sheet on the drawing board or table in a position for comfortable drawing on the sheet. Do not place the sheet too high on the board. It is uncomfortable to reach high up on the board to draw. Long hours leaning or bending over the board cause backaches, so *get comfortable.*

Fastening the Sheet

Use four small pieces of drafting tape; one or 1½ in [25 to 38 mm] is long enough. Tape the paper to the board at the four corners of the sheet, pulling the sheet down tightly after taping the two top corners. Be very sure the drawing board is clean under the taped sheet. Before taping the paper down, the dustbrush should have been used to thoroughly clean every bit of dirt, ribbles (ribbles are the little strings of plastic or rubber that are formed when erasing a drawing), or eraser crumbs from the drafting board surface. Some students may notice black spots on the surface of their drawings. They are caused by high spots on the drawing resulting from some small material which has not been removed from under the drawing sheet. As the tools, triangles, T-square, and so forth, rub over the high spots, dirt is left on the drawing; this will continue to happen until the area under the spot on the vellum is cleaned.

The Need for a T-square

Earlier in the book it was stated that civil drafters seldom use T-squares or parallel rules. This is absolutely true, but students working under nonideal conditions will need a T-square or parallel rule. It will be used to generate horizontal and vertical lines, to put borders on drawing sheets (which do not come preprinted with borders, boxes, and company names), and to drop vertical lines for grids.

BEGIN DRAFTING

Measure in 3 in from the left side of the sheet and draw a vertical line starting 1 in from the top of the sheet and extending to 1 in from the bottom. This is the left-hand border. This edge is always made larger than the other borders because all sets of plans are stapled or fastened by some means at the left-hand side. This larger margin allows space for stapling. (The left and right borders on the plan and profile sheets will be large; they are made that way so that the student can draw the proper number of grid lines without being forced to use unfamiliar fractions.)

Remaining Border Lines

Use an *engineer's scale* now, not an *architect's scale.* The scale should record ten subdivisions (not sixteen) in 1 in. The engineer's scale has the numbers 10, 20, 30, 40, 50, and 60 on the edges. Using the correct scale, start on the rest of the border now. Measure down 1 in from the top of the sheet. Make a dot and draw a horizontal line through the dot all the way across the sheet. Use a hard pencil so that the line will be very light; it can be darkened later or (better) gone over later with a No. 3 Rapidograph or other technical pen. We will erase those parts of the line which hang over; however, we will do that later as these "hangovers" are helpful when inking or darkening the pencil lines. They tell the student where to stop the line. In inking, this is important, as ink is very difficult to remove from vellum.

Now measure 1 in up from bottom of the sheet. Make a dot and draw a horizontal line all the way across the sheet. This is the bottom border line. The next measurement is critical for the correct spacing of the profile grid. Measure 16.75 in horizontally from the left border and put a dot. Draw a vertical line through the dot from the top border line to the bottom border line. It does not matter what the width of the right border measures. We do the border this way on plan and profile sheets to take into account the fact that different schools provide different size C-sheets, and we need just 16¾ in (or 16.75 in on the engineer's scale) for the horizontal distance in the profile grid.

This is the method of developing a border (see Fig. 9-1) for plan and profile sheets—*use it for any plan and profile sheets in this course.* Other sheets will not necessarily have this type of border.

Developing the Sheet for a Plan and Profile Drawing

Now the border is on. The sheet will contain a plan view in the top portion (remember, a plan view is a view of the job looking down from above) and a profile view (a view looking directly at the plan view, but from the side) in the bottom portion of the sheet.

Splitting the Sheet

The vertical dimension of a C-sheet is 17, 17½, or 18 in. We will use a dimension of 15 in within the drawing borders, so that all our drawings have the same size.

Measure up 5 in from the bottom border line. Draw a line all the way from the left to the right border line. The sheet now has a 16.75 × 5-in space for the profile grid; the size of the top space (10 or 10½ in) does not matter. The sheet should look like Fig. 9-2.

Developing the Grid

The sheet would now be a standard plan and profile sheet, but it lacks something: It needs a grid in the bottom portion of the sheet. The grid allows the road profile (or surface) to be drawn at the proper elevation.

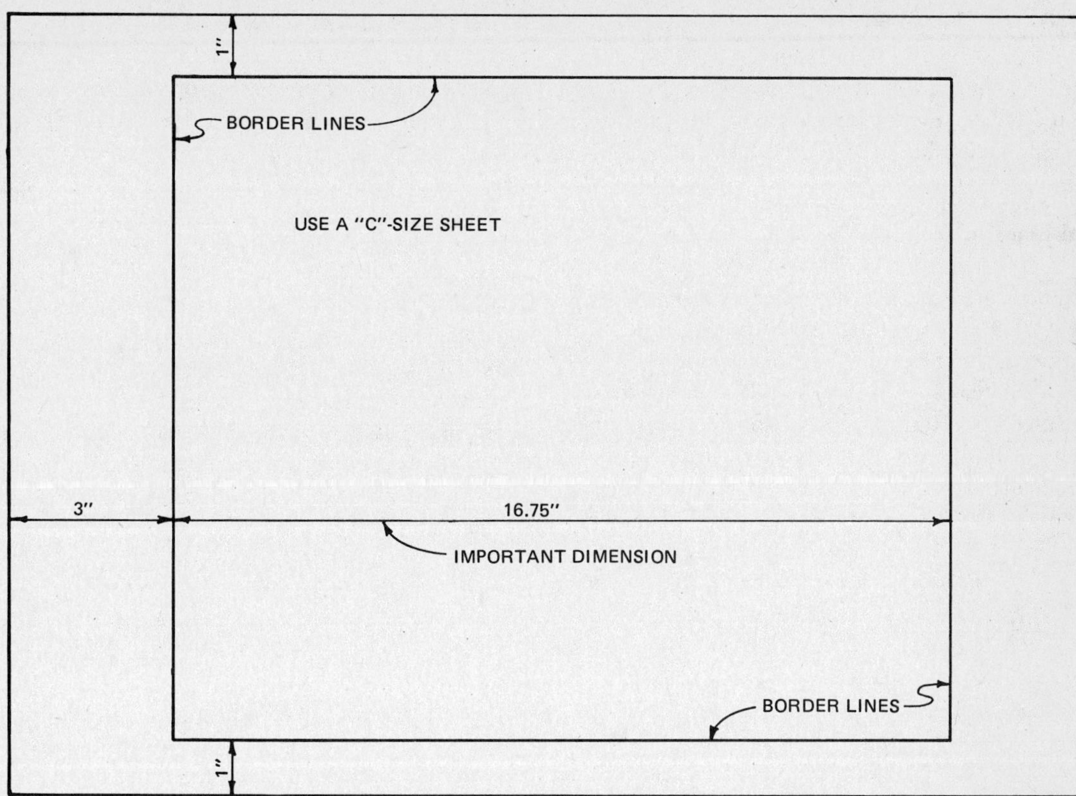

Figure 9-1
Setting up the border lines.

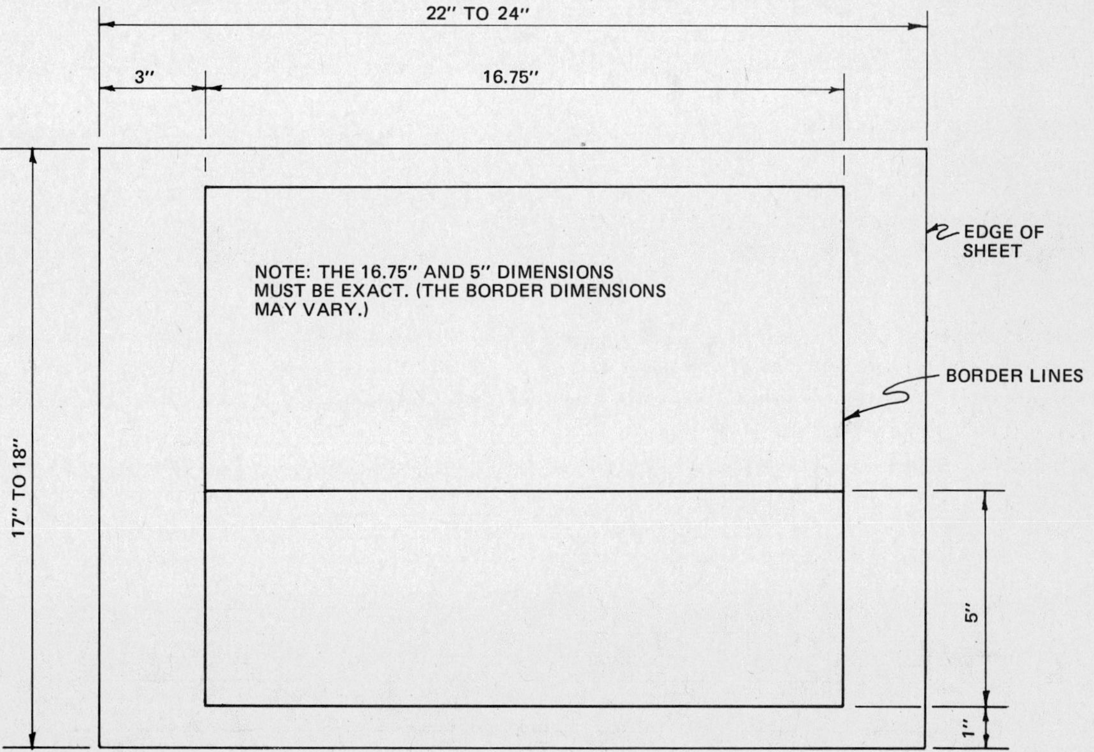

Figure 9-2
Establishing the grid size.

REMEMBER The profile view will show the natural ground as it exists and a new proposed road surface as it will be after construction. Vertical curves are also shown in the profile grid, as well as drainage structures. There must be a grid in order to draw these features properly.

Vertical Lines in the Grid

Measure in 0.75 in from the left border and draw a thin vertical line. This line, like the rest of the vertical grid lines, will be 5 in long and go from the bottom border line to the top of the profile part of the drawing. This line should be Sta. 220. Letter in "220" right above the bottom border for ready identification of this station. Put dots at 0.5-in intervals all the way across the sheet to the right-hand border. Label every fifth station (Sta. 220, then 225, 230, 235, 240, 245, and 250). Following Sta. 250 there will be two more stations, which we will not label. Put a line 0.5 in to the left of the starting station (Sta. 220) for Sta. 219, which will not be labeled. Note that there is still half a station to the left; that is the way the sheet should be.

Draw lines through the individual dots, from the bottom border line up 5 in to the line that splits the drawing surface of the sheet. The vertical part of the grid is now complete.

Horizontal Part of the Profile Grid

At 0.5-in intervals put dots on the vertical Sta. 219 line of the grid. Since there is 5 in of space for the grid, it will be divided into 10 equal 0.5-in spaces. Draw horizontal lines (thin and light) through the dots from the left border to the right border. We now have a standard C-size plan and profile sheet (see Fig. 9-3).

SCALE

We will deviate from the standard scale of 1 in = 100 ft and 1 in = 10 ft to produce a drawing of the size that is sent to the contractor. This will make the drawing easier for the student, without detracting from the learning process. The size the contractor receives is one-half the original size done in the consulting engineer's office. So our scales will be:

Horizontal scale: 1 in = 200 ft
Vertical scale: 1 in = 20 ft

CENTERLINE OF SURVEY

Directly above the lower grid Sta. 220, which is 0.75 in from the left border line, project a thin light line vertically, top to bottom, through the 10 in plan drawing

Figure 9-3
Putting in the grid.

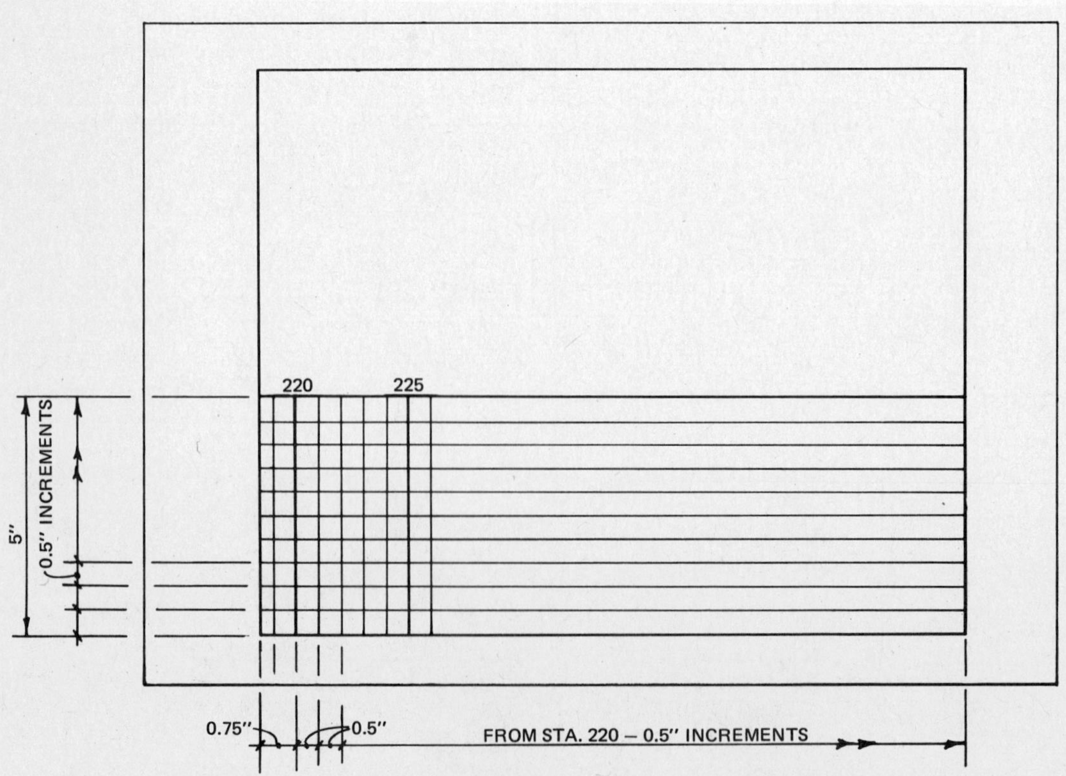

space. This will be the location of Sta. 220 in the plan view. Notice that it is directly above Sta. 220 in the profile view. This is the starting point for the centerline of survey.

Measure down 5 in from the top border line; the point where the Sta. 220 line and the 5-in measurement intersect will be the start of the centerline of survey for this project.

Drawing the Centerline

Project a thin vertical line up from Sta. 250 on the grid below. This will give the stop point for the centerline. When drawing the centerline in heavy, do not pass this point. Now draw the horizontal centerline, thick and heavy. If using pencil, go over the line several times to make a line 1/16 in thick. If using a technical pen, use a No. 3 or No. 4 on the Rapidograph scale of pen lines.

NOTICE we began the centerline at an even station. Directions insist that our stations begin and end with even stations. This gives 30 stations per sheet—count them to see for sure.

Ticking the Centerline

Now we have a good dark centerline, but without some method of measuring we would not know where we were on the line. Knowing that the profile views are directly under the plan views, we can establish a system of measurement. Using a T-square and a triangle (preferably 30–60°), or a parallel rule and triangle, project the grid lines of all stations vertically up to the centerline. Do not draw vertical lines, just make little dots at the top of the centerline where the upward projection intersects the centerline.

The general directions specify that ticks should be 0.1 in high, with ticks at the numbered stations (every fifth station) 0.2 in high. Our drawing is at half scale, so our ticks will be half this size. What is the easiest method of measuring this? We are using a scale of 1 in = 200 ft, so take the engineer's scale and on the left-hand edge select the No. 20 scale (see Fig. 9-4). Use the smallest tick on the scale to measure 0.1 in—do not divide by two, the scale has already done it. The larger ticks are to be 0.2 in long—use the 0.2 in mark on the 20 scale. It is the correct size automatically. This is the way scales are supposed to be used. To check this, take the architect's scale and compare the ticks to the small scale on the drawing. The 0.1-in tick will be a little less than 1/16 in, and the 0.2-in tick will be a little less than 1/8 in.

All these ticks should be made darker. Make them dark but not quite as thick as the centerline. These ticks are to the centerline as the graduations are to the scales; without them the scales and the centerline are useless.

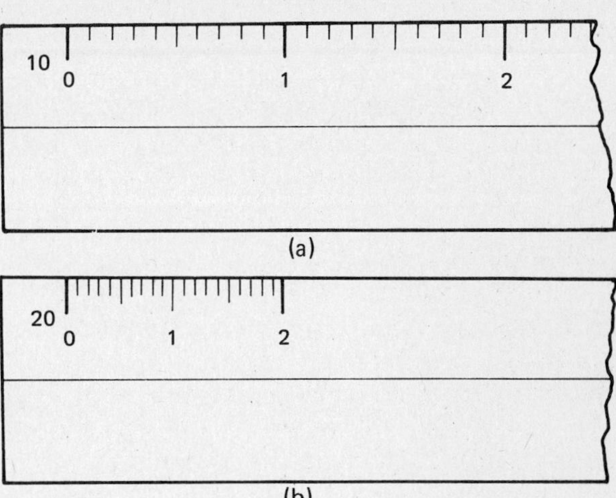

Figure 9-4
Engineer's scale: (*a*) 10 scale. One inch equals 10 ft. Notice that 1 in has 10 divisions. (*b*) 20 scale. Here 1 in equals 20 ft, and 1 in has 20 1-ft divisions.

DRAWING THE PROPOSED ROADWAY

We now have a grid for the profile view. Above this grid are the ticks which give the exact stationing on what will be the centerline of the road. This road, like all roads, has a typical section (something we have yet to study), see Fig. 9-5. Figure 9-5 shows a section of the road cut through vertically from north to south; this gives a cross-section view of the roadway, which goes east and west. On either side of the centerline a dimension of 32 ft [9.8 m] is indicated; this is the median strip, which is 64 ft [19.5 m] wide. Then the typical section shows 24 ft [7.3 m] on each side beyond the median strip. Most roadway lanes must be 12 ft [3.7 m] wide, so each 24-ft [7.3-m] roadway has two lanes of traffic. Two lanes go east and two lanes go west. Overall this is a four-lane highway with a 64-ft [19.5-m] median. This is a very typical cross section of roadway for a fairly high density road in the country.

The Median Edges

The typical section of this highway shows a distance of 32 ft [9.8 m] from the centerline to each edge of the road surface. We need to draw a line on each side of the centerline to represent the inside edge of the road surface; it should be parallel to the centerline, 32 ft [9.8 m] away from it, and it should run from Sta. 220 to 250.

Since our scale is 1 in = 200 ft, take the engineer's scale and find the 20 scale. The scale is divided so that 1 in = 20 ft, so multiply every tick on the scale by 10. This will give 1 in = 200 ft. To measure 32 ft [9.8 m] from the centerline, count three small ticks and estimate two-tenths of the next tick. Multiply 3.2 by 10, and this gives 32 ft [9.8 m] on a scale of 1 in = 200 ft. Draw the two lines that represent the two innermost edges of

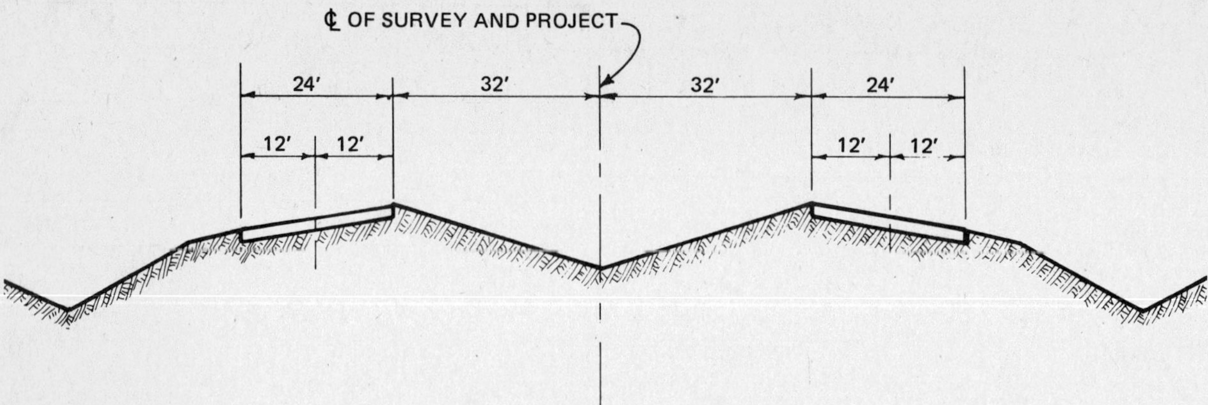

Figure 9-5
Typical road section.

the new roadway, the edges which are close to the centerlines on the typical section shown in Fig. 9-5.

The Outer Road Edges

Note that the roadways in Fig. 9-5 are 24 ft [7.3 m] wide. In most states, each driving lane is legislated by state law to be a minimum of 12 ft [3.7 m] wide. A few old roads may be as small as 9 ft [2.7 m] wide. New projects, however, will be designed 12 ft [3.7 m] wide. On our roadway the roads are designated as 24 ft [7.3 m] wide; we need not show lane widths, so just show the 24-ft [7.3-m] road width. Now read 2.4 small ticks on the engineer's scale and multiply by 10 to get the 24-ft [7.3 m] width of road. Measure two 24-ft [7.3-m] distances away from the innermost road edges and draw the outer road eges from Sta. 220 to 250.

NOTES FOR THE ROADWAY

Starting at about Sta. 226 above the outside edge of the roadway, label the baseline of survey and the centerline of construction. Baseline is abbreviated by a capital *B* with a capital *L* running through its center. Centerline of construction is abbreviated by a capital *C* with a capital *L* running through the center. Throw arrows from the notes to the centerline of the project. Refer to Drawing No. 23 and Fig. 9-6 when necessary.

Bearing of Centerline

The survey team has found the bearing on this section of the roadway to be N89°17′36″E, so under the centerline of project letter in "N89°17′36″E."

RIGHT-OF-WAY LINES AND STATION NUMBERS

At present it is difficult to count the stationing on the plan view. Project all the stations vertically (using tick marks) from the grid in the profile view.

Put on the right-of-way lines 150 ft [45.7 m] from each side of the centerline. Notice that right-of-way lines have a long dash, then two small dashes, then another long dash. In this case the R/W lines have a slash at 45° between the two small dashes. This indicates a limited access right-of-way. Put station numbers above the top right-of-way line at every fifth station starting with Sta. 220.

Who Owns the Right-of-Way?

The city, state, or county must own the land on which the roadway is constructed, see Fig. 9-7. This land, called the *right-of-way* is purchased from private individuals who own it. It is assessed by the government body that wants to purchase it, at what they feel is fair market value. An owner who refuses to sell can take the government to court. Sometimes the private individual wins, but the road always goes through. The government has the right of *eminent domain*, and thus the road cannot be blocked by individual property owners who want to hold out for more money or who just do not want to sell.

Right-of-Way in the City

In city subdivisions the city usually buys 50-ft [15.2-m] wide strips for the city roads. Outside the front edge of a city lot or beyond the sidewalk, if there is one, is about 12 or 13 ft [3.7 or 4.0 m] of land that belongs to the city. Lot owners cannot put permanent construction on this strip. They usually are permitted to gravel this portion, put grass on it, or in some subdivisions plant trees, but this is at the discretion of the individual city or subdivision.

Right-of-Way in the Country

The highway we are drawing is a highway of relatively large size, a four-lane highway like the one in Fig. 9-8. The state (the little block in the upper right-hand corner indicates that this is a state project) has purchased a 300-

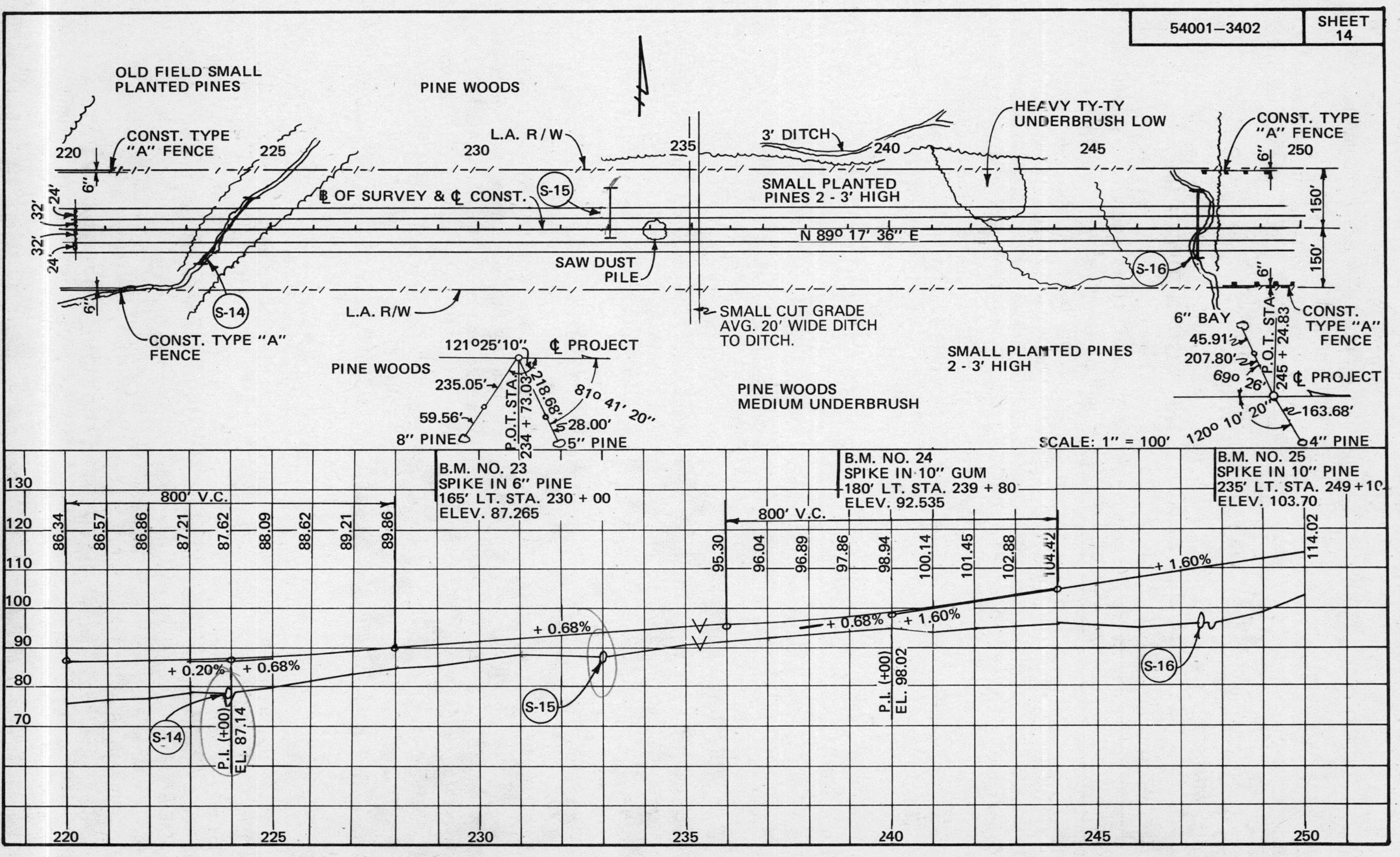

Figure 9-6
The plan and profile drawing in this chapter, Project 54001–3402, Sheet 14. Note: The student should remove Drawing Plate No. 23, p. 177, from the text and refer to it while reading the instructions in this chapter.

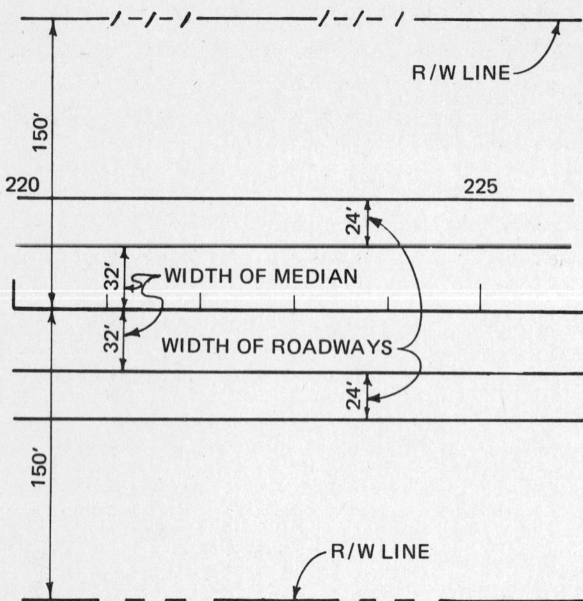

Figure 9-7
Right-of-way, roadways, and median.

Figure 9-8
Four-lane highway similar to the one we are drawing *(Florida Department of Transportation).*

ft [91.4-m] right-of-way on which to build the proposed highway. Three hundred feet is a big right-of-way—this is the size used for most interstate highways. The state will then be responsible for maintenance on the road, on the median strip, and on both sides to the edges of the right-of-way.

In Germany the farmers cultivate the sides of the roads and harvest enough hay from their section of the right-of-way to feed many cattle each winter. Doing the same thing in this country would save money in several ways. The farmers take full responsibility for cutting and maintaining the sides of the roads bordering their farms. This saves the state the expense of the personnel and fuel to run big mowing tractors to haul the mowings away from the site. The farmer gets free use of the land (it may be in tens of acres), which reduces the cost of feed and consequently the cost of farm products. Many of the German highways are beautiful and look as though the grass is cut daily.

THE EXISTING TOPOGRAPHY

Starting from the left side at Sta. 220, we find an old field of small planted pines. This is shown in Fig. 9-6 by a bushlike symbol which runs along the far left side of the drawing above Sta. 220 at an angle of about 60°, again parallel to the centerline near the symbol at the top, and through the centerline at Sta. 223 + 30. Label the area "OLD FIELD SMALL PLANTED PINES."

At Sta. 225 on the centerline another edge-of-wooded-area symbol is shown. It occurs again at Sta. 233 above R/W line to Sta. 244 and branching off at Sta. 241 to 246 + 00.

Place these wooded area symbols as shown in Fig. 9-6 and label them neatly.

DITCHES

There are also a few ditches crossing the roadway. Draw in the meandering ditches as shown on Fig. 9-6; there are three of them. Draw them in freehand as much like Fig. 9-6 as possible.

DRAINAGE

Notice the 3-ft [0.9-m] bottom ditch from Sta. 220 to 225; some sort of drain has been installed where it crosses our roadway. It has a number S-14, which we call out. Drainage structure S-14 is shown on Fig. 9-9. A contractor would need a full set of plans in order to know what S-14 was, bid on it, and build it. Draw this single-line pipe and end walls; this structure picks up water and discharges it in the ditch after going under the roadway centerline at Sta. 223 + 90.

Do the same at S-15 drain at Sta. 233 + 00. There a drain box picks up water from the median strip and puts it into the pipe going under the road.

At Sta. 236 + 00 and 240 + 00 two small ditches already exist and should be shown and labeled.

Put in the proposed median drain at Sta. 233 and label it S-15.

ADDITIONAL TOPOGRAPHY

Notice (Fig. 9-6) the sawdust pile at Sta. 234 + 10. It is a big pile—it measures 50 ft [15 m] across the bottom. Like the trees and other items that obstruct the road, it

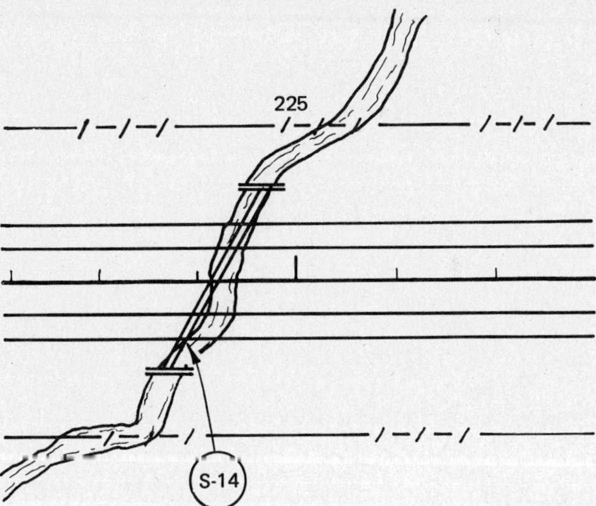

Figure 9-9
Drainage structure S–14.

will be removed. It must be shown on the map and called out.

NORTH ARROW

Put a simple north arrow in the center of the upper plan portion of the drawing. *Never forget the north arrow.*

REFERENCE POINTS

Now the plan part of the plan and profile sheet is done, but the survey crew has provided more information which will be needed in checking the line of survey. This information is in the form of reference points, and they must be put on the drawing.

Put the first reference point above Sta. 231 on the profile grid, on the plan part of the sheet. An arrow indicates centerline of project, and a point of tangency is shown at Sta. 234 + 73.03. An angle of 81°41′20″ is measured from the centerline, and a line is projected from the point of tangency at this angle. A marker (usually a square stake) is located 218.68 ft [66.654 m] out along this line; then the line intersects a 5-in [13-cm] diameter pine tree. From the same point of tangency (POT), an angle turned back 121°25′10″ from the centerline of the project gives a line of sight from the transit to a marker 235.05 ft [71.643 m] away and to an 8-in [20-cm] pine tree 59.56 ft [18.15 m] beyond. This field book information must be put on the sheets, since the field books are not available to the contractor.

After drawing this reference point, add the one at the point of tangency Sta. 245 + 24.83. Now the plan view is complete except for the scale, which is 1 in = 200 ft. Add the scale to complete the plan view and then go on to the profile view.

INFORMATION FROM FIELD BOOKS

All the information for the profile view comes to the drafter from a set of field notebooks made by the survey team. The information is given here as though it had come from the field books.

Infallibility of the Field Books

The field books are infallible on survey information. These field books are developed by the survey crew. They must never have an erasure in them. When erroneous material is entered, it must be crossed out and started over. Hard pencil is used in the books, so erasures would be visible. An erasure found in the book invalidates the material in the book.

The field books are kept in the state department of transportation in a very safe area (Fig. 9-10) where they are protected from fire and access by unauthorized personnel. In lawsuits or other legal situations, the field books are the ultimate authority on a survey.

Bench Marks and Ground Elevations

First, the field book gives bench marks. This information is put at the top of the grid in the profile view. The ground elevation data follow; they will be plotted on the drawing.

Station	Elevation, ft [m]	Station	Elevation ft [m]
220	75.0 [22.9]	237	92.0 [28.0]
221	76.4 [23.3]	239	93.5 [28.5]
222	76.4 [23.3]	240	94.3 [28.7]
223	78.2 [23.8]	241	94.0 [28.7]
223 + 80	78.0 [23.8]	242	94.5 [28.8]
224	77.0 [23.5]	243	94.5 [28.8]
224 + 20	78.2 [23.8]	244	96.0 [29.3]
225	80.0 [24.4]	245	96.0 [29.3]
227	84.0 [25.6]	246	95.0 [29.0]
228	85.0 [25.9]	247	95.2 [29.0]
229	85.0 [25.9]	247 + 60	95.0 [29.0]
230	86.5 [26.4]	247 + 70	94.2 [28.7]
231	88.0 [26.8]	247 + 80	96.0 [29.3]
232	87.0 [26.5]	248	96.0 [29.3]
233	87.0 [26.5]	249	98.5 [30.0]
234	88.5 [27.0]	250	103.0 [31.4]
235	90.5 [27.6]		

First put a vertical scale on the grid in order to plot the elevations. (The horizontal scale is already set up.) Start three lines up from the bottom of the grid and letter a "70" on the left-hand portion of the grid; increase by 10 ft per line. The vertical scale is 1 in = 20 ft. Plot the elevations as close as possible to the right point. Since the vertical scale on the grid shows only 10-ft intervals,

Figure 9-10
Storage of field books *(Florida Department of Transportation).*

the student should use the engineer's 20 scale to divide the grid blocks into feet. Now we will plot the first elevation of 75.0 ft [22.9 m] at Sta. 220. Put the engineer's scale along line 220, find the 70-ft mark and measure up 5 more ft on the 20 scale. This will give an accurate 75 ft.

The Natural Ground Line

Use the preceding chart of natural ground elevations and plot the elevations (use dots) at all the station points. Now connect the dots by straight lines to give the natural ground line.

DRAINAGE STRUCTURES IN THE PROFILE

There are three drainage structures visible in the plan view, S-14, S-15, and S-16. Features shown in the plan view must also be shown in the profile view. In the profile view, these structures will show up at the elevation where they cross the project centerline. Remember that the scales for horizontal and vertical measurement differ. If they were the same, a round pipe would show up as a circle in the profile grid. But since the vertical scale is much greater than the horizontal one, the round pipes show up as ellipses. Therefore, show the drainage pipes at the proper elevation but use elipses where they appear on the grid. S-14 will be at Sta. 223 + 90 with the flow line of the pipe at 78.0 ft [22.9 m]. S-15 will be at Sta. 233 at elevation 88.2 ft [26.3 m] and S-16 will be at Sta. 247 + 50, elevation 94.0 ft [28.7 m].

ROADWAY PROFILE VIEW

Now all we need is the new proposed roadway profile view. A civil engineer figures this out, considering the high water elevation in the area and many other factors. The drafter's job is to draw it on the sheet in pencil or ink.

Drawing the Highway Profile

From Sta. 220 the tangent (or straight line of the profile) is at elevation 86.34 ft [26.32 m] rising slowly at +0.20 percent grade to a point of intersection at Sta. 224 + 00, where the elevation is 87.14 ft [26.56 m]. From here the tangent portion rises at +0.68 percent, but there is a vertical curve 800 ft [244 m] long between Sta. 220 and 228. For the vertical curve, station elevations must be given at every station. There is a similar vertical curve between Sta. 236 and 244.

Marking Off the Elevations

The elevations to be marked on the grid follow in a chart. These elevations, remember, are not in the field books—they do not yet exist. These are the elevations of the new roadway which will be constructed. The design engineer, knowing high water levels, terrain, the speed autos will travel, and many other factors, has designed the profile grade to meet certain design specifications. The elevations on the following chart have come from the design engineer's calculations for vertical curves and slopes. This proposed road profile is the ultimate goal of all the drafting that we have done so far.

Stations for Proposed Road Profile

NOTE If there are no elevations given for several stations, this indicates a tangent area (or a straight line). This line will always be at plus (+) or minus (−) some percentage grade. In these cases just join the last two stations for which elevations are given with a straight line.

Station	Elevation, ft [m]	Station	Elevation, ft [m]
220	86.34 [26.32]	237	96.04 [29.27]
221	86.57 [26.39]	238	96.89 [29.53]
222	86.86 [26.47]	239	97.86 [29.83]
223	87.21 [26.58]	240 (PI)	98.02 [29.88]
224 (PI)	87.14 [26.56]	241	100.14 [30.52]
225	88.09 [26.85]	242	101.45 [30.92]
226	88.62 [27.01]	243	102.88 [31.36]
227	89.21 [27.19]	244	104.42 [31.83]
228	89.86 [27.39]	250	114.02 [34.75]
236	95.30 [29.05]		

When these points have been plotted, the plan and profile sheet will be complete. Before going on to the problems, see Fig. 9-11 through 9-14 for some photographs of equipment and personnel involved in the production of road plans.

Figure 9-11
Print reproduction machine and operator *(Florida Department of Transportation).*

Figure 9-12
Flat and round storage files *(Florida Department of Transportation).*

Figure 9-13
Small section of a design squad. The man with the pipe has been a road design technician for 35 years *(Florida Department of Transportation).*

Figure 9-14
Atlantic Vocational Technical Center at Pompano Beach, the first school to teach civil drafting in southern Florida. *(Broward County School Board).*

PROBLEMS

1. The student will draw the plan and profile view from sheet 17 of State Project 54001–3402.
   (a) Remove Drawing No. 24 from the textbook. Place it on the drawing board or side table for convenient reference. We will reproduce this drawing at a larger scale.
   (b) Use a C-size (17 × 22 in) sheet of vellum. Refer to Fig. 9-1, 9-2, and 9-3 for the border and grid sizes for the problem.

NOTE Do not put in the stationing views in Fig. 9-3. This problem will involve a new area and will use different stationing.

Plan View

(c) Scale: Horizontal 1 in = 200 ft
Vertical 1 in = 20 ft

(d) Draw in the centerline of survey about midway between the top and bottom of the plan section of the drawing. Note that the starting station is Sta. 310, located ¼ in from the left border. Look back at Drawing No. 23, which is the master drawing for plan and profile drawings, to see the correct starting point for the centerline of construction.

(e) Draw in the baseline of survey and centerline of construction, making them at least 1/16 in thick. Tick the centerline and draw in the proposed roadway. The roadway has the typical section shown in Fig. 9-5; it will have a median 32 ft [9.8 m] wide on each side of the baseline of survey and two 24-ft [7.3-m] wide roads, just as the first plan and profile project did. This is the same road but at a different location. For this reason the typical road section is the same.

(f) Indicate the physical characteristics of the area—ditches, streams, trees, underbrush, and so forth.

(g) Put in the drainage structures S-23, S-24, S-25, and S-26, the north arrow and the reference point.

Profile View

(h) Letter in the information on Bench Marks 32 and 33 near the top of the profile grid.

(i) Now put in the natural ground line. The stations and their elevations are:

Station	Elevation, ft [m]	Station	Elevation, ft [m]
310	131.8 [40.17]	324	136.5 [41.61]
311	130.5 [39.78]	325	137.0 [41.76]
312	128.5 [39.17]	326	138.0 [42.06]
313	125.5 [38.25]	327	140.5 [42.82]
313 + 80	124.5 [37.95]	328	141.0 [42.98]
313 + 90	122.5 [37.34]	329	145.0 [44.20]
314 + 10	121.0 [36.88]	330	148.0 [45.11]
314 + 20	121.0 [36.88]	331	150.0 [45.72]
314 + 21	122.0 [37.18]	332	151.0 [46.02]
315	122.0 [37.18]	333	151.0 [46.02]
316	124.0 [37.80]	334	153.0 [46.63]
317	125.0 [38.10]	335	156.0 [47.55]
318	127.0 [38.71]	336	158.1 [48.19]
319	128.0 [39.01]	337	161.5 [49.23]
320	130.0 [39.62]	338	164.0 [49.99]
321	132.0 [40.23]	339	167.0 [50.90]
322	133.5 [40.69]	340	171.0 [52.12]
323	134.5 [41.00]		

After plotting all these points on the profile grid, connect them by straight lines. This is the natural ground line for this area.

(j) Add the drainage structures at the elevations shown on Drawing No. 24. Notice the drainage structure at S-24 is not a pipe, but rather a culvert going under the road. It is shown by a rectangle, and it consists of two rectangular boxes going under the road. A double culvert is the proper name for it.

Proposed Roadway Profile View

1. Starting at Sta. 310 the first point to plot has the elevation 136.88 ft [41.721 m]; this is where the roadway begins on this plan and profile sheet. It goes down at a negative slope of −1.08 percent. The next point to plot is at Sta. 312 + 50, which is the start of a vertical curve. At Sta. 312 + 50 plot an elevation of 134.18 ft [40.898 m]. Follow Drawing No. 24 from here on. All vertical curve elevations are written on the station lines of the curve. Station 320 + 50 is the end of the first 800-ft [243-m] vertical curve; its elevation is 135.54 ft [41.313 m]. The proposed roadway then slopes upward at +1.42 percent, with a straight line connecting Sta. 320 + 50 to Sta. 327, which is at elevation 146.19 ft [44.559 m]. Again, an elevation is given for all the vertical curve stations. Use a French curve to put in the vertical curves. Try to connect at least three points at a time, then shift the curve to connect at least three more points. At Sta. 336 the elevation is 163.87 ft [49.948 m], and from there a straight line at +3.00 percent reaches the elevation 175.87 ft [53.605 m] at Sta. 340.

   Check this problem against Drawing No. 23 for completeness, and sign it above the drawing number.

2. Remove Drawing No. 25 from the end of the chapter and cover it with a B-size sheet of vellum. Trace all the items from this drawing, including the profile grid.

   This is a problem in vertical curves. Vertical curves are seen in the profile view. At Sta. 31 + 50 in the plan view a taper which widens the existing 20-ft [6.1-m] pavement to 24 ft [7.3 m] begins. Twenty-four feet is the width required by most state laws, so any road improvement has to increase the road width to a minimum of 24 ft [7.3 m] if it is a two-lane road.

   Notice how the taper is called out; + 50 means the last station (which is 31) plus 50 ft. So the taper starts at Sta. 31 + 50. It ends at Sta. 32 + 25.

Station	32 + 25
	−31 + 50
	75 ft

Therefore, the length of the taper is just 75 ft.

Notice at the start and finish of this job the note to "connect to existing pavement." This means the job is an improvement to an existing road; for the length of the improvement the road will be widened to 24 ft [7.3 m] and new vertical grades will be established.

Drainage structures S-1, S-3, and S-4 are 24-in [60-cm] concrete pipes with endwalls, and S-2 is a 10-ft [3.0-m] wide by 12.5-ft [3.81-m] high culvert under the road.

NOTICE There is a reference station on this sheet. On the baseline of survey the survey crew found a bolt imbedded in the road. But more important is the U.S. Army Corps of Engineers monument found 100°39′00″ northwest of the baseline of survey. This monument is KR 1312. It is recorded in the Army Corps of Engineers' Record of Monuments book with its never changing elevation of 28.93 ft [8.818 m] above mean sea level.

All the information has been put on this map except the elevations on the 200-ft [61.0-m] vertical curve starting at Sta. 38 + 25 and ending at Sta. 40 + 25. The following stations and elevations should be added to the drawing:

Station	Elevation, ft [m]	Station	Elevation, ft [m]
38 + 25	29.75 [9.068]	39 + 50	28.94 [8.821]
38 + 50	29.54 [9.004]	40 + 00	28.80 [8.778]
38 + 00	29.18 [8.894]	40 + 25	28.77 [8.769]
39 + 25	29.05 [8.854]		

3. In this problem the student will put in the natural ground line from the elevations given in a chart. Notice the low elevations in this problem, which involves a street in one of the islands of the Florida Keys. Elevation of Key land is usually in the neighborhood of 4 ft [1.2 m] above mean sea level. Another feature of the area is *caprock.* Caprock occurs here instead of the dirt or sand normally found in other regions. It is very hard material to deal with and requires bulldozers and occasionally dynamite to move it around.

   Remove Drawing No. 26 from the end of the chapter and place it under the center of a piece of B-size vellum. Trace all the items, including the profile grid. Note that a few houses appear on the map. They must always be included in the plan view. Most plan views are now done by aerial photography, using a plane equipped with special mapping cameras. (The cost for one sheet of a job is over $100. This may seem expensive, but if the camera did not do it, a survey crew would have to record every item in a field book, and then a drafting technician would have to reproduce these notes onto a vellum or mylar sheet to make blue-line or black-line prints of the job by machine.) This particular map would not be one requiring aerial photography because it is not complicated. It has a minimum of features for the drafter to record.

   After tracing all the items from Drawing No. 26, the student should add the following items to the drawing:

   (a) The existing road which is 20 ft [6.1 m] wide from Sta. 11 + 10 (where it has flared down from the entrance radii to 20 ft [6.1 m]) to Sta. 23 + 20 (which is the end of project). The road is an old existing road and it should be drawn with dotted lines.
   (b) Make the note: "Baseline of Survey and Centerline of Construction" near the main line running east and west on the sheet, with an arrow pointing to the centerline.
   (c) Call out the right-of-way line by note.
   (d) Note the bearing of the centerline as S89°19′23″E.
   (e) Add drainage structure S-1 located at Sta. 13 + 50 to the profile view. It is a 24-in [61-cm] concrete pipe with a flow line elevation of 1.5 ft [46 cm] above sea level.
   (f) Add a 30-in [76-cm] concrete pipe culvert to the profile view at Sta. 18 + 80. The flow line elevation of this pipe is 1.0 ft [30 cm] above mean sea level.
   (g) Add the natural ground line from the following data:

Station	Elevation, ft [m]	Station	Elevation, ft [m]
10	4.0 [1.2]	18	2.5 [0.76]
11	2.5 [0.76]	18 + 50	2.0 [0.61]
11 + 50	2.3 [0.70]	19	2.3 [0.70]
12	2.6 [0.79]	20	2.8 [0.85]
13	2.0 [0.61]	21	3.0 [0.91]
13 + 50	1.5 [0.46]	22	3.3 [1.0]
14	1.7 [0.52]	23	3.5 [1.1]
15	2.0 [0.61]	23 + 20	3.5 [1.1]
16	3.0 [0.91]		
17	3.5 [1.1]		

   Check the drawing and sign it above the drawing number.

4. Remove Drawing No. 27 from the end of the chapter and place it under the center of a B-size sheet of vellum. Trace all the items included thereon, including the profile grid.

   Notice that most of the profile grid is blank. The problem includes tracing the plan view and completing the profile view. The profile view needs the bench marks, profile grade line, natural ground line, and drainage structures S-6, and S-7.

Bench Marks:

B.M. No. 11
Boat spike in 10-in [25-cm] oak
42 ft [12.8 m] Lt. Sta. 142 + 06
Elev. 8.87

B.M. No. M-306
USC&GS (1970)
125 ft [38.1 m] Lt. Sta. 144 + 05
Elev. 9.64

REMEMBER the bench marks go at the very top of the profile grid. Since the first one is at Sta. 142 + 06, start the B.M. at Sta. 142. The second B.M. should start at Sta. 144; notice that it has a marker number of M-306. It was put into place in 1970 by the United States Coast and Geodetic Survey.

Drainage Structures

Locate S-6 at Sta. 144 + 50 with a flow line elevation of 6.00 ft [1.83 m]. Remember that the flow line is the inside (inner) bottom of the pipe; the flow line (invert elevation) of the oval shaped pipe should be at 6.00 ft [1.83 m]. This pipe has a diameter of 2 ft [61 cm]; thus it will show as an oval between 6.00 and 8.00 ft [1.83 and 2.44 m] on the profile grid.

Locate the 24-in [61-cm] diameter concrete pipe (structure S-7) at Sta. 145 + 30. The flow line elevation is 6.00 ft [1.83 m] as it was for structure S-6.

Natural Ground Line

This is a map of the Florida Keys; the natural ground is very flat and low. Use the following chart for the points on the natural ground line:

Station	Elevation, ft [m]	Station	Elevation, ft [m]
135	6.00 [1.83]	141	6.50 [1.98]
136	6.00 [1.83]	142	6.50 [1.98]
137	6.00 [1.83]	143	7.00 [2.13]
138	6.50 [1.98]	144	7.00 [2.13]
139	6.50 [1.98]	145	7.00 [2.13]
140	6.00 [1.83]		

Connect the points and put in an arrow to the line with a note saying "Natural Ground."

Profile Grade Line

The profile grade line starting at Sta. 135 is 7.2 ft [2.2 m] above sea level and rises at +0.20 percent. It is already shown as far as Sta. 137.

At Sta. 137 its PI elevation is 8.00 ft [2.44 m]. Draw the profile grade line between Sta. 137 and 143, where the PI elevation is 9.50 ft [2.90 m]. A straight line should connect these two PI's. On top of the line a note should call out "Profile Grade" with an arrow from the note to the profile grade line. In addition, on top of the line add "+0.25%" with an arrow to the line. This is the percentage of slope between these two points.

From Sta. 143 to Sta. 144 + 84 the profile grade is level. Draw a line between these two stations at elevation 9.50 ft [2.90 m]; since it is level, add "+0.00%" with an arrow to the line.

The last item to add for completion of this map problem is the end-of-project flag. Flag the profile grade line at Sta. 144 + 84.00 with "END OF PROJECT" and the stationing.

5. In this problem the student will add items to the plan view. This is part of an orange grove in Florida. Do not worry about the road running through the existing orange trees. The trees will be cleared and grubbed from the area where the road will run. Show the road and the right-of-way lines running right through them.

   The trees in the orange grove need water, which is provided from a well to ditches which run alongside the proposed road. Motorized pumps feed the water from the well to the ditches.

   Notice that one existing corrugated metal pipe at about Sta. 116 + 20 is called out by note "to be removed." There is nothing for the student to do here, but the road contractor will remove this pipe and add two others which will be shown in the plan view.

   Place Drawing No. 28 under a B-sized sheet of vellum. Trace all the items in the plan and profile views, including the profile grid.

Additions to the Plan View

At the begin project flag, letter "Begin Project" on top of the horizontal flag line. Under the horizontal line write "Sta. 106 + 50."

Now draw in the new road to be constructed. It will have two lanes—one 12-ft [3.7-m] lane north of the baseline of survey and one 12-ft [3.7-m] lane to the south. Be sure to dimension these two lanes. The road should be drawn with solid lines.

The bearing of the baseline of survey should be noted. It is N89°45′10″E.

The two right-of-way lines should be drawn in and noted as right-of-way lines ("R/W line"). They extend 40 ft [12 m] on each side of the centerline for a total right-of-way of 80 ft [24 m]. Be sure to dimension each 40-ft [12-m] R/W line from the baseline of survey. Be sure you add the tick marks for all the stations on the centerline.

Drainage Structures

At Sta. 111 + 45, at the point indicated by the arrow from S-1, there is a 24-in [61-cm] corrugated metal pipe (C.M.P.) running south from the 8-in [20-cm] flow well under the road to the drainage ditches. Put this structure in. It should be a heavy line with perpendicular lines at the ends representing end walls.

At Sta. 116 + 70 run another C.M.P. under the road from the north drainage ditch to the south side of the new road. This will be a 30-in [76-cm] (diameter) corrugated metal pipe.

Bench Marks

Add the following bench marks to the profile view near the stations where they occur:

B.M. No. 7
BOAT SPIKE IN 12-in [30-cm] CABBAGE PALM
53 ft [16 m] RT. STA. 105 + 00
ELEV. 4.42

B.M. No. 8
BOAT SPIKE IN MANGO TREE
42 ft [13 m] LT. STA. 108 + 57
ELEV. 4.62

Check the drawing and sign it above the drawing number.

6. Notice that there are no beginning and ending flags on Drawing No. 29. It is part of a longer job; the start and end stations for this sheet are given by solid lines through the centerline of construction. These lines match up with lines on other sheets to show a continuous roadway; they are called match lines.

Remove Drawing No. 29 from the text. Place it under a B-size sheet of vellum and trace all the items, including the profile grid.

There are several drainage ditches. In the interest of simplicity, not all the ditches shown in the plan view are shown in the profile view.

From the following chart, put in the natural ground line:

Station	Elevation, ft [m]	Station	Elevation, ft [m]
120	1.0 [0.30]	126	1.5 [0.46]
121	1.5 [0.46]	127	2.0 [0.61]
122	2.0 [0.61]	128	2.5 [0.76]
123	1.0 [0.30]	129	3.0 [0.91]
124	1.5 [0.46]	130	3.5 [1.1]
125	1.5 [0.46]	131	4.0 [1.2]
125 + 50	1.0 [0.30]		

As with Drawing No. 28, be sure all of the stations have tick marks.

7. Remove Drawing No. 30 from the back of the chapter and center a B-size sheet of vellum on top of it. Trace all the items on the map, including the profile grid. Notice that the existing road wanders around and becomes smaller. This is often the case. Here an old road has become inadequate, so the state is building a new and better one to replace it.

In this problem the student will put in most of the profile grade line from the profile grade PI's on the map. The student will also put in the natural ground line from the following data:

Station	Elevation, ft [m]	Station	Elevation, ft [m]
50	5.00 [1.52]	57	3.00 [0.914]
50 + 50	4.50 [1.37]	58	2.50 [0.762]
51	3.00 [0.914]	59	2.50 [0.762]
52	3.50 [1.07]	60	3.00 [0.914]
53	4.00 [1.21]	61	3.50 [1.07]
54	3.50 [1.07]	62	3.50 [1.07]
55	3.50 [1.07]	63	4.00 [1.21]
56	3.50 [1.07]		

LEARNING ACTIVITY PACKAGE

Read Chap. 9 and be sure the objectives are understood.

Chapter 9 read ______________ *(date)*.

Objectives completed ______________ *(date)*.

Now it is time to take the Chap. 9 quiz. Remove it from the text and answer all the questions.

Quiz completed ______________ *(date).*

All students should do Problem 1 and Problem 2.

Problem 1 completed ______________ *(date).*

Problem 2 completed ______________ *(date).*

Problem 3 completed ______________ *(date).*

Problem 4 completed ______________ *(date).*

Problem 5 completed ______________ *(date).*

Problem 6 completed ______________ *(date).*

Problem 7 completed ______________ *(date).*

9

QUIZ

Refer to Drawing No. 23 when necessary.

1. The profile view is directly under the plan view. (T or F) ____________
2. This drawing is made on a ____________ size sheet.
3. A smooth, clean surface is needed for drawing. (T or F) ____________
4. Black spots on a drawing are caused by ____________ spots on the paper.
5. Students need a T-square or parallel rule to generate horizontal and vertical lines if they do not have printed grid paper. (T or F) ____________
6. The architect's scale is used for plan and profile drawings. (T or F) ____________
7. For the drawings in this chapter, the horizontal distance required for the grid is ____________ inches.
8. The vertical sheet dimension within the borders for drawing is ____________ inches.
9. The space required for the ____________ ____________ is 16.75 in × 5 in.
10. A grid allows the road profile (or surface) to be drawn at the proper elevation. (T or F) ____________
11. Natural ground is the ground as it ____________ in nature.
12. A proposed road surface is the surface of the road as it will be after construction has been completed. (T or F) ____________
13. Horizontal curves show up in the profile grid. (T or F) ____________
14. Stations on the drawings are 0.5 in apart. (T or F) ____________
15. If one station is 0.5 in in length and two stations is 1 in, what is the scale 1 in = ____________ ft
16. Station 220 in the plan view is directly above Sta. 220 in the profile view. (T or F) ____________
17. The centerline of survey starts at Sta. ____________.
18. The stop point of the centerline of survey is Sta. ____________.
19. The centerline of survey is a heavy line about ____________ in thick.
20. There are always ____________ stations per sheet.
21. Normal ticks are 0.1 in high, and every fifth tick is 0.2 in high on full-scale drawings. (T or F) ____________
22. Ticks on our drawing are one-half size. (T or F) ____________
23. Ticks are to the centerline as graduations are on a scale. (T or F) ____________

24. Each roadway has two ___12___ ft lanes.

25. To use the engineer's 20 scale for 1 in = 200 ft, multiply each division by ___10___.

26. What is the bearing of the centerline of this project? ___N89°17'36"E___

27. Looking at the typical section of the project (Fig. 9-5). How wide is the median of the road? ___64___ ft

28. Right-of-way lines are 150 ft from the centerlines. What is the total right-of-way for the job? ___300___ ft

29. Three government agencies can own right-of-way. Name them:
___city___, ___state___, ___county___.

30. The right of eminent domain can keep private individuals from blocking passage of a public road. (T or F) ___True___

31. City rights-of-way for streets are usually 60 ft wide.
(T or F) ___50 false___

32. Can citizens put permanent construction on the city right-of-way abutting their lots? (*yes* or *no*) ___no___

33. What is S-14? ___drainage structure___

34. Reference points must be laid out on the plan and profile sheet, since the contractor will not have a set of field books. (T or F) ___True___

35. Surveyors make erasures in field books to make corrections.
(T or F) ___false___

36. Natural ground elevations must be plotted on the profile grid.
(T or F) ___True___

37. Drainage structures show in the plan but not in the profile view.
(T or F) ___false___

38. Vertical curves are shown on the profile grid. (T or F) ___True___

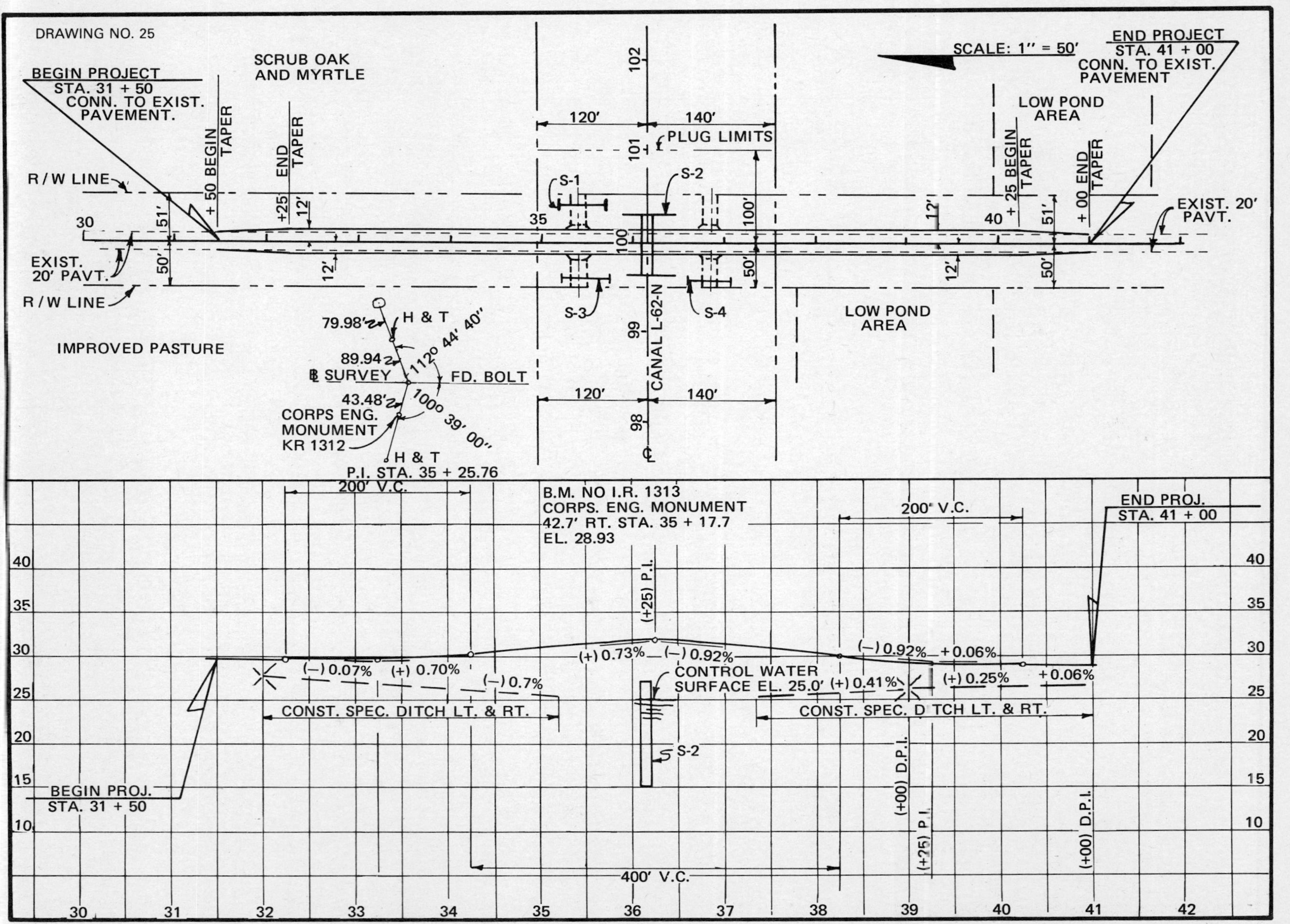
DRAWING NO. 25
SCRUB OAK
AND MYRTLE
BEGIN PROJECT
STA. 31 + 50
CONN. TO EXIST.
PAVEMENT.
+ 50 BEGIN
TAPER
+25 END
TAPER
R/W LINE
EXIST.
20' PAVT.
IMPROVED PASTURE
120'
140'
PLUG LIMITS
S-1
S-2
S-3
S-4
CANAL L-62-N
SCALE: 1" = 50'
END PROJECT
STA. 41 + 00
CONN. TO EXIST.
PAVEMENT
LOW POND
AREA
+ 25 BEGIN
TAPER
+ 00 END
TAPER
EXIST. 20'
PAVT.
79.98'
H & T
112° 44' 40"
89.94
℄ SURVEY
FD. BOLT
43.48'
100° 39' 00"
CORPS ENG.
MONUMENT
KR 1312
H & T
P.I. STA. 35 + 25.76
200' V.C.
B.M. NO I.R. 1313
CORPS. ENG. MONUMENT
42.7' RT. STA. 35 + 17.7
EL. 28.93
200' V.C.
END PROJ.
STA. 41 + 00
(+25) P.I.
(−) 0.07%
(+) 0.70%
(−) 0.7%
(+) 0.73%
(−) 0.92%
(−) 0.92%
+0.06%
CONTROL WATER
SURFACE EL. 25.0'
(+) 0.41%
(+) 0.25%
+0.06%
CONST. SPEC. DITCH LT. & RT.
CONST. SPEC. D TCH LT. & RT.
S-2
BEGIN PROJ.
STA. 31 + 50
(+00) D.P.I.
(+25) P.I.
(+00) D.P.I.
400' V.C.

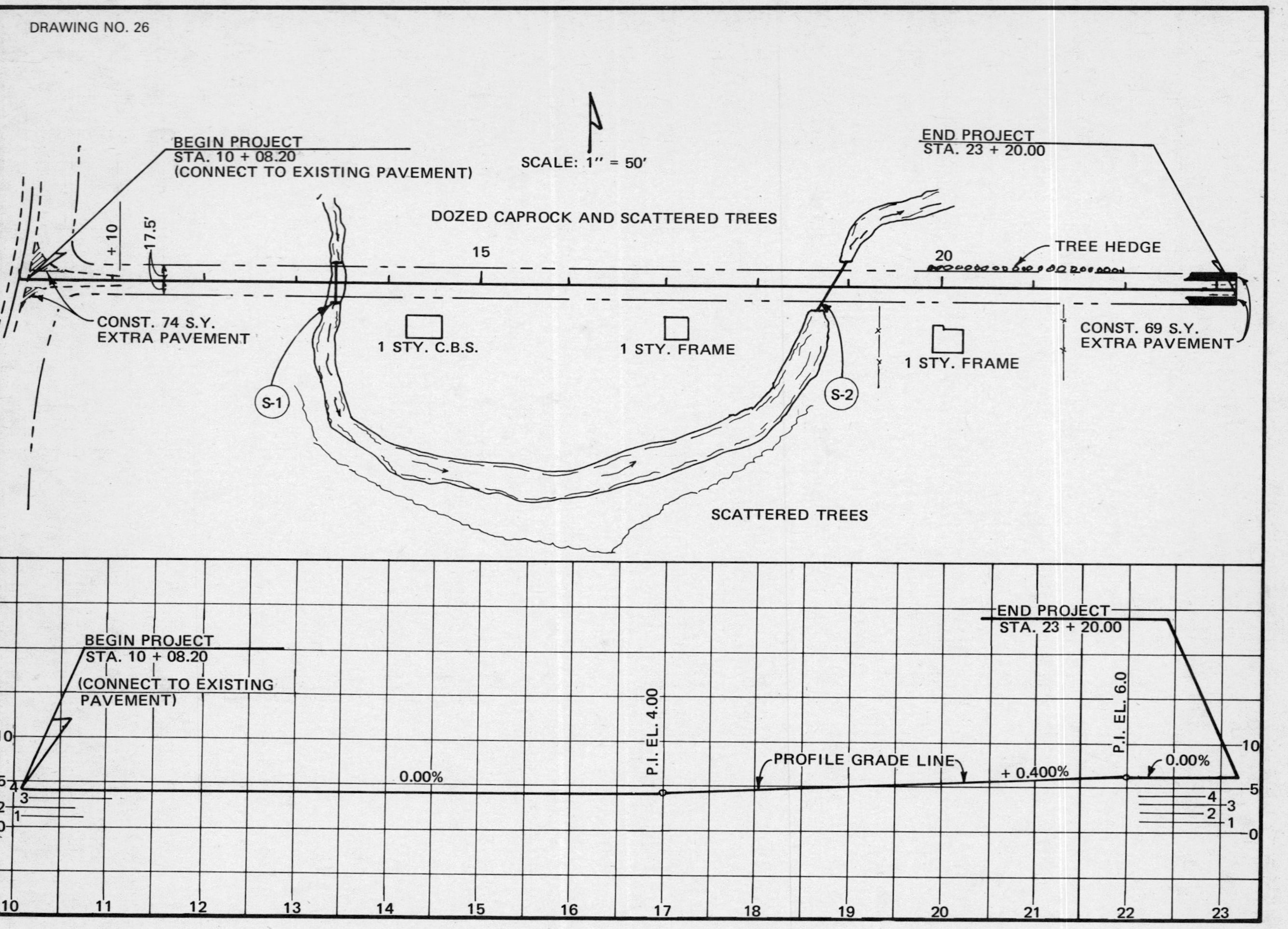

DRAWING NO. 26
BEGIN PROJECT
STA. 10 + 08.20
(CONNECT TO EXISTING PAVEMENT)
SCALE: 1" = 50'
END PROJECT
STA. 23 + 20.00
DOZED CAPROCK AND SCATTERED TREES
+ 10
17.5'
15
20
TREE HEDGE
CONST. 74 S.Y.
EXTRA PAVEMENT
1 STY. C.B.S.
1 STY. FRAME
1 STY. FRAME
CONST. 69 S.Y.
EXTRA PAVEMENT
S-1
S-2
SCATTERED TREES
END PROJECT
STA. 23 + 20.00
BEGIN PROJECT
STA. 10 + 08.20
(CONNECT TO EXISTING
PAVEMENT)
P.I. EL. 4.00
P.I. EL. 6.0
0.00%
PROFILE GRADE LINE
+ 0.400%
0.00%
10 11 12 13 14 15 16 17 18 19 20 21 22 23

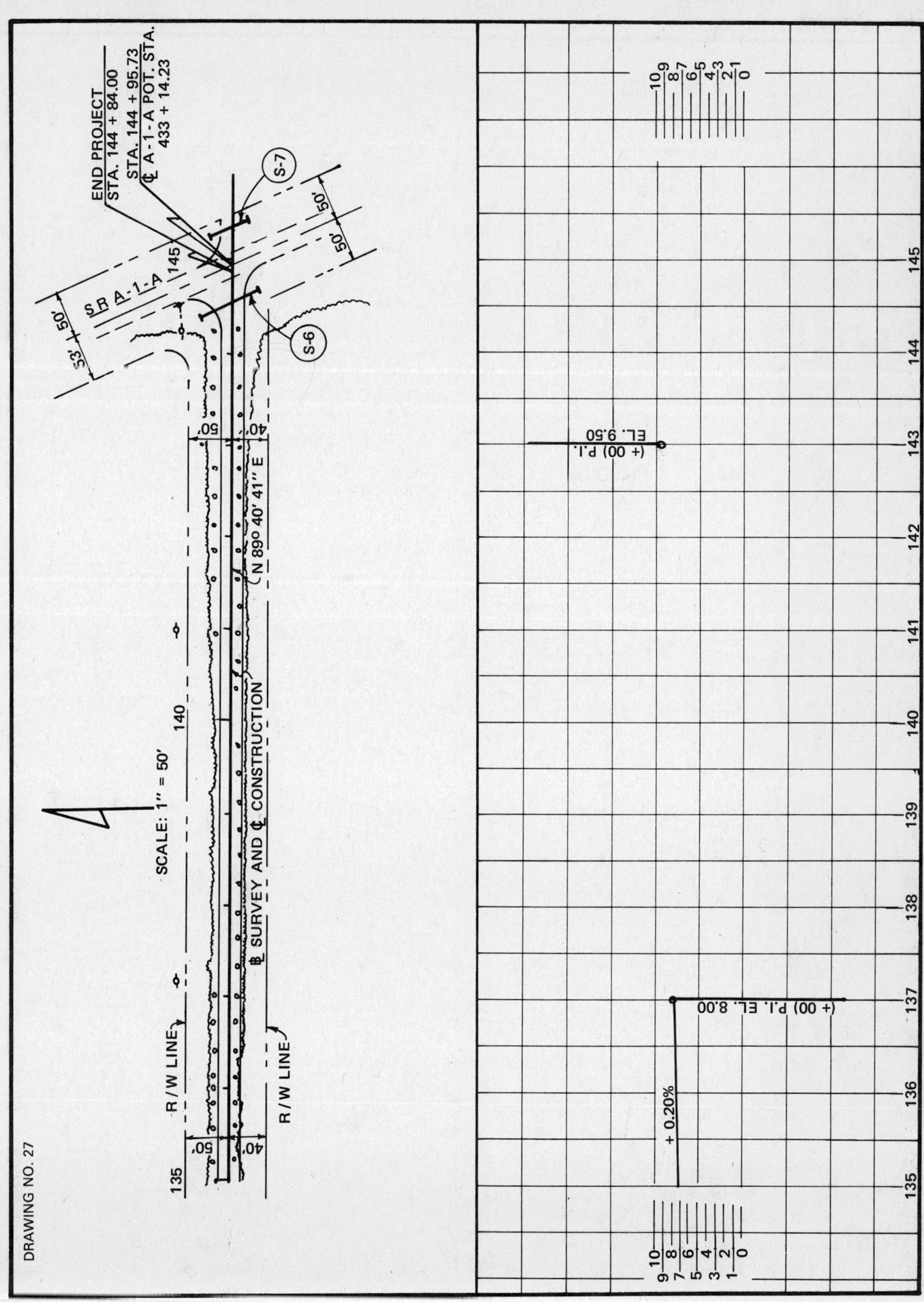
DRAWING NO. 27
SCALE: 1" = 50'
END PROJECT
STA. 144 + 84.00
STA. 144 + 95.73
℄ A-1-A POT. STA.
433 + 14.23
S-7
S-6
SR A-1-A
145
50'
53'
R/W LINE
R/W LINE
℄ SURVEY AND ℄ CONSTRUCTION
N 89° 40' 41" E
40'
135
140
(+ 00) P.I.
EL. 9.50
(+ 00) P.I. EL. 8.00
+ 0.20%
135
136
137
138
139
140
141
142
143
144
145

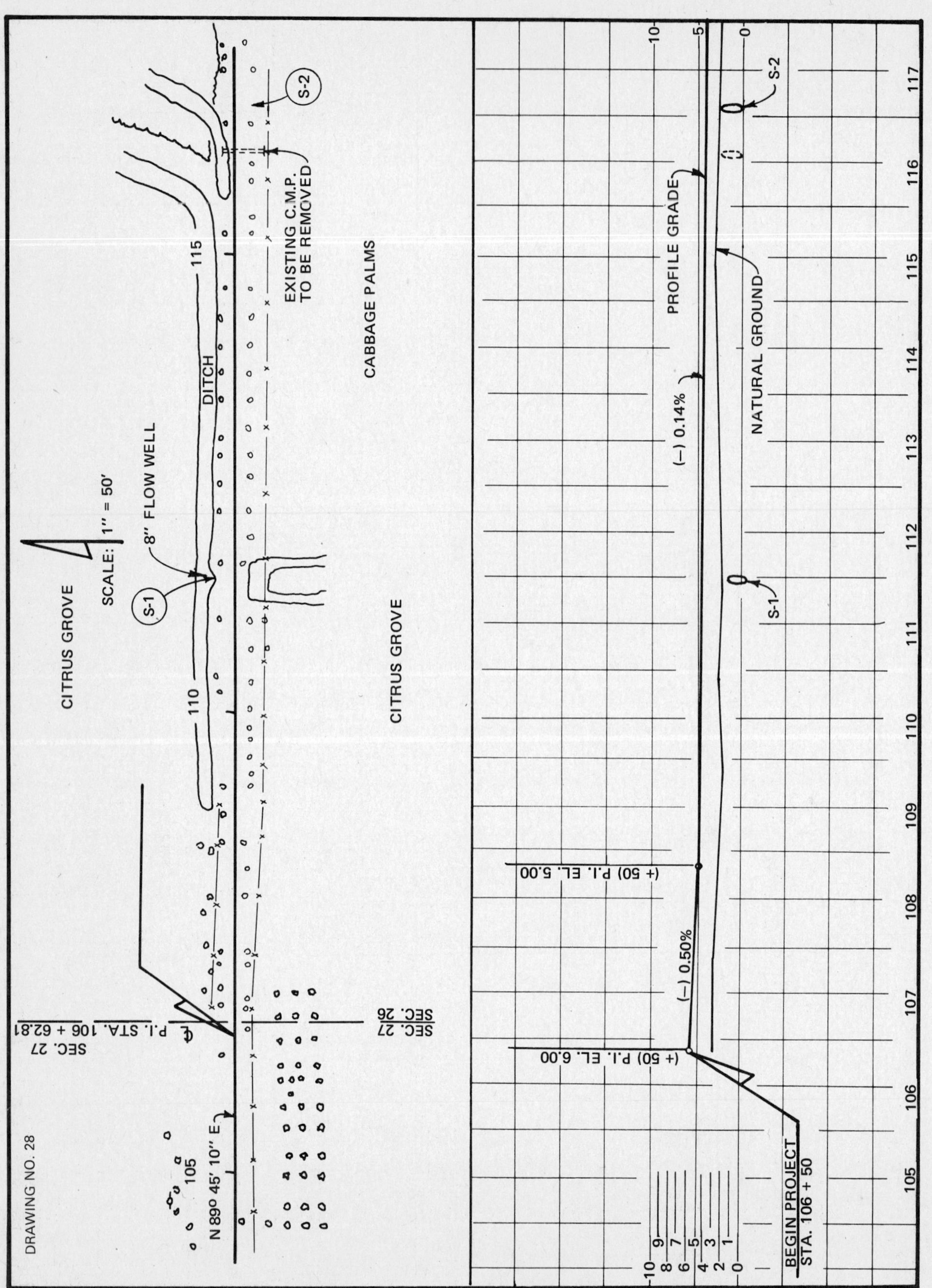
DRAWING NO. 28
CITRUS GROVE
SCALE: 1" = 50'
8" FLOW WELL
S-1
DITCH
110
115
EXISTING C.M.P. TO BE REMOVED
S-2
CABBAGE PALMS
CITRUS GROVE
105
N 89° 45' 10" E
SEC. 27
℄ P.I. STA. 106 + 62.81
SEC. 27
SEC. 26
(+ 50) P.I. EL. 6.00
(−) 0.50%
(+ 50) P.I. EL. 5.00
(−) 0.14%
PROFILE GRADE
NATURAL GROUND
S-1
S-2
10
5
0
BEGIN PROJECT
STA. 106 + 50
105
106
107
108
109
110
111
112
113
114
115
116
117

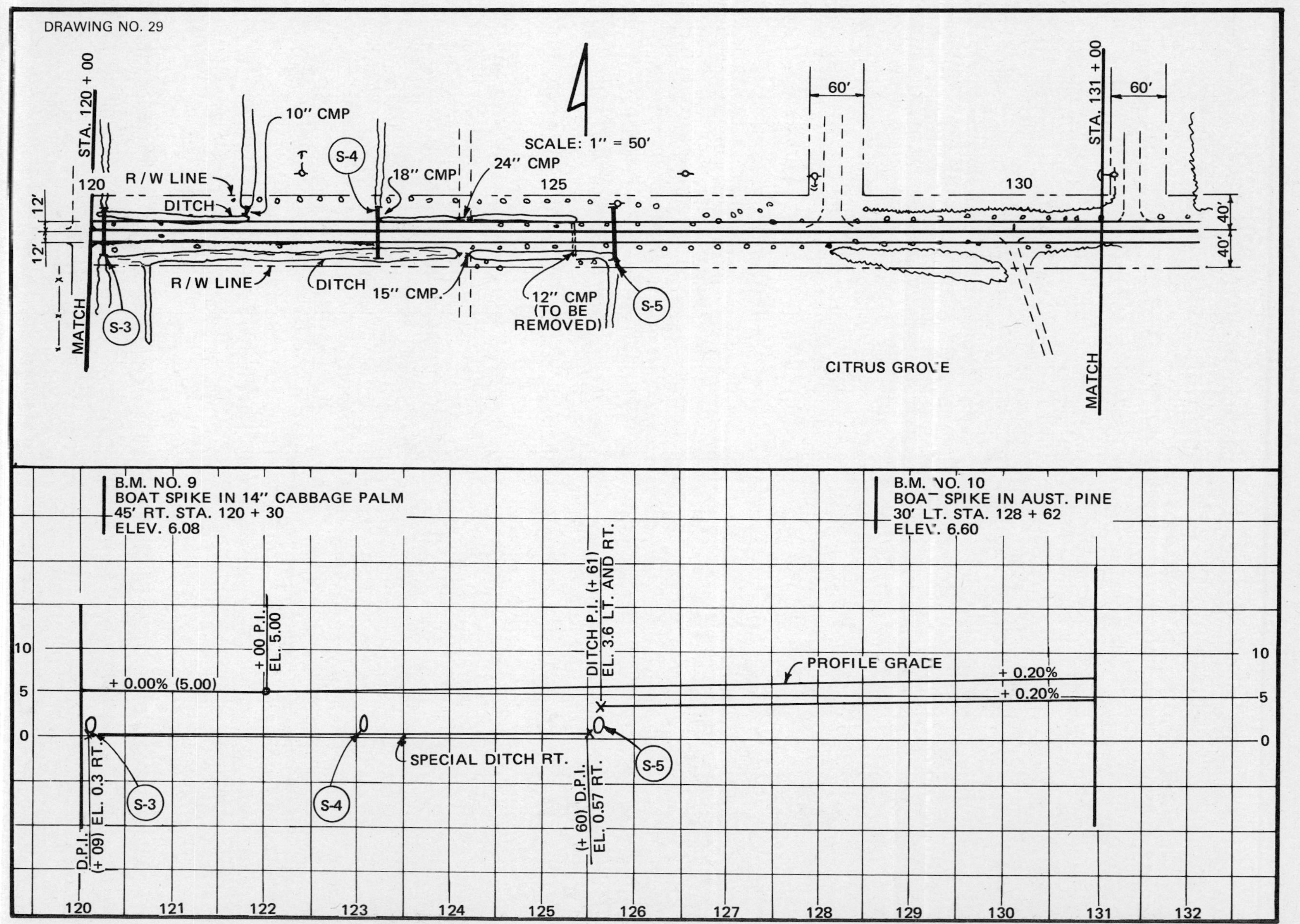
DRAWING NO. 29
STA. 120 + 00
MATCH
12'
12'
120
R/W LINE
DITCH
R/W LINE
S-3
10" CMP
S-4
18" CMP
24" CMP
SCALE: 1" = 50'
125
DITCH
15" CMP.
12" CMP (TO BE REMOVED)
S-5
60'
130
STA. 131 + 00
60'
40'
40'
CITRUS GROVE
MATCH
B.M. NO. 9
BOAT SPIKE IN 14" CABBAGE PALM
45' RT. STA. 120 + 30
ELEV. 6.08
B.M. NO. 10
BOAT SPIKE IN AUST. PINE
30' LT. STA. 128 + 62
ELEV. 6.60
+ 00 P.I.
EL. 5.00
DITCH P.I. (+ 61)
EL. 3.6 LT. AND RT.
+ 0.00% (5.00)
PROFILE GRADE
+ 0.20%
+ 0.20%
SPECIAL DITCH RT.
D.P.I.
(+ 09) EL. 0.3 RT.
S-3
S-4
(+ 60) D.P.I.
EL. 0.57 RT.
S-5
10
5
0
120
121
122
123
124
125
126
127
128
129
130
131
132

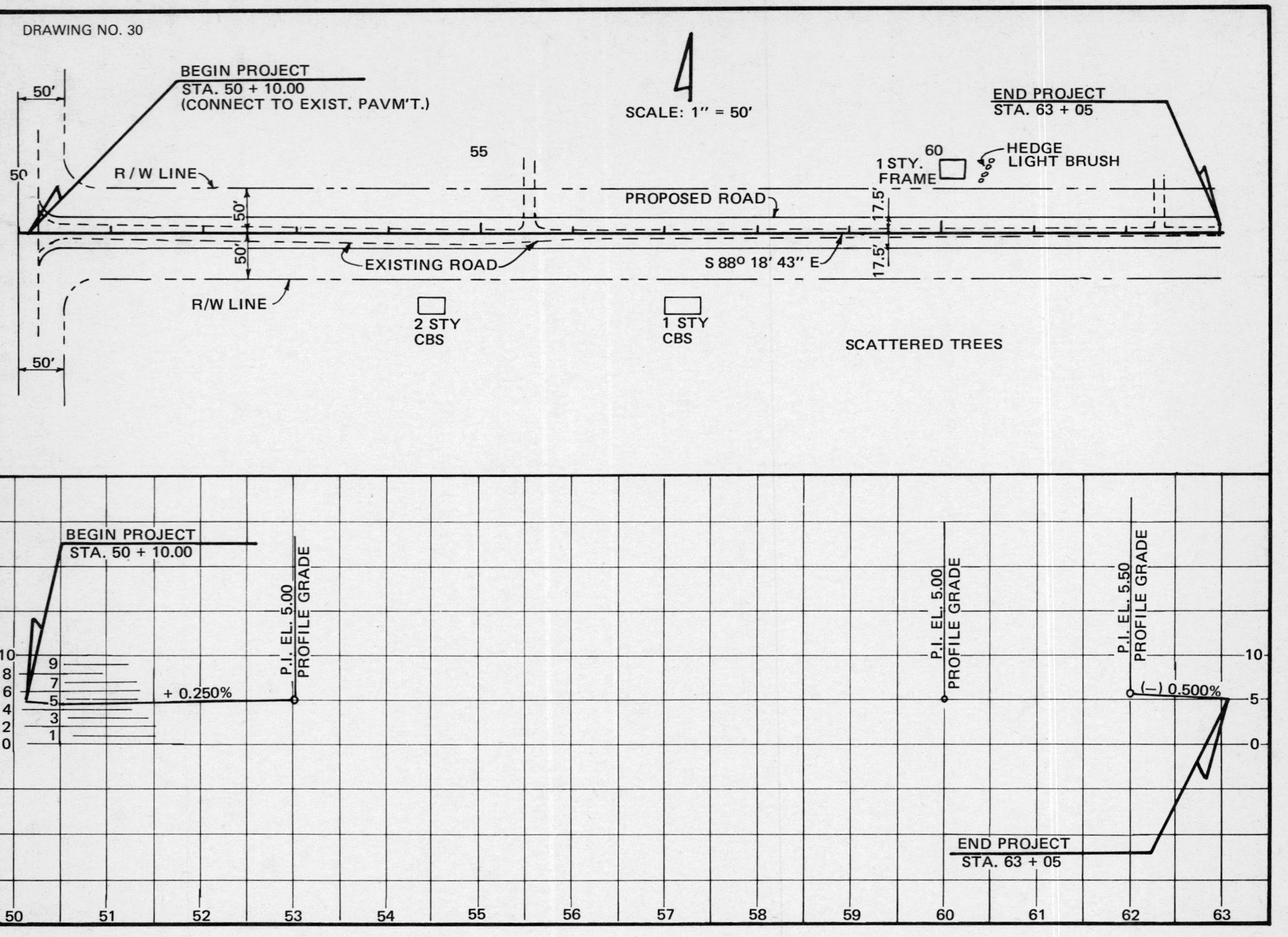

DRAWING NO. 30
BEGIN PROJECT
STA. 50 + 10.00
(CONNECT TO EXIST. PAVM'T.)
SCALE: 1" = 50'
END PROJECT
STA. 63 + 05
50'
50
55
60
1 STY.
FRAME
HEDGE
LIGHT BRUSH
R / W LINE
PROPOSED ROAD
17.5'
EXISTING ROAD
S 88° 18' 43" E
R/W LINE
2 STY
CBS
1 STY
CBS
SCATTERED TREES
BEGIN PROJECT
STA. 50 + 10.00
P.I. EL. 5.00
PROFILE GRADE
+ 0.250%
P.I. EL. 5.00
PROFILE GRADE
P.I. EL. 5.50
PROFILE GRADE
(–) 0.500%
END PROJECT
STA. 63 + 05

10 TYPICAL ROADWAY CROSS SECTIONS

Objectives

a. Understand cross-section views
b. Understand the profile grade point and the profile grade line
c. Study cut and fill sections
d. Understand the relationship of typical sections to plan and profile sheets
e. Know how to read the roadway cross sections
f. Read all the traffic definitions carefully

Rationale

Drafting technicians need to know what the roadway cross sections look like; without this knowledge, roadways cannot be designed. The student will learn to draw typical roadway cross sections and will do a number of problems for practice.

In earlier chapters we learned about the meanings of different views. Remember that a cross section is a view of the inside of an object, as if the object had been cut open. A cross section of a highway project is a view of the inside of the project cut open at right angles to the survey centerline. We will discuss three types of cross sections (see Fig. 10-1), cross sections of the natural ground, typical sections, and roadway cross sections.

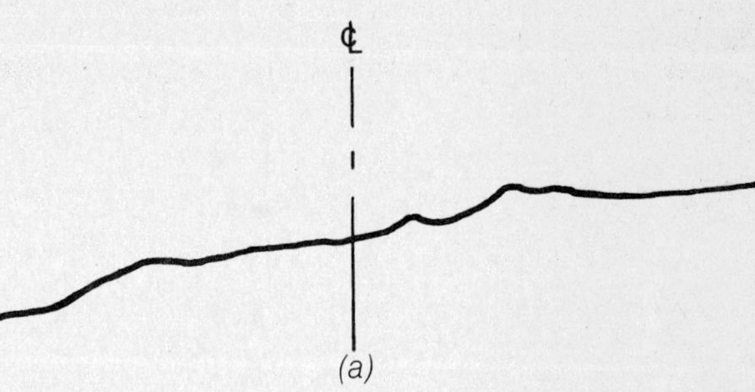

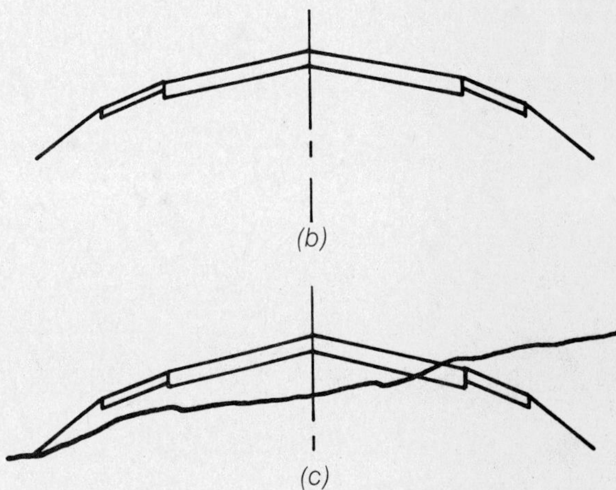

Figure 10-1
The steps in superimposing a ground line on a typical road section.

CROSS SECTIONS OF THE NATURAL GROUND

Before highway construction begins, a field survey is made along the proposed highway centerline. Elevations of the natural ground at various points on the centerline and on either side are recorded as shown in Fig. 10-2.

These elevations are plotted for each station to give *cross sections* of the natural ground. A sample cross section is shown in Fig. 10-3.

TYPICAL SECTIONS

One other type of cross section—the *typical section*—is important to drafting highway plans. A typical section is nothing more than a typical cross section of the road to be built, which is similar throughout most, or all, of the project.

Typical Section Terminology

The terminology used in a typical section of a two-lane highway is illustrated in Fig. 10-4. The *finished grading template* is the final shape of the roadway before paving materials are placed. The *subgrade* is the portion of the

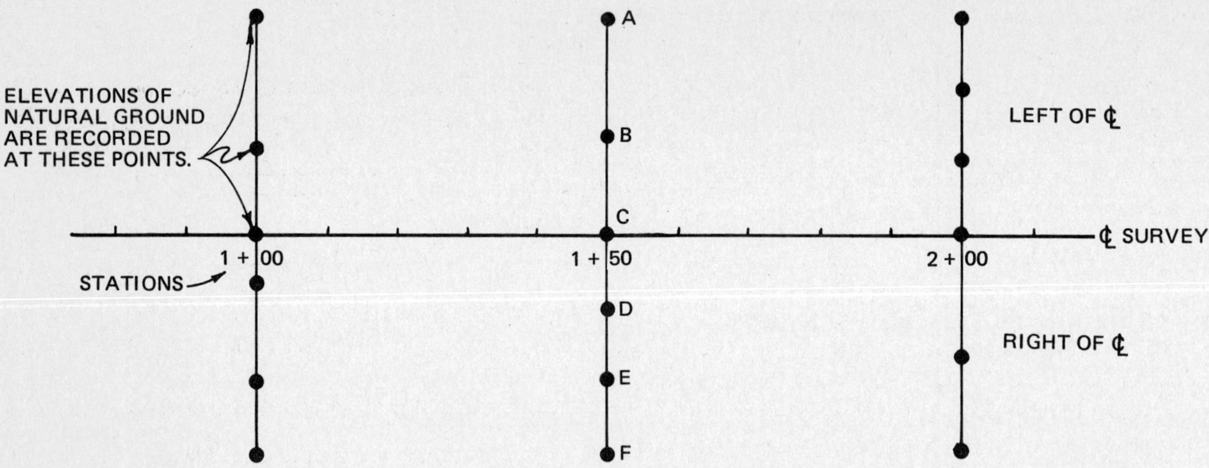

Figure 10-2
Plan view showing the recording of natural ground elevations at various points perpendicular to the road centerline.

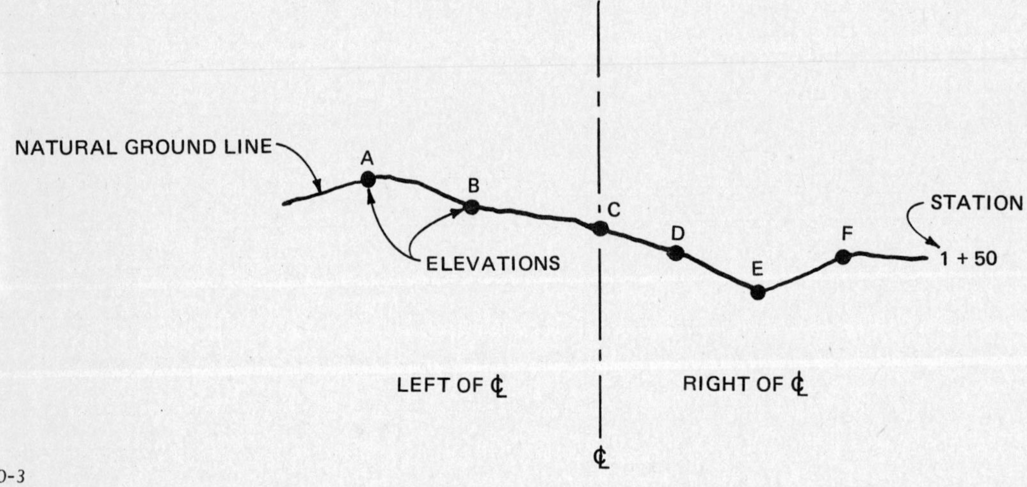

Figure 10-3
A cross-section view of natural ground.

Figure 10-4
Terminology for a typical section of a two-lane highway.

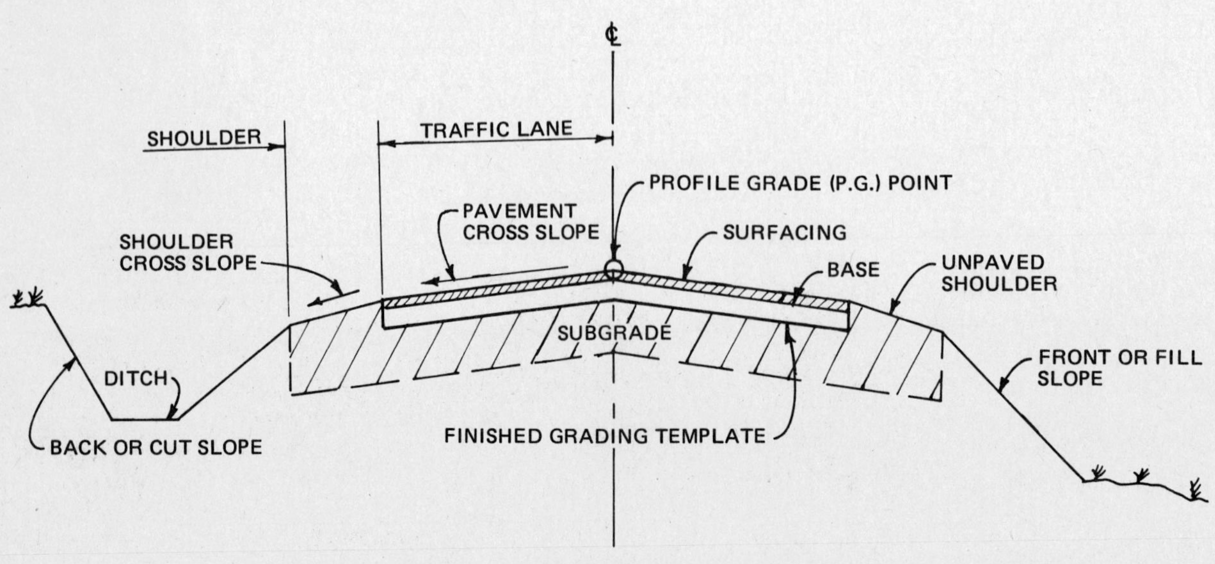

roadbed immediately below the finished grading template. Usually it is about 12 in [30 cm] thick. Notice that the *shoulder cross slopes* are steeper than the *pavement cross slopes*. These cross slope differences are common in some states. The *profile grade point* is the point plotted on profile views to form the smooth, continuous, profile grade line.

Typical Section of Divided Highway

A typical section for a *divided* highway might look like Fig. 10-5. Nearly the same terms apply to both single roadways and divided highways. The only differences are: (1) on divided highways, a distinction is made between inside and outside shoulders, but there is no such distinction between shoulders on single roadways, and (2) divided highways have medians, but single roadways, of course, do not.

Multiple Typical Sections

Sometimes several typical sections are needed for one project. This is the case for Project 54001–3402 in this text. Go to the first typical section sheet for that project; it is labeled as Sheet 5 of this project and is shown in Fig. 10-6. Two complete typical sections are shown on Sheet 5. The one on top is for the main highway; the one on the bottom is a typical section for ramps at the interchanges of Interstate 10 with other roads.

The next sheet on this project, Sheet 6, (Fig. 10-7), shows typical sections of two roads which intersect Interstate 10—S.R. 59, a divided highway, and S.R. S-158, a two-lane highway.

Sometimes several typical sections are needed for the same project. The sections of road to which each typical section applies are noted under the typical section.

QUIZ

On the first typical section of Project 54001–3402 (for the main highway) the median width is measured between the ____P.G.____ points.

The region below the finished grading template on which the paving materials rest is called the ____Subgrade____.

A road's horizontal alignment is shown on ____two____ views.

A diagram shows a plot of the natural ground elevations on both sides of the centerline at a certain station. It thus shows a ____relevation____ of the ____road____ at that station.

Refer to Sheet 5 (Fig. No. 10-6) of Project 54001–3402. On the main highway, what are the dimensions of the following?

Pavement cross slope ____.02'/feet____

Cross slope of inside shoulders ____.05'/feet____

Cross slope of outside shoulders ____.06'/feet____

Width of each roadway ____24'____

Width of pavement on each of the outside shoulders ____10'____

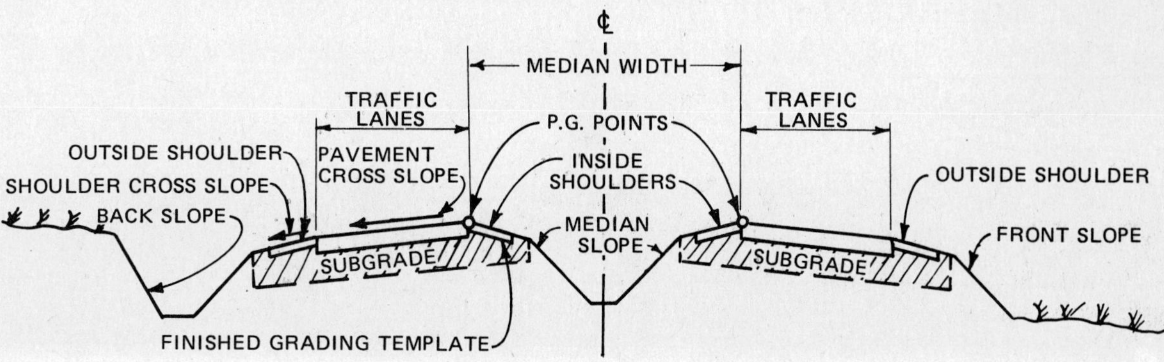

Figure 10-5
Terminology for a typical section of a two-lane highway with a median ditch.

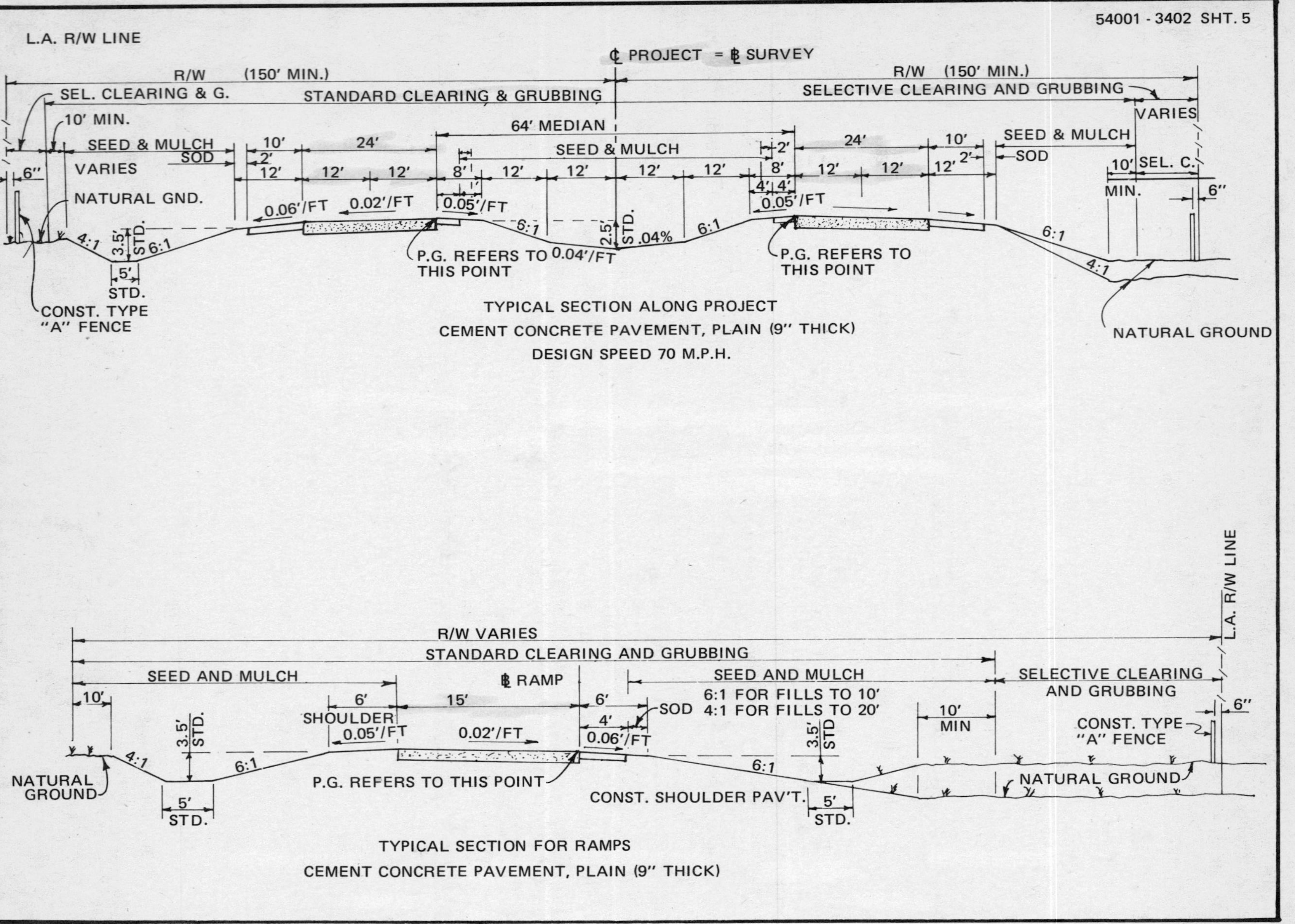

Figure 10-6
Typical sections for I-10 (Job No. 54001–3402, Sheet 5).

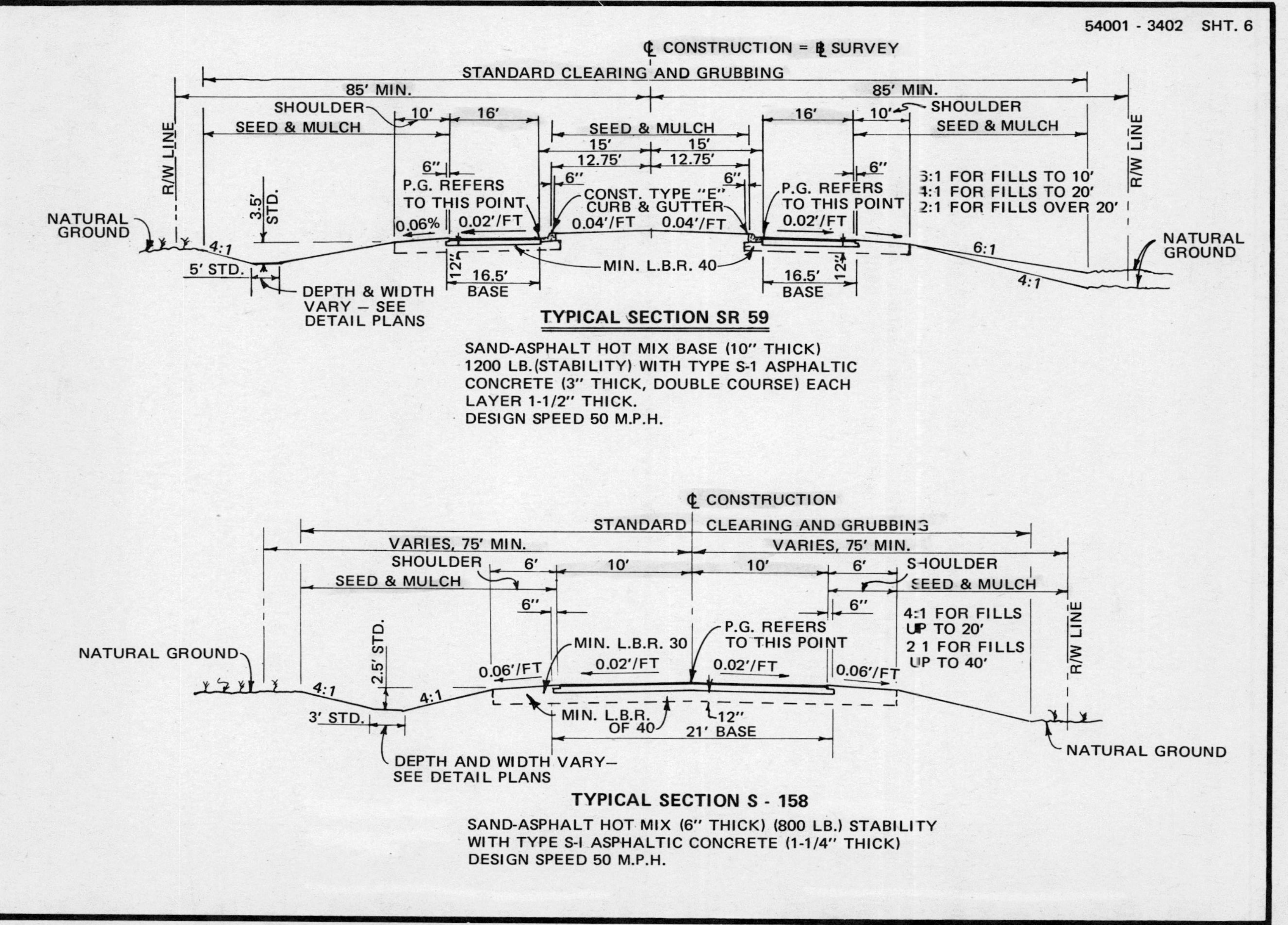

Figure 10-7
Typical sections of SR-59 and S-158 (Job No. 54001–3402, Sheet 6.

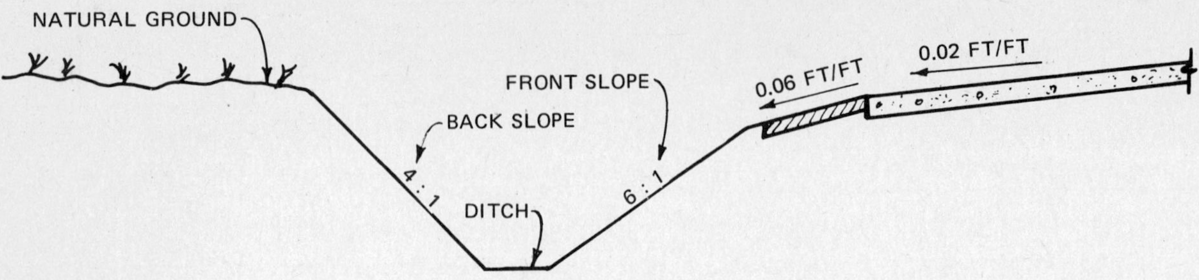

Figure 10-8
Cut section details.

Cut Sections

Cut sections are areas where the existing ground must be "cut" (excavated) in order to shape the roadway. For an example, refer to the first typical section in Project 54001–3402, Fig. 10-6. The details on the left side of this typical section show how the slopes will be graded in cut sections. In *cut* sections, the road is built *below* the existing ground. Some of the cut section details are explained in Fig. 10-8. On this typical section, cut section details are on the left side of the typical section. This does *not* mean that all cuts will be made on the left side of the road. The same details apply to the right side of the road when the natural ground on the right side is higher than the road.

Fill Sections

The details on the right side of this typical section show how the slopes will be graded in fill sections. In *fill* sections, the road is built *above* the natural ground. The fill-section details are explained in Fig. 10-9. Even though fill-section details are shown on the right side of this typical section, they also apply to the left side if the natural ground on the left side is lower than the road.

Relating Typical Sections to Plan and Profile Sheets

There are several similarities between typical sections and plan and profile sheets. We will first compare typical sections to plan views.

NOTE The student will be asked to compare views on certain projects, and the text will give the sheet number required in that particular project. This will give the student the same experience finding the drawings as would be encountered in industry. The necessary sheets are all in the text in the area where that particular phase of drafting is explained; usually they are not far from the sheet the student is working on.

Typical Sections and Plan Views

Refer to Project 54001–3402 and compare the first typical section on Sheet 5 (Fig. 10-6) with the plan view on Sheet 17 (Fig. 10-10). In both views there are two limited access/right-of-way fences, two 24-ft [7.3-m] roadways and a 64-ft [19.5-m] median.

Typical Sections and Profile Views

Now compare the same typical section with the profile view on Sheet 17 (Fig. 10-10). The profile grade line shows the elevations of the profile grade point (in the typical section). To see how this works, closely study Fig. 10-11.

Figure 10-9
Fill slope for different heights. Fill slopes fall moving outward from the centerline of survey. They are *front slopes.*

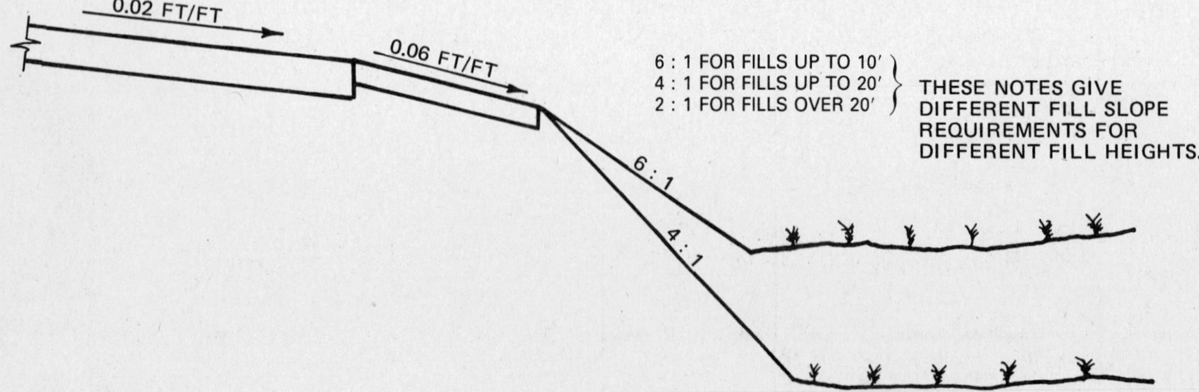

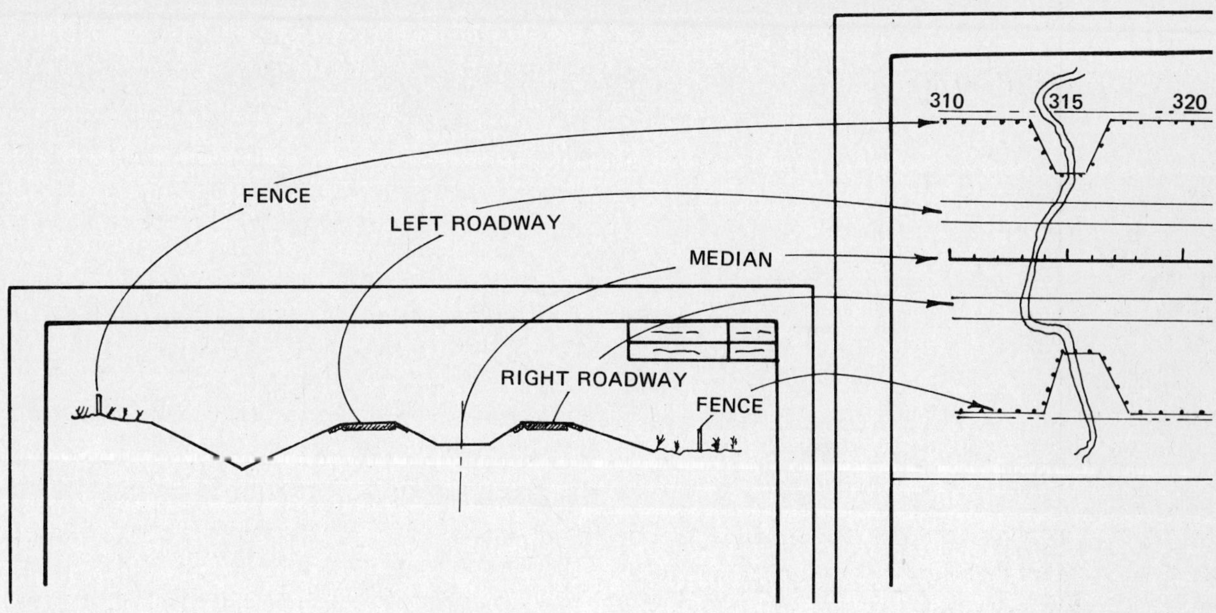

Figure 10-10
Compare the plan view to the typical section.

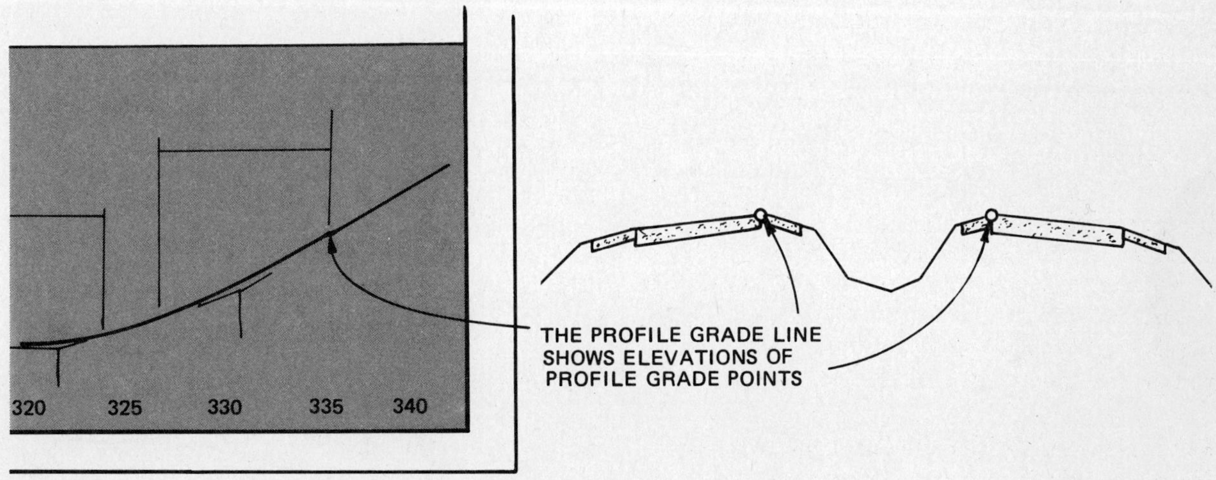

Figure 10-11
The profile grade line and profile grade points in the template.

Figure 10-12
Quiz. Name the slopes on this typical section.

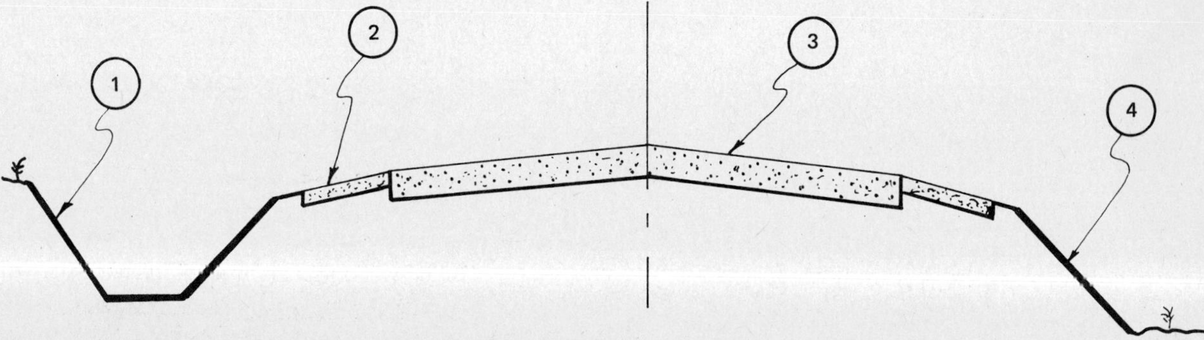

QUIZ

Name the marked and numbered slopes shown in Fig. 10-12.

(1) black slope

(2) outside shoulder

(3) surfacing

(4) front or fill slope

The profile grade point is represented on three types of sheets. Name them.

(5)

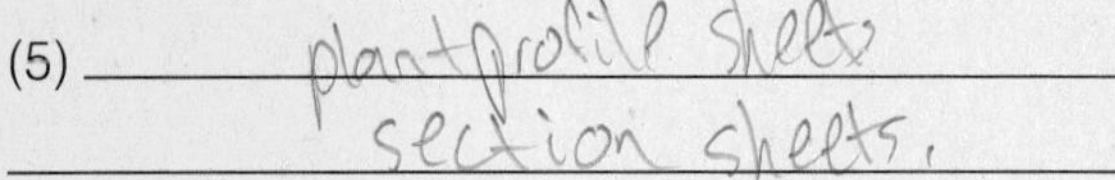

ROADWAY CROSS SECTIONS

Roadway cross sections show typical sections (see Fig. 10-13*a*) superimposed on cross sections of the natural ground (see Fig. 10-13*b*). An example of a roadway cross section is shown in Fig. 10-14.

Now turn to Fig. 10-15, which is also part of Project 54001–3402. This sheet, a roadway cross-section sheet, shows roadway cross sections at these stations: 120 + 00, 121 + 00, and 122 + 00. The cross section at the bottom of the sheet is taken at Sta. 120 + 00. Reading upwards, the next cross section is taken at Sta. 121 + 00, and the last one is taken at Sta. 122 + 00. Roadway cross sections are read from *bottom to top,* reading *up* while going *ahead* on the highway. Examine Fig. 10-16.

REMEMBER On all cross sections, the left side of the section is the *left* side of the highway, and the *right* side of the section is the *right* side of the highway, as if the reader were standing on the centerline looking *ahead* (*up* the sheet).

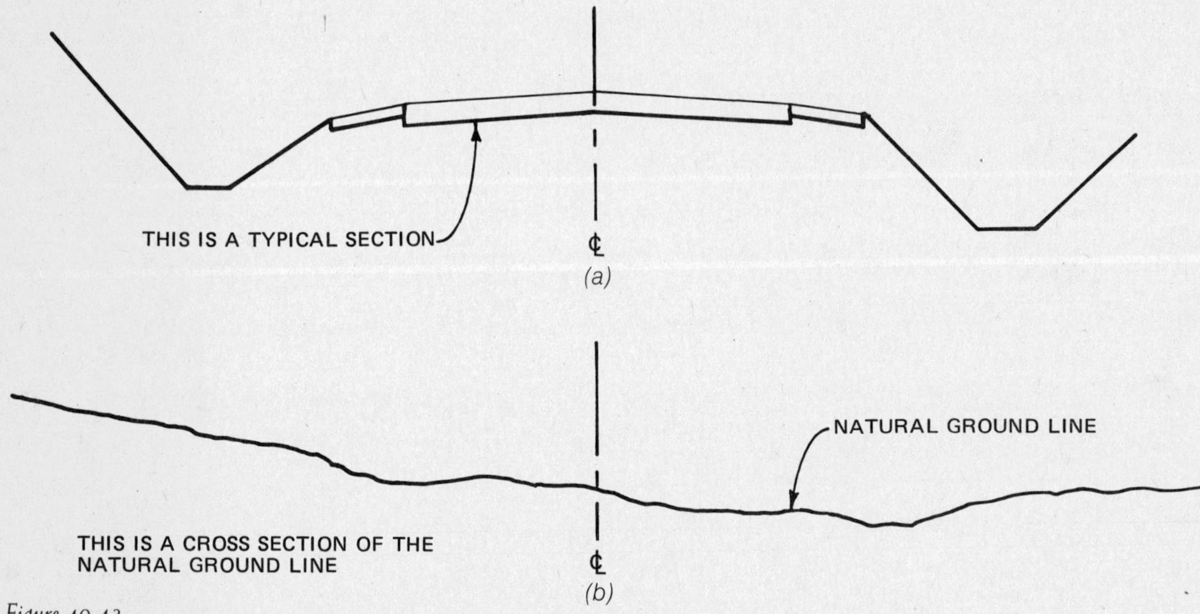

Figure 10-13
(*a*) Roadway cross section and (*b*) a natural ground line cross section.

Figure 10-14
A typical section superimposed on the existing ground line.

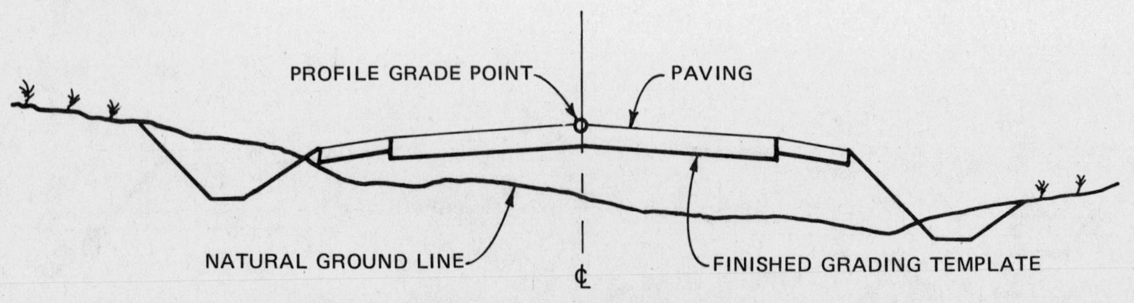

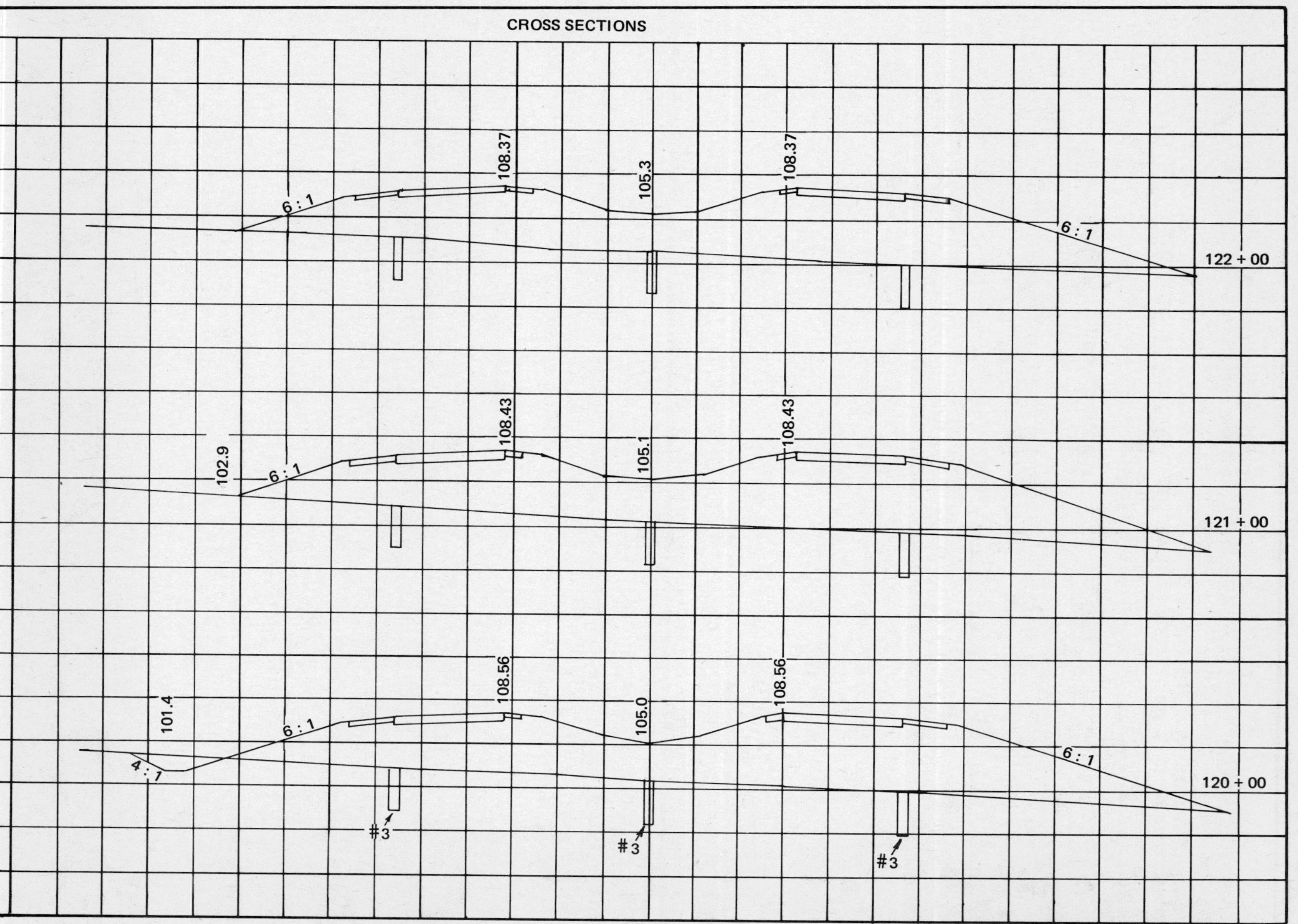

Figure 10-15
Roadway cross-section sheet.

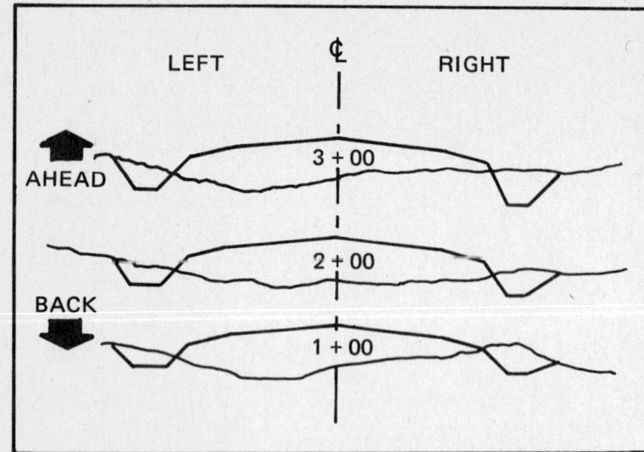

Figure 10-16
The method of reading roadway cross-section sheets.

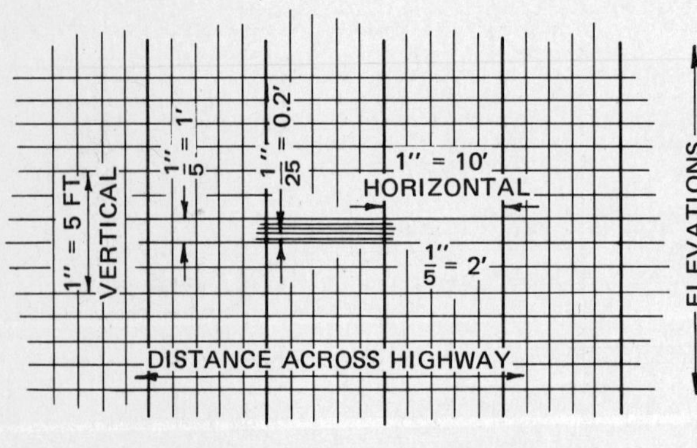

Figure 10-17
Close-up of a roadway cross-section sheet.

Figure 10-18
Study of a roadway cross section.

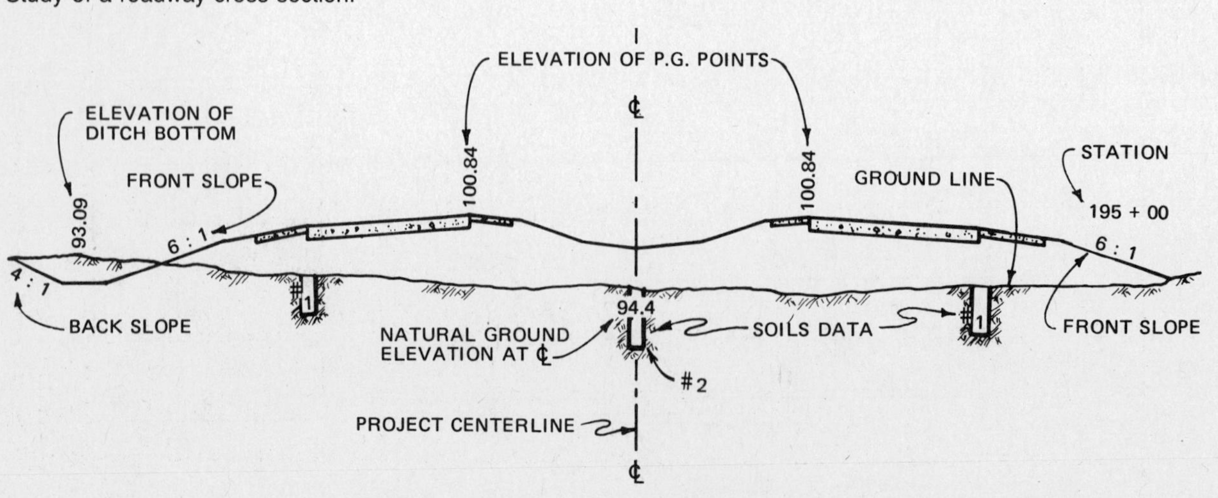

Before going on to the following quiz, the student should be familiar with all the terms and features of roadway cross sections shown in Figs. 10-17, 10-18, and 10-19.

QUIZ

See Fig. 10-20 and fill in the station numbers:

Cross Section	Station Number
A	______
B	______
C	______
D	______

Figure 10-21 shows a small part of a roadway cross section with scales, an elevation, and six points marked on it. The first two points are examples.

Point 1 is at an elevation of 40.00 ft and is located on the centerline.

Point 2 is at an elevation of 41.00 ft and is 6 ft right of the centerline.

1. Point 3 is at an elevation of __41__ and is __6__ ft __left__ of centerline.
2. Point 4 is at an elevation of __39__ and is __4__ ft __left__ of centerline.
3. Point 5 is at an elevation of __43__ and is __4__ ft __right__ of centerline.
4. Point 6 is at an elevation of __38.5__ and is __4__ ft __right__ of centerline.
5. Point 5 is __4__ ft __ahead__ point 6.
6. The horizontal distance between point 2 and point 3 is __12__ ft.

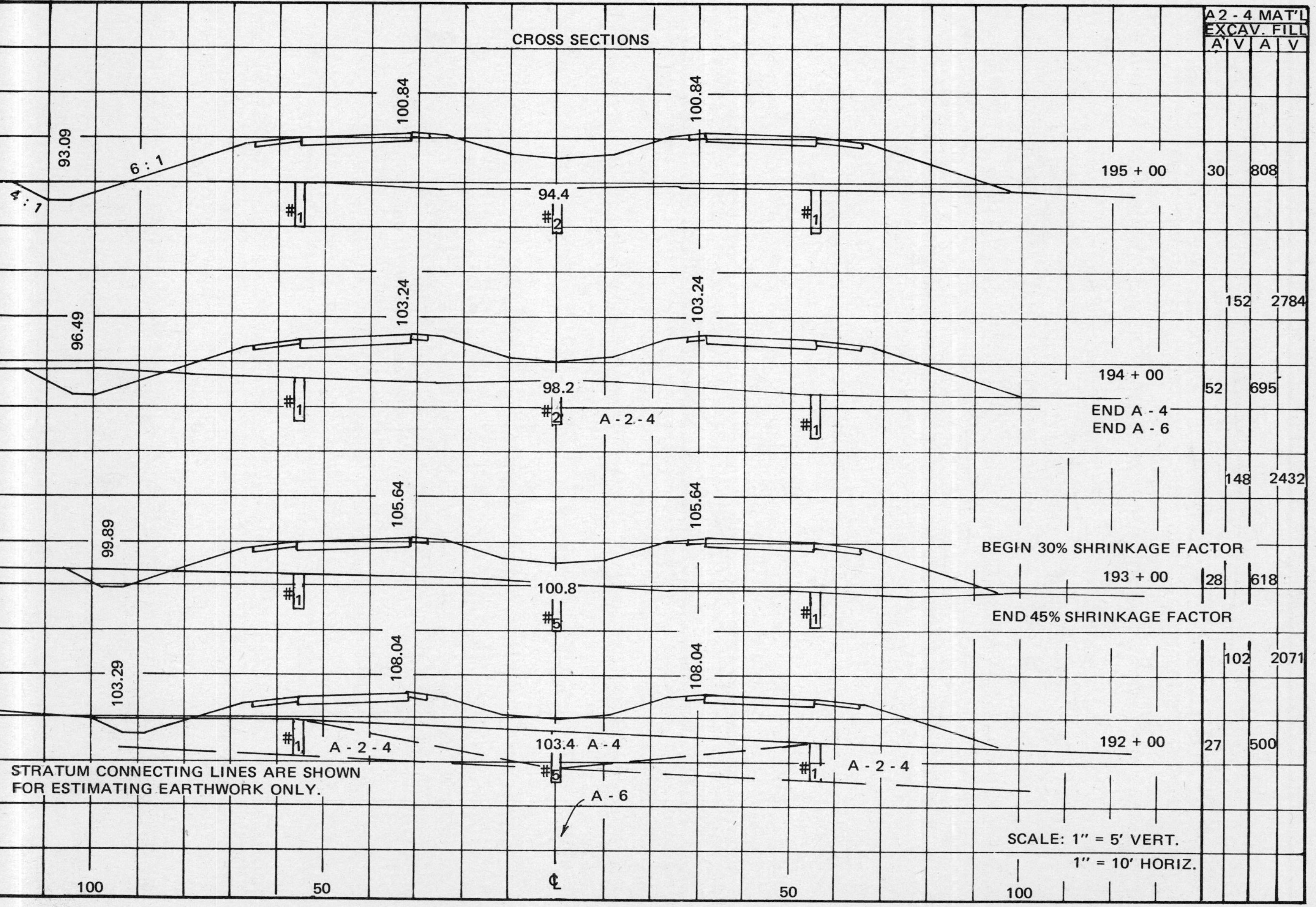

Figure 10-19
Sheet of roadway cross sections for study with Figure 10-20.

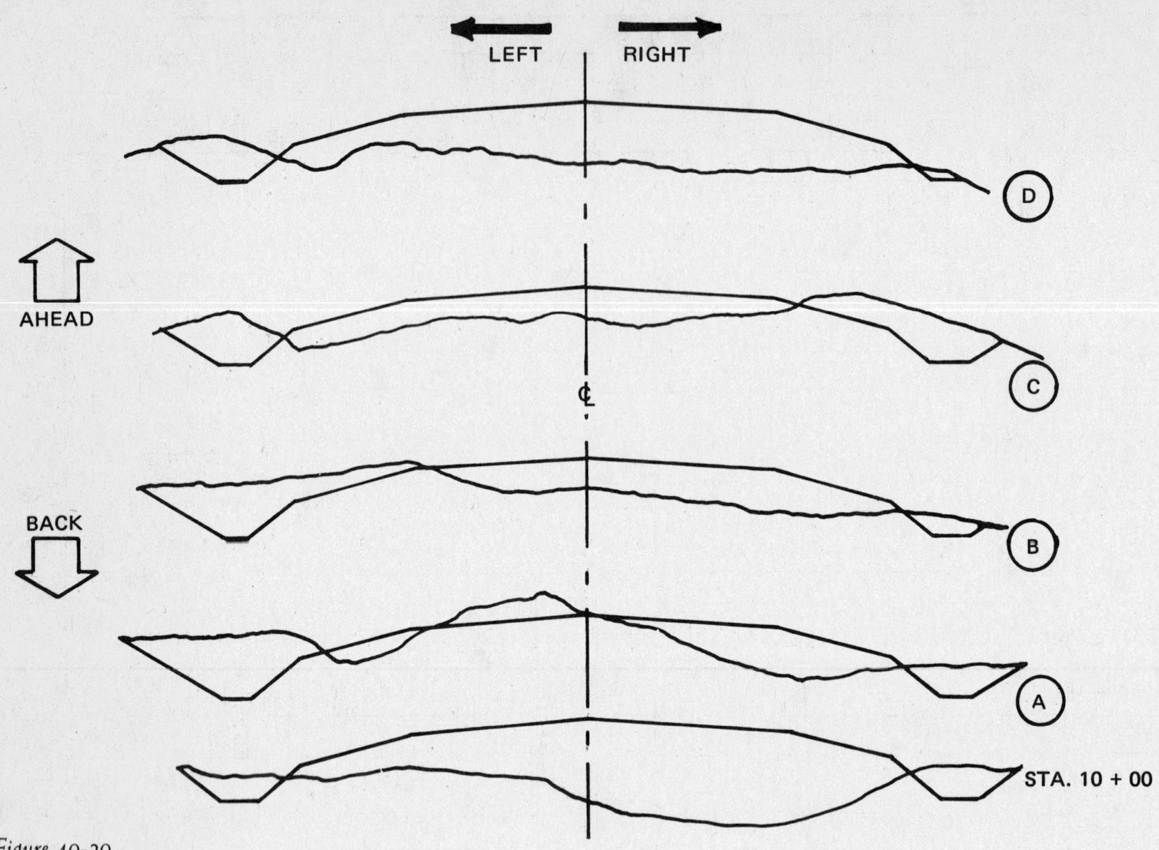

Figure 10-20
Quiz on station numbers.

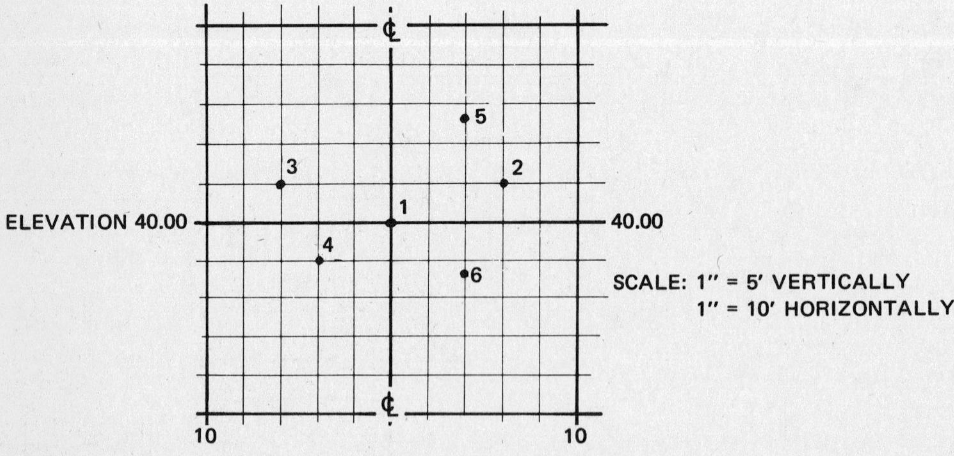

Figure 10-21
Quiz on roadway cross-section sheet.

Answer these questions about the typical section of S.R. 59 on Project 54001–3402, Fig. 10-7.

7. What is the width of the median? 30'
8. What is the standard width of the outside ditch? __________
9. What is the shoulder slope rate? .06%
10. Each shoulder is 10 ft wide.
11. For fills under 10 ft [3.0 m] high, the fill slope ratio is 6:1.
12. For fills over 20 ft [6.1 m] high, the fill slope ratio is 2:1.

13. What type of curb will be constructed on the inside edge of pavement? E

curb+gutter

TRAFFIC DEFINITIONS

Abbreviations that may be confusing are often found on typical sections. The following series of traffic definitions will make these abbreviations clear. They apply to traffic discussions and to typical sections.

ADT: current average daily two-way volume of traffic, with the year specified.

ADT: future average daily two-way volume, with the year specified. The student should note that on most typical sections a current ADT is given and then a second and sometimes a third ADT is given for the future (projected) average daily traffic. Roads stay in place a long time and the engineer must design the roads for the traffic expected in the future. Usually the projected ADT is at least ten years in the future.

DHV: future design hourly volume, the 30th highest hour; two-way unless specified otherwise.

K: the ratio of DHV to ADT, generally ranging between 12 and 18 percent, representing two-way traffic.

D: directional distribution of DHV, one-way volume in predominant direction of travel expressed as percentage of total; *D* varies from 50 to about 80 percent of two-way DHV.

T: percentage of trucks, exclusive of light delivery, expressed as a percentage of DHV. On main rural highways, T might average 5 to 12 percent of DHV during the design hour.

Calculating the Design Hourly Volume (DHV)

When designing interchanges and major intersections, it is advantageous to know the design year DHV for one direction. This value is determined from the projected factors for ADT, *K*, and *T* using the following formula:

$$\text{DHV (one way)} = \text{ADT} \times K \times D$$

Example ADT (1989) = 24,000, K = 12%, D = 60%, T = 7%

$$\text{DHV} = 24{,}000 \times 0.12 \times 0.60 = 1728 \text{ vehicles}$$

When determining the DHV for design, the value obtained from the preceding formula is usually increased to reflect the percentage of trucks (*T*). The overall effect of one truck on traffic operations is often equivalent to that of several passenger vehicles. One truck can be considered to be equivalent to two to four passenger vehicles, depending upon the *K* and *T* factors and terrain.

Example If DHV = 1728 vehicles (1607 passenger cars and 121 trucks), the DHV is adjusted by considering one truck equivalent to two passenger cars:

Adjusted DHV = 1849 vehicles (1607 passenger cars and 242 equivalent vehicles)

The adjusted DHV value can also be determined from the following formula:

$$\begin{aligned}\text{Adjusted DHV} &= \text{DHV} \times 1 + [T \times (\text{equivalent cars} - 1)] \\ &= 1728 \times 1.07 = 1849 \text{ vehicles}\end{aligned}$$

GENERAL DESIGN ELEMENTS FOR A TYPICAL ROAD SECTION

Many of the mathematical aspects of road design are now done by computer (see Fig. 10-22 and 10-23), but the computer requires specific information from the design engineer. Many of the elements that the design engineer must consider are features of typical sections. The following paragraphs will give the drafter some of the details of the design elements that may occur on typical roadway sections.

Figure 10-22
Technician operating the CRT (cathode ray tube). This machine edits math problems before putting them into the computer *(Florida Department of Transportation)*.

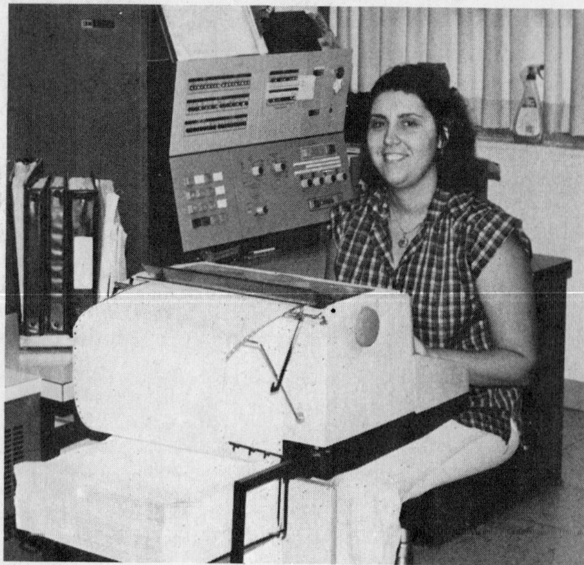

Figure 10-23
Technician running the large computer which does math problems on road design for an entire district *(Florida Department of Transportation).*

Pavement Cross Slope on Straight Road

Rates of cross slope should be as low as possible consistent with the expected accuracy of construction, structural stability, and adequate drainage.

One-fourth inch per foot is a common pavement slope. Where there is more than one lane, each lane may have a different slope. For example, on a three-lane roadway, the lane nearest the central median might have a slope of ¼ in/ft [21 mm/m] across its 12-ft [3.6-m] width. The center lane might have a slope of ⅜ in/ft [31 mm/m] across its width, then the outside lane might have a slope of ½ in/ft [42 mm/m] out to the shoulder or gutter.

Traffic Lane Widths

These lane widths for through traffic are standard:

Interstate and other divided highways—12 ft
Two lane highways and city streets—11 to 12 ft
Low volume highways—10 to 11 ft

Shoulders

Usable shoulders of appropriate width should be provided on all highways where the construction cost is not prohibitive. The shoulder cross-slope rate generally should be ¾ in/ft [62 mm/m]. The shoulders should be of sufficient stability to provide a haven for disabled vehicles in all kinds of weather and should contrast in color and texture with traffic lanes.

In general, usable shoulders with a minimum width of 10 ft [3.0 m] are desirable for all types of highways; however, narrower widths may be indicated for low volume highways or if dictated by economic considerations. DHV should also be considered when selecting shoulder widths, as shown by the following guide.

Minimum Usable Shoulder Widths (Two-Lane Rural)

DHV	Shoulder Width, ft [m]
Less than 100	6—8 [1.8—2.4]
100–400	8—10 [2.4—3.0]
Over 400	10—12 [3.0—3.7]

The width given is to the intersection of the side slope and the shoulder slope.

Median Shoulders. On four-lane divided highways having wide medians and side slopes of 4:1 or flatter, the recommended usable width for a median shoulder is 8 ft [2.4 m]. Where side slopes are greater than 4:1 and a guardrail is to be used, the recommended median shoulder width is 10 ft [3.0 m]. This design will provide continuity of usable shoulder width.

On divided highways having three or more lanes in each direction, a driver in the lane nearest the median may have difficulty maneuvering to the right-hand shoulder. Consequently, a full-width median shoulder of 8 to 10 ft [2.4 to 3.0 m] is desirable for multilane highways having six lanes or more.

When the pavements of a divided highway are at different levels, the left shoulder assumes greater importance, because drivers have a sense of insecurity where a narrow shoulder is coupled with a downward side slope. The recommended usable left shoulder is 8 ft [2.4 m] for 4:1 or flatter slopes and 10 ft [3.0 m] for slopes steeper than 4:1.

Roadway Side Slopes and Ditches

In general, side slopes should conform with these rates:

Fill Height, ft [m]	Rate of Slope
0–10 [0–3.0]	6:1
10–16 [3.0–4.9]	4:1
over 16 [4.9]	2:1 with shoulder curb

Ditch back slopes should be 4:1 if the right-of-way width permits.

Guardrail

Guardrails should be constructed on all high fills, regardless of whether a curb and gutter are to be constructed. Guardrail protection is also provided at roadside obstructions and hazards such as endwalls, deep canals, signs, light posts, bridge approaches, and so forth. On divided highways, median guardrails are installed at bridge approaches and other hazardous locations.

Guardrail details are found in standard drawings. The installation diagrams are minimum requirements and the designer is responsible for determining if more guardrail should be used to insure adequate safety.

Curbs

Curbs are provided generally for five purposes.

Curb and Gutter. The construction, shown in Fig. 10-24, consists of a combination curb and waterway. It is indicated for construction on municipal projects at the outer edge of the pavement and, in the case of superelevated divided highway projects, on the inside edge of the outer roadway. When it is placed at the edge of a traffic lane, the face of the curb should be offset 1.5 ft [46 cm] from the lane line.

Mountable Curb. This is a low, easily mounted curb used only to outline channeling islands at intersections. It should not be used adjacent to other types of curbs.

Median Curb. This is a barrier type of curb, provided to outline raised medians and used in conjunction with traffic lanes. The face of the curb should be offset 1.5 ft [46 cm].

Barrier Curb. This construction is used only for protection at bridge piers or other structures that may be subject to impact by a vehicle out of control.

Shoulder Gutter. This is a shallow gutter section constructed at the shoulder line on high roadway fills. It is designed to channel the runoff from the roadway pavement. Drainage inlets are constructed in conjunction with this gutter.

Sidewalks

Sidewalks are built in conjunction with highway construction at locations of community development such as schools, businesses, industrial plants, and so forth, where the need is apparent. When sidewalks are built along a rural highway, they should be well removed from the traveled way.

Justification for the construction of sidewalks depends upon the vehicle-pedestrian hazard, which is governed chiefly by the volume of pedestrian and vehicular traffic,

Figure 10-24
Standard Curbs and gutters.

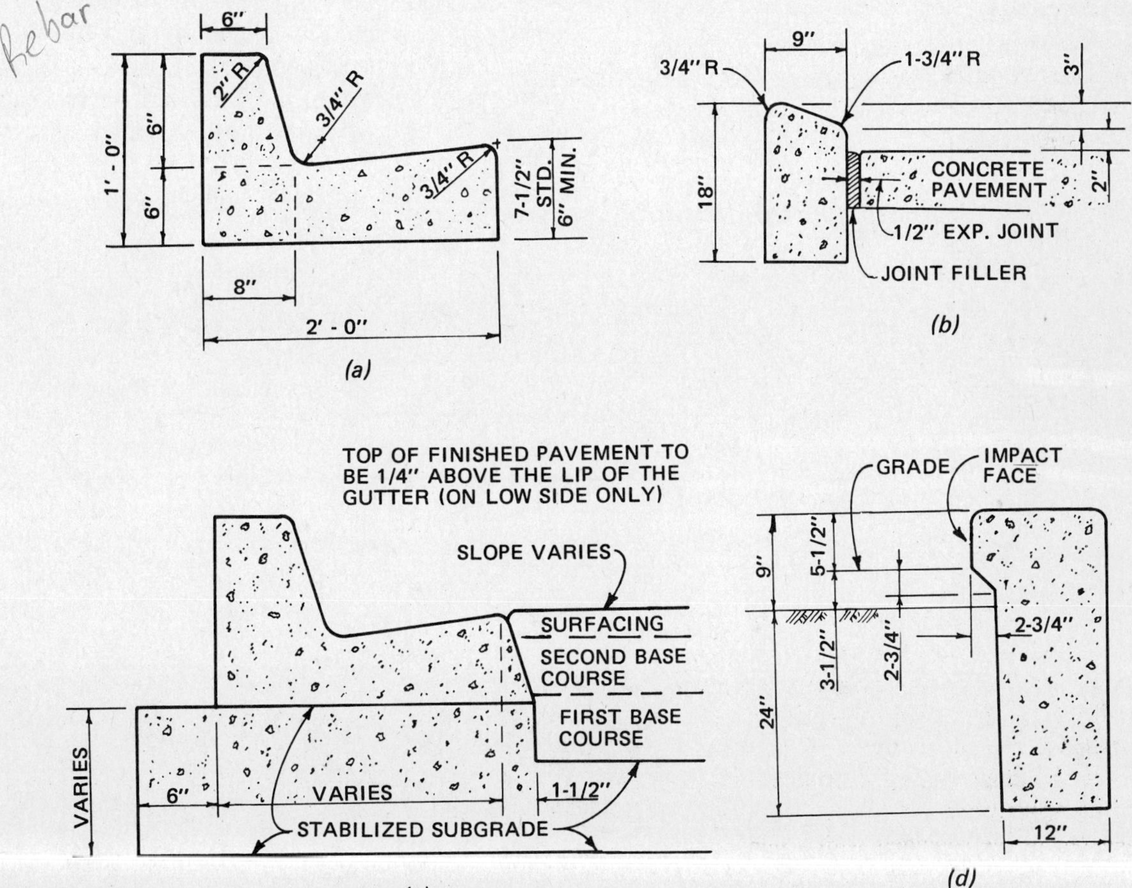

their relative timing, and the speed of vehicular traffic. Sidewalks may be required on one or both sides of the highway. Pedestrian traffic volume warrants for sidewalks along highways are not established. The designer should study the conditions which can be expected at locations of community development and determine if sidewalk construction is justified.

Medians

Medians should be as wide as practical depending on the availability of right-of-way and the balance with other elements of the section. Median width transitions should be obtained by the use of flowing curved alignment; forced alignment should be avoided.

The median shoulder slope on tangent sections is ⅝ in/ft [52 mm/m], and the median ditch slope is preferably 6:1 and not steeper than 4:1.

Median curbs should be provided for all medians which are not of sufficient width to allow an adequate drainage ditch within the median. Curbs should be offset 1.5 ft [46 cm] from the through-traffic lane. The minimum horizontal clearance on the left side must be maintained in medians where guardrails or bridge piers are constructed.

Medians are provided on all multilane highways except in cases where right-of-way costs would absolutely prohibit their construction, in which case every effort should be made to obtain the necessary right-of-way adjacent to intersections for the construction of left-turn lanes. Medians should contrast in color and texture with the through traffic lanes.

A HINT FOR THE EXERCISES

An easy way to make one line parallel to another is to use two sliding triangles to reproduce a second line parallel to the first. Put one triangle on the line in the typical section that is to be paralleled. Slip the other triangle up against the side of the first. Now hold the triangle on the typical section line tightly against the paper and slide the second triangle up or down as needed. The line drawn along the sliding triangle will be parallel to the original line in the typical section.

All the slope lines in typical sections are easily reproduced like this. After the first typical section has been traced, project lines vertically downward from all the stopping points; then use the triangles to produce the parallel lines for the required slopes.

EXERCISES

Exercise 10-1. A Rural Typical Section

Remove Exercise 10-1 from the book and center it under a B-size sheet of vellum. Trace the typical section for State Road 510 and all the notes which accompany it.

Note the following:

Design speed is 45 miles per hour (mph) [72 km/h], indicating that this probably is no superhighway. In addition, the ADT (average daily traffic) is only 1080 cars (Some municipal intersections have 45,000 cars per day), so this is probably a rural road.

The *K* factor is lower than the 12 to 18 percent typical for two-way traffic.

The *D* factor, or directional distribution of design hourly volume, is 58 percent, which fits the proper 50 to 80 percent range.

The *T* factor is large. Twelve percent is a high truck factor, which again indicates a country road.

Notice how the *T* factor influences the lane width. Trucks need more lane width than passenger cars. On this country road the lane width could easily have been 10 to 11 ft [3.0 to 3.4 m] because of the low volume of traffic, but since the road gets a lot of truck use the lane width is 12 ft [3.7 m] and the shoulder is a generous 10 ft [3.0 m].

These are the factors that influence the designer in developing typical road sections.

To complete this exercise the student should reproduce a similar typical section, with all notes, below the traced typical section. This will give the student a little practice doing a rural (high truck count) typical section.

EXERCISE 10-2. TYPICAL SECTION FOR WIDENING A ROAD

Remove Exercise 10-2 from the text and center it under a B-size sheet of vellum. Trace the entire typical section with all notes. Reproduce, without tracing, an identical typical section under the traced one. Use the centerline that appears on the exercise to center the typical section.

NOTICE This typical section is designed to widen the lanes from 12 ft [3.7 m] to 17 ft [5.2 m]. Instead of using a 12-in [30-cm] deep stabilizing bed of limerock mixture, called subgrade, a 6-in [15-cm] thick asphaltic concrete is used under the additional 5 ft [1.5 m] of extra width. Also, the shoulder and slope are machine-dressed where they meet natural ground.

Complete both typical sections and check them for accuracy.

B size

EXERCISE 10-3. TYPICAL SECTION OF A TWO-LANE ROAD

Remove Exercise 10-3 from the text and place it beneath a B-size sheet of vellum. Trace the typical section and draw a similar one, without tracing, below it. Use the centerline already on the sheet to locate the grade point and the center of the new typical section.

EXERCISE 10-4. A TYPICAL SECTION WITH CURBS, GUTTERS, AND SIDEWALK

We need to learn a lot about typical road sections, and this one includes a curb, gutter, and sidewalk. Remove Exercise 10-4 from the text and center it under a B-size sheet of vellum. Trace everything shown on this typical section and then reproduce it in the area below the first traced section.

NOTICE The driving lanes are only 11 ft [3.4 m] wide—this project is a little short on either right-of-way or money. The extra 1 ft [0.3 m] multiplied by five lanes would mean the road would be 5 ft [1.5 m] wider. An extra 5 ft [1.5 m] of limerock base, stabilizing operations to make the subgrade, and all the extra asphalt surface course would increase the costs of construction very greatly.

Notice that the lanes closest to the median almost always have a slope away from the median at ¼ in downward vertically for every 1 ft outward horizontally [21 mm/m]. The next lane slopes at ⅜ in/ft [31 mm/m], and then the last lane slopes ½ in downward vertically for 1 ft horizontally [42 mm/m]. These are very standard slopes.

There are concrete curbs and gutters similar to those in Fig. 10-24 on both the left and right sides of the road, with a concrete sidewalk on the left side of the road adjoining the curb.

The median strip is 15 ft [4.6 m] wide edge-of-gutter to edge-of-gutter, and it is sodded between the curbing.

EXERCISE 10-5. RESURFACING A ROAD

This is a very simple typical section. It is, however, all that is needed to do this particular job.

Here the designer is faced with an existing road 20 ft [6.1 m] wide, which will not be widened at all. The road will just be resurfaced with new asphaltic concrete surface at 175 lb/yd^2 [94.9 kg/m^2]. This will, of course, make the new road several inches higher. Notice that the 5-ft [1.5-m] shoulders are also higher, since they slope continuously down from the road surface. The construction workers will use rollers on the road and then machine dress the 5-ft [1.5-m] shoulders. The rest of the slope will be machined out to end up at the 60-ft [18.3-m] right-of-way.

Remove Exercise 10-5 from the book and center it under a B-size sheet of vellum. Trace the typical section in the top half of the sheet and reproduce another similar typical section (without tracing) on the bottom half.

EXERCISE 10-6. A COMMON TYPICAL SECTION

Remove Exercise 10-6 from the book and center it under a B-size sheet of vellum. Trace all of this typical section on the top half of the B sheet; then reproduce a similar typical section on the bottom half of the sheet, without tracing.

NOTE This is a much-used section set up by the state for the designer. Note that "00" is used to denote a spot the designer must fill with his figures:

00 R/W, K = 00%, D = 00%, T = 00%, and so forth.

This time the roadways are 24 ft [7.3 m] wide; there are two 12-ft [3.7-m] lanes with just one standard elevation drop—¼ in for every 1 ft horizontally [21 mm/m]. Estimate the design speed, R/W, K, D, and T factors and put them in the typical section. (Refer back to the chapter for definitions of these items.)

EXERCISE 10-7. A CITY TYPICAL SECTION

This is a city typical section with a 5-ft [1.5-m] sidewalk on both sides of the roadway. It also has a curb and gutter on both sides and an 8-ft [2.4-m] parking lane on both sides.

Remove Exercise 10-7 from the text and center it under a B-size sheet of vellum.

Trace the typical section on the top half of the vellum and make a reproduction of the same typical section on the bottom half of the sheet.

LEARNING ACTIVITY PACKAGE

Read through Chap. 10 carefully and look back in the chapter for guidance when working the drafting problems at the end of the chapter.

Chapter 10 completed ______________ *(date)*.

Reread the list of objectives and make sure they are understood.

Objectives completed ____________ *(date).*

Answer all the questions on the Chap. 10 removable quiz.

Quiz completed ____________ *(date).*

Do all the exercises for this chapter.

Exercise 10-1 completed ____________ *(date).*

Exercise 10-2 completed ____________ *(date).*

Exercise 10-3 completed ____________ *(date).*

Exercise 10-4 completed ____________ *(date).*

Exercise 10-5 completed ____________ *(date).*

Exercise 10-6 completed ____________ *(date).*

Exercise 10-7 completed ____________ *(date).*

10 QUIZ

1. A cross-section view is a view of the ______________ of an object.
2. There are ______________ types of cross sections discussed in this chapter.
3. Elevations of the natural ground, at and on either side of, the centerline are recorded so that a natural ground line can be drawn.

   (T or F) ______________
4. A typical road section is just a ______________ cross section of the road to be built.
5. The finished grading template is the final shape of the roadway before paving materials are placed. (T or F) ______________.
6. How thick is a usual subgrade? ______________.
7. Shoulder cross slopes are less steep than the pavement cross slopes.

   (T or F) ______________
8. The profile grade point is the point plotted on profile views to form the smooth, continuous profile grade line. (T or F) ______________
9. Divided highways do not have medians. (T or F) ______________
10. Is more than one typical section ever used on the same job?

    (*yes* or *no*) ______________
11. A cut section is a section of road that has been excavated.

    (T or F) ______________
12. A detail on the left side of a typical section cannot apply to the right side.

    (T or F) ______________
13. As one reads *up* on a roadway cross section sheet, one goes *back* on the highway. (T or F) ______________
14. One stands on the centerline of a project and looks ahead (up the sheet) to work on cross sections. (T or F) ______________
15. The design engineer bases the use of guardrails on the need for driver safety.

    (T or F) ______________

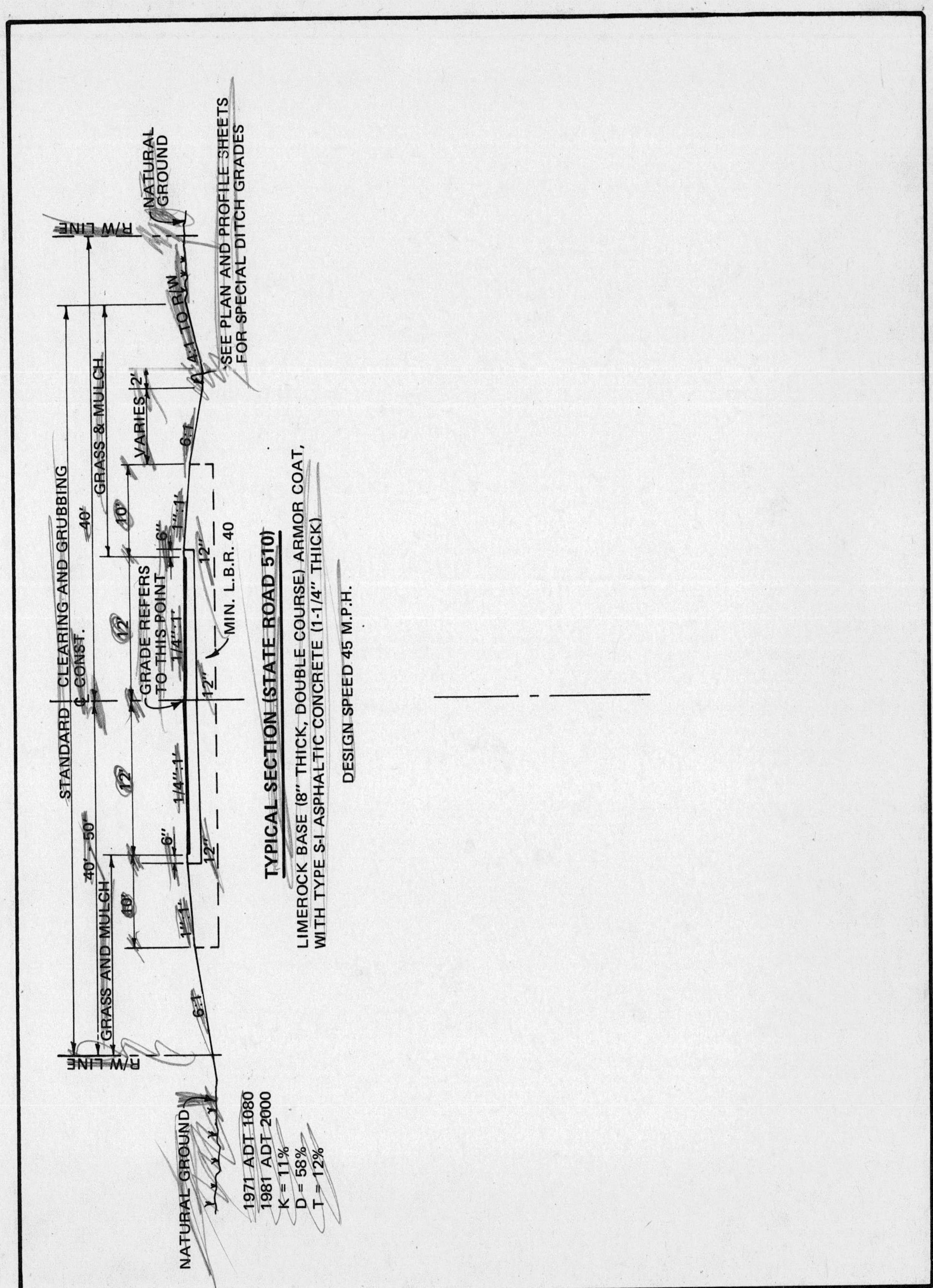
NATURAL GROUND
R/W LINE
GRASS AND MULCH
40' - 50'
STANDARD CLEARING AND GRUBBING
40'
GRASS & MULCH
R/W LINE
NATURAL GROUND
4:1 TO R/W
SEE PLAN AND PROFILE SHEETS FOR SPECIAL DITCH GRADES
VARIES
2'
6:1
10'
12'
12'
10'
6"
6"
1":1'
1/4":1'
1/4":1'
1":1'
℄ CONST.
GRADE REFERS TO THIS POINT
MIN. L.B.R. 40
12"
12"
12"
1971 ADT 1080
1981 ADT 2000
K = 11%
D = 58%
T = 12%
TYPICAL SECTION (STATE ROAD 510)
LIMEROCK BASE (8" THICK, DOUBLE COURSE) ARMOR COAT,
WITH TYPE S-I ASPHALTIC CONCRETE (1-1/4" THICK)
DESIGN SPEED 45 M.P.H.

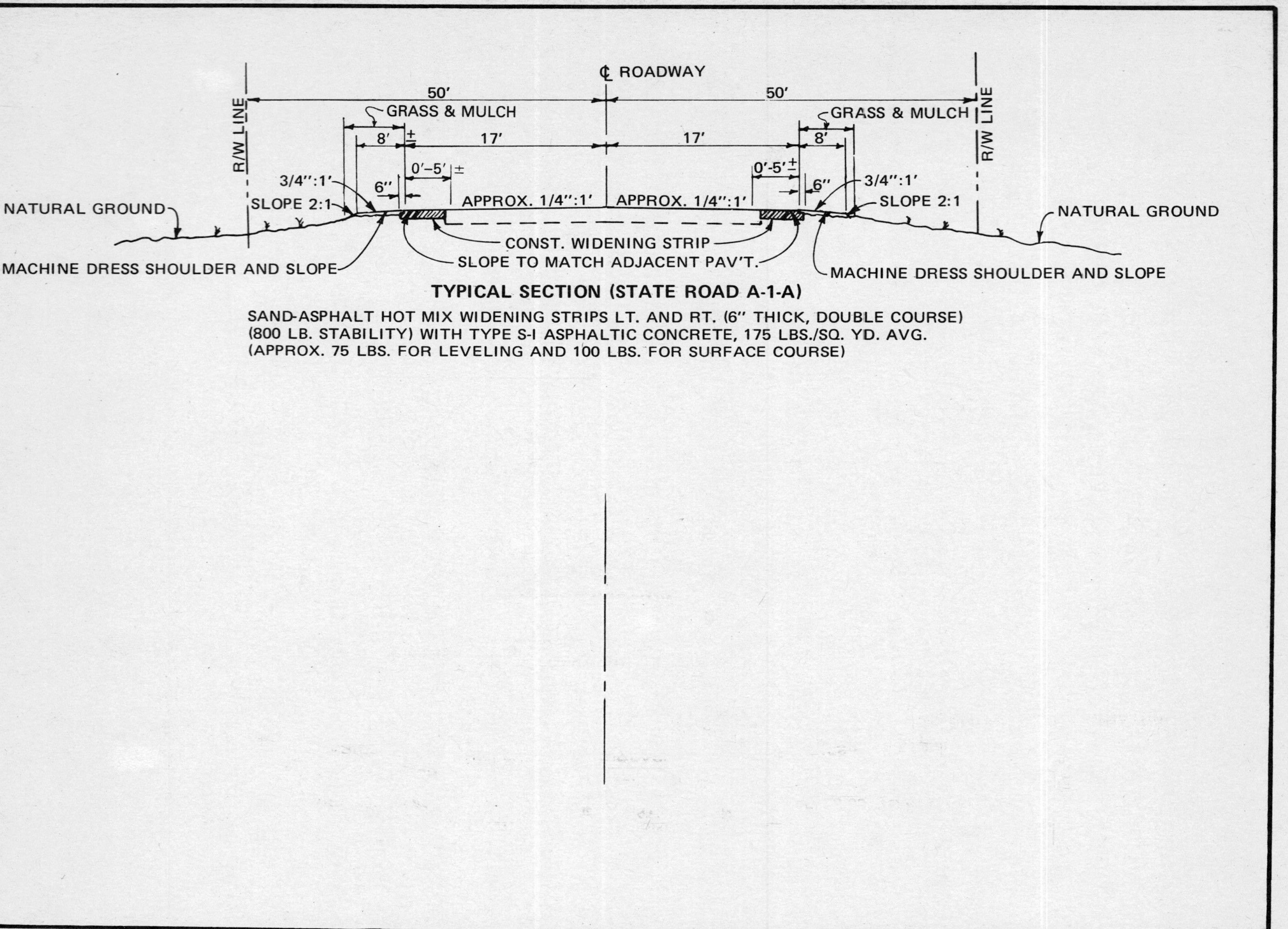
℄ ROADWAY
50'
50'
R/W LINE
GRASS & MULCH
GRASS & MULCH
R/W LINE
8'
17'
17'
8'
0'-5' ±
0'-5' ±
3/4":1'
6"
6"
3/4":1'
NATURAL GROUND
SLOPE 2:1
APPROX. 1/4":1'
APPROX. 1/4":1'
SLOPE 2:1
NATURAL GROUND
CONST. WIDENING STRIP
MACHINE DRESS SHOULDER AND SLOPE
SLOPE TO MATCH ADJACENT PAV'T.
MACHINE DRESS SHOULDER AND SLOPE
TYPICAL SECTION (STATE ROAD A-1-A)
SAND-ASPHALT HOT MIX WIDENING STRIPS LT. AND RT. (6" THICK, DOUBLE COURSE)
(800 LB. STABILITY) WITH TYPE S-I ASPHALTIC CONCRETE, 175 LBS./SQ. YD. AVG.
(APPROX. 75 LBS. FOR LEVELING AND 100 LBS. FOR SURFACE COURSE)

Exercise 10-2

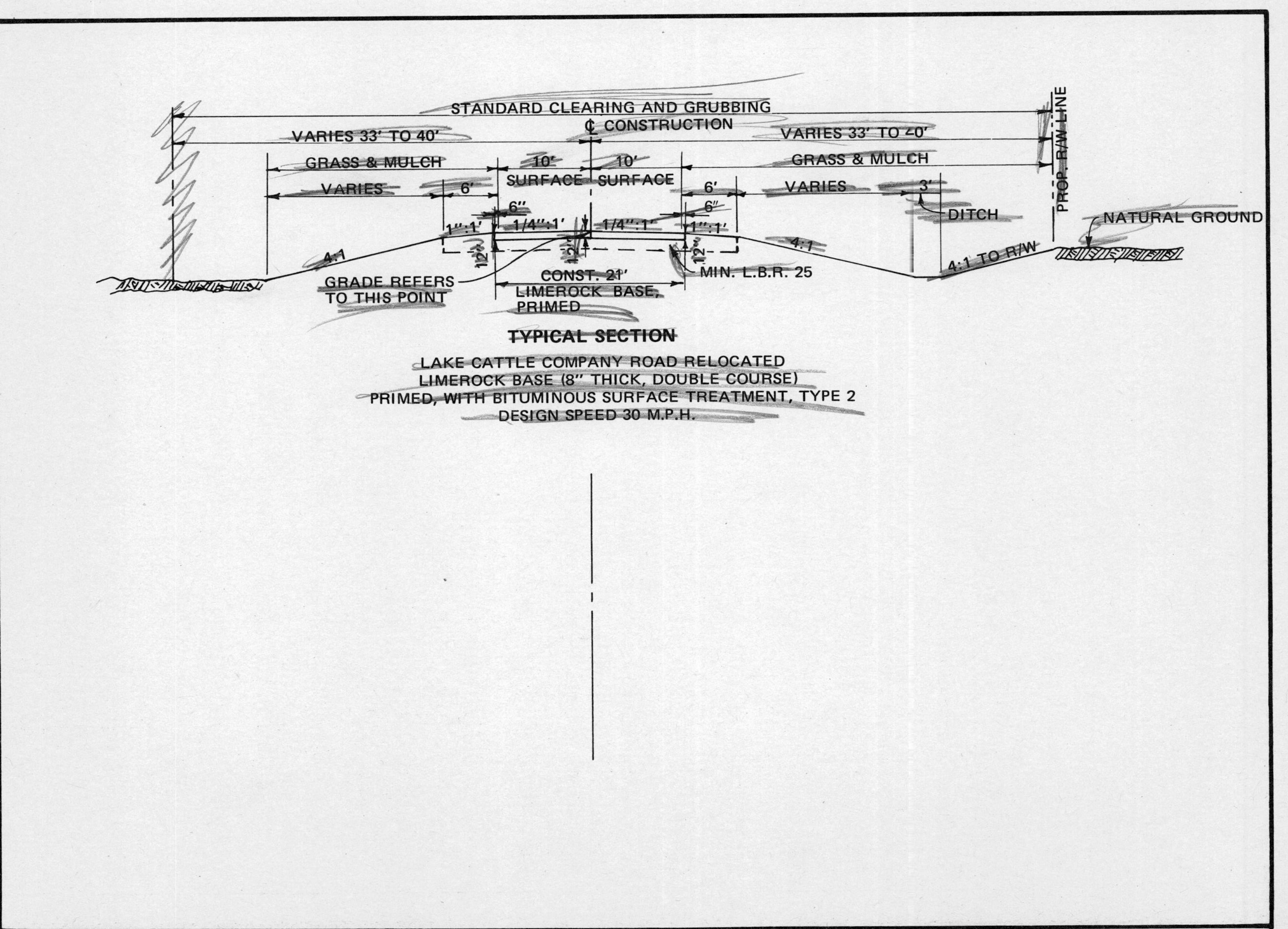

Exercise 10-3

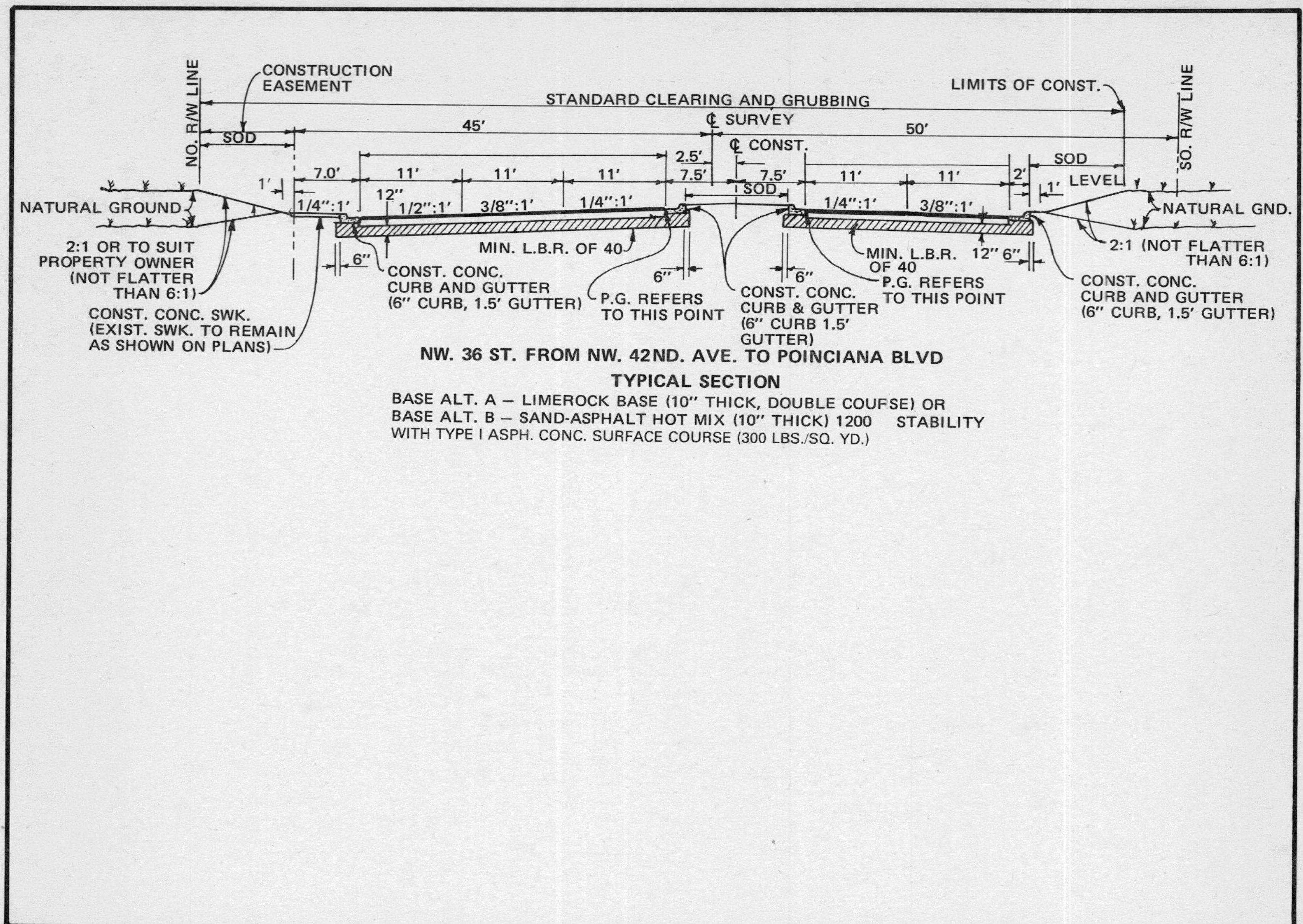
NO. R/W LINE
CONSTRUCTION EASEMENT
STANDARD CLEARING AND GRUBBING
LIMITS OF CONST.
SO. R/W LINE
SOD
45'
℄ SURVEY
50'
℄ CONST.
2.5'
SOD
7.0'
11'
11'
11'
7.5'
7.5'
11'
11'
2'
LEVEL
1'
12"
SOD
1'
NATURAL GROUND
1/4":1'
1/2":1'
3/8":1'
1/4":1'
1/4":1'
3/8":1'
NATURAL GND.
MIN. L.B.R. OF 40
6"
6"
6"
MIN. L.B.R. OF 40
12"
6"
2:1 OR TO SUIT PROPERTY OWNER (NOT FLATTER THAN 6:1)
CONST. CONC. CURB AND GUTTER (6" CURB, 1.5' GUTTER)
P.G. REFERS TO THIS POINT
CONST. CONC. CURB & GUTTER (6" CURB 1.5' GUTTER)
P.G. REFERS TO THIS POINT
2:1 (NOT FLATTER THAN 6:1)
CONST. CONC. CURB AND GUTTER (6" CURB, 1.5' GUTTER)
CONST. CONC. SWK. (EXIST. SWK. TO REMAIN AS SHOWN ON PLANS)
NW. 36 ST. FROM NW. 42ND. AVE. TO POINCIANA BLVD
TYPICAL SECTION
BASE ALT. A – LIMEROCK BASE (10" THICK, DOUBLE COUFSE) OR
BASE ALT. B – SAND-ASPHALT HOT MIX (10" THICK) 1200 STABILITY
WITH TYPE I ASPH. CONC. SURFACE COURSE (300 LBS./SQ. YD.)

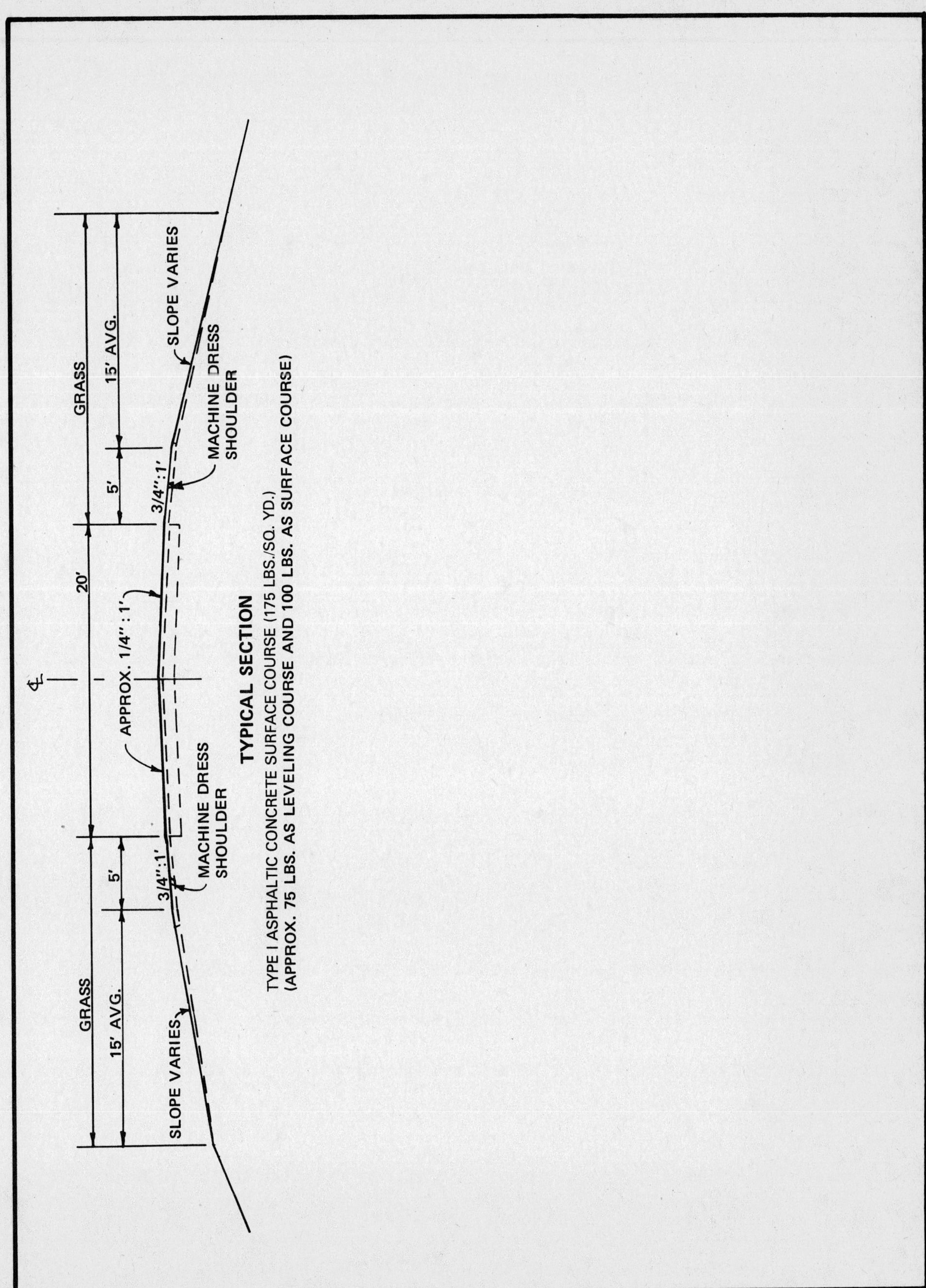

Exercise 10-5

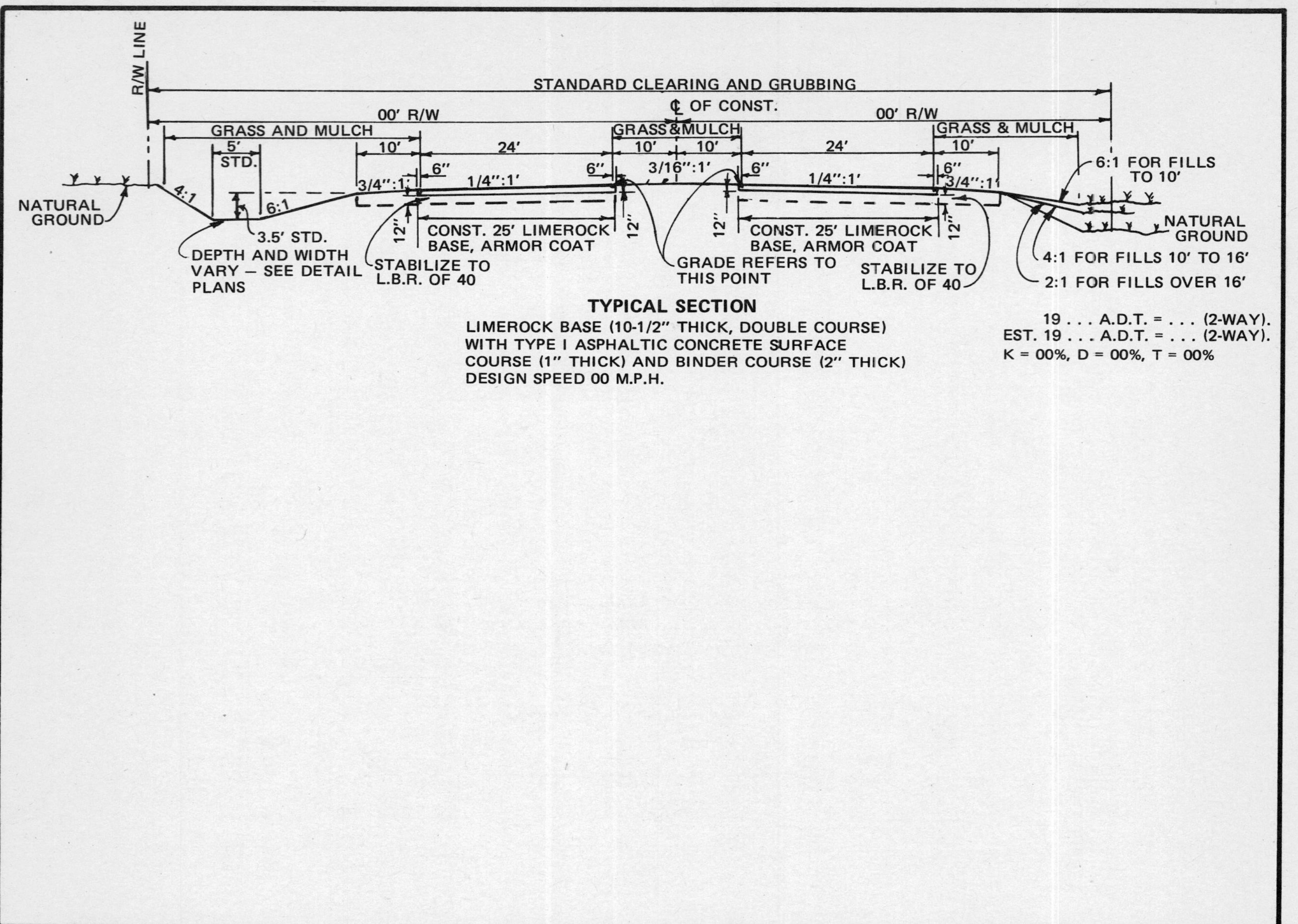

R/W LINE
STANDARD CLEARING AND GRUBBING
℄ OF CONST.
00' R/W
00' R/W
GRASS AND MULCH
GRASS&MULCH
GRASS & MULCH
5'
STD.
10'
24'
10'
10'
24'
10'
6"
6"
6"
6"
3/4":1'
1/4":1'
3/16":1'
1/4":1'
3/4":1'
4:1
6:1
NATURAL GROUND
3.5' STD.
DEPTH AND WIDTH VARY – SEE DETAIL PLANS
12"
12"
12"
12"
CONST. 25' LIMEROCK BASE, ARMOR COAT
STABILIZE TO L.B.R. OF 40
GRADE REFERS TO THIS POINT
CONST. 25' LIMEROCK BASE, ARMOR COAT
STABILIZE TO L.B.R. OF 40
6:1 FOR FILLS TO 10'
NATURAL GROUND
4:1 FOR FILLS 10' TO 16'
2:1 FOR FILLS OVER 16'
TYPICAL SECTION
LIMEROCK BASE (10-1/2" THICK, DOUBLE COURSE)
WITH TYPE I ASPHALTIC CONCRETE SURFACE
COURSE (1" THICK) AND BINDER COURSE (2" THICK)
DESIGN SPEED 00 M.P.H.
19 . . . A.D.T. = . . . (2-WAY).
EST. 19 . . . A.D.T. = . . . (2-WAY).
K = 00%, D = 00%, T = 00%

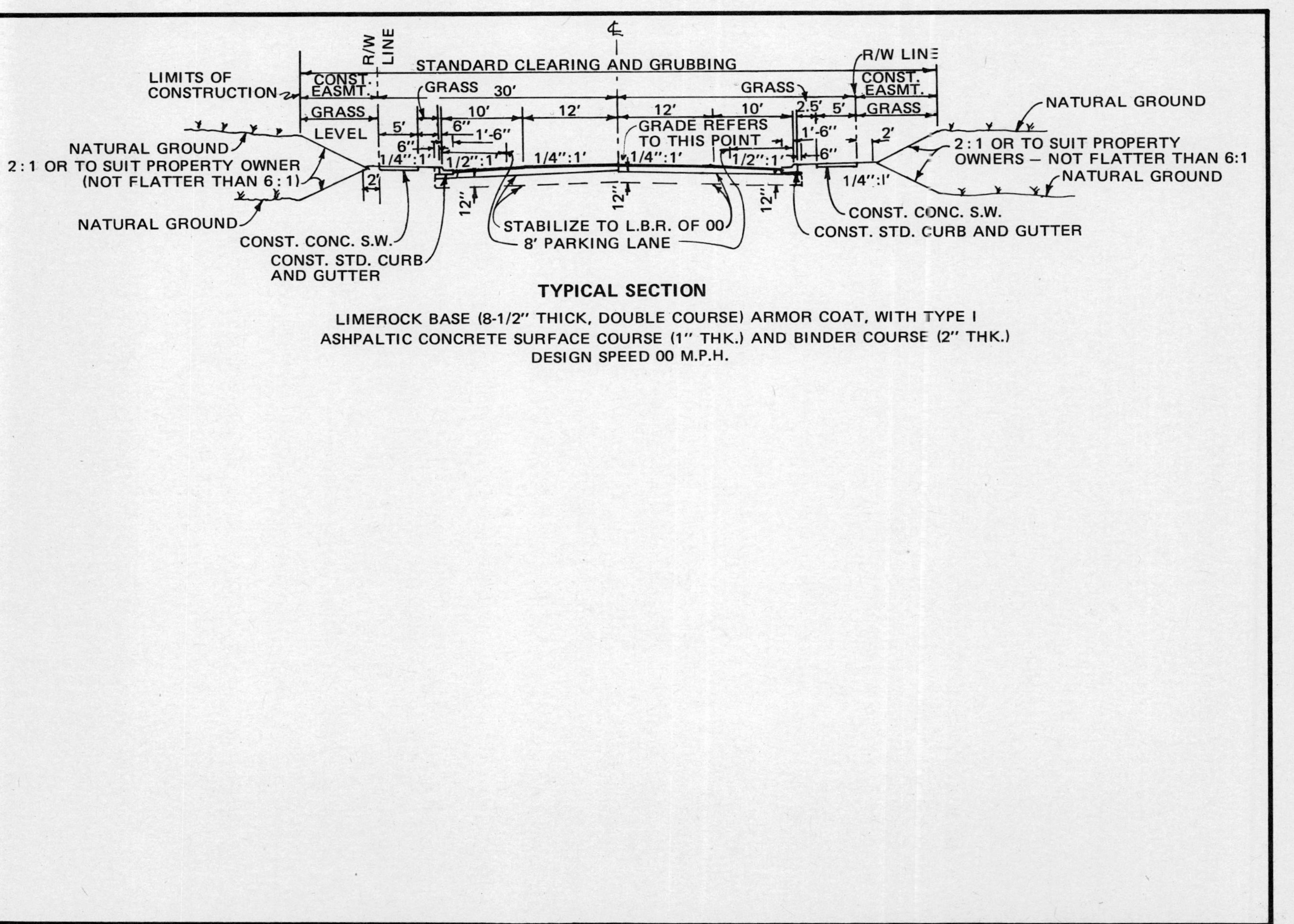

Exercise 10-7

11 SUPER-ELEVATION

Objectives

a. Understand normal crown of a roadway
b. Understand what happens to the roadway surface in a superelevated section of the road
c. Study superelevation transitions
d. Learn to make transition length calculations for superelevation of divided and undivided highways
e. Understand the shoulder construction in a superelevated road section

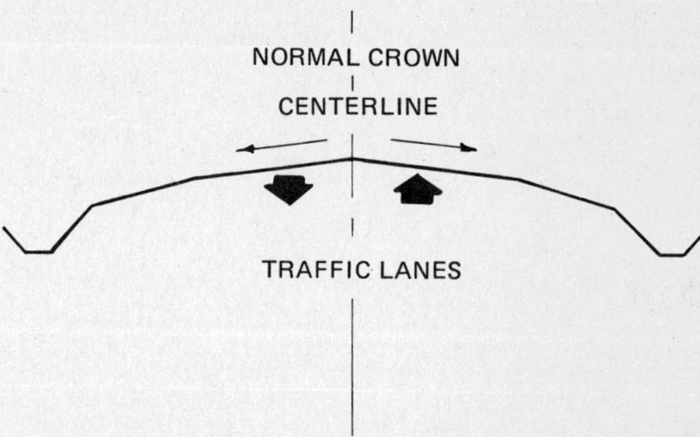

Figure 11-1
Normal crown of a roadway.

Rationale

Superelevation is such an important feature of road design that the student must become familiar with the method of its application. All of us have gone around curves at high speeds and felt the effect of centrifugal force acting upon the vehicle and our own bodies. If the curved part of the road were flat, as it is in a straight stretch, and if the tires were not gripping the road with the most tenacity, the car would slide right off the road. To avoid this, a rise is imposed on one side of the road; this is called superelevation. The superelevation of any road can be calculated from formulas.

Roadways on most horizontal curves are superelevated. If a roadway is superelevated, the edge of the roadway on the outside of the curve is higher than the edge on the inside; thus the roadway surface slopes down from the outside to the inside of the curve.

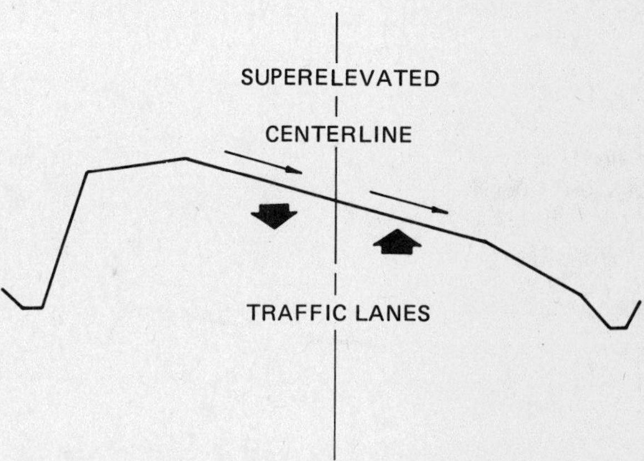

Figure 11-2
Superelevated roadway.

NORMAL CROWN

When a roadway is *not superelevated*, the cross slopes are just like those of any tangent segment of the roadway, and we say the roadway is at *normal crown*. The slope usually falls on each side of the centerline as shown in Fig. 11-1.

SUPERELEVATION OF ROADWAY

When a roadway is *superelevated*, the outside edge is higher than the inside edge. The whole roadway slopes down toward the inside of the curve (this is shown in Fig. 11-2).

Figure 11-3 shows how the outside edge of the roadway is raised—superelevated—in relation to the inside edge. Study Fig. 11-3 carefully to understand how superelevation affects roadways on horizontal curves and to see the difference between right- and left-turning curves.

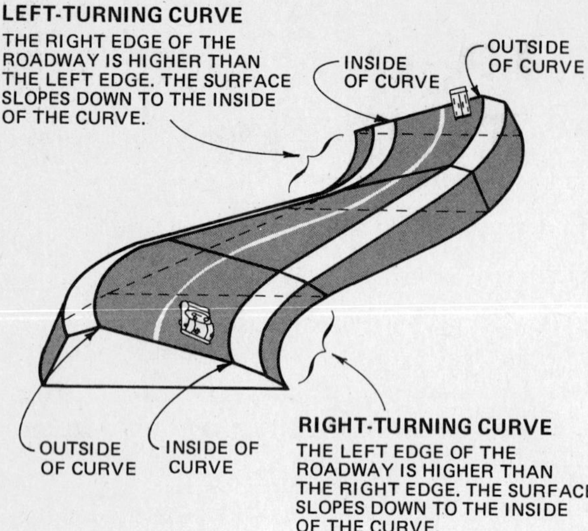
LEFT-TURNING CURVE
THE RIGHT EDGE OF THE ROADWAY IS HIGHER THAN THE LEFT EDGE. THE SURFACE SLOPES DOWN TO THE INSIDE OF THE CURVE.
INSIDE OF CURVE
OUTSIDE OF CURVE
OUTSIDE OF CURVE
INSIDE OF CURVE
RIGHT-TURNING CURVE
THE LEFT EDGE OF THE ROADWAY IS HIGHER THAN THE RIGHT EDGE. THE SURFACE SLOPES DOWN TO THE INSIDE OF THE CURVE.

Figure 11-3
Left- and right-turning curves.

QUIZ

If a horizontal curve on a two-lane road turns to the left, which of the following statements would be true? Circle the correct answer.

1. Only the outside lane slopes down to the right.
2. Both the outside and inside lanes slope down to the left.
3. Only the inside lane slopes down to the left.
4. Both the inside and outside lanes slope down to the right.
5. For Fig. 11-4*a*, label the cross sections as "LEFT TURN" or "RIGHT TURN." For Fig. 11-4*b*, label the cross sections as "SUPERELEVATED" or "NORMAL."

SUPERELEVATION TRANSITIONS

When constructing a horizontal curve in a roadway, the change from normal crown to full superelevation is not made all at once. Instead, there is a gradual transition. Superelevation is built up gradually at the beginning of the curve and then reduced gradually at the end of the curve.

Superelevation of Undivided Highways

Let's see what happens to the cross-section view of a two-lane, undivided highway as superelevation is being applied. Refer to Fig. 11-5.

1. This is a cross section of the roadway on a tangent section—the roadway is at *normal crown*. Both lanes fall from the profile grade point, at the normal cross-slope rate.
2. When transition begins the outside lane rotates upwards about the profile grade point. The inside lane still holds its normal slope until . . .
3. The outside lane has risen to the normal cross slope rate of the inside lane. Now both lanes begin to rotate about the profile grade point until . . .
4. Full superelevation is reached.

Figure 11-4
Quiz on superelevation.

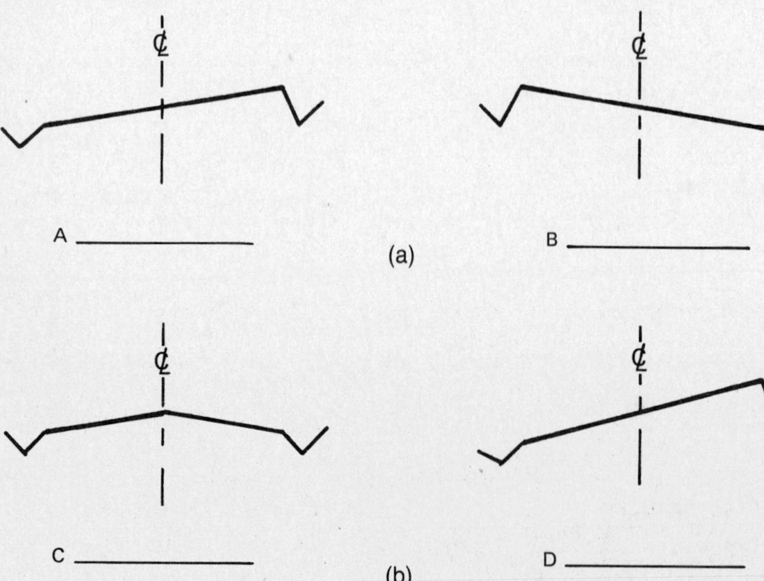
℄
A ____________
(a)
B ____________
C ____________
(b)
D ____________

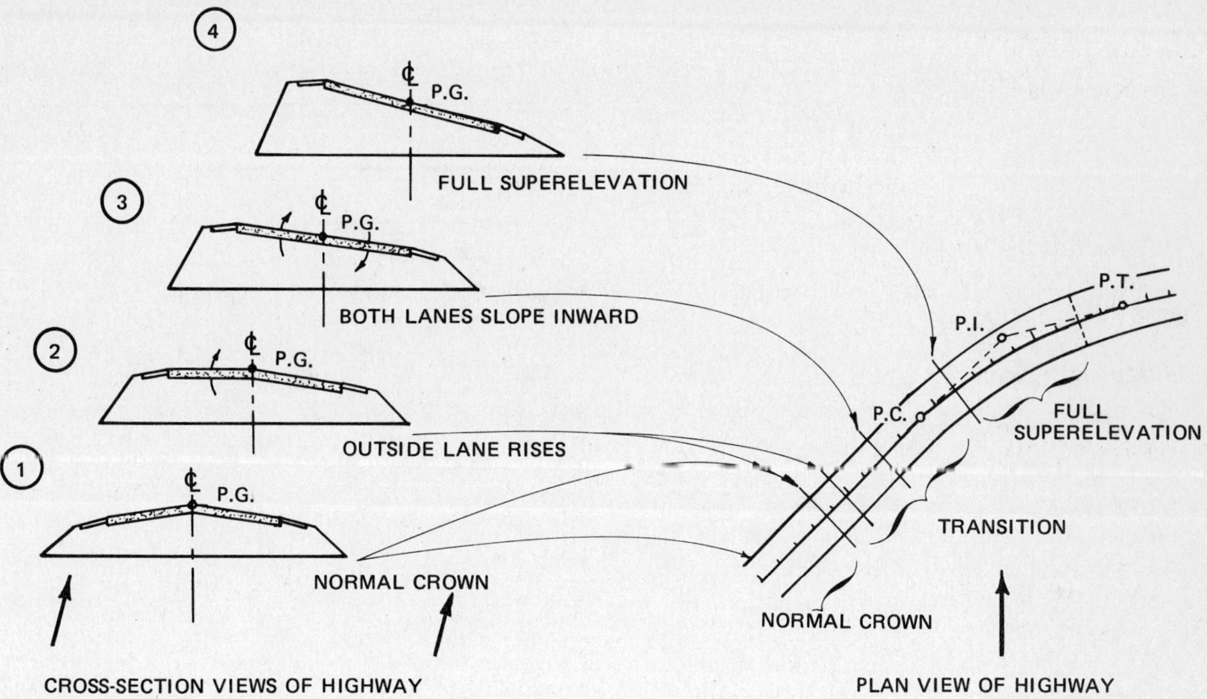

Figure 11-5
Cross-section and plan views of a highway in superelevation.

Superelevation is reduced gradually at the end of the curve by reversing these steps.

Remember that when profile grade points are plotted on profile views, they form a smooth line called the profile grade line. During superelevation transitions, the profile grade line is the *axis of rotation* about which the pavement lanes rotate.

Transition Length Calculation for Undivided Highways

To understand and calculate transitions, look at a profile view of the superelevation transition. (Refer to Fig. 11-5 and Fig. 11-6.) To calculate the transition length *L*, the following facts about the curve must be known (the symbols given are used in the transition formula):

Figure 11-6
Profile view of a superelevation transition.

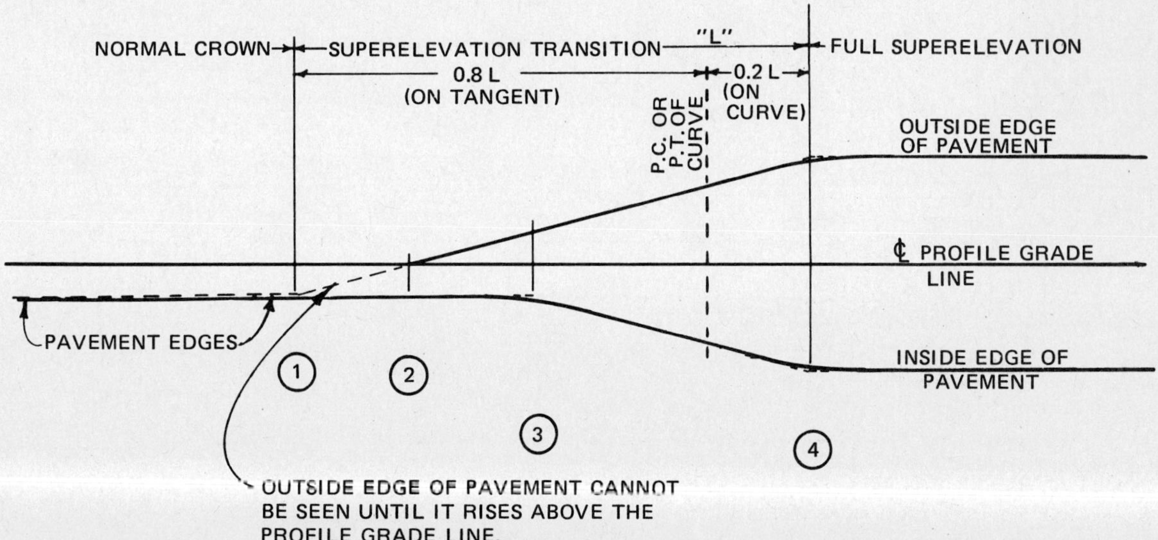

1. The *type* of highway (divided or undivided) and the number of lanes. We will first deal with undivided highways. The calculations for divided highways are slightly different and will be discussed later in this chapter.
2. The *width W* (in feet) and the *normal cross slope rate n* (in feet per foot) of the pavement.
3. The *design speed* of the highway.

The first three facts are found on typical section sheets.

4. The superelevation rate *e* (in feet per foot) for the curve; this is found in the curve data on plan and profile sheets. (It is obtained by the designer from a chart like the one in Fig. 11-7).
5. The *pavement edge slope ratio* (1:*d*). This fact is found in the table in Fig. 11-8. There are three standard slope ratios, corresponding to different design speeds (this is why fact 3 is needed).

When all these facts about a curve are known, the transition length is found using the formula:

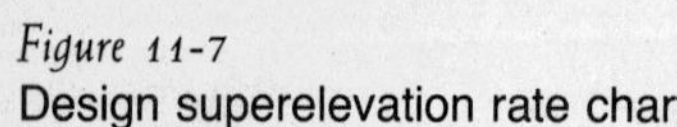

$$L = \frac{W}{2} \times d \times (e + n)$$

SLOPE RATIOS FOR SUPERELEVATION TRANSITIONS			
DESIGN SPEED	M.P.H. 45 - 50	M.P.H. 55 - 60	M.P.H. 65 - 70
1 : d	1 : 200	1 : 225	1 : 250

Figure 11-8
Slope ratios for superelevation transitions.

EXAMPLE Let's work out the transition length for a specific curve, the curve at Sta. 537 + 33.88 on Project 32030–3504. From the typical section (Fig. 11-9) we find:

1. This is an undivided, two-lane highway.
2. Width of pavement W = 24 feet (ft) [7.3 m].
   Normal crown cross slope rate n = 0.02 feet per foot [0.02 m/m].
3. The design speed is 65 miles per hour (mph) [105 km/hr].

From the curve data on the plan and profile sheet (see Fig. 11-10):

Figure 11-7
Design superelevation rate chart

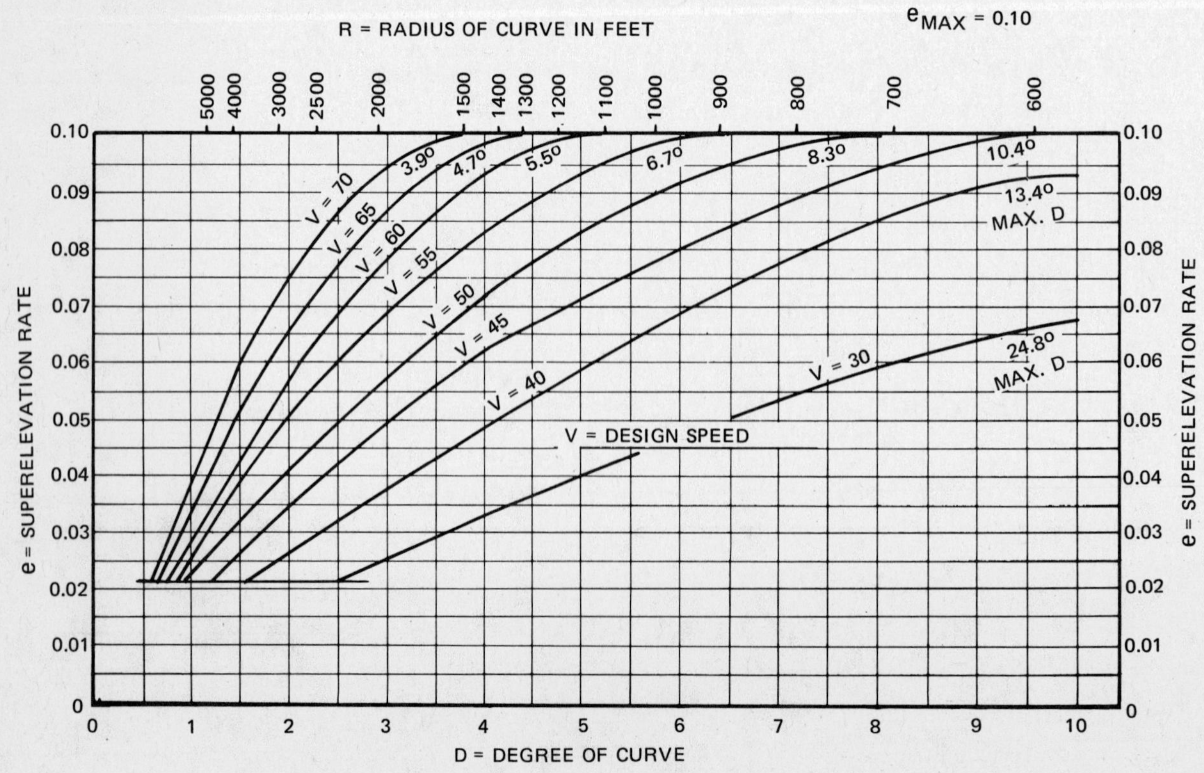

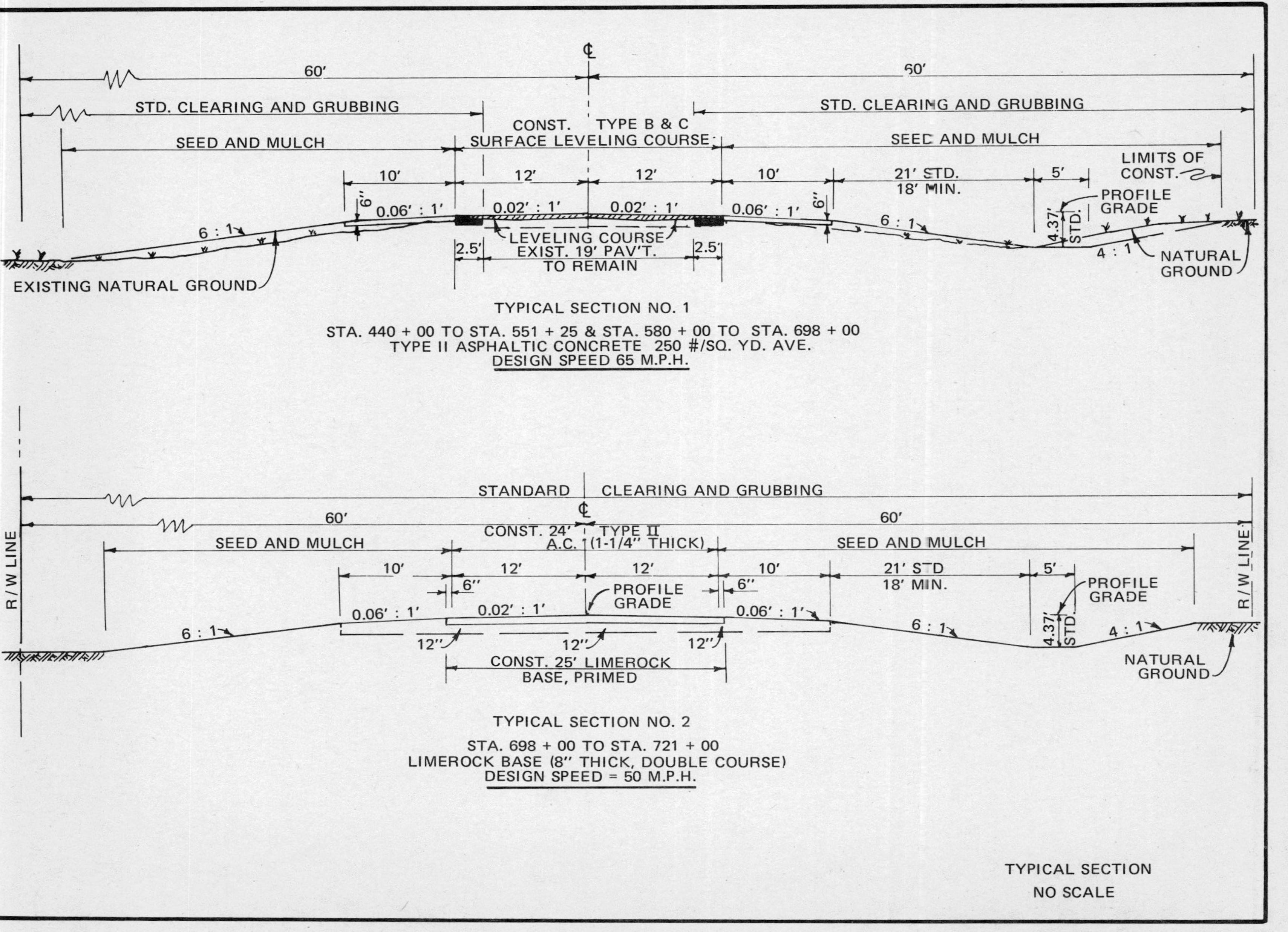

Figure 11-9
Typical sections for projects 32030–3502 and 32030–3504.

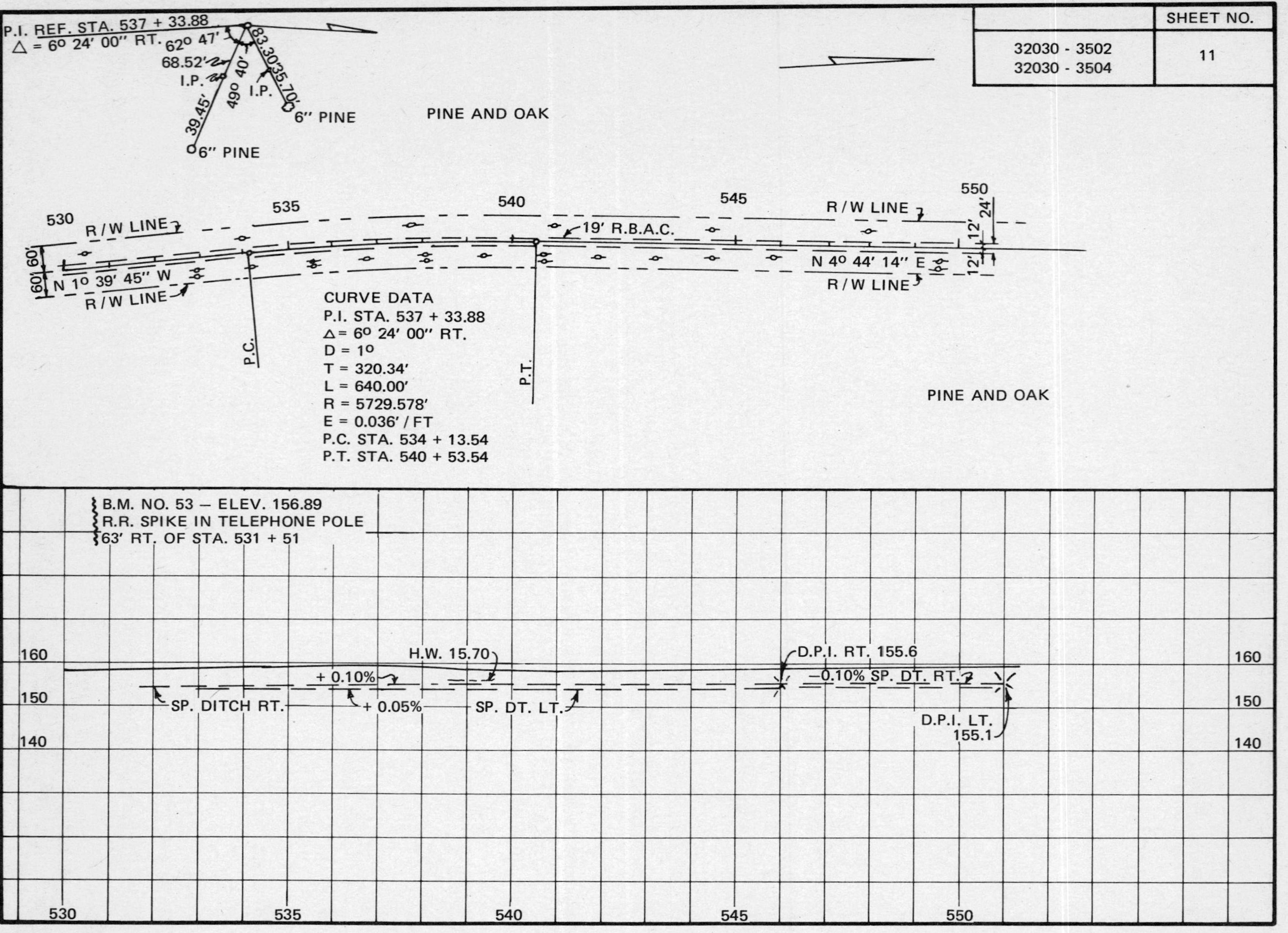

Figure 11-10
Part of Sheet 11 For Projects 32030–3502 and 32030–3504.

4. Superelevation rate e = 0.036 feet per foot [0.036 m/m].

From the standard drawing or Fig. 11-8:

5. For a design speed of 65 mph [105 km/hr], $1{:}d$ = 1:250.

Using all these facts, we calculate:

$$L = \frac{W}{2} \times d \times (e + n)$$

$$= \frac{24}{2} \times 250 \times (0.036 + 0.02)$$

$$= 12 \times 250 \times 0.056$$

$$= 168 \text{ ft (Superelevation transition length)}$$

Superelevation of Divided Highways

Much of the information about superelevation of undivided highways also applies to divided highways. However, there are several differences in the calculation of transition lengths.

The transition lengths for the outer and inner roadways of a divided highway are independent of each other. Figures 11-11 and 11-12 show how transition is applied. Let's see what happens to the cross-section view of a divided highway as superelevation is applied. Refer to Fig. 11-11.

Outer Roadway

1. Normal crown. Transition begins.
2. Pavement rotates about profile grade point.
3. Pavement rotates about profile grade point.
4. Pavement rotates about profile grade point.
5. Full superelevation is reached.

Inner Roadway

1. Normal crown.
2. Normal crown. Transition begins.
3. Pavement rotates about profile grade point.
4. Full superelevation is reached.
5. Full superelevation.

Profile Views of Divided Highways with Superelevation

Divided highways have two axes of rotation, the profile grade lines for each roadway. Figure 11-12 shows the profile view. Notice the *two* superelevation transitions, L_1 and L_2. L_1 is for the outer roadway, while L_2 is for the

Figure 11-11
Cross-section views of highways in superelevation.

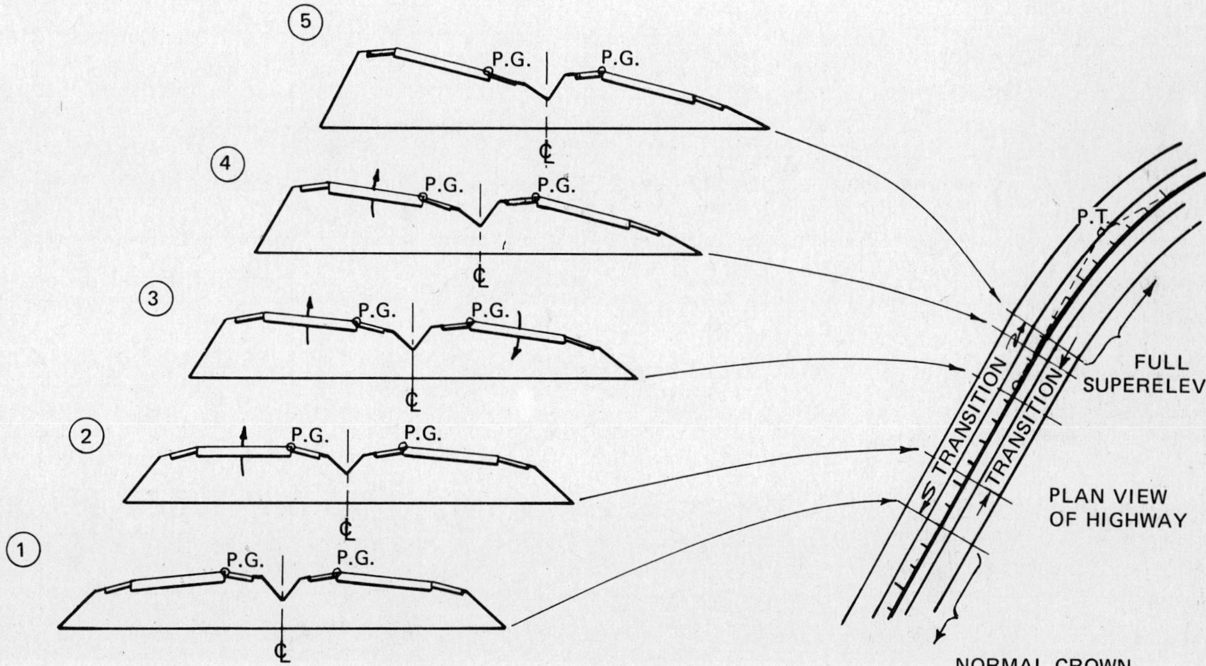

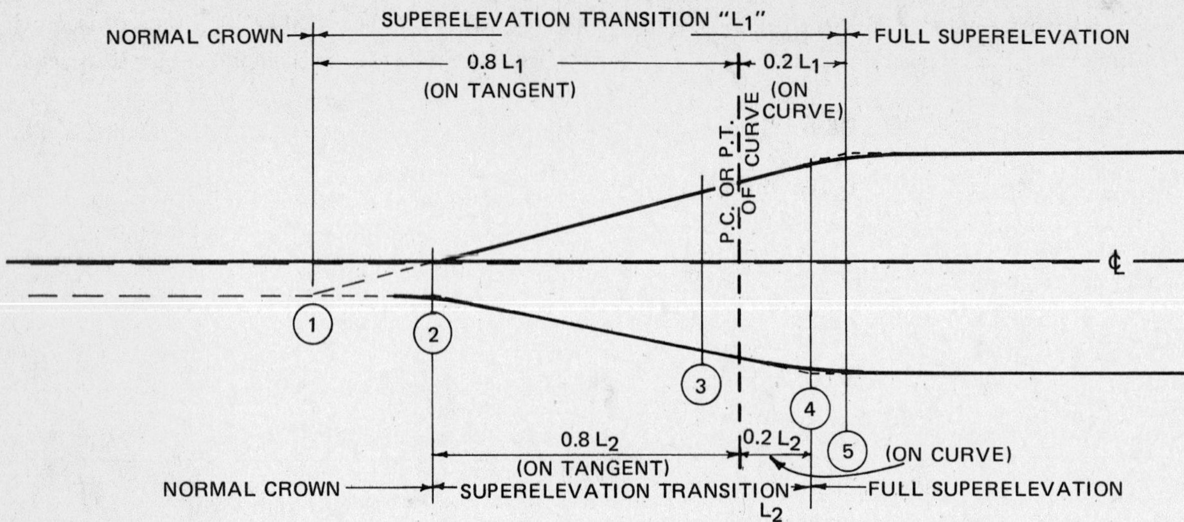

Figure 11-12
Profile of divided highway in superelevation.

inner roadway. These two transition lengths are calculated independently and are not related in any way except in their positions relative to the point of curvature (PC) or point of tangency (PT).

Calculating Transition Lengths for Divided Highways

In order to calculate L_1 and L_2, the transition lengths, the same facts that were required for undivided highways must be known:

1. *Type* of highway, and number of lanes
2. *Width W* (in feet) of each roadway, and *normal cross slope rate n* (in feet per foot).
3. *Design speed*

These first three facts are found on the appropriate typical section sheet.

4. *Superelevation rate e* (in feet per foot) for the curve.

This is found at the end of the curve data on the appropriate plan and profile sheet.

5. The pavement edge slope ratio $(1{:}d)$.

This is found in Fig. 11-10.

When all these facts are known, the transition lengths are calculated using the formulas:

$$L_1 = W \times d \times (e + n)$$
$$L_2 = W \times d \times (e - n)$$

EXAMPLE Now we will work out the transition lengths for a specific curve, the curve at Sta. 173 + 74.60 of Project 54001–3402. From the typical section (top section) on Sheet 5, Fig. 10-6, we find:

1. This is a divided four-lane highway.
2. Width of each roadway W = 24 ft [7.3 m].
   Normal cross slope rate n = 0.02 ft/ft [0.02 m/m].
3. The design speed = 70 mph [113 km/hr].

From the curve data on plan and profile Sheet 12, Fig. 11-13:

4. Superelevation rate e = 0.039 ft/ft [0.039 m/m]

From the table in Fig. 11-10:

5. Pavement edge slope ratio for design speed of 70 mph [113 km/hr] $1{:}d = 1{:}250$

Using all these facts, L_1 and L_2 can be calculated:

$$L_1 = W \times d \times (e + n)$$
$$= 24 \times 250 \times (0.039 + 0.02)$$
$$= 24 \times 250 \times 0.059$$
= 354 ft (superelevation transition length, outer roadway)

$$L_2 = W \times d \times (e - n)$$
$$= 24 \times 250 \times (0.039 - 0.02)$$
$$= 24 \times 250 \times 0.019$$
= 114 ft (superelevation transition length, inner roadway)

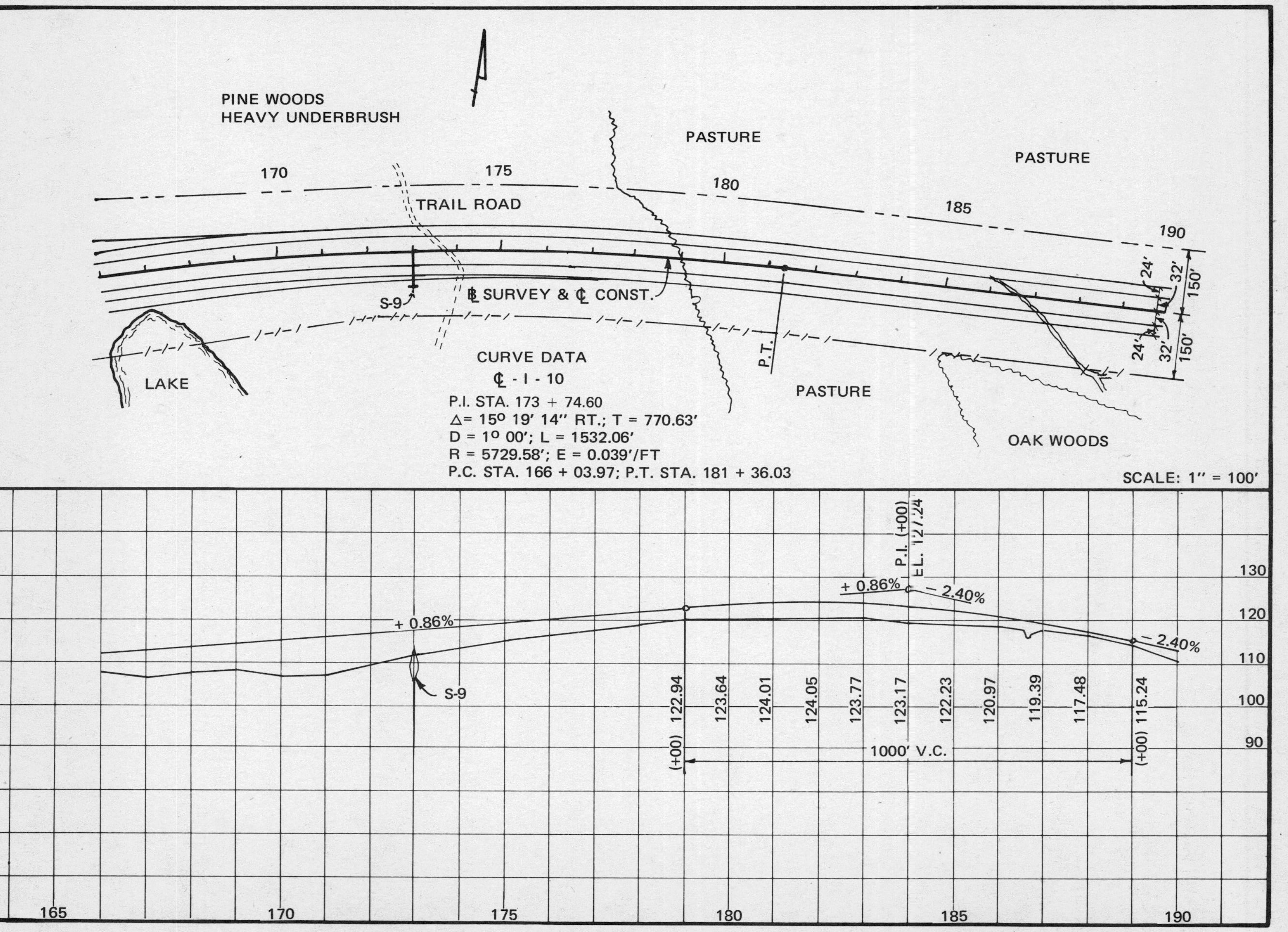

Figure 11-13
Partial plan and profile view with a curve.

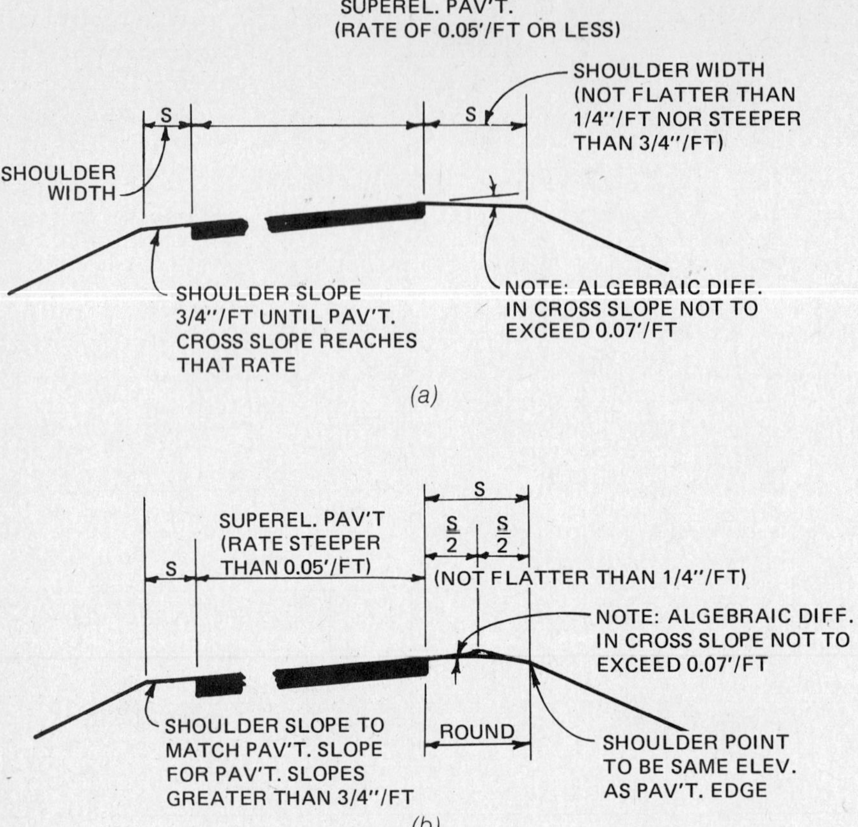

Figure 11-14
Details of shoulder construction with superelevation.

Figure 11-15
This figure shows the changes made in the high side shoulder slopes as the pavement is superelevated.

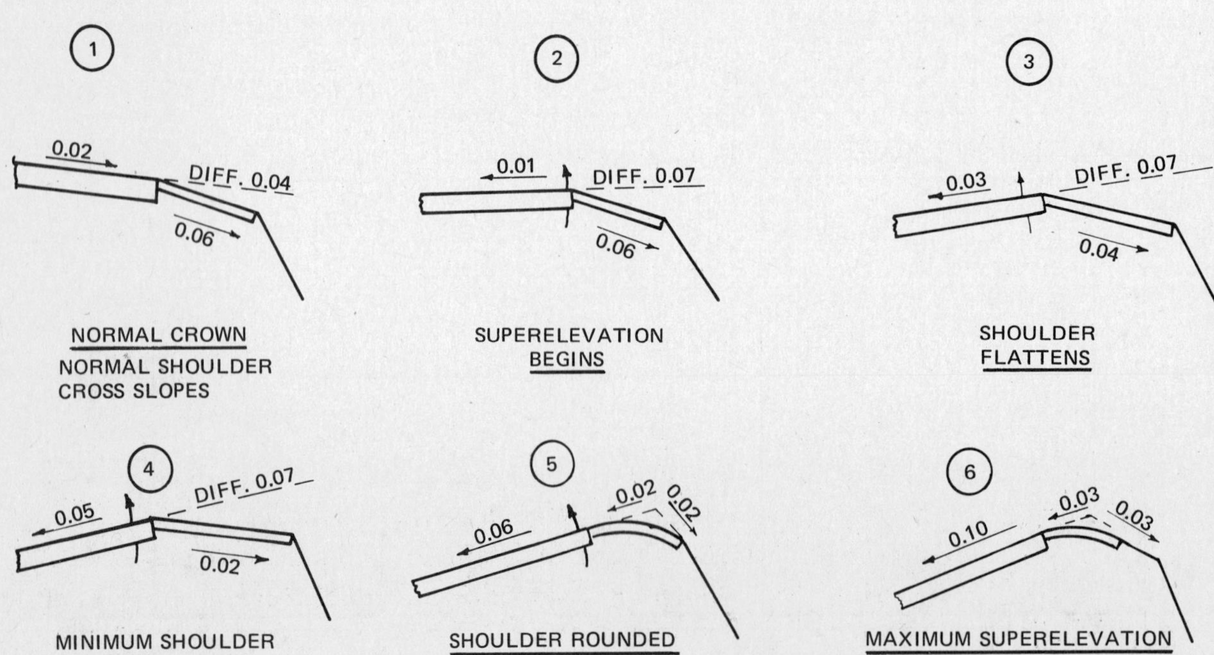

SHOULDER CONSTRUCTION WITH SUPERELEVATION

On most highways, the outside shoulders have a cross slope of 0.06 feet per foot [0.06 m/m]; the inside (median) shoulders on divided highways have a cross slope of 0.05 ft/ft [0.05 m/m]. When the highway is superelevated, the shoulder slopes must be changed to avoid sharp angular breaks in the roadway cross section. The maximum permissible break is an algebraic difference of 0.07 ft/ft [0.07 m/m] between the shoulder slope and the pavement cross slope.

Study Fig. 11-14, which shows details of shoulder construction for superelevated curves. These details apply to both paved and grassed shoulders. Notice that when the shoulder is on the *low side*, as in Fig. 11-14*a*, all that is required is that the 0.06 ft/ft [0.06 m/m] shoulder cross slope be maintained until the pavement cross slope reaches 0.06 ft/ft [0.06 m/m]. If the pavement cross slope is greater than 0.06 ft/ft [0.06 m/m], the shoulder has the same slope as the pavement.

When the shoulder is on the *high side*, the details are more complex. Figure 11-14*b* shows a shoulder on the high side. A shoulder slope of ¾ in/ft downward from the edge of the pavement will be maintained until a 0.07 ft/ft break in slope at the pavement edge is reached due to superelevation of the pavement. As the pavement superelevation increases, the 0.07 ft/ft break in slope will be maintained and the shoulder flattened until the shoulder slope reaches the minimum of ¼ in/ft downward from the edge of pavement. Any further increase in pavement superelevation will necessitate sloping the inside half of the shoulder toward the pavement and the outer half outward, *both* at ¼ in/ft. These slopes will be held with further increase in pavement superelevation until the maximum break of 0.07 ft/ft at the pavement edge is again reached. This maximum break will then be held and shoulder slopes steepened with additional superelevation.

Compare Fig. 11-14 and 11-15.

Figure 11-16 gives some general notes on superelevation. Also see Fig. 11-17 to 11-19 for some views of actual roadway construction.

Figure 11-17
A big bulldozer used to put the superelevation grading on a highway.

Figure 11-16
General notes for superelevation.

GENERAL NOTES FOR SUPERELEVATION

1. USE NORMAL SECTION WITH NO SUPERELEVATION FOR CURVES UP TO 0°-20′ (0°-14′ FOR DESIGN SPEEDS OF 70 MPH).
2. WHEN THE DEGREE OF CURVE IS 0°-21′ OR GREATER (0°-15′ FOR DESIGN SPEEDS OF 70 MPH) AND IS IN THE RANGE OF THE HORIZONTAL PORTION OF THE CURVE, SUPERELEVATE AT THE NORMAL CROSS SLOPE RATE OF 1/4"/ FOOT OR AS INDICATED BY THE CURVE FOR THE APPROVED DESIGN SPEED.
3. THE LENGTH OF SUPERELEVATION TRANSITION IS TO BE DETERMINED BY USING A RELATIVE SLOPE OF PAVEMENT EDGE TO PROFILE GRADE GIVEN IN FIG. 11-10 - MIN. LENGTH OF TRAN. SHALL BE 100 FT.
4. FOR PAVEMENTS WIDER THAN TWO LANES, THE SUPERELEVATION RUNOFF LENGTHS SHOULD BE:
   a. THREE LANE PAVEMENTS: 1.2 TIMES THE LENGTH FOR A TWO LANE HIGHWAY.
   b. FOUR-LANE UNDIVIDED PAVEMENTS: 1.5 TIMES THE LENGTH FOR 2 LANE HIGHWAY.
   c. SIX-LANE UNDIVIDED PAVEMENTS: 2.0 TIMES THE LENGTH FOR 2 LANE HIGHWAY.

Figure 11-18
Setting up a transit on a normal crown street.

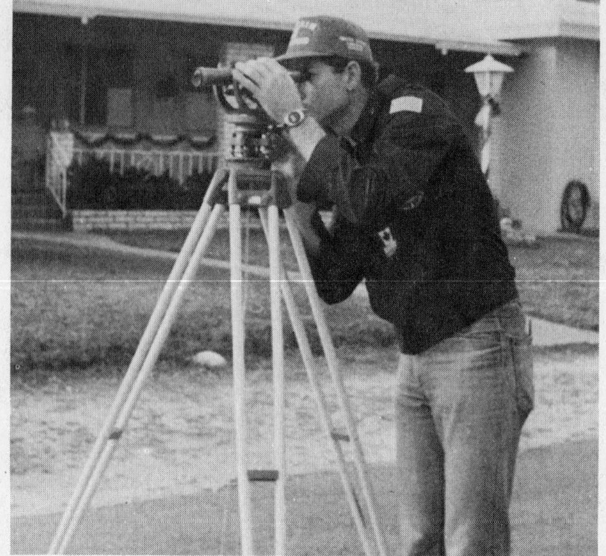

Figure 11-19
Surveyor taking a sighting down the street.

LEARNING ACTIVITY PACKAGE

Read Chap. 11 carefully to become acquainted with superelevation.

Chapter 11 read ____________ *(date)*.

If the student has read Chap. 11 but has still not understood some of the objectives (a) through (e), the paragraphs containing those topics should be reread.

Objectives completed ____________ *(date)*.

Remove the Chap. 11 quiz from the text and answer all the questions.

Quiz completed ____________ *(date)*.

11

QUIZ

1. Vertical curves require superelevation on highways. (T or F) ____________
2. Most horizontal curves are superelevated. (T or F) ____________
3. In superelevation the outside of the curve is lower than the inside. (T or F) ____________
4. If a roadway is *not* superelevated, the cross slopes are at normal ____________ .
5. In fig. 11-3 note the right-turning curve. The surface slopes ____________ to the inside of the curve, and the left edge of the roadway is ____________ than the right edge.
6. Look at Fig. 11-5. When transition begins at (2) the outside lane rotates ____________ about the profile grade point.
7. In Fig. 11-5 at (2) the inside lane holds its ____________ slope.
8. Superelevation is taken down gradually at the end of the curves by reversing the steps that build up the superelevation. (T or F) ____________
9. During superelevation transitions, the profile grade line is the axis of rotation about which the pavement lanes rotate. (T or F) ____________

Here are some of the steps which occur during transition from normal crown to full superelevation. Put them in their correct order.

A. Full superelevation reached.
B. Roadway at normal crown.
C. Both lanes rotate about the axis of rotation.
D. The outside edge of the pavement rises, the inside lane holds a normal crown slope.

10. First: ____________
11. Second: ____________
12. Third: ____________
13. Fourth: ____________
14. A two-lane, undivided highway has a pavement width of 24 ft [7.3 m], with normal crown cross slopes of 0.02 feet per foot [0.02 m/m], and a design speed of 50 mph [80 km/hr]. A curve on this highway is to be superelevated at a rate of 0.06 ft/ft [0.06 m/m]. Calculate the length of the superelevation transition. The formula is:

$$L = \frac{W}{2} \times d \times (e+n)$$

The normal crown cross slope is n. Look at Fig. 11-8 to find $1{:}d$ for a design speed of 50 mph. Do the calculations here: ____________

____

$L =$ ____________ ft

15. Calculate how much of this transition in question 14 will occur *ahead* of the PC (that is, on the curve). *Answer* = ____________ ft.
NOTE: The minimum transition length is 100 ft [30.5 m]. This minimum length should be used if the calculated value of L is less than 100 ft [30.5 m].

16. A four-lane divided highway has 24 ft [7.3 m] wide roadways, with normal cross slopes of 0.02 ft/ft [0.02 m/m] and a design speed of 60 mph [97 km/hr]. A curve on this highway is to be superelevated at a rate of 0.045 ft/ft [0.045 m/m]. Calculate the transition lengths for:
(a) The outer roadway: $L_1 = W \times d \times (e+n)$

L_1 = ____________ ft

(b) The inner roadway: $L_2 = W \times d \times (e-n)$

L_2 = ____________ ft

17. The control point on a finished roadway surface is the ____________ ____________ point.

18. On a divided highway, the median width is measured between the ____________ ____________ points.

19. A project where the shape or width of the roadway changes will require more than one ____________ section.

20. The median width of a highway can be found on three kinds of sheets. Name them.
(1) ________________________________ sheets
(2) ________________________________ sheets
(3) ________________________________ sheets

21. Roadway cross-section sheets are read from the ____________ to the ____________ of the sheet.

22. Vertical measurements on roadway cross-section sheets give ____________.

12 EARTHWORK

Objectives

a. Learn how cut and fill operations are used to construct a roadbed
b. Learn the various types of earthwork
c. Understand borrow pits and the reasons for their use
d. Understand subsoil excavation for the removal of unsatisfactory material
e. Study end areas showing earthwork quantities
f. Understand balancing of earthwork quantities
g. Study shrinkage factors
h. Understand a mass diagram

Rationale

Various types of earthwork are used to develop the roadway. The student should become familiar with these basic processes and the terminology used in earthwork, such as borrow, fill, embankment, balancing of earthwork quantities, and shrinkage factors. The material in this chapter, although brief, will give the student a beginner's knowledge of the subject of earthwork.

Figure 12-1
Cut and fill sections of a roadway.

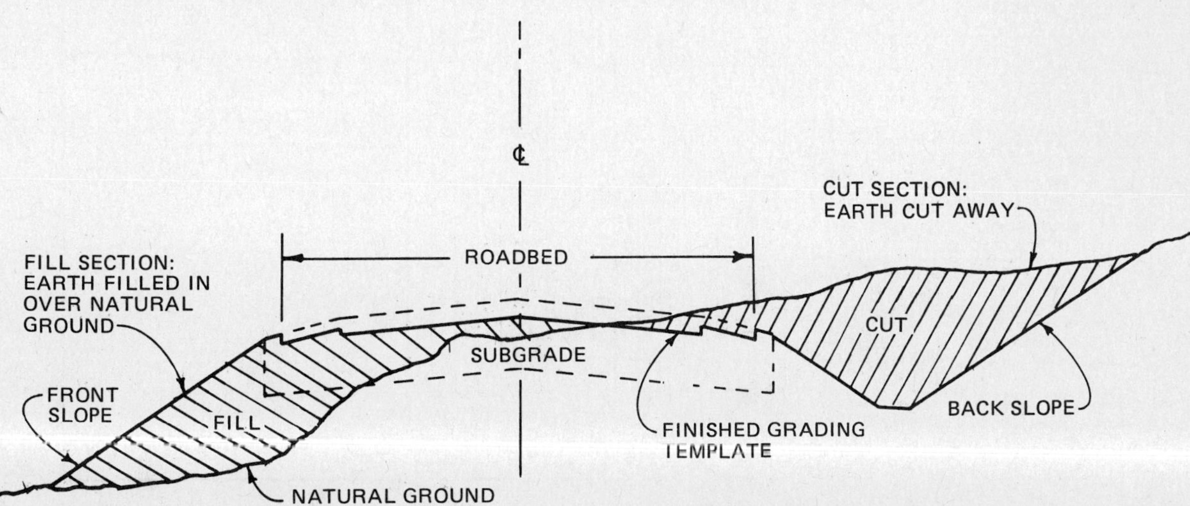

BASIC EARTHWORK PROCESSES

The most important operation involving earthwork is construction of the roadbed. The roadbed is constructed by excavating soil from cut sections and placing soil as embankments in fill sections (see Fig. 12-1).

In cut sections, the roadbed is built below the natural ground, that is, the natural ground is excavated to the elevation of the proposed roadbed. In fill sections, the roadbed is built above the natural ground; the earth fill is an embankment.

TYPES OF EARTHWORK

On many projects, several types of earthwork are required. The type of earthwork usually depends on its location or its purpose. Information on earthwork is found on three kinds of sheets:

1. Summary of quantities sheets
2. Roadway cross-section sheets
3. Mass diagram sheets

SUMMARY OF QUANTITIES SHEET

SUMMARY OF SODDING			
STATION TO STATION	SQ.YDS.		
	LEFT	RIGHT	TOTAL
149 + 90 – 150 + 40 LT. RDWAY	50		50
149 + 43 – 150 + 43 RT. RDWAY	125		125
148 + 68 – 150 + 43 RT. RDWAY		175	175
152 + 60 – 160 + 50 LT. RDWAY	800		800
152 + 60 – 153 + 85 LT. RDWAY		125	125
152 + 60 – 158 + 97.5 RT. RDWAY		637.5	637.5
213 + 15 – 214 + 15 RT. RDWAY	125		125
212 + 40 – 214 + 15 RT. RDWAY		175	175
218 + 50 – 220 + 25 LT. RDWAY	175		175
218 + 50 – 219 + 50 LT. RDWAY		125	125
			2510

SUMMARY OF PAY ITEMS			
ITEM NO.	ITEM	UNIT	QUANTITY TOTAL
103–37	MAINTENANCE OF TRAFFIC	LUMP SUM	1
104–31	ARTIFICIAL COVERINGS	SQ. YD.	6,000
104–37	MULCHING (TEMPORARY)	SQ. YD.	10,000
104–34	SODDING (TEMPORARY)	SQ. YD.	20,000
104–37	SAND BAGGING	CU. YD.	50
104–58			
110–1	CLEARING AND GRUBBING		
110–2	CLEARING AND GRUBBING – BORROW PITS		
110–4			
135–1	GRADING		
135–6	BORROW EXCAVATION		
135–7	SUBSOIL EXCAVATION	CU. YD.	13,954
160–42	TYPE "B" STABILIZATION	SQ. YD.	50,918
162–33	TOPSOIL	SQ. YD.	585,334
170–30	CEMENT TREATED SUBGRADE	SQ. YD.	172,596
170–33	CEMENT		3,573
305–30	SAND COVER MATERIAL	CU. YD.	959
310–4	COVER MATERIAL FOR SEAL COAT	CU. YD.	13
331–32–1	TYPE S–1 ASPHALTIC CONCRETE	SQ. YD.	81,901
336–30–61	SAND ASPHALT MIX	SQ. YD.	2,221
350–1–4	PLAIN CEMENT CONCRETE PAVEMENT	SQ. YD.	148,909
400–1–1	CLASS "A" CONCRETE CULVERTS	CU. YD.	1,241
425–1–1	INLETS (CURB)	EACH	8
425–1–2	INLETS (DITCH BOTTOM)	EACH	19
425–34	SHOULDER GUTTER INLETS	EACH	8
430–1–26	CONCRETE PIPE CULVERT 36"	LIN. FT.	358
430–1–28	CONCRETE PIPE CULVERT 42"	LIN. FT.	500
524–1–1	CONCRETE DITCH PAVEMENT 13" THICK	NO. YD.	9,464
570–2	SEEDING AND MULCHING	SQ. YD.	663,500

Figure 12-2
Summary of quantities sheet.

Summary of Quantities Sheets

Summary of quantities sheets give capsule estimates of each type of earthwork to be done. For example, look at Fig. 12-2, which is the summary of quantities sheet for Project 54001–3402. Near the top of the summary of pay items are listed the three major types of earthwork—grading, borrow excavation, and subsoil excavation.

Grading (Roadway Excavation and Embankment)

Grading consists of making *cuts* (excavation of all types of materials, such as sand, clay, rock, and muck, from inside the right-of-way and above the finished grading template) and *fills* (the placement and shaping of suitable materials to form an embankment).

Borrow Excavation

Borrow excavation is excavation from selected areas (borrow pits) outside the right-of-way; it is necessary when roadway excavation does not supply sufficient suitable materials for construction of the embankments. The locations of borrow pits are shown at the top of the mass diagram, and information on their layout and soil types is found on borrow pit soil survey sheets.

Subsoil Excavation

If the results of the roadway soils analysis show unsatisfactory material at any point beneath the finished grading template, subsoil excavation is carried out to remove the unsatisfactory material. The holes are then filled with suitable material obtained by either roadway or borrow excavation.

EARTHWORK QUANTITIES

Quantities (volumes) of earthwork in cubic yards are calculated from the data on roadway cross-section sheets.

Figure 12-3 shows cross sections of the cut and fill areas at two consecutive stations along a road project. The *end areas* of cut and fill (excavation and embankment) for each cross section are shown in square feet in the columns headed *A* to the right of the cross sections. The *volumes* of this cut and fill between the two cross sections are then calculated and shown in cubic yards in the col-

Figure 12-3
End areas showing square feet of cut and fill.

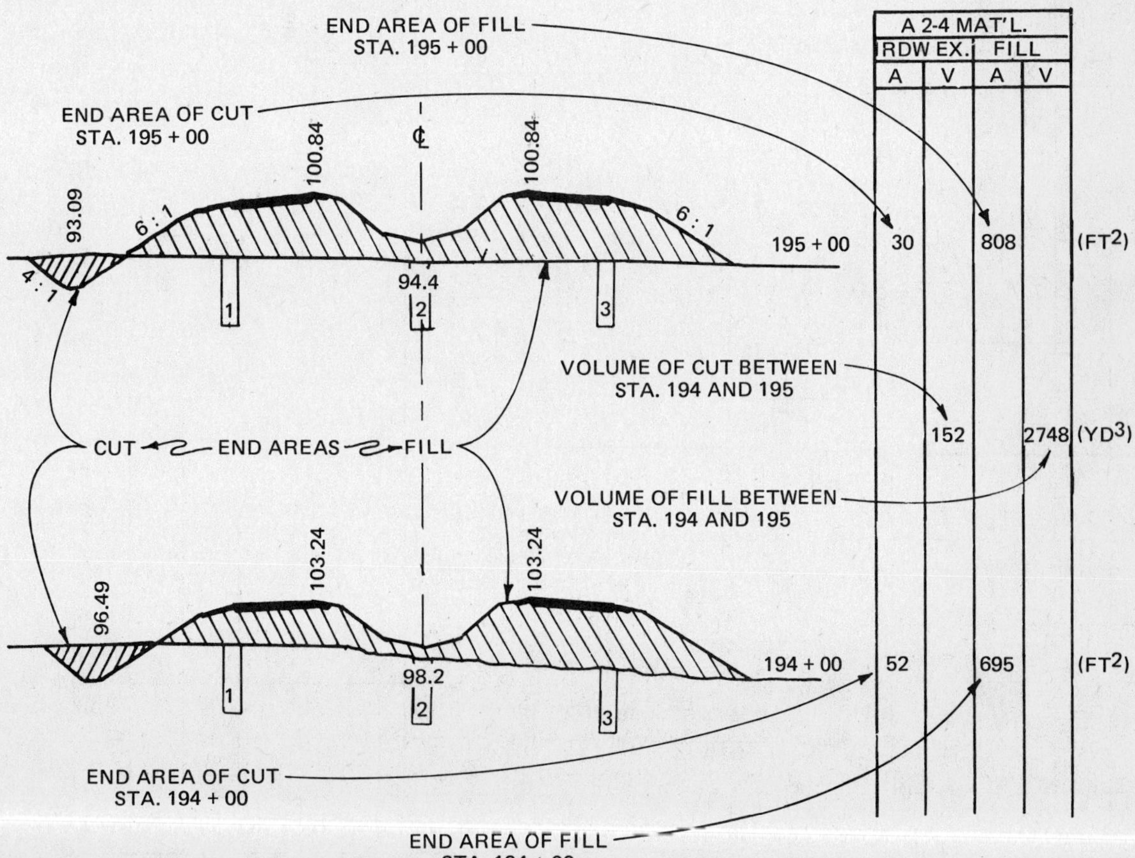

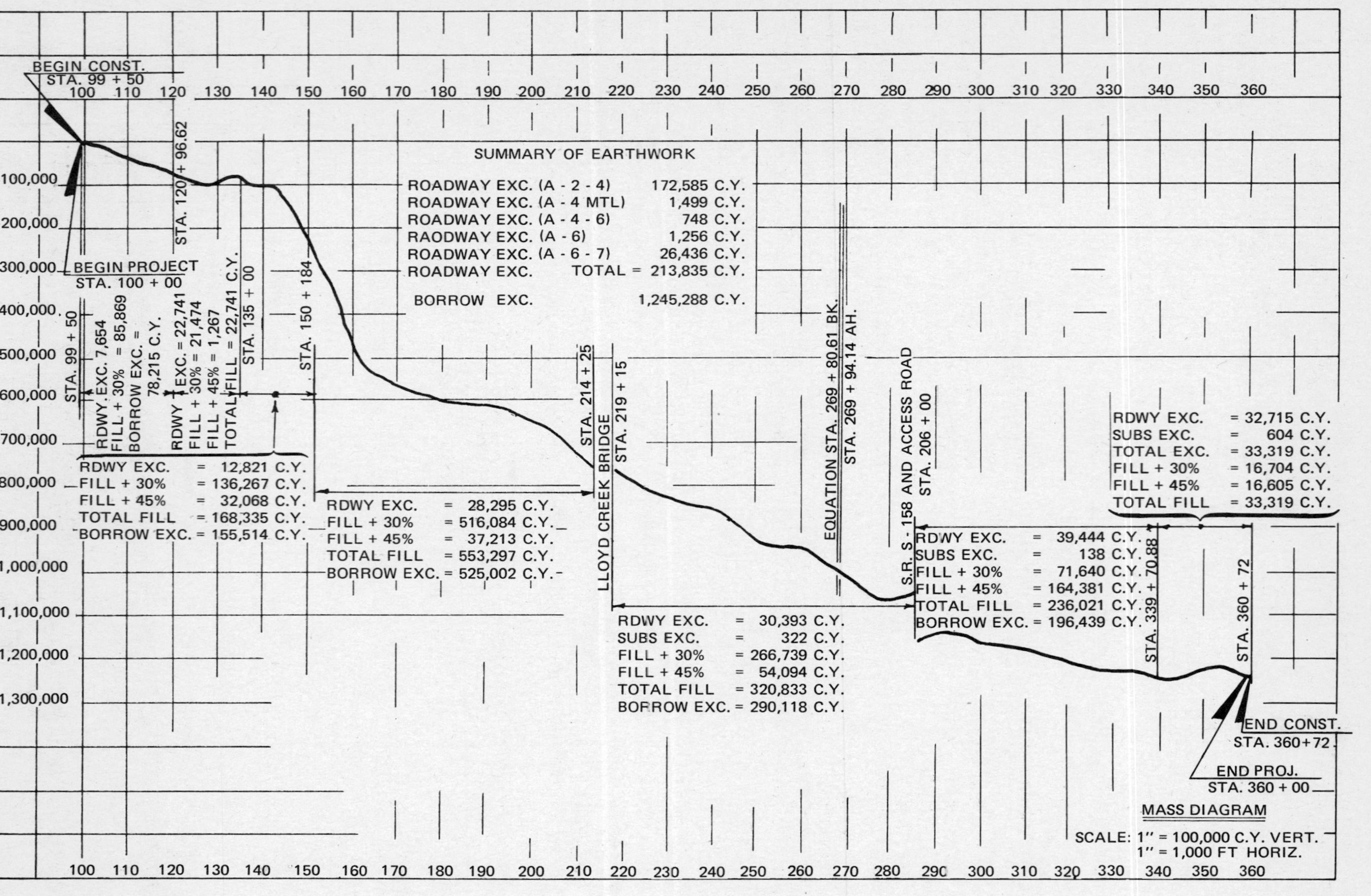

Figure 12-4
A mass diagram.

umns headed *V* to the right of, and between, the cross sections.

Balancing Earthwork Quantities

In order to minimize earthwork, highway designers try to balance excavation quantities with embankment quantities at frequent intervals along the proposed highway. This way, earth is moved only a relatively short distance from its original position.

Balance Areas

A portion of a project where the total roadway excavation is equal to the total fill (plus shrinkage) is called a *roadway balance area.* If some or all of the fill has to be obtained by borrow excavation, the area is called a *borrow balance area.*

All balance areas for a project are shown on the mass diagram. Look at Fig. 12-4, the mass diagram of Project 54001–3402, and find the roadway balance area between Sta. 120 + 96.62 and 135 + 00; notice that the roadway excavation is equal to the total fill, both are 22,741 cubic yards (C.Y.), without the need for borrow excavation. Between Sta. 99 + 50 and 120 + 96.62 is a borrow balance area; the borrow required [78,215 C.Y.] is the total fill (85,869 C.Y.) minus the roadway excavation (7,654 C.Y.).

Shrinkage Factors

The volume of excavation is calculated before the earth is moved. When the excavated material is compacted into an embankment (a fill section) it will occupy *less* than its original volume. This decrease in volume is the *shrinkage factor.* Shrinkage factors vary considerably—between about 10 and 100 percent—depending on the type of soil; shrinkage factors are given along the top of the mass diagram.

To see how shrinkage factors are used, look at the mass diagram in Fig. 12-4. The total fill between Sta. 120 + 96.62 and 135 + 00 on Project 54001–3402 is calculated by adding the volumes of fill in the columns at the right of the cross sections between these stations. (We can get a close approximation of the fill by using the mass diagram instead of the cross sections.)

1. Between Sta. 120 + 96.62 and 127 + 00, 16,518 C.Y. of fill are required; the fill has a shrinkage factor of 30 percent.
2. Between Sta. 127 + 00 and 135 + 00, 874 C.Y. of fill are required; the fill here has a shrinkage factor of 45 percent.
3. 16,518 C.Y. + 30% shrinkage
   = (16,518 × 1.30)C.Y. = 21,474 C.Y.
   874 C.Y. + 45% shrinkage
   = (874 × 1.45)C.Y. = 1,267 C.Y.

Thus the total fill (plus shrinkage) required is

(21,474 + 1,267)C.Y. = 22,741 C.Y.,

which is the same as the volume of roadway excavation. Thus this is a roadway balance area.

MASS DIAGRAM

We have already referred to the mass diagram. There is one for each project; for example, Fig. 12-4 is the summary of earthwork over the entire Project 54001–3402. It shows:

1. All balance areas, with balanced quantities of excavation and embankment
2. Earthwork quantities grouped by soil classification number

LEARNING ACTIVITY PACKAGE

Read Chap. 12 carefully.

Chapter 12 read ____________ *(date).*

Objectives read and studied ____________ *(date).*

Remove the quiz from the book and answer all the questions.

Quiz completed ____________ *(date).*

12

QUIZ

1. What is the most important operation involving earthwork? ______________
2. Soil is excavated from ______________ sections.
3. Soil is placed as embankment in ______________ sections.
4. The roadbed is built below the natural ground in ______________ sections.
5. Cut section of the natural ground are ______________ to the elevation of the proposed roadway.
6. In fill sections, the roadbed is built ______________ the natural ground.
7. Information on earthwork can be found on three kinds of sheets:
   (1) ____________________________ (2) ____________________________
   (3) ____________________________
8. A capsule estimate of earthwork quantities can be found on the
   ____________________________ sheet.
9. Name the three major types of earthwork. (1) ____________________________,
   (2) ____________________________, and (3) ____________________________
10. Grading consists of making ____________________________.
11. The placement and shaping of suitable materials to form an embankment is called a ____________________________.
12. Borrow excavation is excavated from selected areas called ______________.
    ____
13. Volumes of earthwork in cubic yards are calculated from the data on
    ____________________________ sheets.
14. Why are earthwork quantities balanced?
    ____
    ____
    ____
15. All balance areas for a project are shown on the ______________.
16. When the excavated material is compacted into an embankment (a fill section) it will occupy ____________________________ than its original volume.
17. The amount of decrease in volume is called ______________.
18. A shrinkage factor can vary between ______________ and ______________ percent.

13 PROPOSED DRAINAGE STRUCTURES

Objectives

a. Understand the types of drainage structure sheets included in a set of road plans
b. Understand the format for preparation of drainage structure cross-section sheets
c. Understand the successive plotting of drainage structures
d. Read about skewed structures
e. Know where the identification of structures will be found on the drainage structure sheets
f. Understand the importance of plotting underground utilities

Rationale

The student needs a rudimentary knowledge of the inlets, endwalls, and piping used to keep roads from washing out. This chapter will acquaint the student with a few of the basic drainage structures and the way they are shown in road plans.

As previously mentioned, drainage is one of the most important considerations in designing a road. If the roadway has inadequate drainage or is designed too low for the surrounding territory, the road will soon wash out. Many types of drainage structures (examples are shown in Fig. 13-1, 13-2, and 13-3) are therefore required to handle rain water, swamp water, rivers or creeks, or any other water problem likely to affect the roadway.

Figure 13-1
A swale to conduct water off the highway and a roadside drainage ditch *(Florida Department of Transportation).*

Figure 13-2
Drainage canal with a bridge culvert over the canal *(Florida Department of Transportation).*

DRAINAGE STRUCTURE IN ROAD PLANS

Separate sheets of proposed drainage structure cross sections are included in construction plans for both municipal and rural projects.

In the past, attempts have been made to reduce the amount of time consumed in the preparation of plans by omitting the plotting of drainage structures in plans for municipal projects and the plotting of cross drains in the profile portion of the plan-profile sheets for rural projects. Little, if any, time was saved by this omission. On many

Figure 13-3
Repairs being made on a small culvert *(Florida Department of Transportation).*

municipal jobs, more time was spent in duplication of test sections by both design and checking personnel than would have been consumed in the orderly and regular plotting of drainage structures at the outset. Therefore, drainage structure cross-section sheets must be included in plans for jobs requiring drainage structures.

PREPARATION OF DRAINAGE STRUCTURE SHEETS

Drainage structure cross sections are prepared on standard cross-section sheets, usually to the same scale as the roadway cross sections. The centerline of construction is located at or near the center of the sheet, and the existing ground line is plotted at the location of each proposed structure.

Figures 13-4, 13-5, and 13-6 illustrate drainage structure cross-section sheets for rural projects, showing the arrangement of notes and various types of drainage structures and combinations of structures.

Spacing of the Structures

The spacing of sections must be such that the proposed structures can be plotted and proper notes included without overlapping adjacent sections. Sections are plotted successively, beginning at the bottom of the sheet. If, a structure is plotted out of order for any reason, a note should be placed in the correct place in the sequence referring to the sheet on which this structure is plotted.

Existing Ground Line

The existing ground line is inked with a thin, solid line, and the existing ground line elevation is placed immediately below the ground line at the project centerline or baseline. Any existing structures at the location of the proposed structure are plotted using a medium-weight, broken line.

Procedure for Ordinary Cross Drains

For ordinary cross drains, this procedure should be followed:

The roadway template and proposed structure are plotted in pencil using a heavy, solid line, and the proposed profile grade elevation is given above the grade point. The ends of the proposed structure are dimensioned from the centerline or reference line.

Elaboration in plotting the structures is to be avoided; they should be plotted simply as sections along the centerline of the structure. Lines representing the outside of the shell of pipe culverts are not plotted.

Skewed Structures

In the case of skewed cross-drain structures, the section must be along the centerline of the structure. A note is placed below the plotted structure giving the station, length and size of proposed pipe, right and left flow lines, skew angle in the case of a skewed structure, and standard index numbers for endwalls, inlets, or other accessory structures.

Identification of Structures

It is helpful to show the station of the structure in fairly large letters near the right border of the sheet. Ordinarily, no separate notes are used for endwalls, except for the case when the pipe is placed parallel to the project and endwalls are required; then the station, index number, and flow line of each are given.

MUNICIPAL DRAINAGE STRUCTURES

The procedure in plotting drainage structures for municipal construction is similar to that for rural construction with a few exceptions. A large proportion of structures for municipal construction are for the purpose of drainage within the lateral limits of the right-of-way; the existing ground line is not pertinent in these cases and may be omitted.

The ground line, however, should be plotted for cross drains, for stubs to inlets or endwalls outside the sidewalk lines, and for ditch bottom inlets placed at side streets. When mains or laterals run diagonally across the project, they should be plotted in a manner that indicates the minimum cover that will result over the pipe. Longitudinal pipes are plotted as shown in Fig. 13-4, 13-5, and 13-6.

Sequence of Plotting

The structures of the storm sewer mains along the project should always be plotted in proper sequence and without

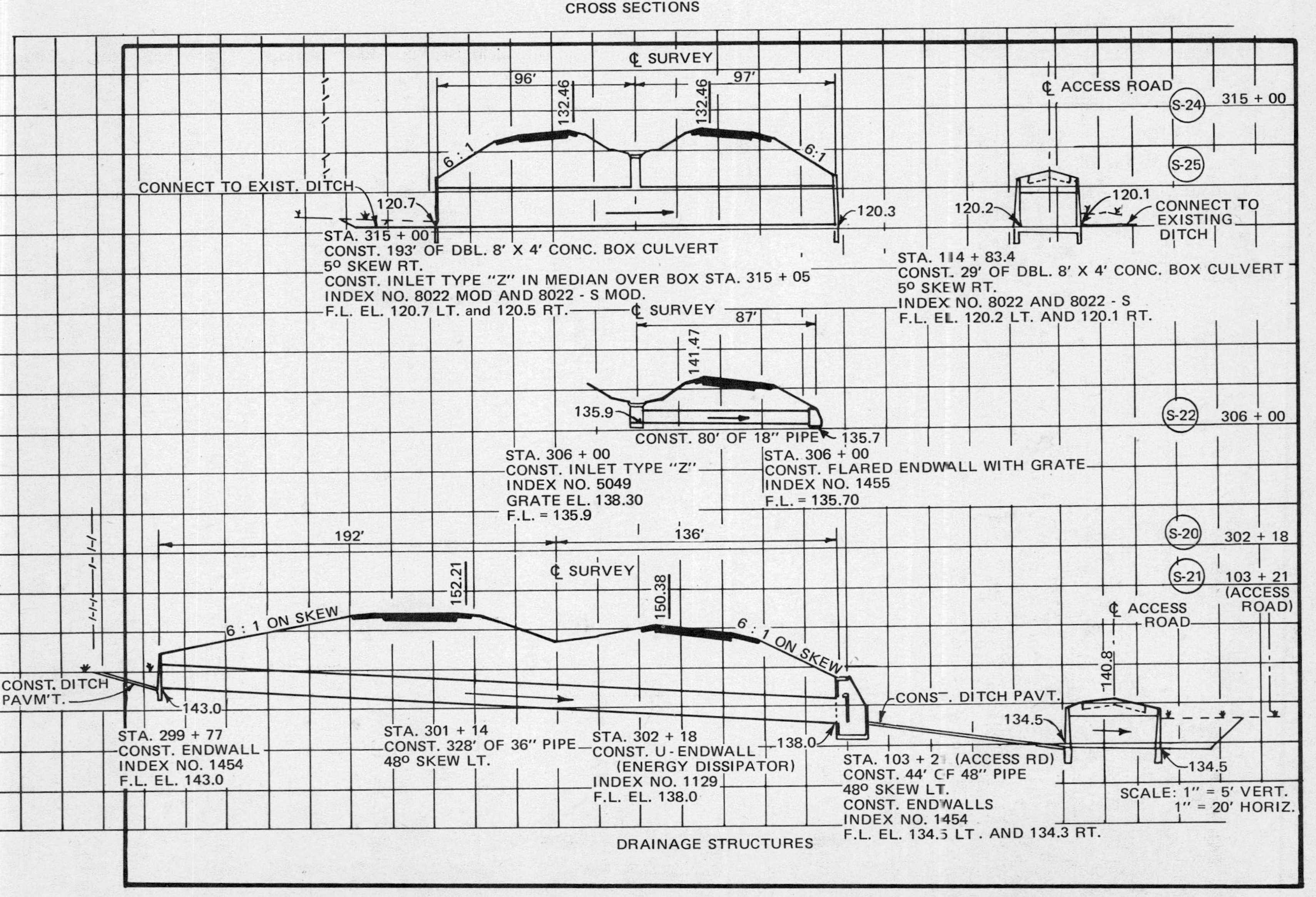

Figure 13-4
A drainage structure cross-section sheet showing a box culvert, an inlet and pipe, an endwall-pipe, and a U endwall with an energy dissipator.

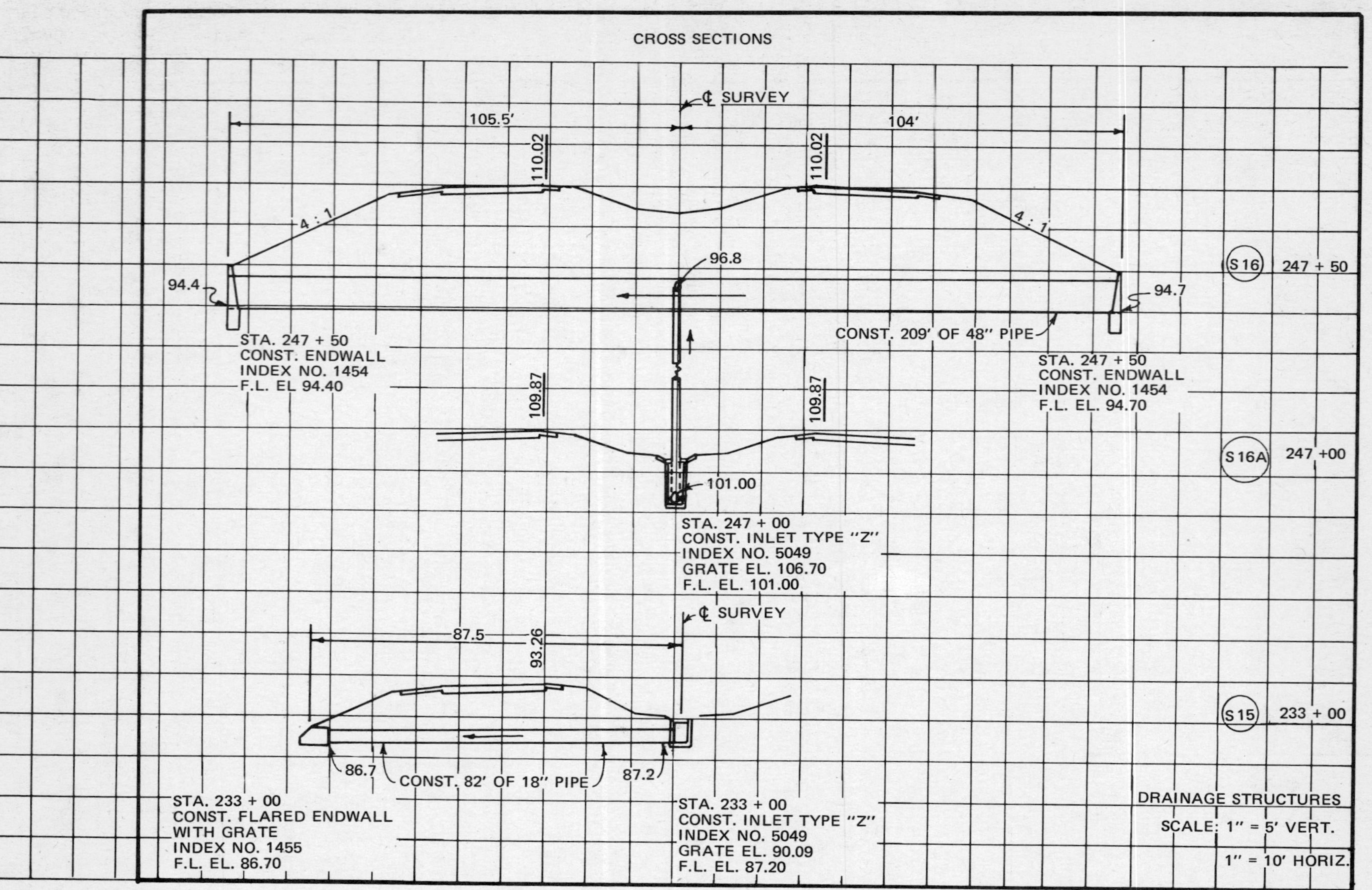

Figure 13-5
A drainage structure cross-section sheet showing endwalls, inlets, and pipe.

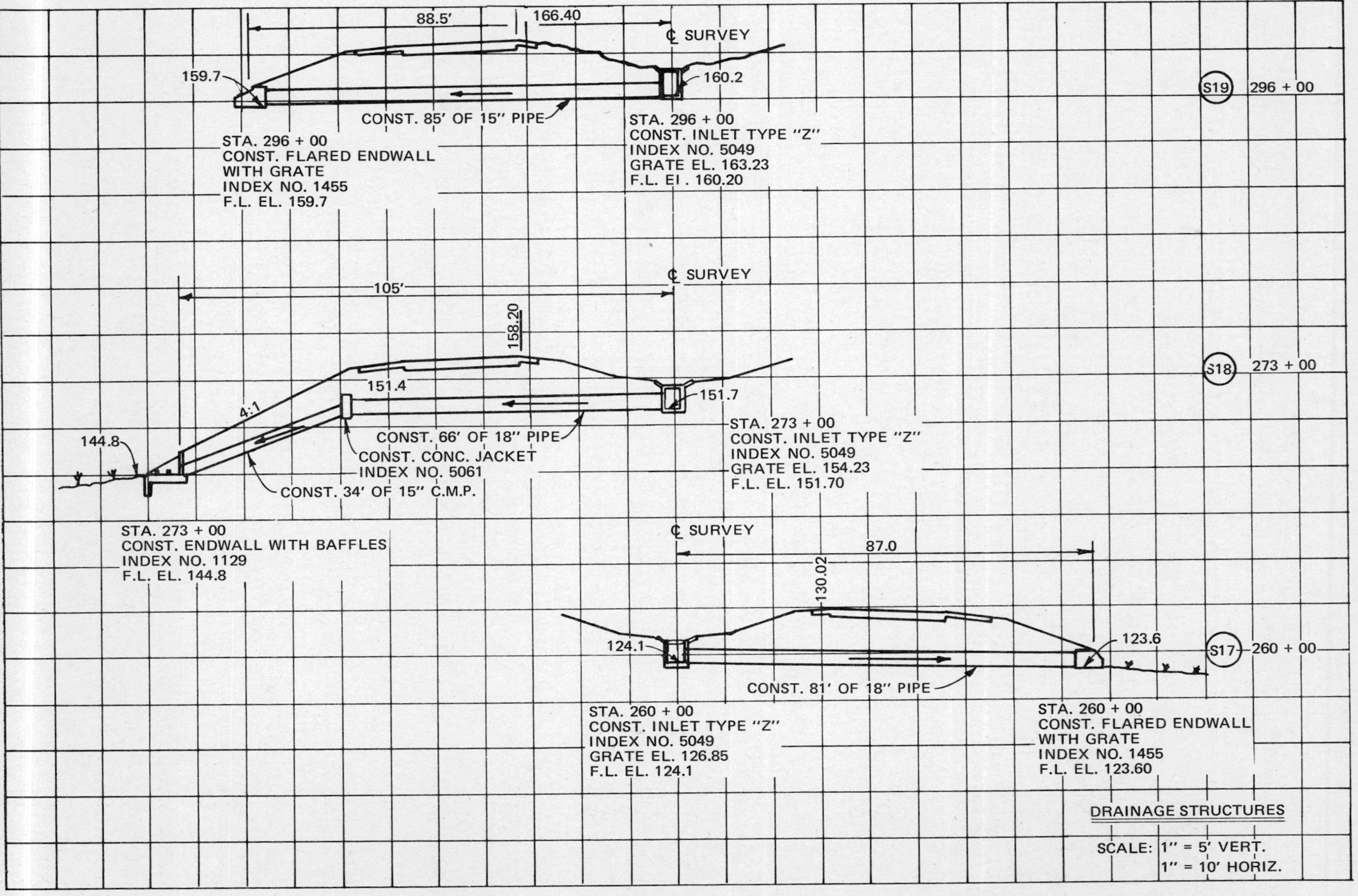

Figure 13-6
A drainage structure cross-section sheet showing a flared endwall with grate, inlets and pipe.

interruption. When inlets are placed at the ends of the returns on cross streets, they should be plotted with a section normal to the side street. These sections usually can be placed to one side of the sheet without interrupting the continuity of plotting.

Order of Systems

When systems extending along cross streets cannot be placed in regular order without interrupting plotting of the main system along the project, these structures should be plotted on separate sheets with cross references to the appropriate sheets given.

Underground Utilities

It is very important to indicate existing underground utilities on the drainage cross sections in order to detect conflicts and to alert the construction crews to instances of near conflict. The same utilities shown on the profile portion of the roadway plan-profile sheets should be shown on the drainage structure sheets in conjunction with each plotted structure. In the case of longitudinal pipes, a section should be plotted for each location where an underground line is crossed.

Notes on the Cross Drain Structure Sheets

Notes for cross-drain structures should conform to those of rural construction plans. For storm sewer systems where cross drains are not involved, notes for proposed inlets, manholes, junction boxes, and endwalls should indicate the station, type, index number, and flow line elevation. The top grade elevations of proposed manholes are also given, as are grating and inlet elevations of proposed ditch bottom inlets. Notes for pipes are to include only size and length.

Flow Line Grades

Flow line grades are indicated at appropriate places on the plotted sections. Arrows indicating the direction of flow for each pipe should be included for cross drains and in storm sewer systems. Existing structures which are to be abandoned but are to be plugged and remain in place must be plotted along with the proposed template at that location.

LEARNING ACTIVITY PACKAGE

Read Chap. 13 carefully.

Chapter 13 read ____________ *(date)*.

If the student has not understood some of the objectives (a) through (f) after completely reading the chapter, the portions of the chapter which contain those objectives should be reread.

Once the objectives in this chapter are understood, the student will be familiar with drainage structures and will be able to read the drainage structure sheets included in sets of road plans.

Objectives read and studied ____________ *(date)*.

Now take the quiz on Chap. 13. Remove it from the book and answer all the questions.

Quiz completed ____________ *(date)*.

13

QUIZ

1. What is the most important consideration in designing a road?

   ____

2. Can time be saved by the omission of drainage structures from the plans?

   ____

3. Are drainage structure sheets, like right-of-way maps, excluded from the plans? __________

4. Where are existing ground lines plotted on drainage structure sheets?

   ____

5. Sections are plotted __________ beginning at the __________ of the sheet.

6. The existing ground line elevation is placed immediately __________ the ground line at the project centerline or baseline.

7. Structures should be plotted elaborately on the drainage structure sheets. (T or F) __________

8. In skewed structures the skew angle should be noted on the sheet. (T or F) __________

9. It is helpful to show the __________ of the structure in fairly large letters near the right border of the sheet.

10. The existing ground line may be omitted from municipal drainage structures. (T or F) __________

11. Structures must always be plotted in proper sequence and without interruption. (T or F) __________

12. Underground utilities need not be shown. (T or F) __________

13. The top grade elevation of proposed manholes is given on drainage structure sheets. (T or F) __________

14. Arrows indicate the direction of water flow. (T or F) __________

15. All existing structures need to be plotted. (T or F) __________

14 RIGHT-OF-WAY

Objectives

a. Understand the method of delineating the land used for building highways
b. Understand who owns right-of-way land
c. Understand the symbols used to mark right-of-way on maps
d. Understand the United States Coast and Geodetic Survey (USC&GS) grid system with its principal meridian and base line
e. Understand the breakdown of a section into its quarters
f. Understand range and township lines

Rationale

Although right-of-way maps are not included in sets of road plans, it is important that they be explained to the student. This short chapter also explains the makeup of the grid system established by the United States Coast and Geodetic Survey to identify property.

The right-of-way (R/W) is the publicly-owned land used to build roadways, see Fig. 14-1 and 14-2.

RIGHT-OF-WAY INFORMATION

Right of way (R/W) land is used for the paved roadway and for the shoulders, ditches, and slopes. Information concerning R/W land is found in:

Figure 14-1
Right-of-way for an individual roadway.

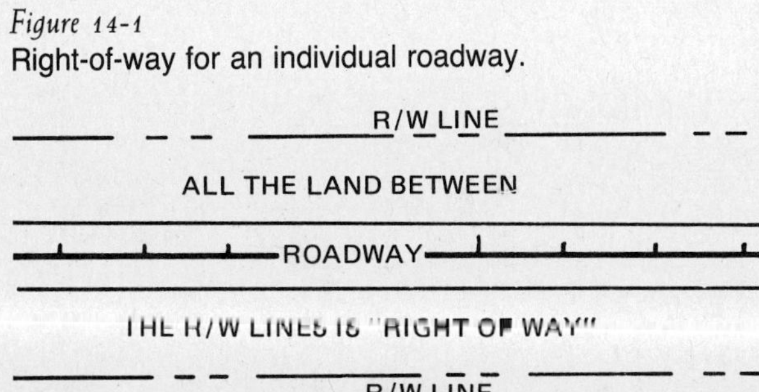

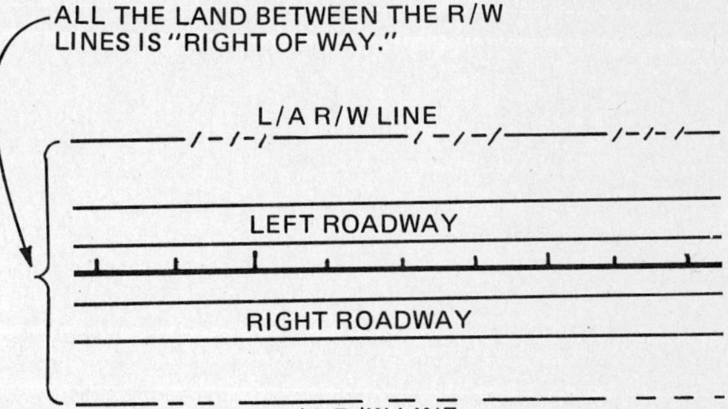

Figure 14-2
Right-of-way for a limited access divided roadway.

1. The contract plans—plan and profile sheets and typical section sheets
2. Special maps called *right-of-way maps*

Inspectors work mostly with contract plans, but sometimes it is necessary to refer to right-of-way maps. Right-of-way maps are *not* normally part of the contract plans; they are part of the *legal* description of the project.

GRID SYSTEMS

Land survey grid systems are often used to identify property. The grid system established by the United States Coast and Geodetic Survey (USC&GS) is based on lines running north-south and east-west. The lines running north and south are *principal meridians*. Those running east and west are *base lines,* see Fig. 14-3.

Township lines are established on each side of a base line and parallel to it at 6-mile (mi) [9.7-km] intervals, as shown in Fig. 14-4. The "rows" of land between township lines are identified as Township 1 North (T1N), Township 2 South (T2S), and so forth.

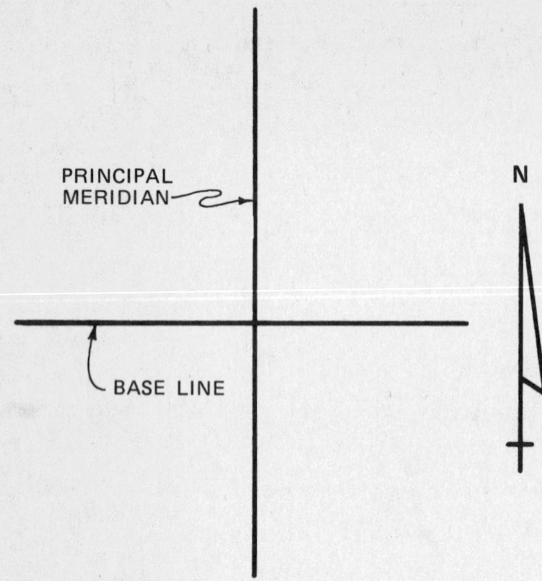

Figure 14-3
Principal meridian and base line.

Range lines are established parallel to the principal meridians at 6-mi [9.7-km] intervals as shown in Fig. 14-5. The "columns" of land between range lines are identified as Range 1 West (R1W), Range 2 East (R2E), and so forth.

When these lines are combined, a grid system is formed. Each block is 6 mi [9.7 km] square. Look carefully at Fig. 14-6, and notice that the exact location of any square can be identified by:

1. Its row north or south of the *base line*.
2. Its column east or west of the *principal meridian*.

Each of the squares in Fig. 14-6 is called a *township*. (Don't confuse this with township lines, which are the dividing lines.) *Township* means the square area of land 6 mi [9.7 km] on each side.

Usually, it is necessary to describe areas of land much smaller than a township. Since a township is 6 mi square, a logical division is 36 1-mi [1.6-km] squares. Each of these 1-mi [1.6-km] squares is called a *section*; the sections within a township are numbered as shown in Fig. 14-7.

Often a section of land must be divided into smaller pieces. The standard way of doing this is to divide the section into four quarters (quarter-sections) and if necessary each quarter is divided into four smaller quarters (quarter-quarter sections). Figure 14-8 shows how this is done and how the quarters are named.

A section —divides into→ *four quarters* —and→ *sixteen quarter-quarters*

Each quarter —divides into→ *four quarter-quarters*

Land areas usually are measured in acres. A standard section contains 640 acres [259 hectares] [1 square mile

Figure 14-4
Township lines.

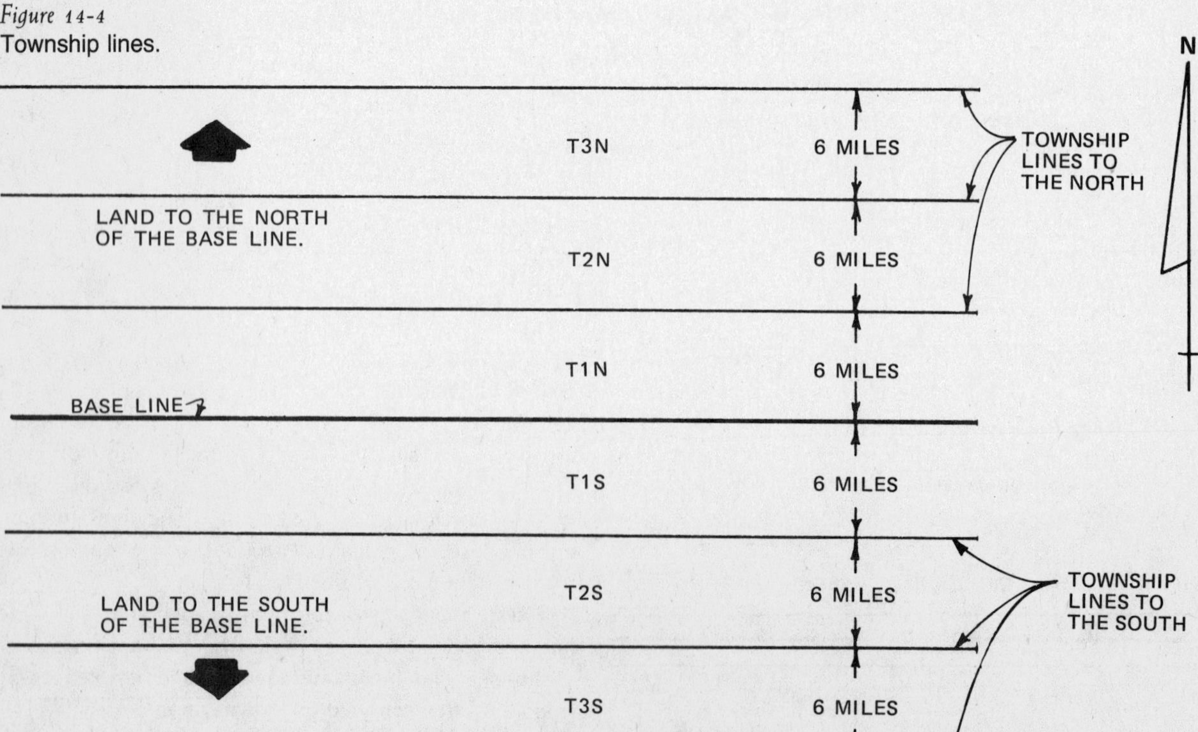

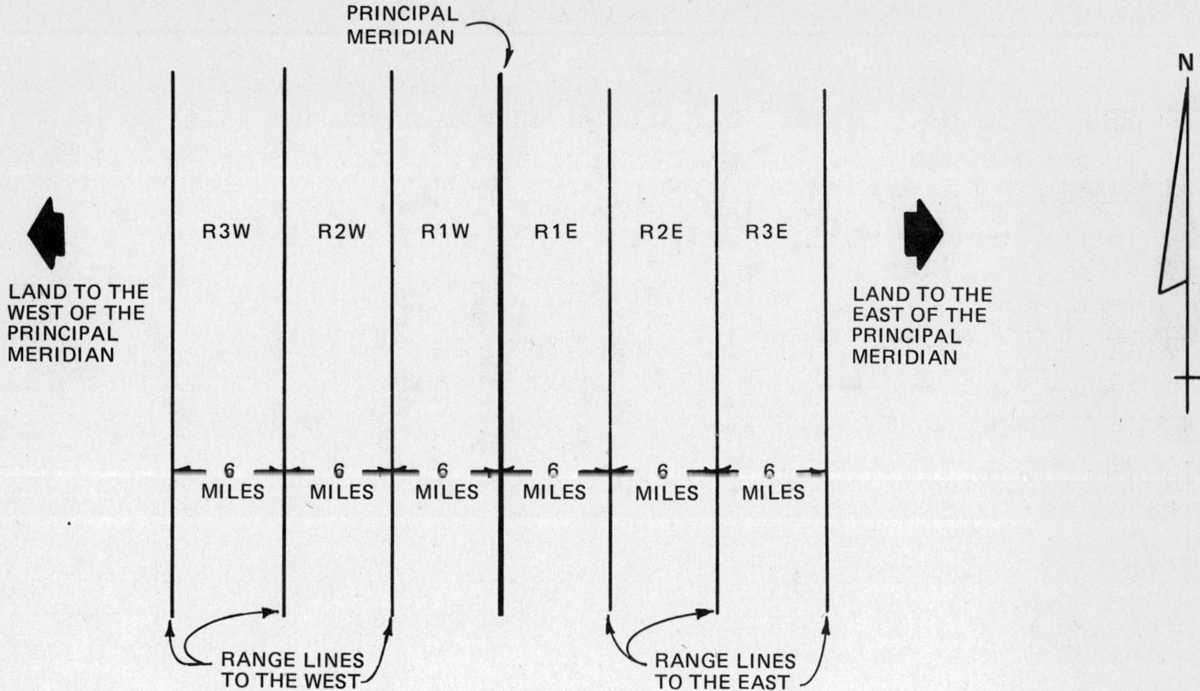

Figure 14-5
Range lines.

Figure 14-6
Grid system.

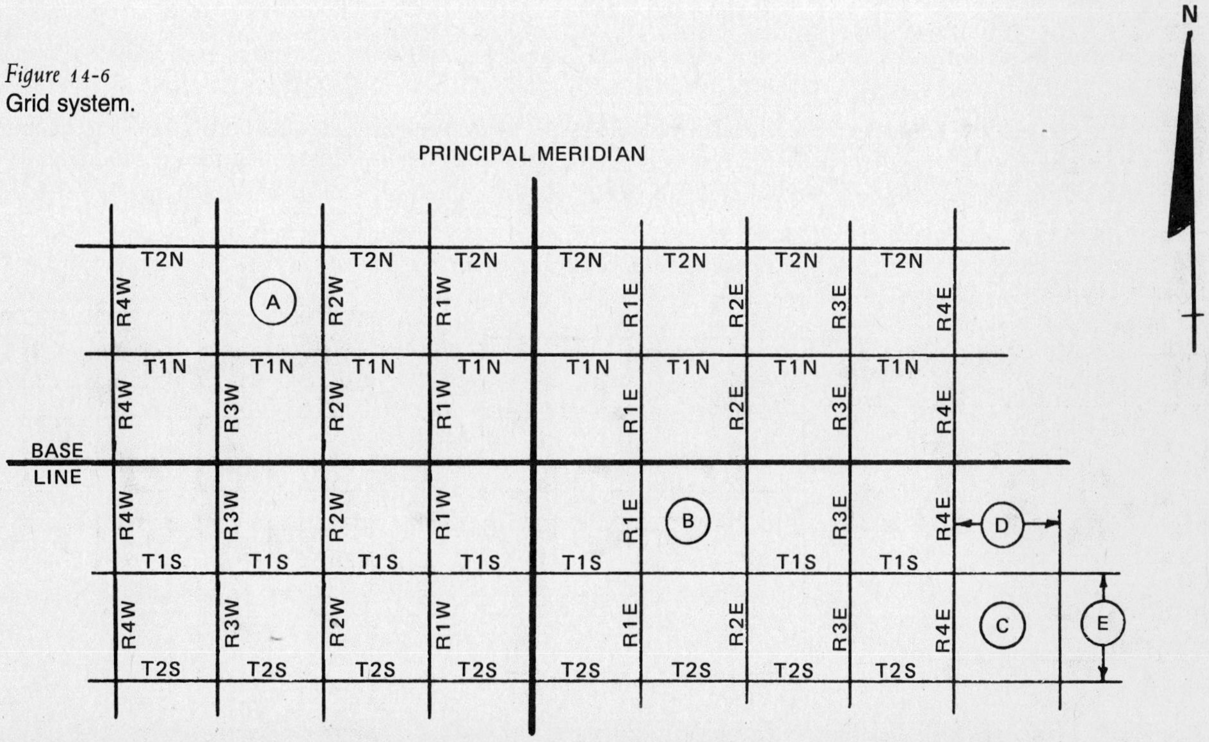

(sq mi) = 640 acres]. Generally, each quarter contains 160 acres [65 hectares], and each quarter-quarter contains 40 acres [16 hectares]. However, since some section lines are not exact or may not have been exactly marked, this is not always true.

PARCELS

Right-of-way land is secured in parcels (small parts) from the property owners. On federal-aid and limited access (L/A) projects, parcels are numbered on the R/W map and tabulated in the table at the foot of the map.

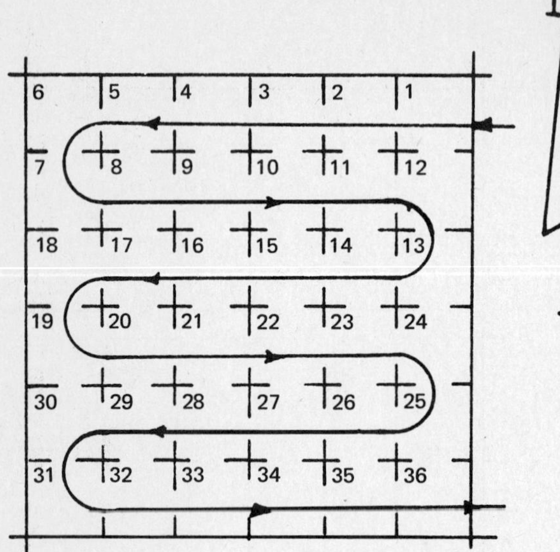

Figure 14-7
Division of a township into numbered sections.

EASEMENTS

An easement is the right or privilege of using something that is not one's own. Easements sometimes are acquired from parcel owners by the transportation department when land is required outside the R/W for a specific purpose, such as drainage, detour construction, or slope construction.

LEARNING ACTIVITY PACKAGE

Read Chap. 14 carefully.

Chapter 14 read ____________ *(date).*

If some of the objectives (a) through (f) are not clear after a complete reading of the chapter, please reread the portions of the chapter which contain those objectives. An understanding of the objectives will give the student a fair command of right-of-way; it will be enough for a start in civil drafting.

Objectives read and studied ____________ *(date).*

Now take the removable quiz on Chap. 14. Remove it from the book and answer all the questions.

Quiz completed ____________ *(date).*

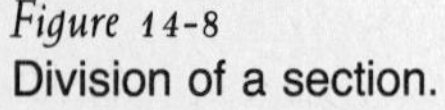

Figure 14-8
Division of a section.

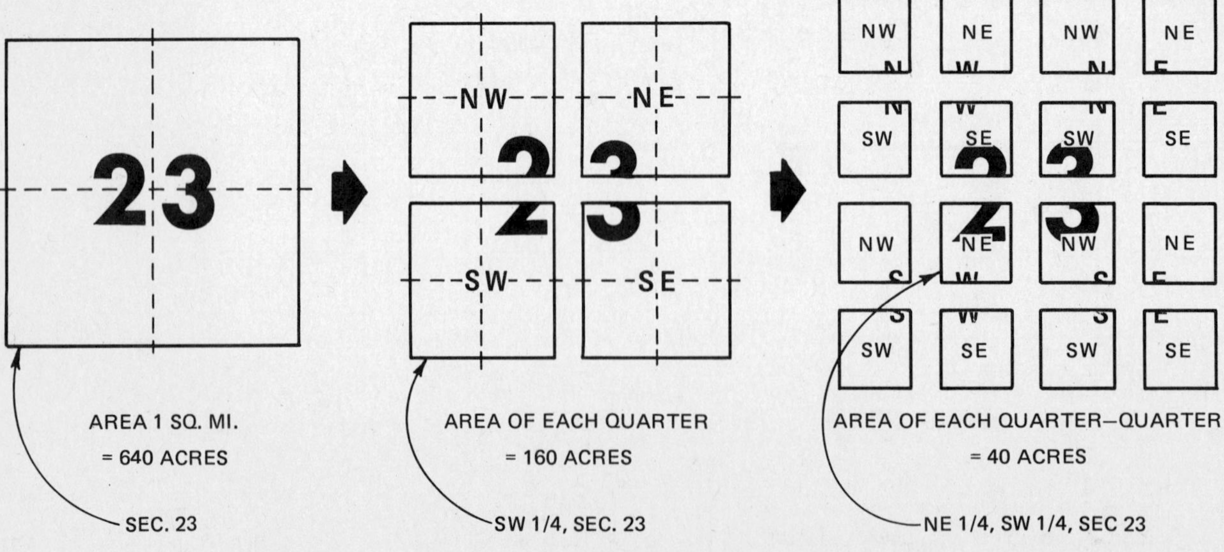

14 QUIZ

1. Highways are constructed within the ____________________.
2. Who owns the right-of-way? ____________________
3. Information about the right-of-way can be found in the ____________ and in ________________.
4. Are right-of-way maps normally part of the contract plans? __________

Refer to Fig. 14-6 for questions 5 through 10.

5. The description for square *A* is ____________________.
6. The description for square *B* is ____________________.
7. The description for square *C* is ____________________.
8. Dimension *D* is __________ mi.
9. Dimension *E* is __________ mi.
10. The area of square *C* is __________ sq mi.
11. Two lines are established as starting points for land survey grids: The east-west line is the __________ and the north-south line is the __________
12. Lines 6 mi [9.7 km] apart and parallel to the base line are __________ lines.
13. Lines 6 mi [9.7 km] apart and parallel to the principal meridian are ________________ lines.
14. The areas defined by township and range lines are called __________
15. The area of each township is __________ sq mi.
16. Townships are divided into 36 areas called __________
17. The area of each section is __________ acres.
18. Sections are divided into __________ sections and __________ sections.

15 MATHEMATICAL PROCEDURES

Objectives

a. Learn how to use a planimeter and a planimeter conversion chart.
b. Learn to calculate roadway and pipe slopes
c. Learn to calculate cubic yards of excavation the easy way through the use of charts
d. Study Fig. 15-6, the chart for calculating vertical curves. (Beginning drafters are not required to calculate curves, but after a few years it will be part of their work.)
e. Become aware of the useful relations and formulas available at the end of the chapter

Rationale

Students should know how to use a planimeter and a conversion table for a planimeter. The student should also learn how to do slope calculations; they are very simple, and the beginning drafter may be required to compute slopes. It is also useful to be able to use charts to quickly estimate the displaced soil volume for pipes.

SCOPE OF THE MATHEMATICS CHAPTER

Since this is a text on drafting, not engineering, we will give only a few types of problems. Beginning drafters in industry are not required to solve even the few types of problems presented here. Charts which give the excavation in cubic yards per lineal foot of corrugated pipe culvert or concrete pipe culvert are given here, since they would be of value to beginning technicians. Some useful formulas are also provided for future reference.

PLANIMETER

A planimeter (Fig. 15-1) is a device used to measure areas directly from a map or chart. Drafters often employ a planimeter to measure square yards or acres of land enclosed within a certain area. The volume of material (in cubic yards) per 50-feet (ft) [15.2-m] length of various geometric areas can also be obtained by using a planimeter. A technician can planimeter the roadway ditch cross sections and compute how much earth will be removed in digging the roadside ditches.

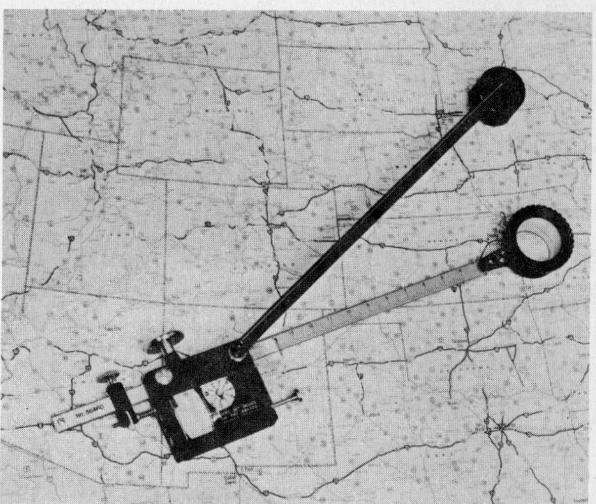

Figure 15-1
Planimeter

Conversion Table

After circling an area with the pin and movable arm of a planimeter, a reading appears on the planimeter dial. This dial reading in itself would mean nothing, but by using the horizontal and vertical scales of the map from which the reading was taken, a conversion can be made that will give the enclosed area in square yards or acres (or the actual cubic yards for every 50 ft [15.2 m] of length).

Figure 15-2 is the conversion chart to be used with a planimeter.

SLOPE CALCULATIONS

The method of calculating slopes for roadways, pipes, or anything else that is not horizontal is given in Fig.

CONVERSION TABLE FOR PLANIMETER

PLANIMETER SET FOR DIRECT READING OF
CUBIC YARDS FOR 50 FEET

SCALES	MULTIPLY PLANIMETER READING BY	TO GET
1″ = 5′ VERT. 1″ = 5′ HORIZ.	0.50	CU. YDS. PER 50′
1″ = 5′ VERT. 1″ = 10′ HORIZ.	1.00	CU. YDS. PER 50′
1″ = 10′ VERT. 1″ = 10′ HORIZ.	2.00	CU. YDS. PER 50′
1″ = 10′ VERT. 1″ = 20′ HORIZ.	4.00	CU. YDS. PER 50′
1″ = 20′	0.48	SQ. YDS.
1″ = 30′	1.081	SQ. YDS.
1″ = 40′	1.922	SQ. YDS.
1″ = 50′	3.000	SQ. YDS.
1″ = 100′	12.000	SQ. YDS.
1″ = 200′	0.009917	ACRES
1″ = 300′	0.02231	ACRES
1″ = 400′	0.03967	ACRES
1″ = 500′	0.06198	ACRES
1″ = 600′	0.08926	ACRES

Figure 15-2
Planimeter conversion chart.

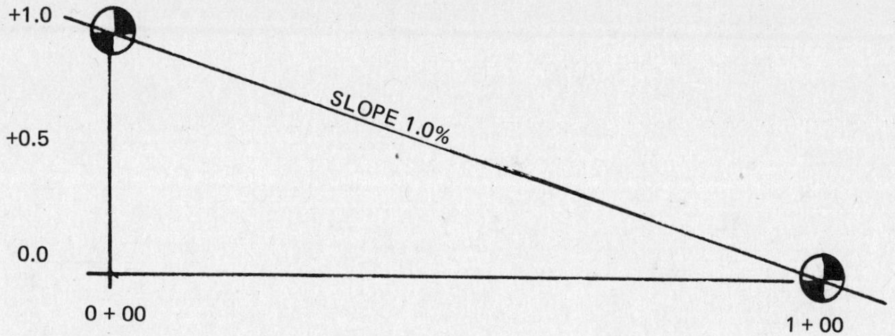

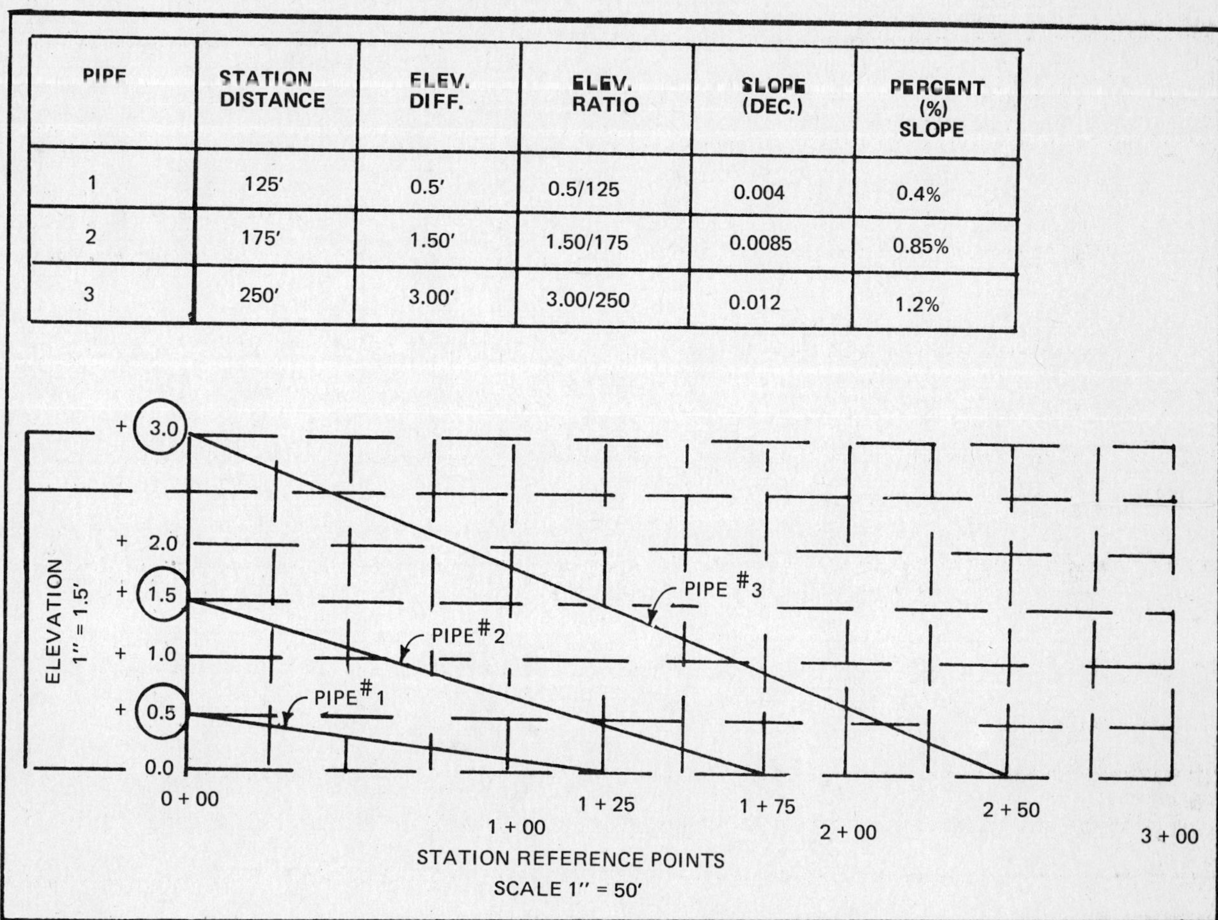

PIPE	STATION DISTANCE	ELEV. DIFF.	ELEV. RATIO	SLOPE (DEC.)	PERCENT (%) SLOPE
1	125′	0.5′	0.5/125	0.004	0.4%
2	175′	1.50′	1.50/175	0.0085	0.85%
3	250′	3.00′	3.00/250	0.012	1.2%

Figure 15-3
Slope determination chart.

15-3. Figure 15-3 is made up for three pipes on different slopes, but it can also be used for a section of highway.

DRAINAGE STRUCTURE EXCAVATION

Drainage structures require excavation, and it is necessary to calculate the number of cubic yards of dirt to be removed. This calculation can be done easily just by consulting the charts in Fig. 15-4 and 15-5. Calculation of dirt excavation is especially difficult if the pipe culvert is the arched variety, but even this calculation can be done easily by reading the corrugated arch pipe culvert chart in Fig. 15-4.

Although it is not anticipated that beginning drafters would be called upon to calculate vertical curves, contained in Fig. 15-6 are formulas and examples for such calculations.

Figure 15-7 gives a group of useful relations that will be of help in industrial drafting work. They are not to be learned but should serve as a handy reference.

DIAMETER SIZE	EXCAVATION YD3/LIN. FT
6″	0.00704
8″	0.01296
10″	0.02037
12″	0.02926
15″	0.04556
18″	0.06556
21″	0.08926
24″	0.11630
30″	0.18185
36″	0.26185

DIAMETER SIZE	EXCAVATION YD3/LIN. FT
42″	0.35630
48″	0.46556
54″	0.58889
60″	0.72740
66″	0.88000
72″	1.04704
78″	1.22889
84″	1.42555
96″	1.86185

SIZE			EXCAVATION
RISE		SPAN	YD3/LIN. FT
11″	X	18″	0.04074
13″	X	22″	0.05926
16″	X	25″	0.08148
18″	X	29″	0.10370
22″	X	36″	0.16296
27″	X	43″	0.23704
31″	X	50″	0.32222
36″	X	58″	0.42222
40″	X	65″	0.52963
44″	X	72″	0.65185

Figure 15-4
Volume of excavation when using corrugated arch pipe culvert.

EXAMPLE A drafter might need to convert acres into square yards. To convert 4.65 acres into square yards, multiply 4.65 times 4840 to give 22,506 square yards.

These useful formulas also are not to be studied or memorized but should be used as reference material (also refer to Fig. 15-8).

INSIDE DIAMETER (INCHES)	SHELL THICKNESS (INCHES)	DISTANCE F.L. TO TOP SHELL (FEET)	WATER AREA (FT2)	DISPLACED SOIL VOL. YD3/LIN. FT
12	2	1.17	0.785	0.05171
15	2	1.42	1.227	0.07293
18	2	1.67	1.767	0.09777
24	2-1/2	2.21	3.142	0.16989
30	3	2.75	4.909	0.26181
36	3-1/2	3.29	7.069	0.37349
42	4-1/2	3.88	9.621	0.52543
48	4-1/2	4.38	12.566	0.65631
54	6	5.00	15.904	0.87994
60	6	5.50	19.635	1.04718
66	6-1/2	6.04	23.758	1.26070
72	7	6.58	28.274	1.47327
78	7-1/2	7.13	33.183	1.74715
84	8	7.67	38.485	2.02004
90	8-1/2	8.21	44.179	2.31273
96	9	8.75	50.265	2.62519
102	9-1/2	9.29	56.745	2.86054
108	10	9.83	63.617	3.30957

Figure 15-5
Displaced soil volume from round pipe.

LEARNING ACTIVITY PACKAGE

Read Chap. 15 carefully. The material in this chapter should be used as reference material and should not be memorized. Though there is no quiz for this chapter, take the time to learn how to use the planimeter with proficiency.

Chapter 15 read ____________ *(date).*

Objectives read ____________ *(date).*

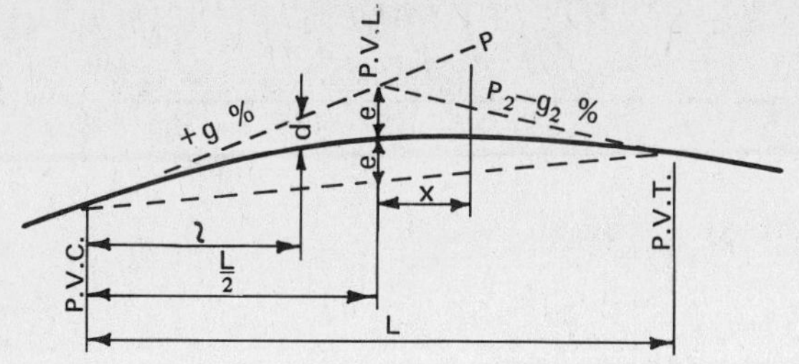

Length of vertical summit curves should provide required sight distance. Note that all horizontal distances shown on this page (L, ζ, ζ_1, ζ_2, χ_1, χ_2) are expressed in 100-ft stations. Work for "e" first and then use

$$y = e\frac{x_2}{\frac{1}{2}L^2}$$

Formulas

x = distance from P.G. to point wanted

L = length of curve in stations

A = algebraic difference of grades $+ g_1\% - (-g_2\%)$

$$e = \frac{AL}{8}$$

$$d = \frac{\zeta \cdot A}{2L} \qquad d = 4e\left(\frac{\zeta}{L}\right)^2 \qquad y = \frac{x^2A}{2L}$$

Example

Given	Required
$g_1\% = +3.00\%$	A, e, and d
$g_2\% = -2.00\%$	
$L = 3.00$	
$\zeta = 0.50$	

Solution

$A = 3.00 - (-2.00) = 5.00$

$$e = \frac{5.00 \times 3.00}{8} = 1.875 \text{ ft}$$

$$d = \frac{0.50^2 \times 5.00}{2 \times 3.00} = 0.208 \text{ ft}$$

$$\text{also, } d = 4(1.875)\left(\frac{0.50}{3.00}\right)^2 = 0.208 \text{ ft}$$

To find Sta. of P.V.I. when elevations of P_1 and P_2 are known.

$$\text{Formula: } x = \frac{\text{elev. } P_1 - \text{elev. } P_2}{A}$$

Example

Given	Required
Elev. $P_1 = 154.50$	x = distance in 100-ft stations from know point to P.V.I.
Elev. $P_2 = 150.00$	
$A = 5.00$	

Solution

$$x = \frac{154.50 - 150.00}{5.00} = 0.90 \text{ (100-ft Stations)}$$

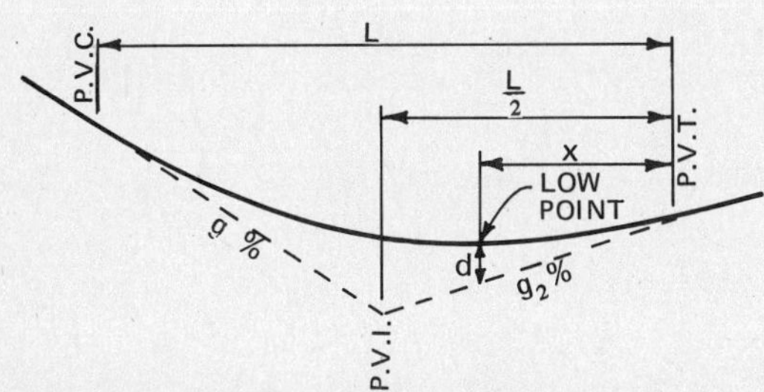

Length of vertical sag curve should provide headlight illuminations for a safe stopping distance.

To find low point on sag curve:
Formulas

$$x = g \text{ (lesser gradient) } \frac{L}{A}$$

$$d \text{ (at low point)} = \frac{x^2\,A}{2L}$$

Note: High point on summit curve can be found using the same method.

Example

Given	Required
$g_1\% = -3.00\%$	x and d
$g_2 = +2.00\%$	
$L = 3.00$	
$A = 5.00$	

Solution

$$x = 2.00 \times \frac{3.00}{5.00} = 1.20 \qquad d = \frac{1.20^2 \times 5.00}{2 \times 3.00}$$

Figure 15-6
Roads: Vertical Curves (Parabolic); vertical curve calculations.

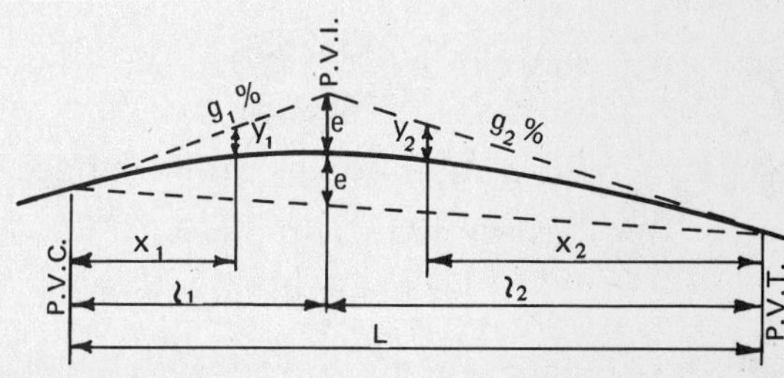

Unsymmetrical Vertical Curves used to fit unusual conditions.

Formulas

$$e = \frac{\zeta_1\zeta_2}{a\,(\zeta_1 + \zeta_2)}\,(A) \qquad y_1 = e\left(\frac{x_1}{\zeta_1}\right)^2 \qquad y_2 = e\left(\frac{x_2}{\zeta_2}\right)^2$$

Example

Given	Required
$g_1 = +3.00\%$	e, y, and y_2
$g_2 = -2.00\%$	
$L = 4.00$	
$\zeta_1 = 1.50$	
$\zeta_2 = 2.50$	
$x_1 = 0.50$	
$x_2 = 1.00$	

Solution

$$e = \frac{1.50 \times 2.50}{2\,(1.50 + 2.50)}\,(3.00 + 2.00) = 2.35 \text{ ft}$$

$$y_1 = 2.35\left(\frac{0.50}{1.50}\right)^2 = 0.26 \text{ ft}$$

$$y_2 = 2.35\left(\frac{1.00}{2.50}\right)^2 = 0.38 \text{ ft}$$

USEFUL RELATIONSHIPS

Lineal feet	×	.00019	=	miles
Lineal yards	×	.0006	=	miles
Square inches	×	.007	=	square feet
Square feet	×	.111	=	square yards
Square yards	×	.0002067	=	acres
Acres	×	4840	=	square yards
Cubic inches	×	.00058	=	cubic feet
Cubic feet	×	.03704	=	cubic yards
Links	×	.22	=	yards
Links	×	.66	=	feet
Feet	×	1.5	=	links
360°	=	21600′	=	1,296,000″
Radius	=	arc of 57.2957790°		

Arc of 1° (radius = 1) = 0.017453292

$\pi = 3.141592654$

$\sqrt{\pi} = 1.772453851$

Curvature of the earth's surface = approx. 0.7 ft in 1 mi.

Error in chaining of 0.01 ft in 100 ft due to:

1. Length of tape error of 0.01 ft.
2. Alignment. One end 1.4 ft out of line.
3. Sag of tape at center of 0.61 ft.
4. Temperature difference of 15°.
5. Difference of pull of 15 lbs.

Figure 15-7
Standard conversions.

USEFUL FORMULAS

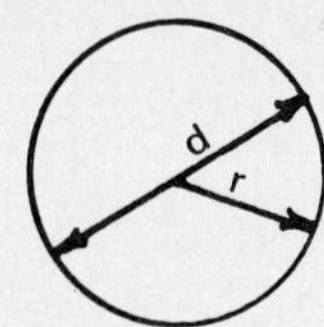

Circumference	$d = 2r$
Diameter	$= 3.1416$
Radius	$C = d$
Area	$A = r^2$

1 mile = 5280 ft

1 sq. acre = 43,560 sq. ft

231 cu. in = 1 gallon

7.48 gallons per cubic foot

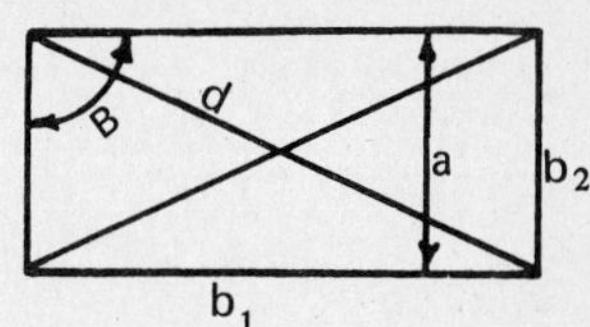

Rectangle: A parallelogram whose sides are perpendicular but unequal.

C = circumference	$C = 2\ (b_1 + b_2)$
$a = b_2$	
A = area	$A = b_1 b_2$
B = angle	$B = 90°$
d = diagonal	$d = b_1^2 + b_2^2$

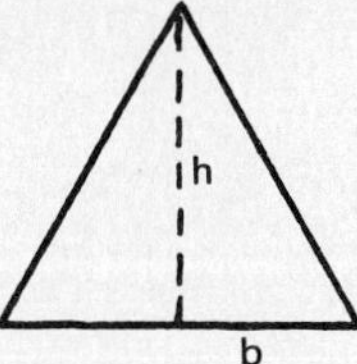

A = Area
h = Height
b = Base

$$A = \frac{1}{2}\ h\ b$$

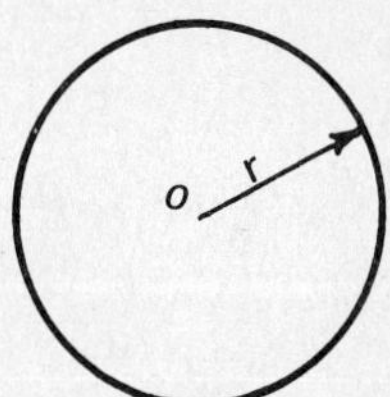

Sphere: A solid figure bounded by a surface all points of which are a distance "r" from a given point "O" called the center.

A = area: r = radius	$A = 4\ r^2$
V = volume	$V = \frac{4}{3}\ r^3$

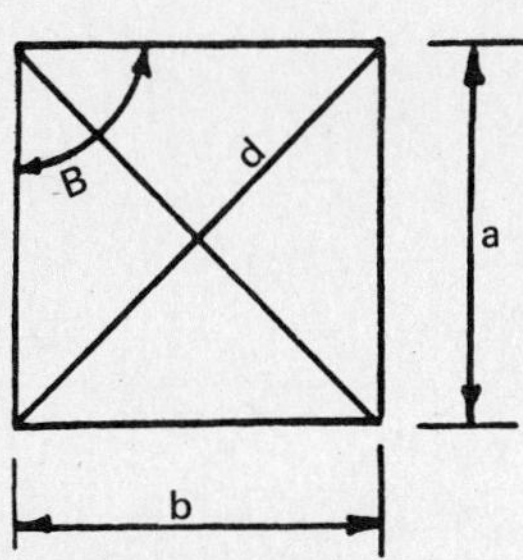

Square: A parallelogram whose sides are equal and perpendicular.

C = circumference	$C = 4b$
d = diagonal	$d = b\ 2$
a = altitude	$a = b$
A = area	$A = b^2$
B = angle	$B = 90°$

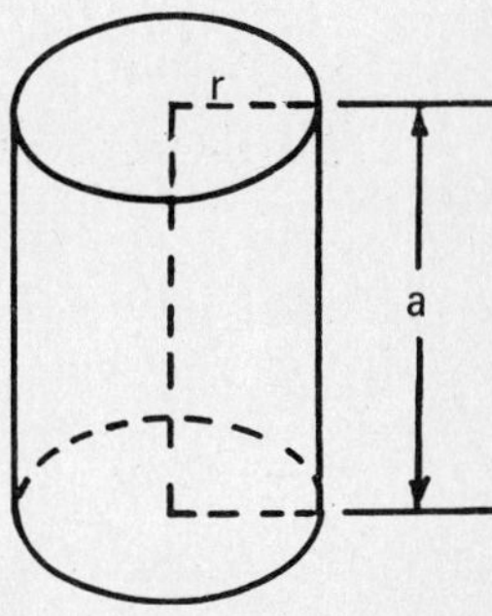

Right circular cylinder: A solid figure traced by a rectangle of height "a" and with "r" rotated about the side "a" as an axis.

$A = 2\ r\ a$

$V = r^2\ a$

Figure 15-8
Further useful formulas.

16 LAND DEVELOPMENT

Objectives

a. Learn who develops land
b. Learn that a legal description of a piece of property is always required
c. Know the importance of the base material under the property to be developed
d. Understand that soil surveys may be necessary, especially for multistory buildings
e. Learn about the use of television cameras to discover the exact locations of connectors and bad spots in underground piping
f. Understand the use of the transit for setting pile locations

Rationale

Land development is an important part of civil engineering drafting. Some consulting engineering offices do no road design; instead they design subdivisions and survey and plot lots for developers and private individuals.

In this chapter a complete land development from vacant property through completion of a four-unit townhouse is shown in detail. The student will learn all the steps necessary in building a typical townhouse. This chapter includes pictures of all stages of the townhouse, a history of the project, descriptions of the property and subsoil, and descriptions for connecting to city sewers and locating and driving piling.

Once the student is acquainted with road design, land development comes easily. Drainage of storm waters, which was covered under road design, especially on drainage maps, is also of great importance in land development.

WHO WANTS LAND DEVELOPMENT?

A landowner (a private citizen, corporation, partnership, realty firm, or the city, county, state, or federal government) owns a parcel of land (large or small) and has an intended use for it.

DEVELOPMENT SIZE

An architect could handle the job of developing a lot into a townhouse complex. Larger developments, because of more complex drainage situations and required environmental studies, are usually handled by consulting civil engineering firms.

A Townhouse Project

We will follow the development of a four-unit townhouse complex. Work on this townhouse is starting just as this textbook is being written, and its construction will be followed step by step. Pictures will show all phases of the work, from clearing the lot through the final topping of the structure.

Legal Description of the Property

The property involved in this project is Lot 10, Block 8, Hillsboro Shores Subdivision, in the city of Pompano Beach, Florida. The lot size is 100 × 100 feet (ft) [30.5 × 30.5 m].

Acquiring the Property

A real estate developing firm has found a choice lot on Spring Street in Hillsboro Shores, which is a subdivision in the city of Pompano Beach, Florida. This land is less than 300 ft [91 m] from historic Hillsboro Inlet on the east coast of Florida. Situated just 300 ft [91 m] from the ocean on a quiet street near the ocean highway, it has a very desirable location.

HISTORY OF THE PROPERTY

The abstract of title shows that the original owners of the land were Spanish conquistadors back in the sixteenth century. At one time within the last 70 years the land was sold for $1 per acre. At this writing, the lot has a value of $350,000 per acre. It has seen a lot of improvement and a lot of inflation.

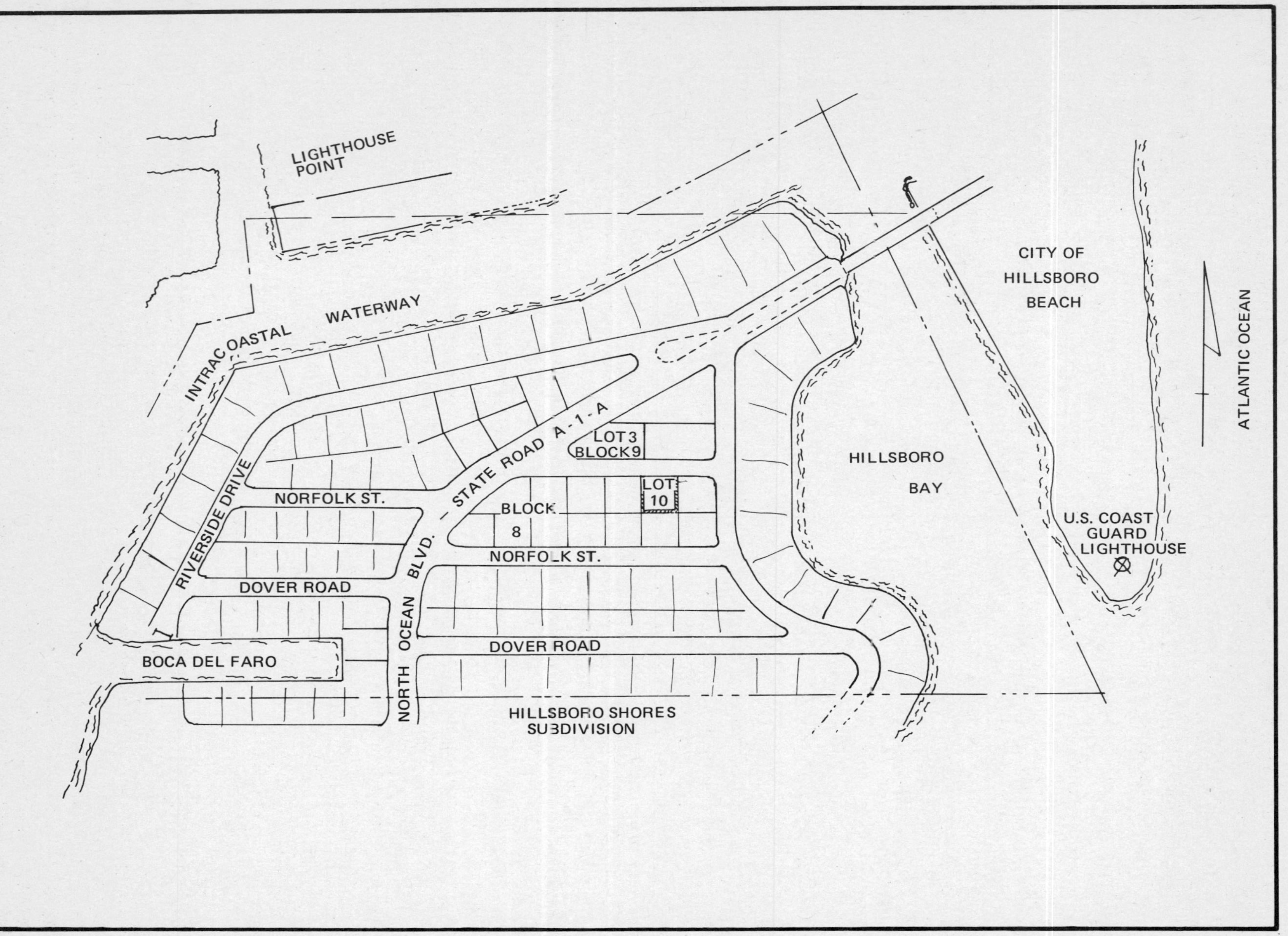

Figure 16-1
Map of the area in which Lot 10 is located.

At one time sailing ships docked at Lot 3 of Block 9, just 200 ft [61 m] northwest of this lot (see Fig. 16-1). What does this mean? It means that most of this area must have been part of the Atlantic Ocean then. Wooden sailing ships drew quite a lot of water. If there were ships with drafts of 8 to 12 ft [2.4 to 3.7 m] docked 200 ft [61 m] from this lot, then Lot 10 must have been covered with at least 6 ft [1.8 m] of water. Over a period of many years, mangrove trees have built up the ocean front land into usable land.

A pioneer developer of the 1940s saw the potential of the area, bought the land for next to nothing, and started pumping ocean sand into the area hydraulically. He reclaimed the mangrove swamp, laid out and built roads, and developed the land into a subdivision. After this subdividing, the land had reached a value of over $8000 per acre.

WHAT KIND OF BASE IS UNDER THE PROPERTY

The student may wonder what kind of base is under the lot and how firm it would be with chopped-down mangrove swamp land beneath it. When the hydraulic dredging of the ocean sand was done, the mangroves were chopped down and allowed to lie where they fell. These trees slowly oxidize and become a muck which settles each year. The new owner also must have wondered about this, as the design for the new townhouse called for two-and-one-half stories with solid poured concrete walls between all the units.

Soil Survey

A soil survey was conducted by a consulting civil engineer, and piling was ordered for the area. The piling was driven 16 to 20 ft [4.9 to 6.1 m] into the ground. This forced the piling into the coral rock which underlies the area. Florida is made up of a gigantic layer of coral rock, which is very stable.

Since mangrove trees oxidize slowly, the land on this lot sinks into the ocean at the rate of 0.021 ft/year [6.4 mm/yr]. To prevent the townhouse from experiencing a Leaning Tower of Pisa effect or having all its door frames crack at the corners in half a century, the engineer said that the townhouse must rest on piling (see Fig. 16-2).

Elevation of the Lot and the Townhouse

This particular lot has a land elevation of 5.5 to 6.0 ft [1.7 to 1.8 m] above mean sea level. Recently the Army Corps of Engineers decided that all property built in the future in this area should have a first floor elevation of 8 ft [2.4 m] above sea level to prevent possible flood damage during hurricanes. This requirement will cost the developer a large sum of money; an extended stem wall will be built on top of the grade beam and the extra space within the grade beam and stem wall will be filled with suitable sand fill. The stem wall structure is shown in Fig. 16-2.

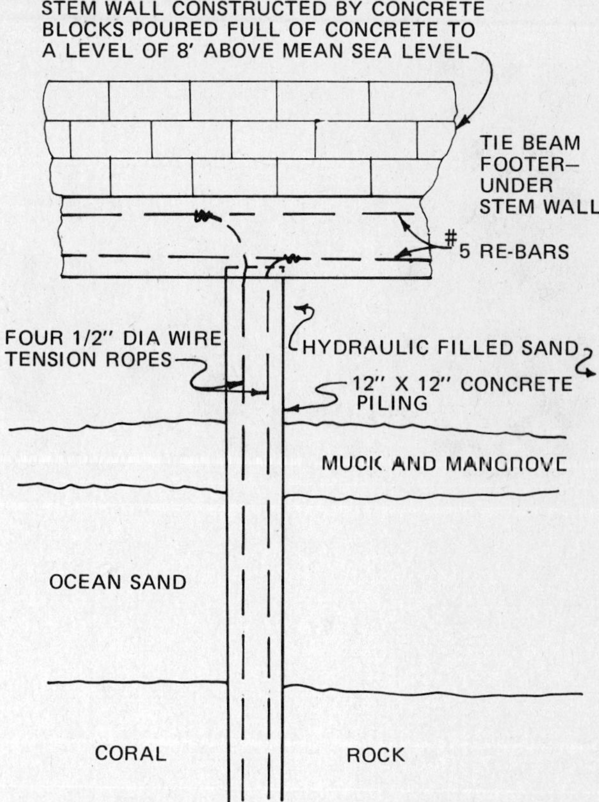

Figure 16-2
Method of connecting piling to the tie beam footer and stem wall.

Cleaning the Lot

In order to lay out the property for piling, the lot had to be cleared of the debris that had accumulated over the past 30 years, since the land was reclaimed from the sea and the mangrove swamps (Fig. 16-3).

CONNECTING THE SANITARY SEWER

The contractor set up a trailer as an office. This trailer had a rest room that served the needs of the workers on the project, but the lot needed a connection to a city sanitary sewer. The trailer was positioned on the lot at the exact location of the connection to the city sanitary sewer, according to city records.

Figure 16-4 shows a digging machine probing for the Y connection to the city sewer line. After probing with

Figure 16-3
Loader clearing the lot of debris *(Atlantic Florida Corp).*

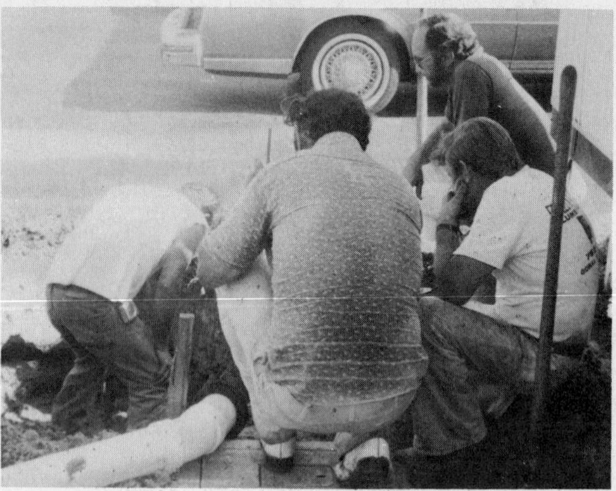

Figure 16-5
Where is the sanitary sewer line? *(Atlantic Florida Corp).*

Figure 16-4
Using a backhoe to probe for the Y connection to the city sewer line *(Atlantic Florida Corp).*

a steel probe and digging with the machine for half a day, the group of workers were forced to abandon the search. The city had indicated that the connection would be found 18 inches (in) [46 cm] west of the east lot line, that is, 18 in [46 cm] inside the boundary of Lot 10, but the city was incorrect.

Finding the Connection to the City Sewer

It was a frustrating experience for the contractor. A little thing like an improper location of the connection to the city sanitary sewer main can cause so much trouble. At today's prices (who knows what they will be in the future) the costs are: two plumbers at $15/hour (hr), plus a grader supervisor at $25/hr, plus the contractor's own salary for four hours. This means that the city's error cost the contractor $220 in labor loss alone, plus the contractor's own salary. Figure 16-5 shows the intensity of the search for the **Y** connection to the city sanitary sewer. The man most concerned is the contractor, who must pay the wages of all the other workers, who get paid whether the work is completed or not.

The City Finds Its Lost Sewer Connection

The next step, since the location given by the city engineer was incorrect, was to make the city provide an accurate location for the connection.

The contractor called the city engineer's office and asked them to bring in their television equipment to locate the connection. The city immediately brought its Telespection system (Fig. 16-6) to the lot. Telespection is a system using a crawling television camera that photographs the inside of the sewer drain lines as it rolls along. The picture is viewed on a screen in a city truck located nearby. The city discovered the connector 10 ft [3.0 m] into the asphalt driveway of the four-unit condominium located on Lot 11, see Fig. 16-7. The city, being at fault, was obligated to dig up the driveway on Lot 11, and then, after the connection was made by the contractor, the city refilled the hole, compacted the dirt, and built a new asphalt driveway for the condominium.

The manhole where the television camera was put down was located 159 ft [48.5 m] west of the east lot line of Lot 10, see Fig. 16-8. The television camera discovered that the exact location of the connection was 11.5 ft [3.5 m] from where the city's records had shown it to be.

Figures 16-9 to 16-11 show details of the rest of the sewer connecting project.

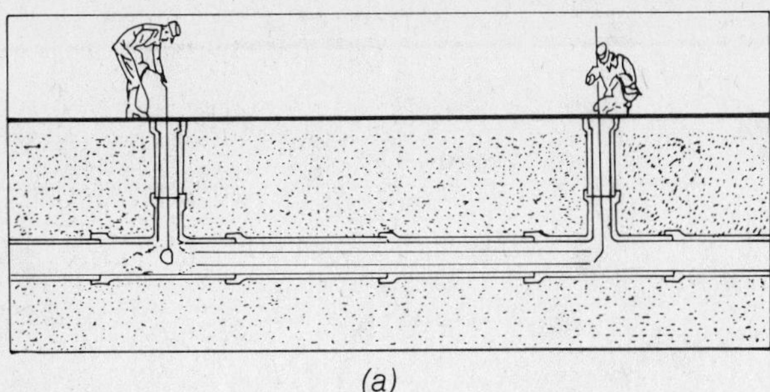

(a)

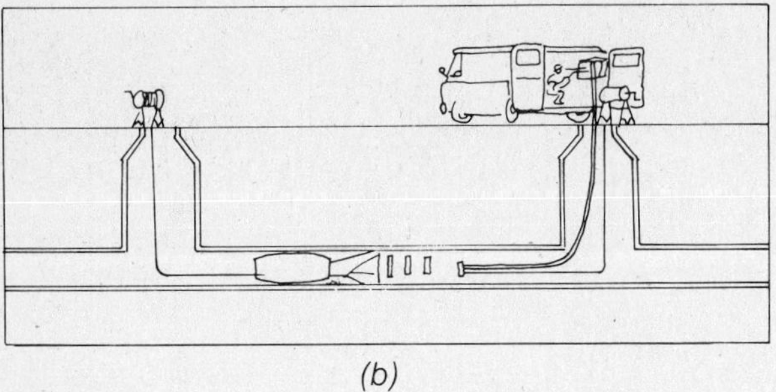

(b)

Figure 16-6
Sewer Inspection (*a*) In the 1920s, "lamping the line" was tops in sewer inspection. (*b*) In the 1980s, Telespection (a television camera sewer line checker) and Telegrout Service Systems are the optimum.

CONNECTING TO CITY WATER

Before making a sewer connection, the city crew came out to make the water connection. Since water was available only on the other side of Spring Street, it was necessary to tunnel under the street to reach the supply.

Jacking Under the Street

The city used a nozzle on a 2-in [51-mm] diameter galvanized iron pipe of 30-ft [9.1-m] length. Attached to the back of the galvanized pipe was a high pressure hose, which gave the "rig" flexibility. The hose was attached to the tank of a large air compressor, and the air was jetted out of the nozzle at high velocity. The effect of this jet of air was to tunnel under the roadway with no damage to the road. The 2-in [51-mm] galvanized pipe was "jacked" under Spring Street and connected to a 2-in [51-mm] line on the north side of the street, see Fig. 16-12 and 16-13.

DEVELOPING THE LOT

Before the pile-driving contractor could drive the piling for the building foundation, each point where a piling was to be driven into the ground had to be located and marked for the pile-driving crew.

Figure 16-7
Location of the Y connection to the future townhouse.

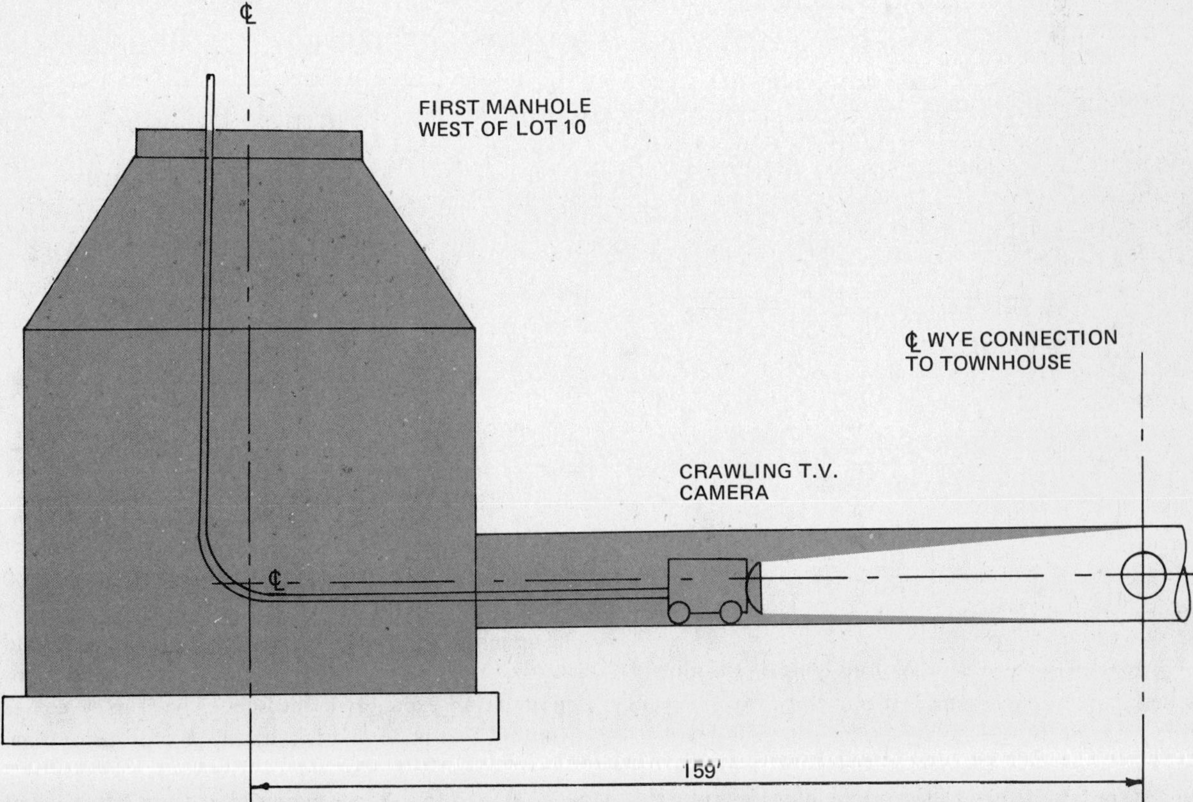

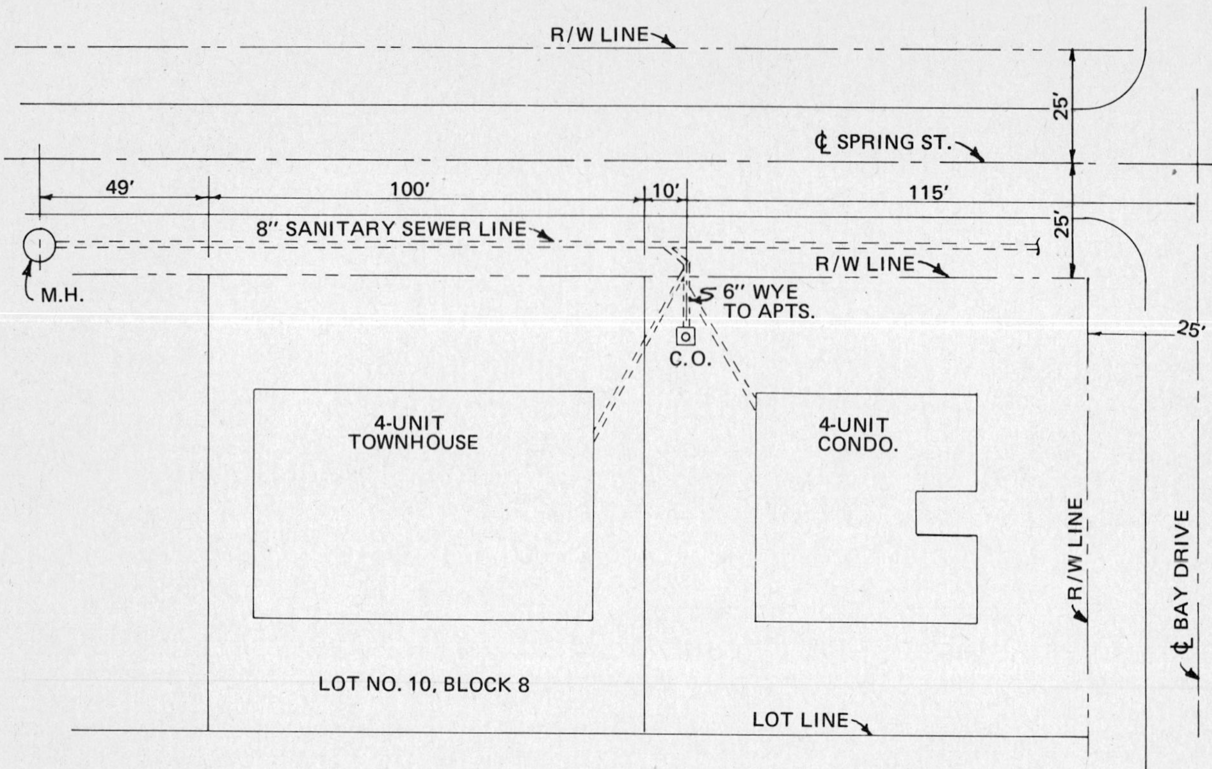

Figure 16-8
How Lot 10 was finally connected to the city sanitary sewer.

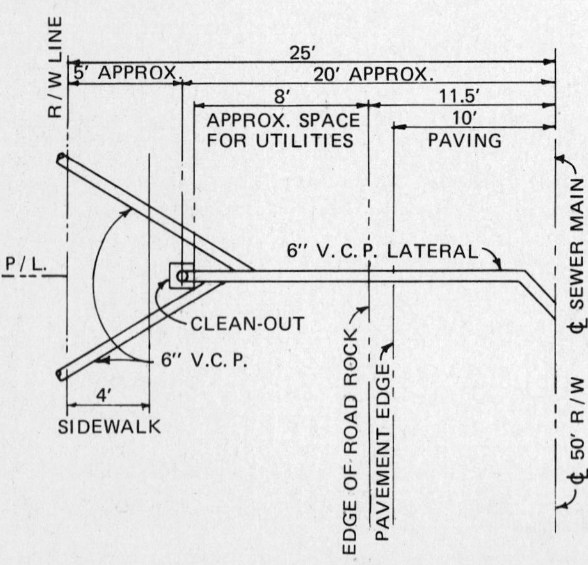

Figure 16-9
Schematic diagram showing double sewer service lateral with surface cleanout in the city right-of-way.

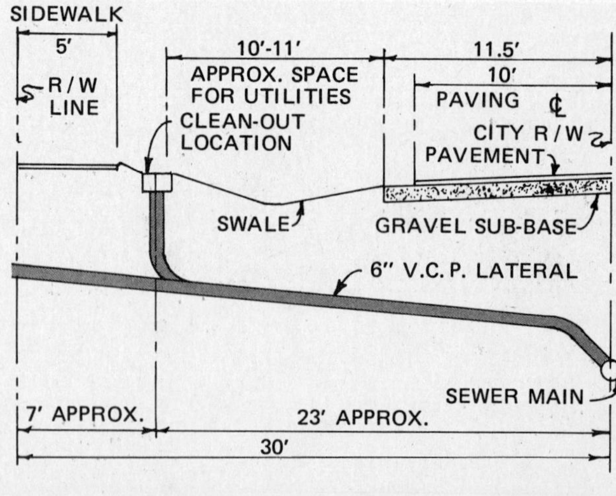

Figure 16-10
Section of city right-of-way and sewer house lateral.

Figure 16-14 shows a set of plans lying on the ground, with a carpenter's hammer keeping them from blowing away. All plans for buildings requiring piling have a foundation plan, which shows where every piling must be driven. It also shows the load the piling must be able to carry. The load is measured in *kips*; a kip is 1000 pounds [454 kg].

The piling locations were done by the contractor and a surveyor. The students should lay out the piling locations as an exercise, if the school has survey equipment. All that is needed is a transit, a good tape, some nails (for points), and 58 wood stakes. The stakes should be 2 × 2 in [51 × 51 mm] and at least 2 ft [61 cm]

Figure 16-11
Providing a surface cleanout for new sewer line *(Atlantic Florida Corp).*

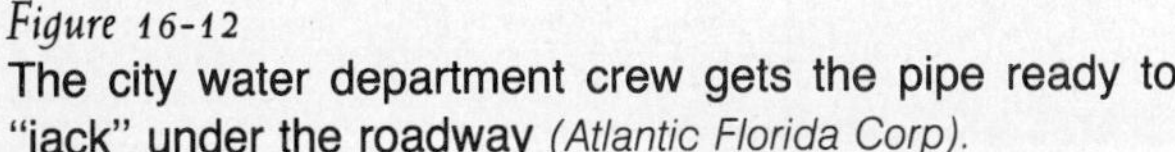

Figure 16-12
The city water department crew gets the pipe ready to "jack" under the roadway *(Atlantic Florida Corp).*

Figure 16-13
Pushing the 2-in galvanized pipe under Spring Street with high pressure air *(Atlantic Florida Corp).*

Figure 16-14
The piling grade beam plan.

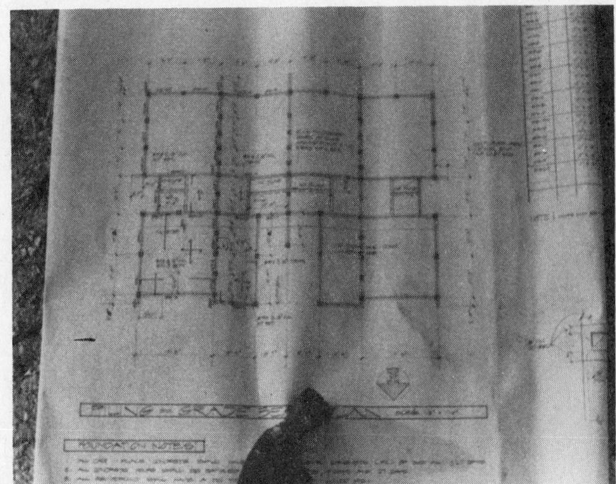

long, pointed at one end so that they can be driven into the ground easily.

The Lot Lines

A surveyor carefully staked out the lot lines and drove in iron pipes at the four corners before the lot was sold. Therefore these points did not need to be located again.

THE LOCATION POINTS FOR THE PILING

From the foundation plan, the contractor had to set up a complete set of locations for the pile-driving company, which then came in to drive all the piles.

Figure 16-15 shows the contractor watching the surveyor set the transit for layout of the piling stakes.

Setting Up the Transit

The surveyor first measured 125 ft [38.1 m] down the center of Spring Street, starting from the nail and tab

Figure 16-15
Contractor and surveyor setting the transit *(Atlantic Florida Corp).*

located in the center of Bay Drive. Figure 16-16 shows the typical section of Spring Street. Notice that the asphaltic surface of the street is 24 ft [7.3 m] wide. To locate the center of the street, the tape was run across the street from edge-of-asphalt to edge-of-asphalt and the center of the road was spotted at 12 ft [3.65 m]. As soon as the center of Spring Street was found and the 125-ft [38.1-m] length measured from the centerline of Bay Drive, a nail and tab were driven into the asphaltic concrete at that point, and the transit was set up over the nail and tab.

Nails and Tabs The nails used for this purpose are concrete penetrating nails. The tabs are tin-coated sheet-steel circles. When used with a concrete penetrating nail, they form a good reference point for the transit. The tabs are similar to those used to fasten roofing tar paper to house roofs. The tabs are about $1\frac{1}{2}$ in [38 mm] in diameter; they are usually painted orange for visibility after they are put in place. The nails easily penetrate the tin tabs if they are not made with a centrally located hole.

Look in the streets for nails and tabs; they can be found everywhere. Survey crews never pull them out, so once driven in they stay there until the city adds another layer of asphalt to fix the streets. Almost any existing street which has been resurveyed will have nails and tabs every 100 ft [30.5 m] all the way down the street. These are the 100-ft [30.5 m] stations which every survey must have.

The Water Main Notice in Fig. 16-16 that the north side of the street has the 3-in [76-mm] galvanized water main to which the city crew "jacked" and connected a 2-in [51-mm] galvanized pipe. Note that the city had to provide a water connection to this lot. It is a city responsibility to see that water and sewer connections are available to all lots within the city limits.

Locating the Stations for the Piling Lines

The east edge of the lot was covered by the transit when it was set up 125 ft [38.1 m] down Spring Street. From here the piling stakes were located. Notice the heavy

Figure 16-16
Typical section of Spring Street.

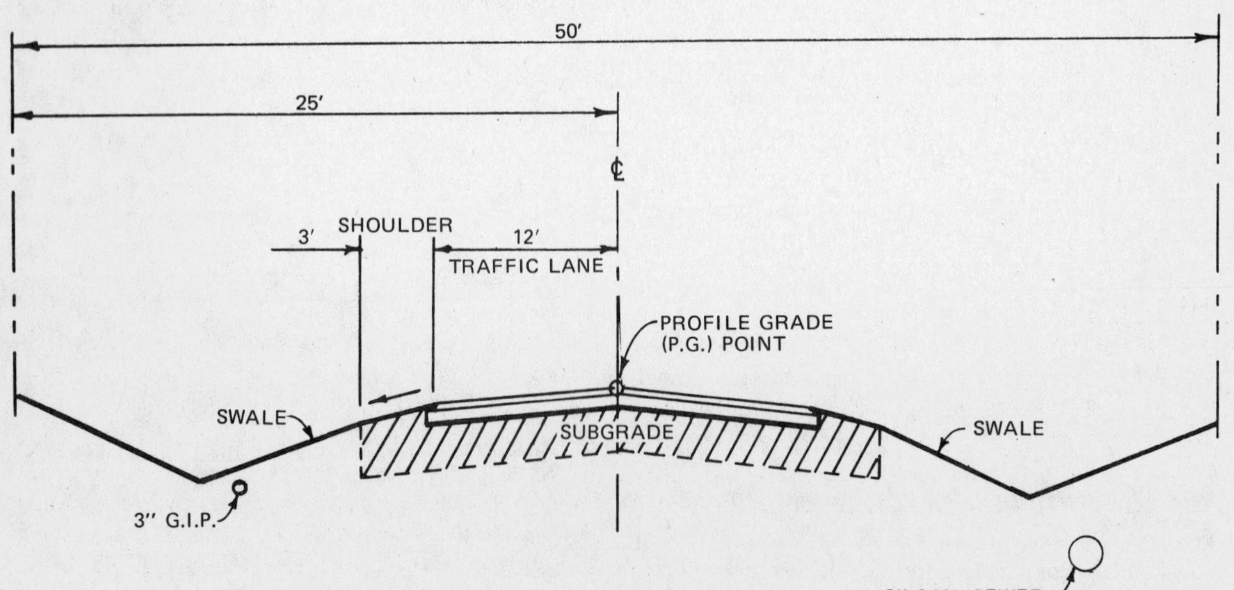

cord extending downward from the center of the transit in Fig. 16-15. At the lower end of the cord is a *plumb bob*. The plumb bob is like a cylindrical arrowhead made of brass. The lower part of the bob has a point. The point is suspended directly over the nail and tab.

The transit was set over Sta. 11 + 25. Notice the numbering (11 + 25). Almost no survey line starts with the number 1. A new survey direction usually starts with the number 10. In this case the surveyor started the Spring Street survey at the centerline of Bay Drive with the number 10. Looking at Fig. 16-17, note that the distance down Spring Street to the east edge of Lot 10 is 125 ft [38.1 m]. One station in surveying is 100 ft [30.5 m], so 125 ft [38.1 m] is one station more than 10, which gives Sta. 11. The additional 25 ft [7.6 m] of the 125 ft [38.1 m] is added following the station number, giving a station of 11 + 25.

Backsighting the Transit The surveyor's next step was to backsight the transit to read the point on Bay Drive. This was Sta. 57 on the Bay Drive survey. The rodperson put the point of the rod on top of the Sta. 57 nail and tab. If the rodperson has a bubble on the rod for keeping the rod vertical, the surveyor can read the rod anywhere. If not, the surveyor can read right at the point where the rod touches the top of the nail.

Turning the 180° Angle The surveyor then turned an angle of 180° 0′00″ from Sta. 57. This gave a straight line looking west down Spring Street, exactly on the centerline of the street. Refer again to Fig. 16-17. Notice that Line 2 has the first row of piling to be staked out. Line 2 is 11 ft ½ in [3.36 m] (by a carpenter's tape measure) from Sta. 11 + 25 on Spring Street. This distance could be measured as given with a carpenter's tape, but it should be converted to the decimal form (feet and decimals of a foot) for stationing.

Converting Inches to Decimal Form One foot divided by 12 inches gives 0.083 ft/in; this is how many feet are in 1 in. To get the station for Line 2, multiply the ½ in by 0.083 ft/in, giving 0.04 ft. The calculation goes like this:

$$1 \div 2 = 0.500;\ 0.500 \times 0.083 = 0.04 \text{ ft}$$

Since the 11-ft dimension did not change, add to it the inch dimension which has just been changed to 0.04 ft, giving 11.04 ft. The station of Line 2 is

$$\begin{array}{r} 11 + 25 \\ +\ 11.04 \\ \hline 11 + 36.04 \end{array}$$

Marking the Stations

The tape was held by one person on the center of the nail and tab at Sta. 11 + 25. The rodperson moved the stretched tape north and south, keeping a thumb on the 11 ft ½ in mark (11.04 feet on a civil engineer's tape), until the transit operator saw it exactly on line in the transit. The rodperson put the point of the concrete penetrating nail and tab at this position and drove the nail into the asphalt. From this point two people (a rodperson and another to hold the tape over the last point determined) could lay out the rest of the points that mark the piling lines. At every point, the transit operator indicated to the rodperson where to stop as the tape was moved north to south over the centerline of the street. The transit operator gave the locations to drive the nails and tabs so that the line would be a true centerline down Spring Street.

The distances laid out on Spring Street went west on Spring Street from Sta. 57 + 00 on Bay Drive, after turning an angle of 90° 00′00″ from the true north direction that was run on Bay Drive. Line 1, which is located at Sta. 11 + 25 on Spring Street, is 125.00 ft from Sta. 57. The additional distances that were laid out by the surveyor and rodperson are:

Line 2	11 ft ½ in [3.365 m]
Line 3	9 ft 7 in [2.921 m]
Line 4	9 ft 7 in [2.921 m]
Line 5	9 ft 7 in [2.921 m]
Line 6	10 ft 8 in [3.251 m]
Line 7	8 ft 7 in [2.616 m]
Line 8	10 ft 9 in [3.277 m]
Line 9	9 ft 7 in [2.921 m]
Line 10	9 ft 7 in [2.921 m]
Line 11	11 ft ½ in [3.365 m]

See Fig. 16-17.

If the entire line of points is converted to feet and decimals of a foot (this will be an exercise for this chapter), the total is 100.00 ft, the exact frontage of the lot.

The nails and tabs marking the centerline of Spring Street were then sprayed with fluorescent paint so that they would always be easy to locate.

Locating the Piling Positions

The front of the lot was thus stationed into the lines on which the pile-driving contractor would drive the piling, but the position of each individual pile had not yet been determined. To get the piling locations, the transit was positioned over each of the stations laid out on the road in front of the lot. After the transit was positioned over each individual station, it was first backsighted to Sta. 57 + 00 on Bay Drive, then an angle of 90 °00′00″ was turned to the south. This made the line of sight through the transit perpendicular to the centerline of Spring Street. The transit was then sighted due south toward the back of the lot. The transit was first set up over Sta. 11 + 36.04, which is Line 2; see Fig. 16-17.

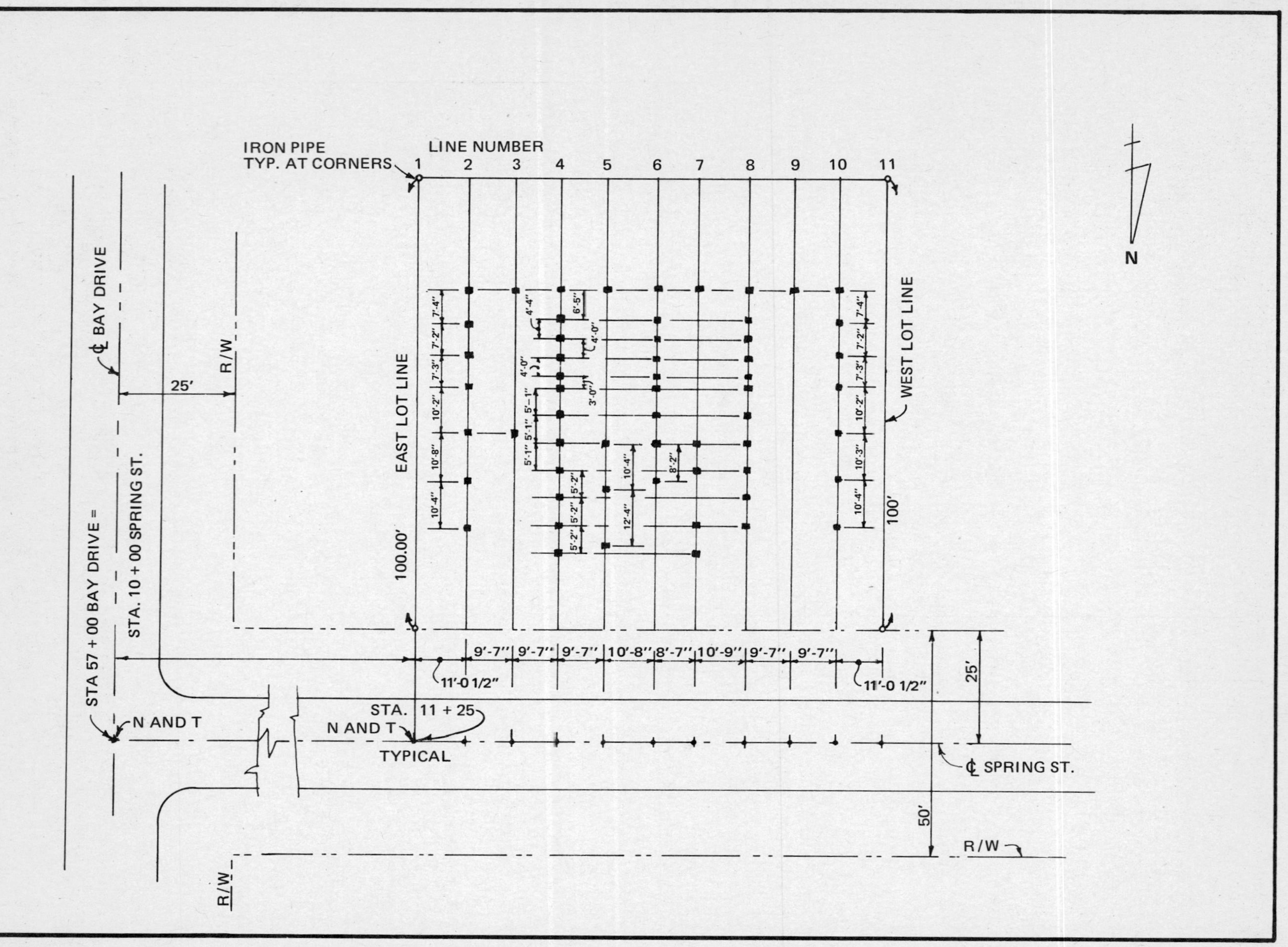

Figure 16-17
Spring Street and Lot no. 10.

Look back at Fig. 16-16, the road template for Spring Street. Notice that the right-of-way extends 25 ft [7.6 m] from the centerline of Spring Street to the edge of the right-of-way line. The edge of the R/W line is always the front of the lot. The lot itself is 100 ft [30.5 m] deep, and there is an additional 25 ft [7.6 m] between the lot and the centerline of Spring Street.

There will be 25 ft [7.6 m] from the back edge of the proposed townhouse to the back lot line. So on Line 2 the crew measured 125 ft [38.1 m] (the distance from the Spring Street centerline to the back of the lot) minus 25 ft [7.6 m] (the distance from the back edge of the lot to the back of the building); 125 ft − 25 ft = 100 ft [30.5 m]. The transit operator gave the exact location to drive the stake as the rodperson moved the tape east and west at a tape distance of 100 ft [30.5 m]. The 100-ft [30.5-m] distance was measured from the nail and tab at Sta. 11 + 36.04 south along Line 2. The tape was held on the nail and tab at Sta. 11 + 36.04 and pulled tight by the rodperson who also moved it east and west until the transit operator said to stop. The rodperson drove the stake at that point.

Always remember to drive the stakes farthest away from the transit first. If the closest stakes were driven first, they would obstruct the transit operator's view of the stakes farther from the transit.

Next, 7 ft 4 in was measured to the next piling marking stake (see Fig. 16-17); when the correct distance was determined by the transit operator and the transit, the stake was driven. Then each successive stake was driven until Line 2 was complete.

The transit was then moved to each station on Spring Street, backsighted to Sta. 57 + 00 on Bay Drive, and turned an angle of 90° to the south; then another line of stakes was set, always starting with the one farthest from the transit. The rearmost stake in every line was exactly 100 ft [30.5 m] from the nail and tab over which the transit was centered for that line.

There were 58 pilings to be driven, and when the surveyor and rodperson had laid out all 58, the foundation plan layout for this townhouse was complete. Figure 16-18 shows the contractor and surveyor measuring between stakes and driving the stakes for the proper positioning of the piling.

THE PILING OPERATION

The piles, when coupled with the tie beam (also called the grade beam or footer), formed the building foundation. The tie beam connected all the pilings. Forms were set up over the tops of the pilings, and poured full of concrete. The forms had steel reinforcing rods inserted throughout their lengths. These rods were tied by steel wire to the steel cables that extended upward from the driven piles (see Fig. 16-2). Steel reinforcing rods were then extended upward beyond the wood forms to engage the concrete block wall which formed the stem wall to a height of 8 ft [2.4 m] above sea level.

Figure 16-18
Driving stakes for pilings *(Atlantic Florida Corp).*

The forms were filled with concrete which was delivered in concrete mixing trucks. The mixing truck which originally transported the concrete to the lot used a hopper to deliver a fixed amount of concrete to a pumping machine. This machine screened the concrete first, then pumped it through long 4-in [10-cm] diameter rubber hoses (much like fire hoses) to the footer or grade beam locations. Using a hose made the concrete very mobile. The hoseperson went all around the grade beam and filled it to the required level, which the contractor had determined using a transit. The level was marked by small stakes which were driven to the proper fill height and left inside the forms after the concrete was poured.

The Pile Driver

Figure 16-19 shows a diesel pile-driving machine invented in Germany during World War II. It is very fast at driving pilings, much faster than the old type of machine, which dropped a heavy hammer on top of the pilings using a dragline crane. This acted like a series of hammer blows on top of the pilings; it was very slow, since the heavy weight that served as a hammer had to be reeled back up to the top of the pile-driving machine after each blow. The diesel driver is just like one cylinder of a diesel engine, and it strikes many times per minute.

Positioning the Pile Driver

The pile driver had to be lifted into position over the positioning stakes which were driven into place by the contractor and surveyor. When the crane had lifted the

Figure 16-19
Diesel pile driver *(Atlantic Florida Corp).*

Figure 16-20
Pile driver in action *(Atlantic Florida Corp).*

Figure 16-21
Markings on piling to show depth *(Atlantic Florida Corp).*

Figure 16-22
Driver and controllers *(Atlantic Florida Corp).*

driver into position vertically, a piling was attached by a chain through a loop near the top of the piling and pulled up into the pile driver by the crane. Figure 16-20 shows the crane with the pile driver vertical and the piling pulled up into driving position. Actually the pile was in the process of being driven (notice the little puff of diesel smoke drifting away from the pile driver).

Figure 16-21 shows the markings on the piling to show how deep it is being driven. In this picture a man is hanging on the driver and shooting ether into the valve on the diesel driver to get it "cooking." This driver had not been used for some time, and a cold diesel driver is difficult to start up. After 5 or 10 minutes of shooting ether into the driver, it got hot and ran well for the driving of the full 58 pilings, which took two days.

Driving the Pilings

Figure 16-22 is a close look at the driver and the two people who control it at the point of driving. Another person had to operate the crane, which did all the positioning work for the pilings. The pilings for this job were 12 in [30 cm] square and weighed well over a ton. Notice the 20-ft [6.1-m] mark on the piling. It was a test piling 24 ft [7.3 m] long which was driven in as far as possible in order to determine the typical depth of the pilings for this job.

Figure 16-23
Pilings driven into the ground. Notice the high test piling *(Atlantic Florida Corp).*

Figure 16-24
Cutting the pilings *(Atlantic Florida Corp).*

On this job the pilings were typically driven 16 to 20 ft [4.9 to 6.1 m] deep. The pilings were driven until they met a standard set up by the architect and engineer for resistance to driving. Figure 16-23 shows the pilings in the ground after being driven to "refusal." Notice the 24-ft [7.3-m] test piling sticking up quite high. This pile must be quite long, since the pile drivers never know just how far the piling must go down to embed itself in the solid coral rock below.

Cutting the Piling

After each piling had been driven to refusal, it was cut by a concrete-cutting gasoline saw almost through to the prestretched wire rope contained inside the piling. Pilings were previously made with reinforcing rods running the entire length of the piling. Now most piling contains steel wire rope that is prestretched before pouring. The tension is released later, after the cement is hard enough. This makes an even stronger piling than the earlier reinforced piling.

Figure 16-24 shows a laborer with a face mask cutting the piling in order to make it easier to knock down with a sledge hammer, which is the next operation to be performed.

Figure 16-25 shows the laborer knocking the rest of the protruding piling off, leaving the four wire ropes standing up out of the piling.

Figure 16-25
Knocking down excess piling *(Atlantic Florida Corp).*

Connecting the Pilings to the Grade Beams

The steel from the pilings was tied with steel wire to the steel reinforcing rods which were formed in the grade beam. The grade beam was a continuous beam made by forming a rectangular box from plywood and pouring it full of concrete. The grade beam was thus tied to the pilings under it, and these pilings were in turn embedded 3 or 4 ft [0.9 to 1.2 m] into the bedrock underlying the ground. The grade beam for this project was again tied by reinforcing steel to the stem wall. This stem wall was made of concrete blocks poured full of concrete. The entire piling, footer or grade beam, and stem wall were unified construction. The top of the stem wall was at an elevation of 8 ft [2.4 m] above mean sea level.

Figure 16-26 shows the supervisor on the job using a transit to line up the plywood forms on top of the pilings.

Figure 16-26
Supervisor lining up plywood forms *(Atlantic Florida Corp).*

Figure 16-27
Consultation on the construction of the concrete forms *(Atlantic Florida Corp).*

Figure 16-28
Forms being Installed *(Atlantic Florida Corp).*

Figure 16-29
Workers installing rebars *(Atlantic Florida Corp).*

Figure 16-27 shows the supervisor and the contractor figuring out how the forms should be constructed. Notice the forms behind them; some are already installed.

Figure 16-28 shows forms being installed by workers. The backhoe is filling in sand around the forms so that the concrete, when poured, will not break out.

Figure 16-29 shows two workers forming the steel to be installed within the forms.

Summary of the Piling Procedure

First the lines of piling were positioned on the street in front of the lot. The foundation plan showed exactly where each line of piling was to be installed. The location of each line was found using a transit and tape. Nails and tabs were driven into the centerline of the street to mark each line of piling.

Then the stakes were set to mark the position of every pile. The piling was driven to "refusal" and then cut with a concrete power saw. The excess piling above the cut was knocked down with a sledge hammer.

Plywood forms were built over the top of all the pilings. Steel from the pilings was tied by wire to steel reinforcing rods placed in the forms.

Concrete was poured or squirted through hoses into the forms. Steel reinforcing rods were placed in the grade beam while the concrete was soft. These rods tied the grade beam to the stem wall. The stem wall was needed on this building to attain the 8 ft above sea level height required by the Army Corps of Engineers.

COMPLETED TOWNHOUSE

Figure 16-30 shows the completed townhouse.

Figure 16-30
The completed townhouse *(Atlantic Florida Corp).*

EXERCISES

EXERCISE 16-1. STATIONING THE CENTERLINE OF SPRING STREET

1. Remove Exercise 16-1 from the book and cover it with a B-size sheet of vellum.
2. Trace the problem on the B-size vellum.
3. Station the centerline of Spring Street. Convert the feet and inches dimensions on the lines to feet and decimals of a foot. The first station (line #1) is 11 + 25.
   The following table gives the distances west of the first station for the various lines; fill in the stations.

Line	Station	Distance West
1	11 + 25	0
2	______	11 ft ½ in
3	______	9 ft 7 in
4	______	9 ft 7 in
5	______	9 ft 7 in
6	______	10 ft 8 in
7	______	8 ft 7 in
8	______	10 ft 9 in
9	______	9 ft 7 in
10	______	9 ft 7 in
11	______	11 ft ½ in

Refer also to Fig. 16-17.

EXERCISE 16-2 LOCATING A POINT BEHIND A BUILDING

In this exercise we will try to locate a point behind a building by turning angles around the obstructing building. Tear out Exercise 16-2 and tape it to the drawing table. Tape a B-size vellum over the exercise.

Measure the 90-ft dimension between point 1 and point 2 with a civil engineer's scale. (The 30 scale should work. This scale is 1 in = 30 ft, which should be close enough. Photographic reduction in printing makes absolute accuracy impossible.)

1. Go from point 1 90.00 ft to point 2.
2. Turn 90° left at point 2 and go 37.00 ft to point 3.
3. At point 3 turn 90° right and go 50.00 ft to point 4.
4. At point 4 turn 45 ° left and go 70.00 ft to point 5.
5. At point 5 turn 90° left and go 70.00 ft to point 6.
6. At point 6 turn 90° left and go 58.00 ft to point X, the point we are trying to locate.

Trace all the lines, and label the dimensions and angles.

EXERCISE 16-3 LOCATING THE CORNERS OF A HOUSE

Use Dummy 16-3 in back of the chapter to set up for drawing this exercise.

1. Lot 17 on Maple Street has a 200.00-ft frontage and is 120.00 ft deep; it is a perfect rectangle.
2. Four corner iron pins have been placed by a registered surveyor.
3. The front of the house must be 25 ft from the front lot line.
4. The first stake used to mark the location of the house is I.P. 1 (iron pipe), located 25 ft north of the R/W line (the front lot line) and 40 ft east of the west lot line.
5. From I.P. 1 go due north 65 ft 4 in and place I.P. 2.

NOTE 65 ft 4 in must be converted to feet and decimals of a foot for the plot plan. Remember how to do this: 4 in divided by 12 in/ft is 0.33 ft. All dimensions on plot plans must be in the same form as dimensions on the civil engineer's tape, which are in feet and hundredths of feet.

NOTE The original drawing was made on a scale of 1 in = 20 ft, which is normal for plot plans in the city. Photographic reproduction should give

Exercise 16-3 a scale of about 1 in = 30 ft. Try the civil engineer's scale on the drawing, and measure a dimension that has been established. For example, if the 25.00 ft dimension reads 25 ft on the 30 scale, then use this scale for measuring all the dimensions. If it does not fit, try all the other scales and use the one that comes closest. The dimensions written on the plans, not the measured dimensions, are the ones which a contractor would follow.

6. Next, go due east 35.00 ft. Call this I.P. 3.
7. Go due north 10 ft 6 in (change this to feet and decimals of a foot) and mark I.P. 4.
8. Proceed due east 30.00 ft and mark I.P. 5.
9. Proceed due south 30 ft 8 in and mark I.P. 6. (Be sure to change the dimension to feet and decimals of a foot).
10. Proceed due east 55.00 ft and mark I.P. 7.
11. Proceed due south for 45 ft 2 in (change to decimal form) and mark I.P. 8.

Be sure to label all these lines in feet and decimals of a foot. The enclosure just drawn is the layout for a house on a plot plan.

EXERCISE 16-4 A SWIMMING POOL

On Lot 53 on Summer Street lay out the city's new swimming pool.

NOTE Students should establish a scale as close as possible to that of the exercise sheet.

(Try 1 in = 30 ft)

Tear out Exercise 16-4 from the textbook. Tape it to the drafting board and overlay it with a B-size sheet of vellum.

1. Trace Summer Street and the outline of Lot 53 on the vellum.
2. Lay out point 1 on the vellum, 25 ft north of the R/W line and 30 ft east of the west lot line.
3. Lay out the following points:

   Point 2—50 ft north of point 1
   Point 3—75 ft east of point 2
   Point 4—30 ft north of point 3
   Point 5—45 ft east of point 4
   Point 6—80 ft south of point 5

   Connect these points. They form the outline of the city swimming pool.
4. Now we will develop the bath house. Point 7 is 170 ft east of the west lot line and 25 ft north of the north right-of-way line of Summer Street.
5. Locate the following corners of the bath house:

   Point 8 is 50 ft north of point 7.
   Point 9 is 25 ft east of point 8.
   Point 10 is 50 ft south of point 9.
6. Connect these points to get the outline of the bath house.

Now locate the swimming pool and bath house from the lot lines using civil engineer's measure (feet and hundredths of a foot).

EXERCISE 16-5 AN INDIRECT ROUTE TO A POINT

In this exercise we will try to reach a predetermined point from a starting point. First use the civil engineer's scale to measure the distance between point 1 and 2 on Exercise 16-5. Use the scale that reads closest to 100 ft for this distance.

1. Tear out Exercise 16-5 from the textbook and tape it to the drawing board. Tape a B-size sheet of vellum over the exercise and trace points 1 and 2 and the line connecting them.
2. At point 2 turn 15° left and go 130.00 ft to point 3.
3. Turn 75° left and measure 110.00 ft. This will be point 4.
4. At point 4 turn left 90° and go 180.00 ft to establish point 5.
5. At point 5 turn 65° left and go 80.00 ft. This should be point X.

   NOTE There were trees and buildings in the area of some sightings so the surveyor had to take an indirect route as we have done.
6. Label the distances on each line.

LEARNING ACTIVITY PACKAGE

Chapter 16 describes work that has been performed by a contractor, or a contractor and a surveyor with a rodperson. The students should read the chapter as though they were doing the work themselves.

This chapter tells about the development of a lot for construction of a townhouse; it will introduce the student to a very practical set of problems.

Chapter 16 read ____________ (*date*).

If after reading Chap. 16 the student has not understood some of the objectives (a) through (f), the paragraphs which contain those objectives should be reread.

Objectives read and studied ____________ (*date*).

Now take the removable quiz on Chap. 16. Remove the quiz from the text and answer all the questions.

Quiz completed ____________ (*date*).

There are five exercises to be completed with this chapter. They include problems in converting the foot and inch scale used by carpenters to the foot and decimals of a foot measurements used by surveyors, taping, transit setup and sighting, and layout of the lot and pilings. If a school does not have the necessary tape, stakes, transit, and so forth, the students can still do the problems graphically.

Exercise 16-1 completed ____________ (*date*).

Exercise 16-2 completed ____________ (*date*).

Exercise 16-3 completed ____________ (*date*).

Exercise 16-4 completed ____________ (*date*).

Exercise 16-5 completed ____________ (*date*).

16

QUIZ

1. Drainage of ______________ water is the most important phase of land development.
2. Large land developments require consulting engineers because of drainage and environmental problems. (T or F) ______________
3. Mangrove trees can reclaim the ocean shoreline into valuable shore land. (T or F) ______________
4. In Florida the sand rests on coral rock. (T or F) ______________
5. In developing a lot it can be assumed that the city has taken care of the storm drainage. (T or F) ______________
6. A connection to the sanitary sewers is unimportant for a city lot. (T or F) ______________
7. In the 1920s "lamping the line" was a sewer inspection procedure. (T or F) ______________
8. The city does not have to make city water available to city lots. (T or F) ______________
9. It is possible to tunnel under a city street using air pressure. (T or F) ______________
10. If there were no pilings in a building foundation, a transit would not be needed. (T or F) ______________
11. Foundation plans are easily set up using a transit. (T or F) ______________
12. Nails and tabs are often used to locate points in paved streets. (T or F) ______________
13. Plumb bobs are not essential when setting up a transit on a point in a city street. (T or F) ______________
14. If a surveyor turns the transit around to look back at a point or monument behind the line of sight, this operation is called a ______________.
15. Dividing 1 ft by 12 in = 0.0833, which is the number of feet per inch of distance. (T or F) ______________
16. To convert feet and inches to decimal form, write down the number of feet then add to this number the number obtained by multiplying the inches by 0.08. (T or F) ______________
17. In the case of Lot 10, the centerline of Spring Street was ______________ ft from the front edge of the lot line.
18. When driving piling location stakes, it is important to drive the stake farthest from the transit first, so that it will not interfere with the line of sight of the transit. (T or F) ______________

19. Diesel pile-driving machines were invented by a Polish immigrant during World War I. (T or F) ____________
20. The dropping-hammer pile-driving machine is more efficient than the diesel driver. (T or F) ____________
21. Test pilings are not used before driving the pilings. (T or F) ____________
22. Pilings are cut to a uniform level after driving, using a concrete saw and sledge hammer. (T or F) ____________
23. Pilings are not tied in any way to the grade beam that sits on top of them. (T or F) ____________
24. Reinforcing steel is placed into the forms that make the grade beam. (T or F) ____________
25. Diesel pile drivers are clean and never emit smoke. (T or F) ____________
26. A transit may be easily aligned over a nail and tab without a plumb bob. (T or F) ____________
27. The lower floor of this townhouse has to be at an elevation of ____________ ft above mean sea level.
28. The agency setting the elevation of property in this area, due to proximity to the ocean, is the Navy Corps of Engineers. (T or F) ____________

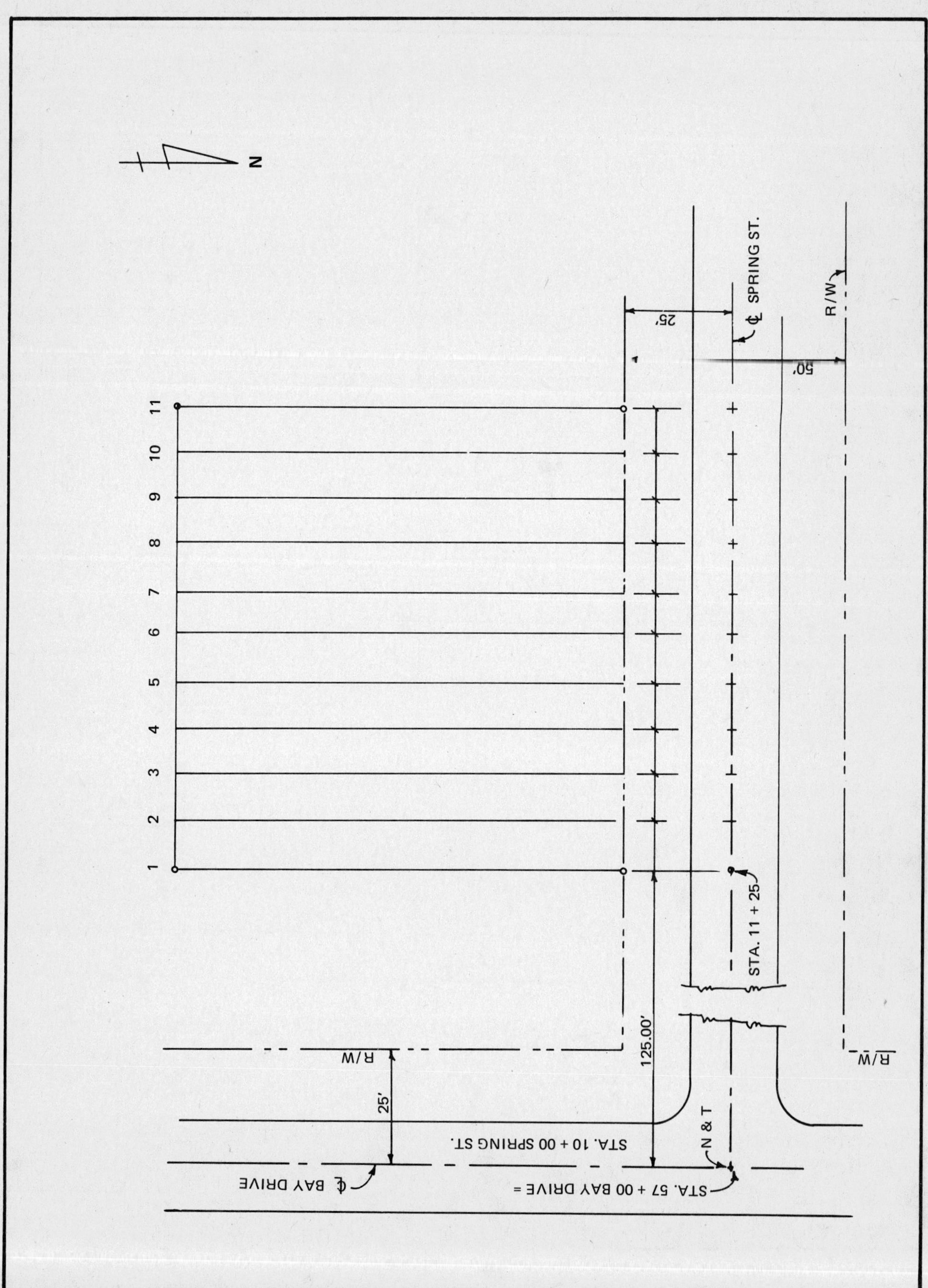

Exercise 16-1

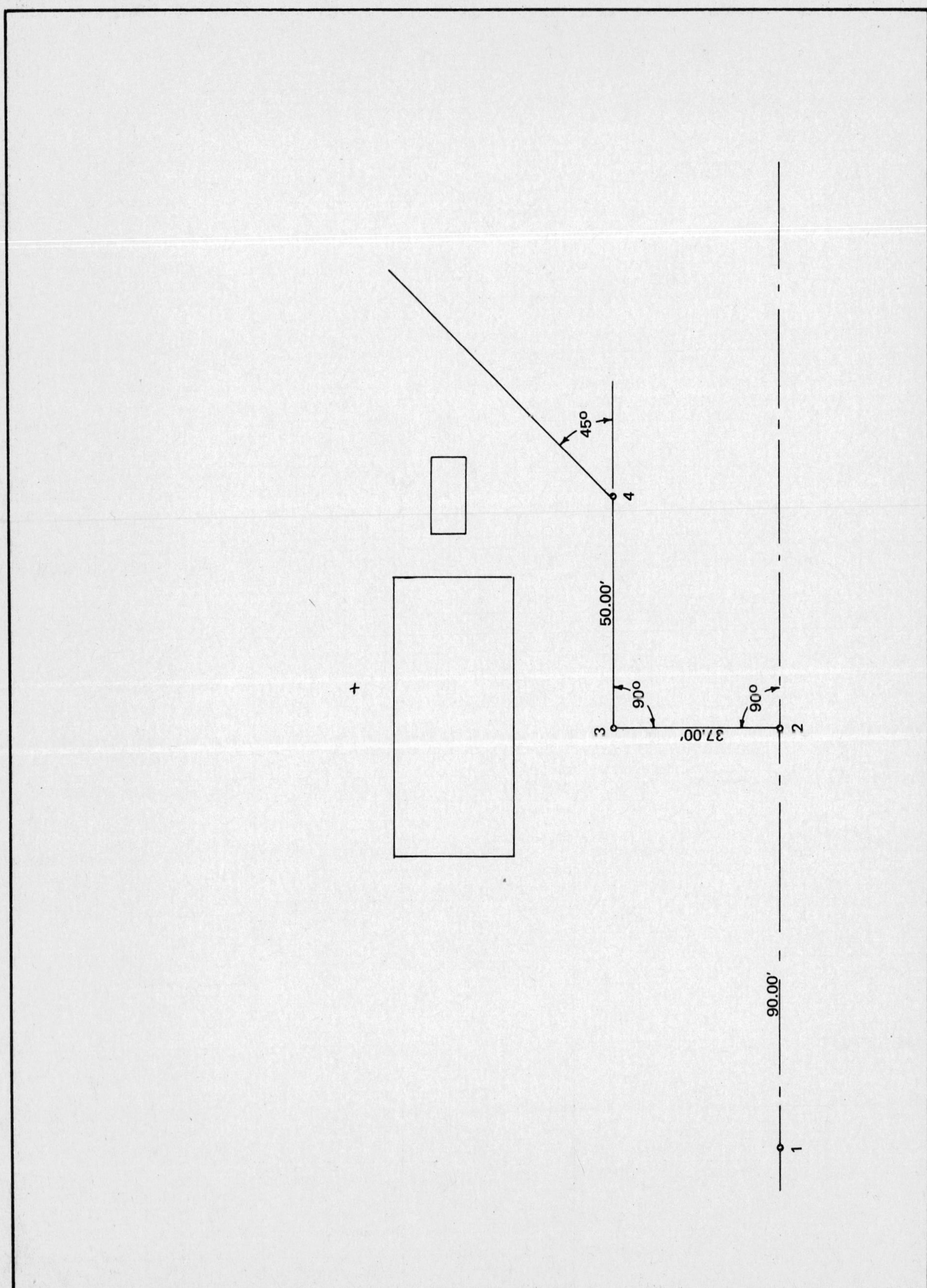

Exercise 16-2

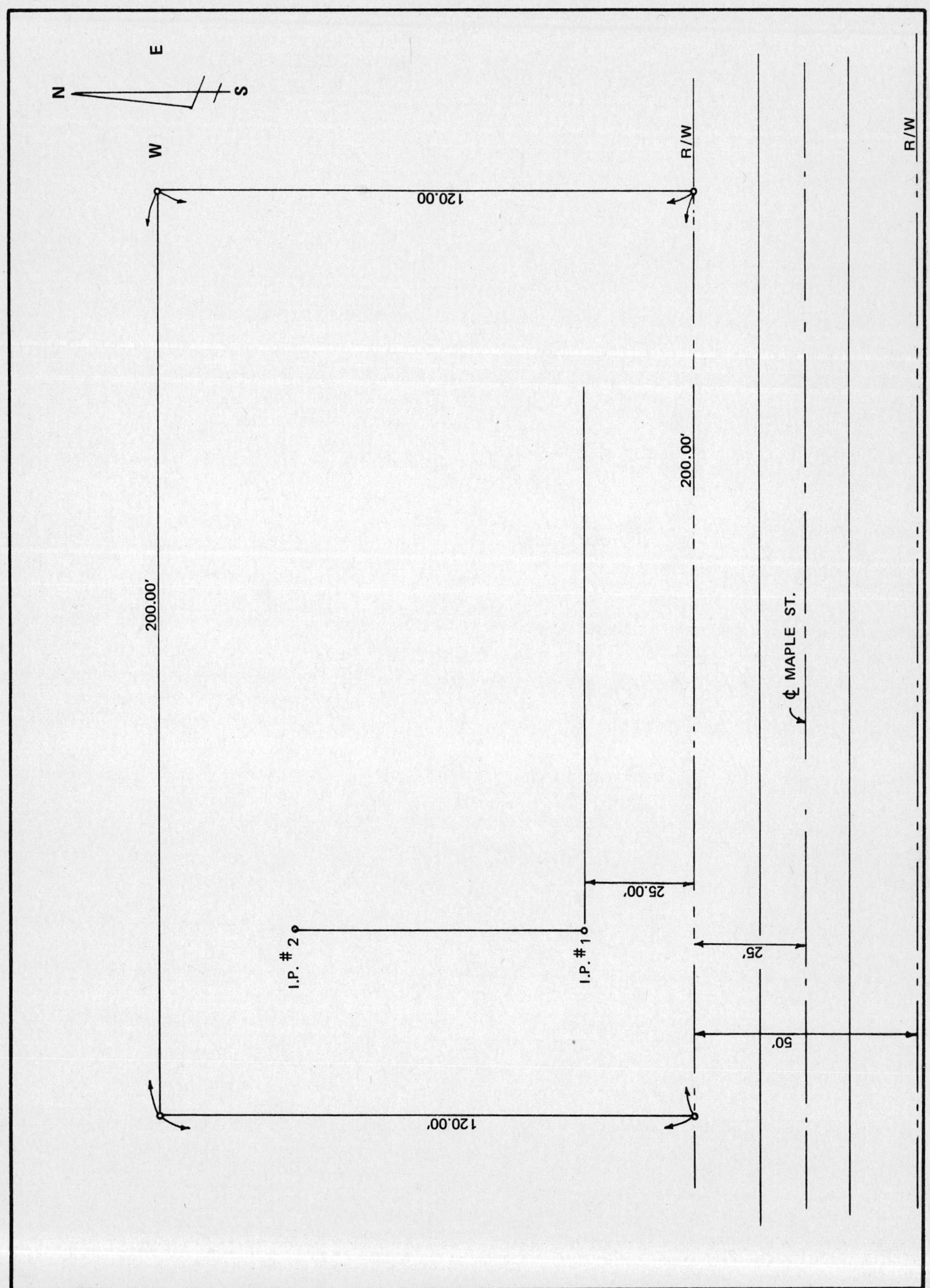

Exercise 16-3

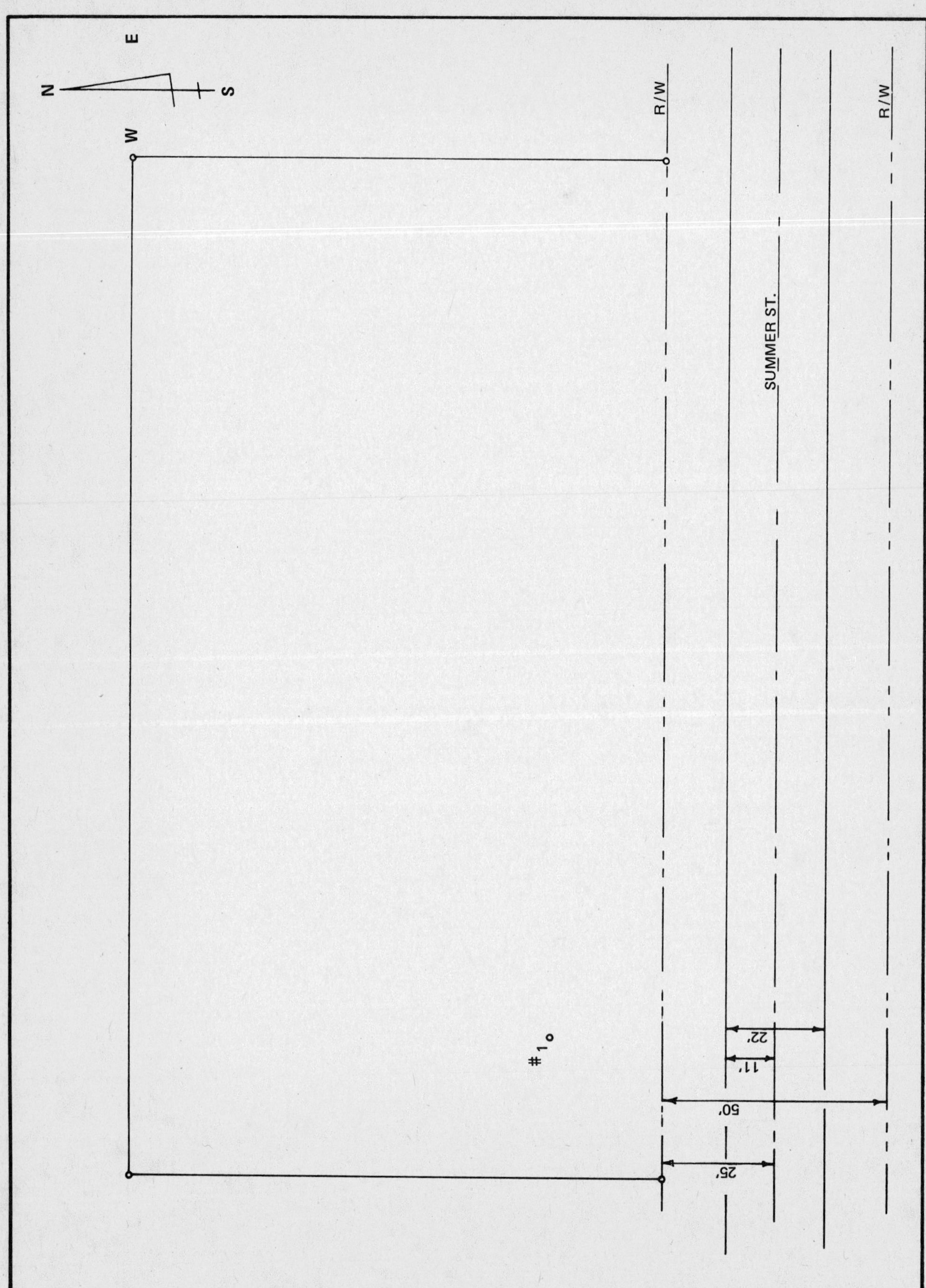

N
E
W
S
R/W
R/W
SUMMER ST.
22'
11'
50'
25'
#1

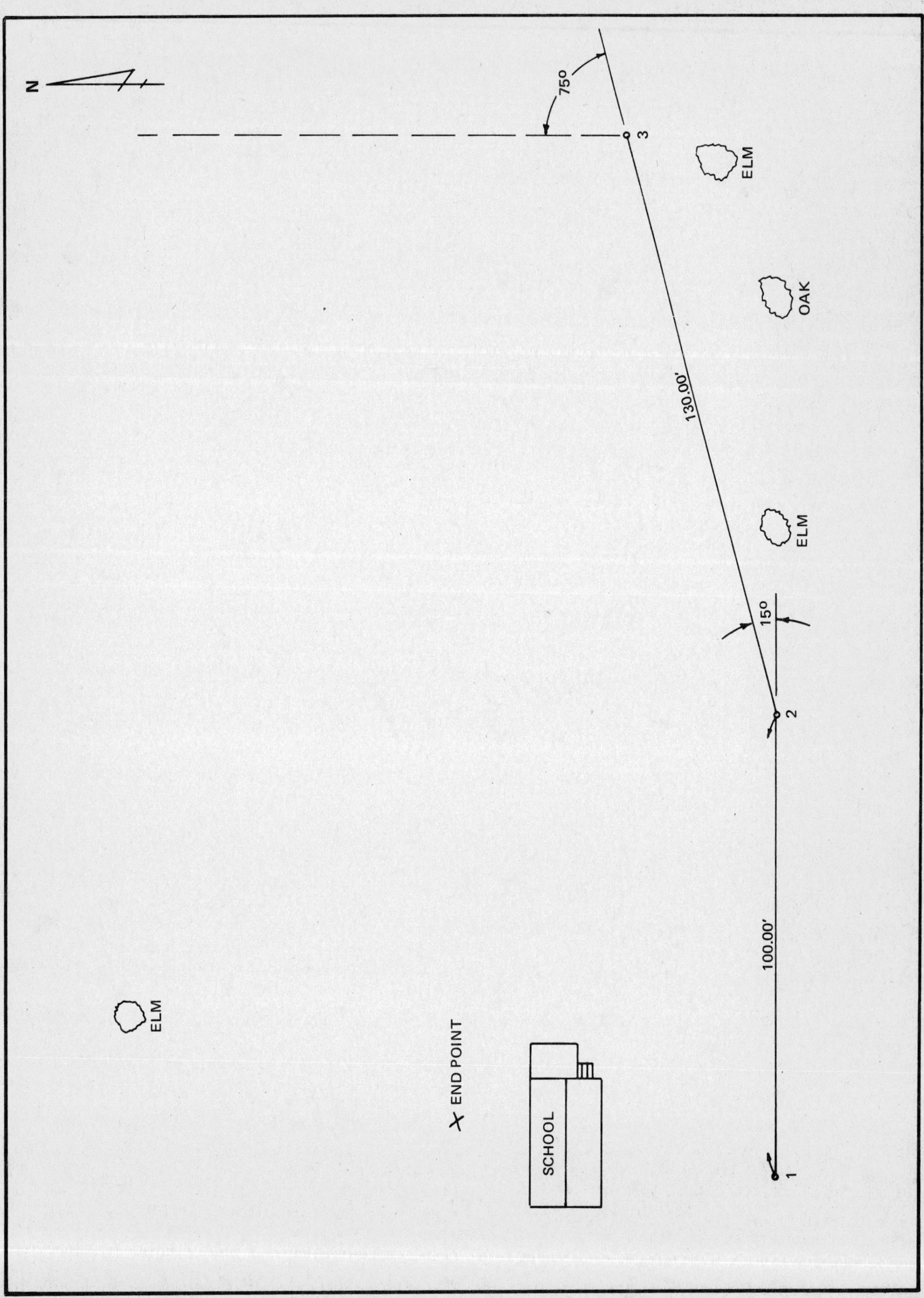

Exercise 16-5

17 SURVEYING EQUIPMENT

Objectives

a. Understand the use of various surveying tools
b. Be able to care for surveying equipment properly
c. Learn the parts of the engineer's level and the engineer's transit
d. Understand the proper operation of the level and the transit
e. Understand some of the limitations of the steel tape and the taping process
f. Be able to use a plumb bob properly

Rationale

Assuming that the students have had no surveying experience, they must learn about the tools of the trade. This chapter will explain surveying tools, their use, and sometimes their care.

The basic surveying that the student will do requires a few major pieces of equipment and several minor items. This chapter will introduce most of the more important ones and describe the parts and terms associated with each one.

LEVELS

The engineer's level can be compared to a carpenter's level. The difference is that the engineer's level is used by mounting it on a tripod (to hold it steady) and sighting through a telescope in order to transfer the level line to another point. While the carpenter's level can be used to determine if two points a few inches apart are level, the engineer's level can tell if two points a few hundred feet apart are level. Just as there are many different types of carpenter's levels, for example, water levels, line levels, and so forth, so too there are many different types of engineer's levels. Although some of these levels have certain features that others do not have, they all share certain basic parts. Figure 17-1 identifies the important parts of an engineer's level:

1. *Eyepiece.* The adjustable lens through which the observer looks. The eyepiece is rotated to bring the crosshairs into focus.
2. *Telescope.* The tube which holds all of the lenses and focusing gears in their proper positions.
3. *Sunshade.* A metal or plastic extension which can be placed over the objective lens to protect the lens from damage and to reduce glare when the level is in use.
4. *Focusing knob.* An adjustment knob which internally focuses the level on the desired target.
5. *Leveling screws.* Adjustable screws used to level the instrument.
6. *Base.* A 3½ × 8 inch (in) [89 × 203 mm] threaded base which secures the instrument to the tripod.
7. *Plumb bob, hook, and chain.* A hook and chain, centered under the level, to which the plumb bob is attached if angles will be turned.
8. *Shifting center.* A design feature which permits exact placement over a given point.
9. *Horizontal tangent screw.* An adjustment which allows exact alignment of the crosshairs and the target within the horizontal plane.
10. *Horizontal clamp screw.* An adjustment which allows approximate alignment of the crosshairs and the target within the horizontal plane.
11. *Level vial.* A graduated, liquid-filled, glass vial which is parallel to the line of sight of the telescope.

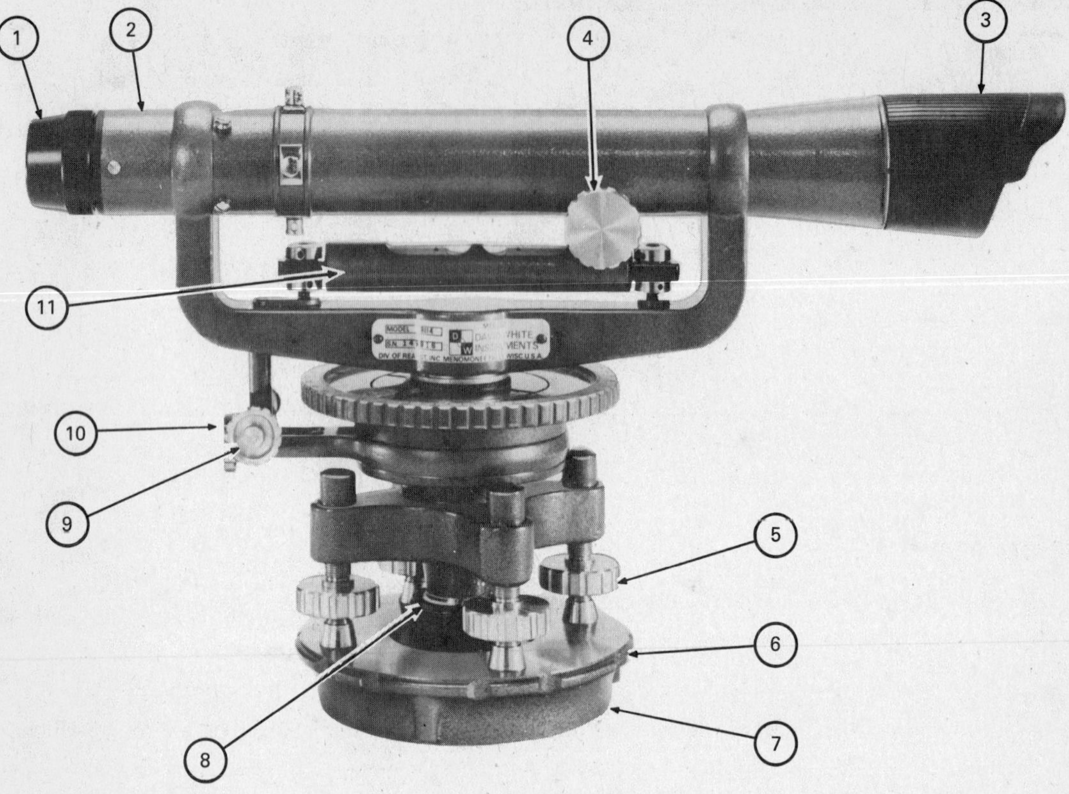

Figure 17-1
Universal level *(David White Instruments).*

TRANSITS

The engineer's or surveyor's transit (see Fig. 17-2 to 17-4) is often called the universal surveying instrument because of its many uses. It can be used for observing horizontal angles and/or directions, for observing vertical angles and differences in elevation, for prolonging straight lines, and for measuring distances by stadia. Although the transits of various manufacturers differ in appearance, they are alike in their essential parts and operation. They also share many parts and functions with the engineer's level. Figure 17-4 identifies the parts of a common transit. The parts which are unique to the transit are listed here.

1. *Plate level vials.* In addition to the telescope level vial like the one on the engineer's level, the transit also has two plate level vials which are used to level the instrument within the horizontal plane.
2. *Compass.* The instrument has a built-in surveying compass for jobs requiring directional readings. The compass is graduated to 1° and numbered in quadrants. The *W* and *E* on the compass are reversed from the normal map position because the dial surface is attached to the instrument and revolves with it. The needle remains the fixed point and indicates the direction the telescope is facing.
3. *Compass locking screw.* The compass locking screw disconnects the needle to reduce wear on the compass when not in use.
4. *Vertical clamp screw.* The telescope can be locked to the approximate vertical angle with the vertical clamp screw.
5. *Vertical tangent screw.* Fine vertical settings can be made with the vertical tangent screw. The clamp must be hand-tightened firmly before the tangent screw will function.
6. *Lower horizontal clamp screw.* The upper horizontal clamp screw secures the horizontal circle to the standard, as it does on the engineer's level. The lower horizontal clamp screw secures the circle to the leveling head.

TRIPODS

The tripod (see Fig. 17-5) is the base or foundation which supports the survey instrument and keepts it stable during observations. It consists of a tripod head to which the instrument is attached, three wooden or metal legs which are hinged at the head, and metal pointed shoes on each leg to press or anchor into the ground to achieve a firm setup.

Figure 17-2
Transit and carrying case.

Figure 17-3
Engineer sighting the transit.

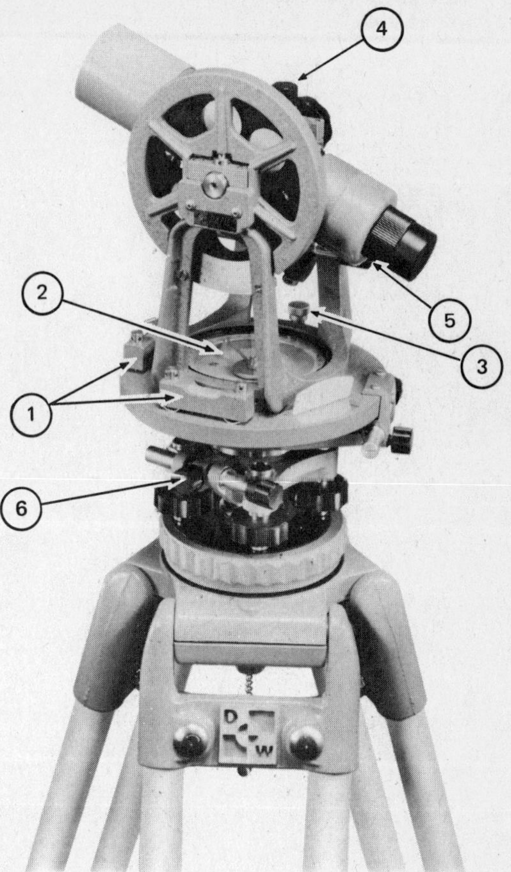

Figure 17-4
Sight path transit *(David White Instruments)*.

Two types of tripods are available to the surveyor—the fixed-leg tripod and the extension-leg tripod. The legs of the fixed-leg tripod are made of a single piece of material, and for this reason, they must be swung in or out in varying amounts in order to level the head and to control the instrument's height. The legs of the extension-leg tripod are made of two sections which slide up and down. This advantage is particularly useful for rough terrain.

RANGE POLE

The range pole, shown in Fig. 17-6, is also called a line rod, flag, or flagpole. It is a wooden or metal rod about 7 feet (ft) [2.1 m] long with a pointed tip at one end. It is painted in alternate red and white bands. The range pole is useful as a target in angle measuring or to mark the direction of a tape line for a taping party. Its coloring makes it highly visible against many backgrounds. At times, small sections may be seen through trees or underbrush to line up a sight on some smaller target.

LEVELING RODS

A leveling rod is essentially a tape supported vertically and used to measure the vertical distance (difference in elevation) between a line of sight and a specific point above or below the line of sight. The point may be a permanent station, such as a bench mark, or it may be some natural or constructed surface.

Leveling rods are available in several different styles. The Florida rod, the California rod, and the Detroit rod are but a few of the possible variations, but the Philadelphia rod is by far the most commonly used type. The

Figure 17-5
Extra-tall tripod and rodperson using a leveling rod *(David White Instruments).*

Figure 17-6
Rodperson with a range pole.

standard Philadelphia rod is a graduated wooden rod made of two sections. It can be extended from 7.1 to 13.1 ft [2.2 to 4.0 m]. The graduations on the rod are feet, tenths of feet, and hundredths of feet. Instead of using a small line or tick to mark each hundredth, the spaces between alternate pairs of graduations are painted black on a white background. Thus, the mark for each hundredth is the line between the colors, the top of the black being even-numbered values, and the bottom of the black being odd-numbered values. The tenths and feet are numbered in black and red respectively. The observer usually reads the rod directly while sighting through the telescope. This rod may be used with the level, transit, theodolite, and occasionally the hand level to measure the difference in elevations.

ROD TARGETS

Conditions which hinder direct readings, such as poor visibility, long sights, and partially obstructed sights through brush or leaves, sometimes make it necessary to use rod targets (Fig. 17-7). The target is also used to mark a rod reading when setting numerous points to the same elevation from one instrument setup.

Targets for the Philadelphia rod are usually oval, with the long axis at right angles to the rod, and the quadrants of the target painted alternately red and white. The target is held in place on the rod by a thumb screw. It has a rectangular opening approximately the width of the rod and 0.15 ft [4.5 cm] high through which the face of the rod may be seen. A linear vernier scale for reading to thousandths of a foot is mounted on the edge of the opening with the zero on the horizontal line of the target.

STADIA RODS

Stadia rods, sometimes called stadia boards, are wooden boards about 12 ft [3.7 m] long which are hinged at the

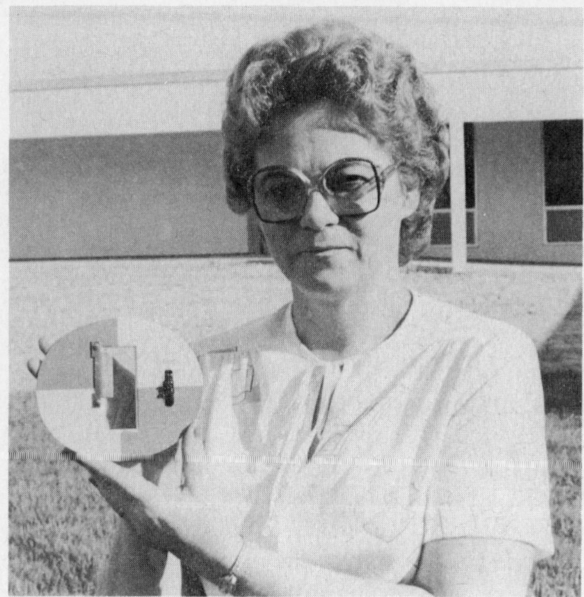

Figure 17-7
Target.

center for quick folding and carrying. The rod has painted graduations in feet, tenths, and half-tenths (1/20) of a foot. The stadia rod is used to measure distance by noting the difference in the readings of the two stadia wires within the telescope.

HAND LEVELS

The hand level, like all surveying levels, is an instrument which combines a level vial and a sighting device, see Fig. 17-8. The locator hand level is so called because it is held by hand in front of the eye. For greater stability, it can be rested against a tree, rod, work tool, or any other handy object. A horizontal line is provided in the sight tube as a reference line. The level vial is mounted on top of a slot in which a reflector is set at a 45° angle. This permits the observer to sight through the tube and see the landscape or object, the position of the level bubble in the vial, and the index line all at the same time. The distance over which a hand level is sighted is comparatively short, so no magnification is provided by the level.

The Abney topographic hand level is a more specialized type of hand level which has a graduated arc so that the vertical angle and the percentage of grade can be measured. This topographic level has a reversible arc assembly mounted on one side. The arc is graduated in degrees on one side and percent of grade on the other. The level vial is attached at the axis of rotation of the index arm. The bubble is centered by moving the arc, not the sight tube as is done with the locator level. Thus, the difference between the line of sight and the level bubble axis can be read in degrees or percent of grade from the position of the index arm on the arc. The 45° reflector and the sighting principle (with its view of the landscape, bubble, and index line) are the same as in the locator hand level.

TAPES

Tapes (Fig. 17-9) are used in surveying to measure horizontal, vertical, and slope distances. This process of measuring distances is called *taping* or *chaining*. The term *chaining* comes from the former surveying practice of using either a 66-ft [20.1-m] or a 100-ft [30.5-m] chain of

Figure 17-8
(Top) Sight Mark hand-held level *(David White Instruments)*. (Bottom) Engineer using a sign post as support for a hand level.

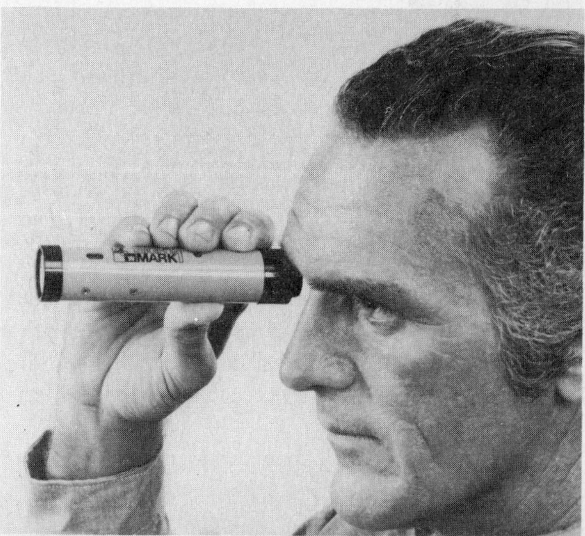

Figure 17-9
Surveyor in field with tape and plans. An assistant is driving a stake *(Mid-South Engineering Co.)*.

100 or 10 links, respectively, to measure distance. The common survey tapes are made of a ribbon or band of steel, an alloy of steel, or a "cloth" of metal and cotton or linen. Tapes are made in various lengths and widths and graduated in a variety of ways.

The metallic tape is made by weaving fine metal wires and cotton or linen threads into a band or tape, ⅝ to ⅞ in [16 to 22 mm] wide and 50 (but sometimes 100) ft [15.2 or 30.5 m] long. The tape is impregnated with a paintlike material for protection, and graduations are applied to the surface. When not in use, the tape is kept in a leather covered metal case with a built-in reel for winding up the tape. The materials in the tape are susceptible to temperature and humidity changes and to being stretched. For this reason, metallic tapes are used for low-accuracy work.

The steel tape is the most common tape used in surveying. It is a ribbon of steel varying in width from ¼ to ½ in [6.4 to 12.7 mm] and in thickness from 0.020 to 0.025 in [0.51 to 0.64 mm]. The tapes most frequently used by the surveyor are 30 meters (18.4 ft), 50 meters (164 ft), 100 ft [30.5 m], and 300 ft [91.4 m] long. Some of these are designed with foot graduations on one side and metric graduations on the other. Loops are riveted to each end of the tape and rawhide thongs may be attached to each loop. Steel tapes are more accurately graduated than metallic tapes and are used to measure distances up to and including second-order accuracy under special conditions.

CAUTION. Although a steel tape is more rugged than a metallic one for normal use, it must never be dragged over any surface. This will wear away enough material to cause the tape to stretch or break when tension is applied. (About 22 to 28 pounds [98 to 125 newtons] of tension is used to offset the sag due to the added weight of a steel tape.) A steel tape should never be jerked, pulled around corners, or run over by vehicles, since it can kink or break.

A steel tape must be carried by the tapepersons, and if necessary, a third person should support it at the center point during movement. The tape should be wiped clean after use and oiled lightly. When not in use, the tape should be stored in its reel.

TAPING ARROWS

Taping arrows are steel pins with a ring at one end and a point at the other end, see Fig. 17-10. They are used for marking measured tape lengths on the ground and for checking the number of tape lengths measured since the last station. The ring and part of the pin are painted red, while the remainder of the pin is white. When they are properly used, taping arrows prevent "dropped" tape lengths, which are a common mistake in distance taping.

Figure 17-10
Set of taping arrows.

Figure 17-11
Important items for the surveyor: straw hat to prevent sunburn, hatchet to drive stakes, roller measurer and carrying case *(Atlantic Vocational Technical Center).*

Figure 17-12
Close-up of carpenters level, plumb bob and holder, hand level and carrying case *(Atlantic Vocational Technical Center).*

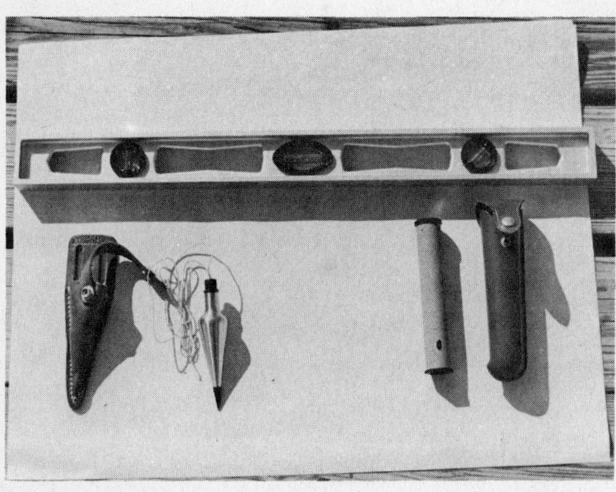

MINOR PIECES OF EQUIPMENT

The surveyor may use a variety of minor items, depending on the job. Some of these are shown in Fig. 17-11 and 17-12 or discussed in the following sections.

Tension Scale

The tension scale, sometimes called the tension handle, is made with an integral scale graduated in pounds and is used for the low orders of accuracy. The tension handle uses a linear scale and is graduated in pounds from 1 to 30 [4.4 to 133 newtons]. It is clipped to the tape loop and tension is applied until the reading specified for the tape appears on the scale.

Scissor Clamp

When measuring less than a full tape length, tension is applied by using a steel tape clamp handle or scissor clamp. This is a mechanical device which grips the flat ribbon of steel without kinking it.

Thermometers

Tape thermometers are used in accurate taping to determine the temperature of the tape at the time of the measurement. The temperature is used to determine a correction to the measured distance. The thermometers are mounted in holders and can be attached near the ends of the tape for reading during the taping operation.

Turning Pins, Plates, and Wooden Stakes

A turning point is a point on which a leveling rod is held between a foresight and the next backsight, while the instrument (the level or transit) is being moved to the next setup. It must be sufficiently stable to maintain the accuracy of the level line. Where the proper natural or artificial features are not available, a turning pin, a turning plate or pedestal, or a wooden stake is used. These not only furnish the solid footing but also identify the same position for both sightings. Normally, the pins or plates are used for short periods and are taken up for future use as soon as the instrument readings are completed. Wooden stakes are used for longer periods except when wood is scarce or when local regulations require their removal.

The turning pin is a tapered steel spike with a round top and a ring through the shaft for pulling the pin out. Turning pins are driven into the ground with a mallet. After they have served their purpose at one point, they are pulled and carried to the next turning point.

Turning plates or pedestals are triangular metal plates with turned-down corners or added spikes which form prongs; they have a projection or bump in the center to accept the rod. Turning plates (or pedestals) are devised for use in loose, sandy, or unstable soils. The plate is set by placing it on the ground, points down, and stepping on it to press it to a firm bearing. After use, it is lifted, shaken free of dirt and mud, and carried forward to the next turning point.

Wooden stakes are used when a point must be marked for some time, but not permanently, or when pins or plates are not available. The stakes may be of precut lumber or may be made by the survey party from locally available timber. Stakes must be long enough to prevent them from being worked out of the ground if they are to remain for a considerable length of time in an area subject to freezing and thawing. Wooden stakes are either placed in locations where they are not likely to be disturbed or driven flush with the surface of the ground.

Figure 17-13
Using a plumb bob for position over a nail and tab in a city street.

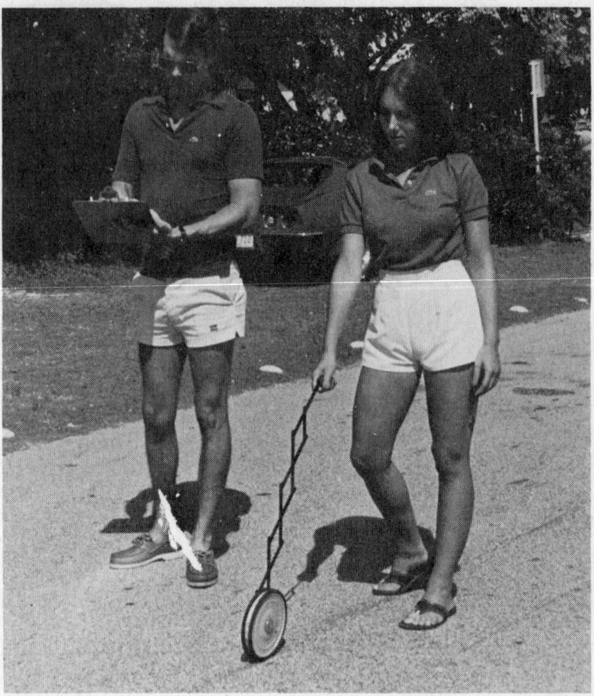

Figure 17-14
A roller marker.

Figure 17-15
An old-time surveyor with a large roller marker *(Mid-South Engineering Co.).*

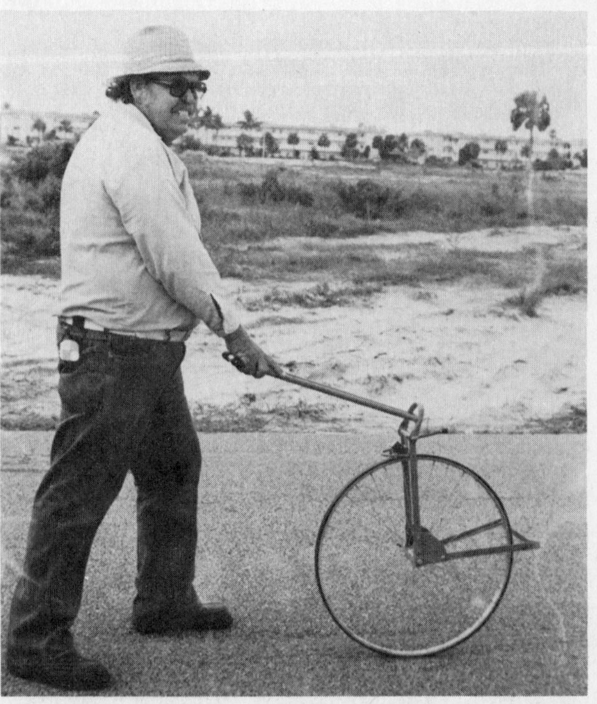

Umbrella

For all leveling of third or higher order accuracy the instrument must be shaded from the direct rays of the sun, both during observations and when moving from one instrument station to another. The surveying umbrella is used for this purpose. When necessary, the umbrella can also be used as a windscreen with good results.

Plumb Bobs

The plumb bob (Fig. 17-13) usually has a body and a removable cap made of brass with a replaceable point made of hardened steel. It is a weight that is tapered so that its point will hang directly below a supporting string. For normal tripod work, a movable slide is mounted on the string and is used to adjust the height of the plumb bob. When the string is hung under the center of the instrument, the point of a freely suspended plumb bob will be directly below this center. The vertical axis of the leveled instrument is then exactly over the point indicated by the plumb bob, or conversely, the point on the ground is exactly beneath the vertical axis of the instrument. In taping, the plumb bob may be used to "drop" a measurement from the tape to the ground or to find the reading on the tape directly above a specific point on the ground. Plumb bobs come in varying sizes and weights, depending upon their use.

Roller Markers

Roller markers (Fig. 17-14 and 17-15) are also used for measuring distances. However, they are not as accurate as a properly used tape.

LEARNING ACTIVITY PACKAGE

Read Chap. 17 carefully.

Chapter 17 read ____________ *(date)*.

If after completely reading the chapter the student has not understood some of the objectives (a) through (f), the portions of the chapter which discuss those objectives should be reread. An understanding of the objectives listed above will give a good command of the basic surveying tools used in elementary surveying.

Objectives read and studied ____________ *(date)*.

Now take the removable quiz on Chap. 17. Remove it from the book and answer all the questions.

Quiz completed ____________ *(date)*.

17

QUIZ

1. What are the basic differences between an engineer's level and a transit?
level transfer the levelline to another point
transit observing horizontal angles and/or direction

2. Name at least five parts of an engineer's level.
Eyepeice Telescope Sunshade
Focusing knob, Leveling screws Base

3. Which instrument is called the universal surveying instrument? Why?
surveyor's transit

4. What is the range pole used for? used as a target in angle measuring

5. What is the most commonly used type of leveling rod? Give a brief description of it. philadephia

6. What additional device might be used if a number of points were being set to the same elevation from one instrument setup? rod targets

7. What is the difference between a metallic tape and a steel tape?
metal wires +cotton ribbon of steel

8. What device is used to mark a tape length on the ground? taping Arrows

9. What three items are commonly used to establish a temporary turning point?
wooden stakes

10. What two purposes does the plumb bob serve?
drop a measurement from the tape to the ground or to find the readins on the tape directly abov

18 DISTANCE MEASUREMENTS

Objectives

a. Know how a taping party is organized
b. Know the duties of all of the taping party personnel
c. Understand the procedure for slope taping
d. Know the procedure for plumbing
e. Know how to measure tape lengths
f. Learn how to "break tape"
g. Know how to determine the taped distance
h. Know how to lay off a given distance
i. Know how to minimize taping mistakes and errors
j. Know what factors influence the measured distance and how the measured distance is corrected
k. Understand the procedure for recording data in field notebooks
l. Become familiar with the stadia method for measuring distances

Figure 18-1
An EDM or electronic distance measuring device in use on State Road A-1-A in Pompano Beach, Florida *(Mid-South Engineering Co.).*

Figure 18-2
Rodperson holding an optical prism which reflects the signal directly back to the electronic distance meter *(Mid-South Engineering Co.).*

Rationale

Measuring the distance from one point to another is a fundamental part of surveying. With today's modern equipment, one can look at the readout of an electronic distance measuring machine and read the exact distance correctly, but since these devices are expensive, they are not always available. In this chapter the students will learn the conventional steel tape and pins method. In addition to taping procedures, this chapter also discusses the duties of the members of a taping party, the method of recording field notes, the corrections applied to measured distances, and the stadia method of measuring.

Distance measuring equipment in use today includes steel tapes, microwave instruments, electro-optical instruments for use in lightwave measuring systems, and stadia boards and calibrated instruments used for the stadia method. When used properly, the microwave and lightwave methods (see Fig. 18-1 and 18-2) yield extremely accurate results over distances ranging from less than 5 feet (ft) [1.5 m] to over 1 mile (mi) [1.6 km]. Unfortunately, this capability is also reflected in the initial cost of the equipment. Thus most schools will only be concerned with teaching the taping and stadia methods. However, knowledge of these two basic methods is very valuable in understanding the other distance measuring techniques and other aspects of surveying.

TAPING

There are two basic methods for measuring distance with a tape. These methods are slope taping and horizontal taping. In the slope taping method, the tape is held as required by the slope of the ground, the slope of the tape is measured, and the horizontal distance is computed. In the horizontal taping method, the tape is held horizontally and the required graduation is projected to the ground with a plumb bob. Under certain conditions, each of the methods of taping has its advantages. The slope taping method is the most precise and is always used for taping baselines and second- and higher-order traverse distances. Third-order traverse measurements are usually made using slope taping; horizontal taping can be used, but it is not recommended. The horizontal taping method is generally used for lower-order tape traverses in mapping projects and construction surveys.

Party Organization

A taping party (see Fig. 18-3) can consist of a minimum of two people for horizontal taping or up to as many as nine people for precise slope taping. When working in areas of heavy underbrush or a wooded environment, an additional clearing party is sometimes required to clear the path of the survey.

Horizontal Taping Party

The minimum taping party consists of two people, one at each end of the tape. However, this is not recommended except for very low order surveys. The standard taping party should consist of at least four people: a recorder, stretcherperson, and rear and front tapepersons.

Recorder. The recorder keeps a complete record of all measurements made by the taping party, makes all necessary sketches, writes descriptions of stations and reference points, records all other pertinent supplementary data, and usually completes all necessary field computations. The recorder is usually the chief of the taping party.

Stretcherperson. The duty of the stretcherperson is to apply and maintain the correct tension to the tape during taping.

Rear Tapeperson. The rear tapeperson holds the tape on or directly over the rear point and also maintains the alignment of the tape between stations.

Figure 18-3
Four-person taping party.

Front Tapeperson. The front or head tapeperson is responsible for making the measurement and marking the new point on the ground.

Slope Taping Party

A slope taping party consists of a minimum of four people or up to as many as nine people, depending on the accuracy requirements. As in all surveys, some of the duties are absorbed by other members of the party if sufficient personnel are not available. The following paragraphs give a general summary of the duties assigned to the party members.

Chief of Party. The chief of the taping party directs all measurements, establishment of stations, and other activities of the party. When traversing, the chief of the traverse party is usually directly in charge of the taping party.

Recorder. The duties of the slope taping party recorder are the same as those of the horizontal taping party recorder.

Front and Rear Tapepersons. The tapepersons' duty is to make actual measurements.

Front and Rear Stretcherpersons. The stretcherpersons' duty is to apply and maintain the proper tension to the tape while the tapepersons are making the measurements.

Level Party

For precise tape measurements, the slope of the tape is usually determined by direct (differential) leveling. This type of leveling requires an instrument person (Fig. 18-4), a rodperson, and a recorder. For third- and lower-order taping, the slope of the tape is usually determined using an Abney topographic hand level. When using the hand level, the tapepersons or the stretcherpersons are responsible for the slope measurement.

Tape Alignment

One of the requirements of taping is that the taping be done on a straight line between stations. The order of the work being done will define the permissible limits of misalignment between stations. For precise taping the allowable misalignment is very small, and a theodolite is used to keep the alignment of the tape within limits. For third- and lower-order taping, the tape can be aligned by having the rear tapeperson "eye in" the tape.

SLOPE TAPING PROCEDURE

In the slope taping method, the tape may lie on smooth ground, on a paved road, or on other fairly smooth and uniformly sloping surfaces, or its ends may be supported by taping stools or stakes. The following procedures are generally used when taping third- or lower-order traverse distances. Normally, the equipment consists of a range pole, one set of taping pins, one steel tape, one tape thermometer, and one Abney hand level.

The range pole is set along the line to be measured and slightly behind the point toward which the taping will proceed.

The rear tapeperson, with 1 of the 11 taping arrows (pins), is stationed at the point from which the taping will start. The head tapeperson, with the zero end of the tape and 10 taping arrows, moves toward the end point. When the head tapeperson has gone nearly the full tape length, the rear tapeperson gives a signal to halt by calling out "tape." The rear tapeperson holds the last graduation at the initial point and directs the head tapeperson into alignment with the previously set range pole. The head tapeperson then pulls the tape taut, bringing it onto the line. The tapepersons exert and maintain the required tension on the tape (assuming no stretcherpersons are used). When the exact graduation is on the initial point, the rear tapeperson calls "mark" or "stick" and the head tapeperson marks the distance by sticking the arrow into the ground at the zero graduation of the tape. The head tapeperson then calls "marked" or "stuck" and both tapepersons release the tension. When ready to repeat the measurement, the head tapeperson calls "check," and the measurement is repeated as a check. The distance is now recorded along with the tape temperature, and an Abney hand level reading is now taken and recorded along the line coincident with or parallel to the slope of the tape.

Figure 18-4
Instrumentperson using a universal level-transit *(David White Instruments)*.

Before moving forward, the rear tapeperson pulls out the rear taping pin and carries it along. The front tapeperson leaves the newly placed pin in its position. Thus, one taping pin always remains in the ground, and the number of pins held by the rear tapeperson indicates the number of full tape lengths from the initial point to the remaining arrow.

Both tapepersons then move forward and make another complete measurement starting from the taping pin that marks the end of the previous measurement.

When the taped distance is more than 10 tape lengths, the head tapeperson signals the rear tapeperson to come forward at the end of the tenth length and to bring the 10 taping pins from the rear. Both tapepersons check the number of pins to see that none have been lost. The head tapeperson checks the recording book to see that 10 taped distances, temperature readings, and slope measurements have been recorded. The rear tapeperson gives 10 pins to the head tapeperson, and the measurement is then continued.

At the end of the line, the head tapeperson holds the zero graduation on the terminal point. The rear tapeperson pulls the tape taut and holds the appropriate full graduation at the taping pin. The fractional unit is now read by the head tapeperson.

At this point, two important items should be noted. First of all, if less than a full tape length is being measured, then the tension applied to the tape must be prorated. This is done by dividing the amount of tension applied to a full tape length by the length of a full tape, then multiplying the result by the fractional length to be measured.

EXAMPLE 20 pounds [89 newtons] of tension is normally applied to a certain 300-ft [91-m] tape. The fractional length at the end of a line is approximately 45 ft [14 m] (within 1 foot).

$$20 \div 300 = 0.0666 \text{ lbs/ft}$$

$$0.0666 \times 45 = 2.997 \text{ ft}$$

Therefore, 3 pounds [13 newtons] of tension would be applied to the final 45-ft [14-m] section.

The second hazard in reading fractional tape lengths is misreading a plus tape for a minus tape, or vice versa. A plus tape is one which, in addition to its standard length (30 meters (m) (98 ft) 50 ft [15.2 m], 300 ft [91 m] and so forth) also has one unit ahead of the zero mark which is subdivided into smaller units. As an example, a metric tape might have an extra decimeter graduated in millimeters prior to the zero. Similarly, a foot tape would have an extra foot divided into tenths and hundredths before the zero. On a plus tape these extra graduations are read from the zero toward the loop, that is, the numbers are read from right to left instead of left to right as is usually done. Conversely, a minus tape has these subdivided graduations between the zero and one marks. Because of this difference between a plus and a minus tape, a fractional length is read on a plus tape by adding the graduation held by the rear tapeperson to the fractional reading obtained by the head tapeperson. On a minus tape the fractional reading is subtracted from the rear tapeperson's reading.

REMEMBER *Add* when using a *plus* tape. *Subtract* when using a *minus* tape.

HORIZONTAL TAPING PROCEDURE

In horizontal taping, the tape is supported only at its ends and it is held in a horizontal position. Plumb bobs are used to project the end graduations of the tape to the ground or to project a point on the ground to the tape. Care must be exercised in the use of the plumb bobs, in exerting a steady pull on the tape ends, and in determining when the tape is nearly horizontal.

Plumbing

Plumbing is accomplished when the tape is aligned horizontally and is under proper tension.

The rear tapeperson holds a plumb bob cord at the proper graduation of the tape, with the point of the plumb bob about ⅛ in [3 mm] above the marker from which the measurement is being made. When the plumb bob is directly over the marker, the rear tapeperson calls "mark."

The head tapeperson holds a plumb bob cord at the correct graduation of the tape (with the point of the plumb bob about 1 in [25 mm] above the ground) and allows the plumb bob to come to rest. The head tapeperson then sees that the tape is approximately horizontal, checks its alignment and tension, and when the rear tapeperson calls "mark," allows the plumb bob to fall and stick in the ground. This spot is then marked with a taping arrow or pin.

Any swinging of the plumb bob is eliminated by gently lowering the tape and plumb bob until the tip touches the ground and then slowly raising the two back to the horizontal position. This procedure may have to be repeated once or twice to stop the swinging entirely.

After the point has been marked, the measurement must be repeated for a check. The tapepersons must be certain that the point on the ground is a good transfer from the elevated tape. This check is very important in horizontal taping.

Leveling the Tape

The head tapeperson can easily keep the tape horizontal by using the level bubble on the hand level. On the Abney hand level, the arc is first set for a level reading, then the level is held against the tape while the downhill person raises the tape until the bubble is centered. This marks the height at which to hold the tape for both tapepersons. Once the height is established, the level is removed and the tape returned to this same height for measuring.

Measuring Full Tape Lengths

Taping consists of measuring some number of full tape lengths plus a partial tape length at the end of the line.

To measure the first full tape length, the front tapeperson keeps 10 taping pins and gives 1 to the rear tapeperson. The pin given to the rear tapeperson represents the first full tape length. The front tapeperson moves toward the forward station with the zero end of the tape. As the end of the tape reaches the rear station, the front tapeperson stops, either on the count of paces or on the command "tape" given by the rear tapeperson. The rear tapeperson sights along the tape toward the forward station and signals the direction that the front tapeperson should move to align the tape, first aligning it with the forward station and then with an estimated horizontal plane. Both tapepersons place leather thongs on their wrists and hold their plumb bob cords on the proper graduations on the ends of the tape. At the command "pull" or "tension," both exert a pull on the tape. After the front tapeperson has properly aligned the tape, the rear tapeperson places the rear plumb bob exactly over the rear station and calls "mark." At this command the front tapeperson drops the front plumb bob and then marks the point of impact with a taping pin. When the pin has been placed in the ground, the front tapeperson reports "marked." The reading is checked, recorded in the notebook, and the rear tapeperson moves forward to measure the next tape length. When a team is taping on sloping ground void of brush and tall grass, the plumb bob need not be used at the uphill end of the tape. The end of the tape can be held on the ground next to the taping pin.

To measure succeeding full tape lengths, the tapepersons use the procedure discussed above, except that the rear tapeperson places the plumb bob exactly over the point at which the taping pin enters the ground. When the measurement is completed, the rear tapeperson pulls the taping pin or arrow from the ground before moving forward to the next pin position. If a taping pin is lost during the measurement of the distance, the tapepersons must make the entire measurement again, instead of completing the measurement from a recovered pin hole. The number of arrows in the rear tapeperson's possession indicates the number of full tape lengths which have been measured.

Breaking Tape

To measure tape lengths when the tape cannot be aligned with a horizontal plane within ½ m (about 1½ ft) because of the slope of the ground, the tapepersons use a special procedure known as "breaking tape."

In this procedure, the front tapeperson first pulls the tape forward a full tape length and lays it approximately on line, then comes back along the tape to a point at which a partial tape length, when held level, is below the armpits of the downslope tapeperson. At this point, the front tapeperson selects any convenient full meter (or foot) graduation. The tapepersons then measure the partial tape length, applying the proper prorated tension to the tape.

After placing the taping pin, the front tapeperson waits until the rear tapeperson has come forward. The front tapeperson tells the rear tapeperson which full graduation was used (for example, "holding 25"); this is repeated by the rear tapeperson, who then holds that graduation on the taping pin when the front tapeperson moves forward. The front tapeperson receives a pin from the rear tapeperson and moves forward, repeating this procedure until the zero mark is reached.

When holding a point on the tape other than the zero graduation, the front tapeperson must receive a pin from the rear tapeperson before proceeding to move forward. At the zero point, the rear tapeperson picks up the pin as in any full length measurement to maintain the count.

Measuring Distances Longer Than 10 Tape Lengths

To measure a distance longer than 10 full tape lengths, the tapepersons use the procedures discussed above and the instructions on how to slope tape in excess of 10 tape lengths.

Measuring Partial Tape Lengths

To measure the partial tape length remaining between the forward station and the taping pin representing the final full tape length, the tapepersons use the following procedure.

The front tapeperson moves to the forward station and places the plumb bob cord on the zero graduation of the tape. The rear tapeperson moves forward along the tape to the taping pin.

If slack is needed, the rear tapeperson allows the tape to move forward. When ready, the front tapeperson calls "tension," and the rear tapeperson exerts a pull on the tape, using the clamping handle to hold the tape. While applying tension to the tape, the rear tapeperson slides the plumb bob cord along the tape until a full decimeter or foot division is reached, then moves the tape until the graduation is exactly over the pin and calls "mark." The front tapeperson slides the front plumb bob cord along the tape until the plumb bob is over the station, reads the value on the tape, and asks the rear tapeperson for the even value above the pin.

The front tapeperson records the reading of the final increment, counting the number of pins in the rear tapeperson's possession. Both tapepersons should now check the taping record.

Determining the Taped Distance

The field notebook contains a record of the number of exchanges of pins (10 tape lengths), plus a number of tape lengths determined by the number of pins held by the rear tapeperson, plus the partial increment measured last. These figures should be checked by both tapepersons and initialed as correct.

Laying Off a Given Distance

Frequently, a taping party is required to "lay off" a given distance and establish a new point on the ground. A known distance on the tape is thus transferred to the ground. All of the procedures described above are used in the same order. The only difference is that a stake or other type of marker is left in the ground at the given distance.

TAPING CORRECTIONS

Every measured distance has to be corrected to reduce it to the true length. These computations are based on known errors, such as errors due to tape length (standardization error), slope, temperature, supports, and tension. Corrections for support and tape length can be made from data supplied by the standardizing agency or by comparing the tape against a calibrated or standardized tape. The comparison is made by applying the standard tension and by using the method of support required by the accuracy of the survey. For example, the tape may be fully supported, supported at the ends only, or supported at the ends and at the midpoint. Once the correction is determined, the amount is applied to each tape length measured. Temperature and slope corrections cannot be predetermined. Slope and temperature readings must be made with each tape measurement and the correction applied to each one. The effect of the correction (that is, whether it is plus or minus) depends upon the type of correction. Tape length and temperature may vary in either direction from a standard. However, horizontal or vertical misalignment in horizontal taping results in a value that is longer than the actual distance; these errors are deducted from the measured value on the tape to get the true distance. In slope taping, vertical misalignment may give a longer or shorter value and is a random error.

Length of Tape

Tape length varies with temperature, tension, and manner of support. The original graduations were placed on the tape under conditions which were not the same as those that are encountered in the field. Thus, the standard length is referred to a definite set of conditions. The conditions encountered in the field are measured and compared to the standard, and the differences are converted into a correction.

Precise tapes are sent to the National Bureau of Standards where the length is determined using a standard tension and several different support conditions. In addition, a specified temperature is maintained during the standardization. A coefficient of thermal expansion is computed for each tape. A tape standardization certificate is issued for the tape, listing all this information. This tape can then be used to calibrate others, which in turn are used to compare field tapes.

The comparison establishes a "standard" length for each tape under specific conditions. Any variation from these conditions is measured, and the correction can then be computed.

Any tape which is to be used for measuring distances should be checked for length against a standardized or a calibrated tape. The result of the comparison is recorded in the taping notebook as a plus or minus correction for each tape length as it is recorded. Since these comparisons are made under a definite applied tension, the same tension must be used in the field.

Method of Support. Even under standard tension, a tape supported or held only at the ends will sag in the center; the amount of sagging is based on its weight per unit length. This sag will cause the recorded distance to be greater than the length being measured. When the tape is supported at its midpoint, the effect of sag in the two sections is considerably less than when the tape is supported only at its ends. As the number of equally-spaced intermediate supports is increased, the distance between the end graduations will approach the length of the tape when supported throughout its length. When more than two supports are used, the tops of all supports must be at the same level. The correction for the error due to the sag between two supports for any section of the tape can be determined by the following equation:

$$C_s = \frac{W^2 l^3}{24t^2}$$

in which C_s is the correction for sag, W is the weight per unit length of the tape, l is the length of the suspended section of tape, and t is the tension applied to the tape. In this equation, W and t must have the same units of weight measure, then C will have the same unit of linear measure as l. The weight W per unit length can be determined accurately enough for most purposes by weighing the tape and dividing the result by the number of units in the tape.

A strong wind acting on an extended tape creates a condition similar to sag. A correction for this condition is almost impossible to determine, so more precise taping should not be attempted in high winds. For lower-accuracy surveys, the wind effect can be minimized by increasing the number of support points or by measuring with a fully supported tape.

Atmospheric Effects. When measuring with a tape, the only atmospheric condition that has to be considered is temperature. The temperature of the tape (not the temperature of the air) is used to determine the thermal expansion or contraction of the tape due to temperature changes. The tape is standardized at a specific temperature, and the temperatures which are recorded during the taping are used to correct the *measured length*. The order of accuracy of the survey and the type of tape determine the number of thermometers used, the placement of the thermometer(s) on the tape, and the required accuracy of the temperature reading.

The standard length of a tape is usually determined at a temperature of 68°F [20°C]. When the temperature of a steel tape is less than 68°F, the length of the tape is less than its standard length; conversely, when the temperature of the tape is greater than 68°F, the length of the tape is greater than its standard length. For example, at temperatures higher than the standard, a tape length measures a distance that is actually greater than the tape value. Therefore, any correction must be added. For colder temperatures, the tape is short and the measured ground distance is less than the value on the tape, so the correction is subtracted (minus).

The change in the length of a steel tape because of a difference between the actual temperature of the tape and the standard temperature can be found by using one of the following formulas:

$$C_t = 0.00000645\,(T-68)\,l$$
$$C_t = 0.00001161\,(t-20)\,l$$

in which C_t is the change in length because of temperature, T is the temperature of the tape in degrees Fahrenheit, t is the temperature of the tape in degrees Celsius, and l is the length of tape used. The value of C is in the same unit of measure as l. The sign of the correction indicates the way the correction is applied to the measured length.

Slope of Tape

When a measurement is made with the tape inclined, the slope distance is always greater than the horizontal distance. The slope of the tape can be determined by making one of two measurements: the difference in elevation between taping stations or the value of the vertical angle. The percent of slope is used as a criterion to determine which formula is used with the difference in elevation method. The small errors that normally occur in the alignment of the tape have no appreciable effect on the measured distance on the lower-order surveys normally associated with this book.

Vertical Angle Method. When the slope is determined from the vertical angle, the correction to be subtracted from the slope distance is determined by the following equation:

$$C_h = s \text{ vers } a$$
$$= s\,(1-\cos a)$$

in which C_h is the correction to the slope distance, s is the measured slope distance (usually one tape length), and a is the vertical angle of slope.

Difference in Elevation Method. The difference in elevation between supports is measured in the same units as the slope distance measurement, and a correction (to be subtracted from the slope distance to obtain the horizontal distance) is computed by the following equation:

$$C_h = \frac{-h^2}{2s}$$

in which C_h is the correction, h is the difference in elevation, and s is the slope distance. This equation gives an approximate value for C_h to be used for slopes of five percent or less.

For slopes greater than 5 percent, a closer approximation of the true value of C_h can be determined by use of the following equations:

$$C_h = \frac{-h^2}{2s\frac{-h^2}{2s}}, \text{ or}$$

$$C_h = \frac{-h^2}{2s} - \frac{h^4}{8s^3}$$

in which C_h, h, and s are as defined above.

TAPING MISTAKES AND ERRORS

Taping, like all survey measurements, is susceptible to mistakes and errors. Most mistakes can be avoided and errors minimized as described below.

Mistakes

Mistakes may result from poor work habits, lack of judgment, or confusion. They are often costly, time consuming, and difficult to detect. The easiest way to avoid them is to establish and follow a definite procedure, being constantly alert during the operations where mistakes are possible. Some of the more common mistakes are:

1. Failing to hold the zero graduation of the tape over the point
2. Transposing figures, such as recording 48.26 for 48.62
3. Reading the figure upside down and obtaining, for example, 9 for 6
4. Measuring from the wrong end of the tape and misreading fractional tape lengths, for example, 28 instead of 22
5. Reading the wrong foot mark, such as 38.32 for 37.32
6. Subtracting incorrectly when reading a tape
7. Omitting an entire tape length

Errors

Errors in surveying can be divided into two classes, systematic and accidental. The relative importance of systematic and accidental errors depends on the purpose of the survey. When the purpose tolerates low accuracy measurements, all errors are often treated as accidental errors, and no effort is made to correct for the systematic errors. If the required accuracy is increased, a corresponding increase in effort must be made to determine the values of systematic errors and correct their effects. In a survey requiring high accuracy measurements, the effects of all systematic errors are first corrected, then the probable value of the accidental errors must be determined.

Systematic Errors. Systematic errors, sometimes called constant errors, occur from well-understood causes and can be reduced by taking proper precautions to eliminate them. For example, the length of a steel tape between the 0 and 50 meter graduations varies. Its length was calibrated as 49.99 m, but it actually is 49.98 m. Each tape length is thus 0.01 m too long. Thus, a systematic error of 1:5000 is introduced in each measured course. Systematic errors can be greatly reduced by methods of observation and by eliminating calibration and adjustment errors in the equipment.

Accidental Errors. Accidental errors are caused by a combination of factors beyond the control of the observer. For example, when determining a horizontal distance with a steel tape, small uncontrollable errors result while applying tension to the tape, determining the temperature of the tape, measuring the slope of the tape, or transferring the positions of the end graduations to the ground. The magnitude and algebraic sign of these errors are matters of chance. A compensating effect results when as many accidental errors are positive in algebraic sign as are negative. Accidental errors remain after mistakes have been eliminated and systematic errors have been reduced. Accidental errors are also called random errors, irregular errors, and erratic errors.

FIELD NOTES

The field notes of the surveyor must contain a complete record of all measurements made during the survey, along with any necessary sketches, diagrams, or narrations which help to clarify the notes. The best field survey is of little value if the notes are not complete and clear. The field notes are the only record that is left after the survey party departs from the field survey site.

Recording

All field notes must be lettered in a neat and legible manner. The lettering should be in a freehand, Gothic style. All notes should be recorded with a 3H or 4H pencil. A hard pencil is used because ink could smear due to moisture on the job (rain, fog, and so forth), and because the pencil will leave indentations in the paper which will indicate if erasures are made. Numerals and decimal points should be legible and permit only one interpretation. Notes must be kept in the standard surveying notebook and not on scraps of paper for later transcription.

Field Notebook Information

The survey notes are usually kept in a field notebook. The following information must appear in each book:

1. Instruction for return of book, if lost.
2. Index of field notes contained in the book.
3. List of party personnel and their duties.
4. List of instruments used, including serial numbers, calibration data, and dates used.
5. A generalized sketch and description of each project.
6. The survey measurement notes. On each page containing the measurement notes, the heading must be filled out to include the station name, date, instrument person, recorder, instrument used, and the weather. The body of the page contains all the pertinent measurement notes. The bottom of each page must be initialed by the instrument person, who checks the page for errors or omissions.

Forms of Recording

Field note recording takes three general forms: tabulation, sketches, and descriptions.

Tabulation. The numerical measurements are recorded in columns according to a prescribed plan depending on the instrument used, order of accuracy of the survey, and the type of measurement.

Sketches. Sketches add much to clarify field notes and should be used liberally. They may be drawn to scale or approximate scale or exaggerated for clarity. A plane-table sheet is an example of a sketch drawn to scale. The measurements should be added directly on the sketch or keyed in some way to the tabular data. Legibility is a very important requirement of any sketch.

Descriptions. Tabulations with or without added sketches can also be supplemented with descriptions. A description may only be one or two words to clarify the recorded measurements, or it may be a lengthy narration if it is to be used at some future date, possibly years later, to locate a survey monument.

Abbreviations and Symbols

It is recommended that standard abbreviations, signs, and symbols be used in field notes. If there is any doubt as to the meaning or interpretation of a symbol or abbreviation, the words must be spelled out.

Corrections

Erasures are not permitted in field notes. Individual numbers recorded incorrectly should be lined out by a single diagonal line and the correct values added above. The circumstance of the correction of all original figures should be explained in the remarks column, except for obvious mathematical errors. No position will be voided or rejected in the field notes, except in the case of bumping the instrument or observing the wrong target, and then a note must be made in the remarks column stating the reason for voiding. Pages that are voided or rejected must be referenced to a substitute page. *The procedure for corrections is mandatory*, since the field notes are considered legal evidence.

Waterproofing Field Notes

During work in parts of the world that are subject to high humidity and/or rain, it has been found that field notes can be waterproofed in the field. This can be accomplished by spraying a thin coat of clear acrylic plastic on the field record. This spray can be applied before the recording to make the paper waterproof; the paper can still be written on with ordinary writing instruments. The field notes can be sprayed again after the recording; the plastic then fixes the writing and prevents water damage to the records. One such spray is Krylon Workable Fixative #1306; however, there are many other sprays on the market, and any of them may be used.

Recording Procedures

The field notebook for taping is prepared in the same manner as all survey notebooks. In addition, as each job is begun, one page of the notebook should contain a record of the comparison or calibration of the tapes (see Fig. 18-5). It should show the points of support and the actual measured distance for the tape length. The rest of the notes (see Fig. 18-6) contain the field-recorded values in the first five columns. The remaining information is computed to reduce all distances to horizontal.

The top of the page shows where the line was run, to what accuracy, by whom, when, and with what equipment. The tension used is also recorded.

The column headings are entered as shown and are self-explanatory.

The stations are entered in column 1.

The method of support, in column 2, explains whether the tape was supported at two points, three points, or in its entirety. Remember that the support points are equally distributed along the tape.

The temperature value, column 3, is the tape temperature.

Column 4 lists the percent of slope. Note that the value could be the difference in elevation (DE) between tape ends; DE is divided by 100 to get the percentage of slope. Tape values of less than 100 ft use a proportional amount of the DE to get percentage of slope.

The measured distance, column 5, is the actual tape reading.

The temperature corrections (TEMP CORR) are determined for each tape length as described in the para-

Figure 18-5
Entries in an Air Force field book *(U.S. Air Force)*.

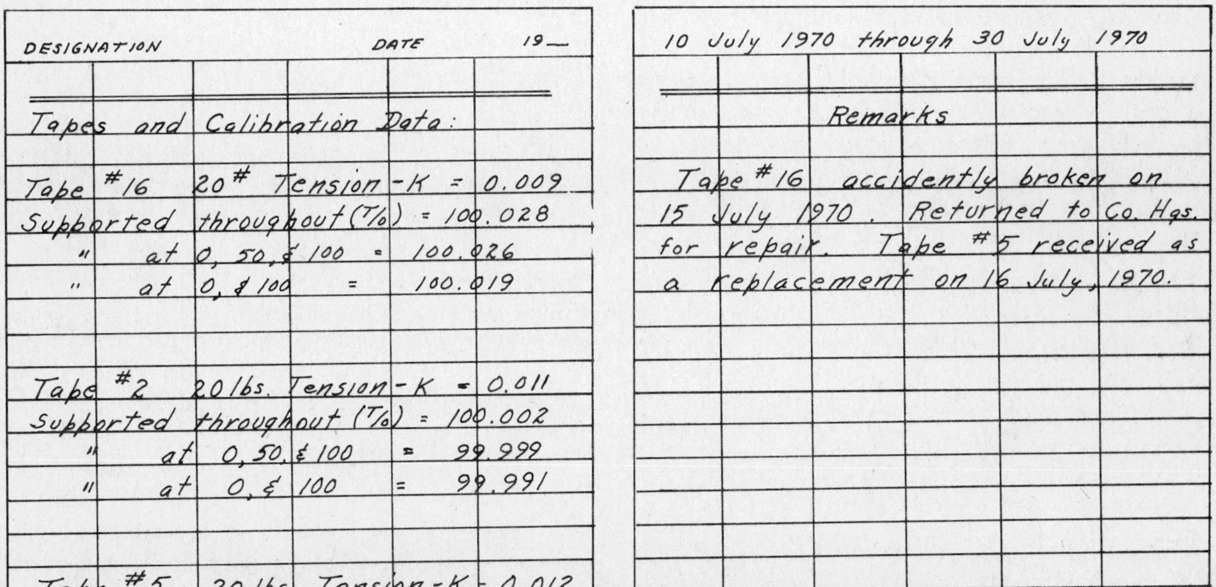

DESIGNATION			DATE		19__
Tapes	and	Calibration	Data:		
Tape	#16	20#	Tension	-K =	0.009
Supported		throughout	(T/o) =	100.028	
"	at	0, 50, & 100	=	100.026	
"	at	0, & 100	=	100.019	
Tape	#2	20 lbs.	Tension	-K =	0.011
Supported		throughout	(T/o) =	100.002	
"	at	0, 50, & 100	=	99.999	
"	at	0, & 100	=	99.991	
Tape	#5	20 lbs.	Tension	-K =	0.012
Supported		throughout	(T/o) =	100.034	
"	at	0, 50, & 100	=	100.031	
"	at	0, & 100	=	100.022	

(1)

10 July 1970 through 30 July 1970					
		Remarks			
Tape #16		accidently	broken on		
15	July	1970.	Returned	to	Co. Hqs.
for	repair.	Tape	#5	received	as
a	replacement	on	16	July,	1970.

DESIGNATION: 3RD Order Taping DATE 11 JULY 1970

FROM: Δ Fox To: Wolf Head Tapeman: J. Doe

Rear tapeman: W. Roe Recorder: R. Coe

Station	Support	Temp.	Slope %	Measured Distance	Temp. Corr.	Slope Corr.	Tape Corr.	Total Corr.	Horiz. DISTANCE	Remarks
Δ Fox	2	72° F	2.5	100.00	+0.003	-0.031	+0.019	-.0.009	99.991	Tape #16
	2	72°	2.8	100.00	+0.003	-0.039	+0.019	-0.017	99.983	Tension: 20 lbs
	2	73	1.5	100.00	+0.003	-0.011	+0.019	+0.011	100.011	
	2	73	1.0	100.00	+0.003	-0.005	+0.019	+0.017	100.017	
	2	74	1.3	100.00	+0.004	-0.008	+0.019	+0.015	100.015	
	2	74	1.8	100.00	+0.004	-0.016	+0.019	+0.007	100.007	
⊙ 1	2	74	0.5	83.72	+0.003	-0.001	+0.018	+0.020	83.740	
Fox to ⊙1	Totals			683.72				+0.044	683.764	
⊙ 1	2	74° F	2.3	100.00	+0.004	-0.026	+0.019	-0.003	99.997	
	2	75	1.8	62.50	+0.003	-0.010	+0.016	+0.009	62.509	
	T/O	75	1.5	100.00	+0.005	-0.011	+0.028	+0.022	100.022	
	T/O	74	1.5	100.00	+0.004	-0.011	+0.028	+0.021	100.021	
	T/O	75	1.5	100.00	+0.005	-0.011	+0.028	+0.022	100.022	
⊙ 2	2	75	0.0	59.77	+0.003	0.000	+0.015	+0.018	59.788	
⊙1 to ⊙2	Totals			522.27				+0.089	522.359	

2

Figure 18-6
Field data in Air Force field book *(U.S. Air Force)*.

graph on atmospheric effects. Then, as a check, the average of all the temperature readings is used to apply a temperature correction to the total line distance.

The slope corrections (SLOPE CORR) are determined as described in the paragraph on slope of the tape. In this instance, the percentage of slope is the difference in elevation in feet for a slope distance of 100 ft. The slope correction must be determined for each measured value.

Values in the column headed TAPE CORR depend on the manner of support of the tape during the measurement; as described, the tape correction depends on whether the tape has two-point support or total support.

Values in the column headed TOTAL CORR are the algebraic sum of the values on the same line, in the three preceding columns.

Values in the column headed HORIZ DIST (horizontal distance) are equal to the "meas dist" (measured distance) corrected by the total correction.

Recording Precautions

The field notes must contain all the data needed to convert the taping information into horizontal distances. Responsibility for this rests with the recorder and the chief of the party. The order of accuracy of the survey will establish the type of taping to be done, the precision of the measurements, and which readings other than tape measurements must be taken. Thus, if the survey calls for slope taping, the slope or the difference in elevation of the tape ends must be measured. If survey precision further requires the temperature correction, the tape thermometer reading must be noted for each tape length. When taping with a a specified tension, not only must the tension be recorded, but a tape calibration against a standard (as in Fig. 18-5) must also be shown.

The techniques described for taping pin exchange and checking notes by both tapepersons should be a standard procedure. The tapeperson should make a practice of pacing the distance while moving forward with the tape. This will call attention to possible mistakes if the paced and measured distance do not agree. Tape measurements are subject to many mistakes which, if not discovered in time, require reruns and waste valuable time. Every attempt should be made to eliminate the practices which cause mistakes. This will minimize the number of reruns.

INDIRECT METHODS

Distance measuring is normally performed with distance measuring equipment. However, there are some indirect methods that employ the use of angle measuring equipment to determine distances. These methods are usually used for fourth- and lower-order surveys when microwave instruments are not available and the terrain is prohibitive to taping. These methods are stadia, short base, and subtense.

The short base and subtense methods of indirect measuring are rarely used and rather complicated. For this reason they will not be discussed here. The stadia method will serve most purposes.

THEORY OF STADIA

Stadia is a method which uses the geometric principle of similar triangles to measure distances. When stadia is used to measure distances, the difference in elevation is also determined, and this is referred to as trigonometric leveling.

Two horizontal lines or hairs are placed at a fixed distance above and below the center hair on the telescope reticle. When viewing a rod some distance away through the telescope (see Fig. 18-7), these two lines (U and L) will appear on the rod at U_3 and L_3. This distance is called the stadia intercept or stadia interval. If the rod is moved to position 2, the stadia interval will be U_2L_2; and at position 1, U_1L_1. The angle UOL is fixed and remains constant regardless of the distance. The stadia hairs are spaced so that the distance UL is some even proportionate value of the distance from O to the line through U and L. By similar triangles, U_1L_1 is the same proportion of the distance from O to U_1L_1, and U_2L_2 and U_3L_3 are similarly related to their respective distances. No matter where the rod is held, the stadia intercept will equal the same proportion of the distance from the instrument to the rod. In surveying, the principle is stated: The distance to any point equals so many times the stadia intercept on a rod held on that point. There are three common stadia intervals in use—1:100, 1:200, and 1:333.

Distances can be measured to any point up to 200 times the length of the rod and visible from an instrument setup. Only the rod has to be moved from point to point for the distance to be determined. To establish a position, the direction from the instrument to the point must be known. This is accomplished by measuring an angle with a transit or theodolite. Another common method uses a planetable and alidade. After orientation, the direction is drawn on the planetable and the distance is plotted to a convenient scale.

Stadia, as described above, assumes a horizontal line of sight. When the line of sight is inclined (see Fig. 18-8) the stadia intercept on a rod held vertically is not a true proportion of the distance since the rod is not perpendicular to the line of sight. To make the rod perpendicular, it would have to be tilted from the X position to a position like Y. This tilt would be almost impossible to maintain. In practice, the rod is held vertically, and not tilted. Notice in Fig. 18-8 that the extension from X is perpendicular to the horizontal distance, H. The angle between X and Y is equal to angle α, and the horizontal distance H and difference in elevation DE can be computed from the intercept read on the vertical rod as follows:

$$H = \frac{f}{i} I \cos^2\alpha + C\cos\alpha$$

$$DE = \frac{f}{i} I \tfrac{1}{2} \sin 2\alpha + C\sin\alpha$$

where $\frac{f}{i}$ is the stadia interval factor. I is the stadia intercept on the rod held vertically at X, and C is the stadia constant of the instrument.

Figure 18-7
Stadia intervals *(U.S. Air Force).*

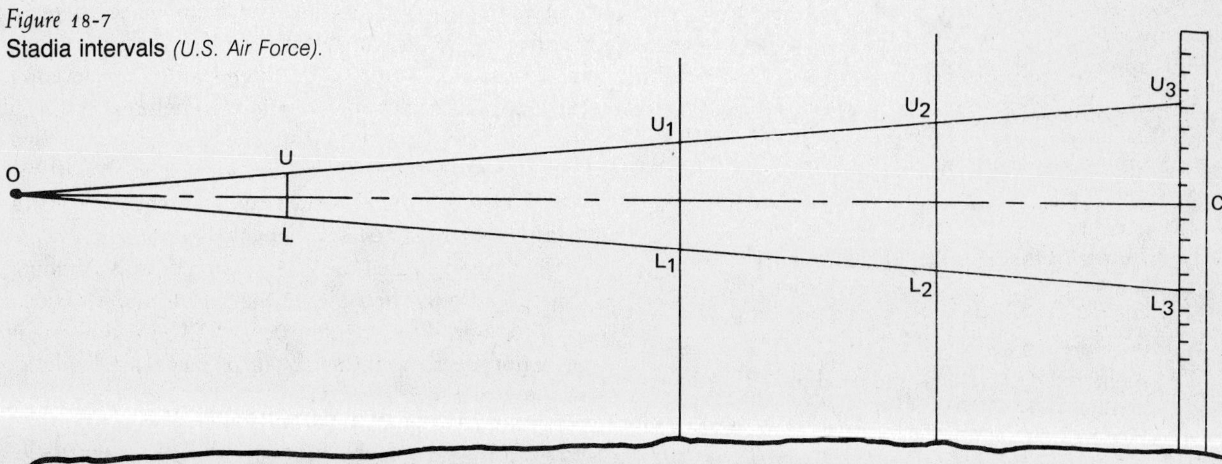

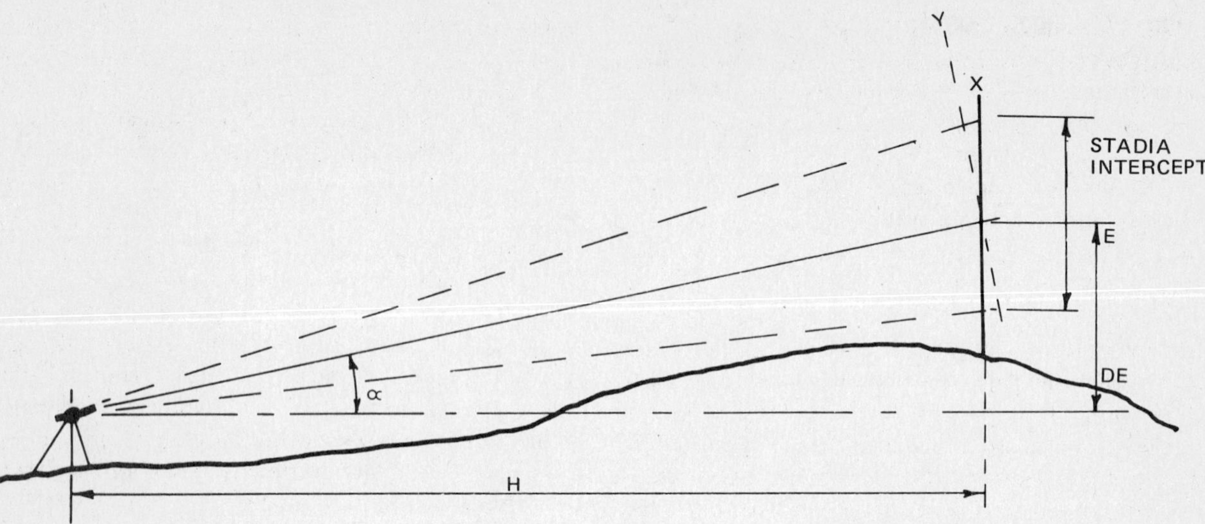

Figure 18-8
Theory of stadia *(U.S. Air Force).*

Stadia Constant

The stadia constant C is equal to $f + c$ (f is the focal length of the telescope's objective lens, c is the distance from the center of the objective lens to the center of the instrument). Ordinarily, this value is determined by the manufacturer and is noted on the inside of the instrument's carrying case. For normal stadia work, the constant C is assumed to be zero for an internal-focusing instrument and 1.0 ft for an external-focusing instrument. The 1.0 ft value is not universal. C is determined by the manufacturer for each instrument and marked on a tag mounted in the carrying case. It must be checked for each instrument.

For internal-focusing instruments, $C = 0$, and the second terms of the equations for H and DE become zero. Thus, both H and DE depend on the intercept, the angle, and the stadia interval factor.

For external-focusing instruments, C equals 1 ft. In the first formula, $\cos\alpha$ is thus multiplied by one. However, when the stadia angles are small (below 10°), $\cos\alpha$ also is near 1 ($\cos 10° = 0.9848$). The term $C \cos\alpha$ is thus approximately equal to 1 ft. For practical purposes, the stadia constant C is added to the horizontal distance, especially when the angle does not exceed about 5°. In the formula for difference in elevation, C is multiplied by $\sin\alpha$. For small angles, $\sin\alpha$ is close to zero, and the product ($C\sin\alpha$) can be considered zero. Then DE depends only on the first part of the formula.

Stadia Interval Factor

The stadia interval factor is the focal length of the telescope's objective lens f divided by the actual distance between the stadia hairs i. When the stadia interval factor must be checked in the field, the following method is used:

1. Select an area where a horizontal sight of approximately 300 m (800 to 1,000 ft) can be made.
2. By taping, mark a series of points at 50-meter (or 100-ft) intervals from the instrument. For external-focusing instruments, only the first 50-m (or 100-ft) point should include the stadia constant C. The remaining points are set at the normal 50-m (100-ft) interval.
3. Read and record the stadia intercept on a rod held on each of the points in turn.
4. Divide the measured distance to each point by the stadia intercept reading for that point. The result is the stadia interval for each distance.
5. Take a mean of all the values as the stadia interval factor $\frac{f}{i}$ for the instrument.

The frequency of the interval factor check depends on the type and accuracy of the survey and the instrument associated with it. For higher orders of leveling, the factor determination is performed before the start of work and anytime the instrument is bumped or jolted. On the lower-order surveys such as planetable-alidade stadia, checks about once a week and when the instrument is jolted may be sufficient.

The formulas used in the reduction of stadia readings can be solved by the tables in the back of the field book, or with slide rules or other devices. The various stadia reduction devices give a tabular or mechanical solution of the stadia formulas in which a standard value is used for $\frac{f}{i}$ (usually 100) and the value for C is disregarded.

Stadia Measurement

Stadia measurement consists of two basic steps; the first step is to determine the stadia intercept for the distance, and the second is to obtain a rod reading and vertical angle or scale reading for the difference in elevation.

The readings are made on a leveling rod or on a specially graduated stadia rod. The foot-graduated stadia rod has painted graduations in feet, tenths, and half-tenths (0.05 or 1/20) of a foot. Both the stadia rod and the leveling rod are normally read to hundredths of a foot for distance and to tenths of a foot for elevation.

To take a reading, the telescope is moved until all three wires fall on the rod. The instrument is clamped in a position as close to horizontal as possible under the given terrain conditions. The vertical reading consists of recording the values of the center wire and the vertical arc, if any. The top and bottom wire values (stadia intercept) are also read at this time. These will be used to determine the horizontal distance.

During stadia surveys, the rod is sometimes held in a location where only two hairs can be seen on the rod, the third hair being obscured. Another possibility, especially on a level sight, is that only one hair intercepts the rod; the other two will be visible but will be above or below the rod. The geometry of stadia can be used to obtain a complete reading.

The two stadia hairs or wires are set at equal intervals on each side of the center wire. When two of the three wires can be read on the rod, the value of the third can be computed. If the center and either outside wire are readable, the difference between their readings (the half-interval) is read and the center wire is moved to the outer wire position. This brings the off-the-rod wire onto the rod. The second half-interval can be read and added to the first to obtain the full value. If only the two outer (stadia) wires are visible, their difference divided by two is the distance from either wire to the center one.

Stadia Accuracy

Stadia measurements are affected by numerous factors that may cause large errors in the horizontal distances and differences in elevation. The use of incorrect stadia constants cause large errors in measurements. Errors in the adjustments of the instrument and incorrect plumbing of the rod cause errors especially when sights are steeply inclined. Inaccuracies in the rod graduations cause erroneous intercept readings. Sights passing close to the ground may be affected by differential refraction. Long sights on sunny days over terrain which reflects the heat result in heat waves in the sights, making accurate rod reading impossible. With reasonably careful stadia measurements over terrain that does not require steep sights, and with the use of the correct values for the stadia constants, horizontal distances can be determined to a degree of accuracy of 1:5000. Under the same conditions, differences in elevation can be determined with errors not exceeding 0.2 ft times the square root of the distance in miles (or approximately 0.048 times the square root of the distance in kilometers).

PROBLEMS

1. With a steel tape and tape holder, range pole, set of 11 tape arrows, clip board, pencil, hatchet, and stakes, tape a distance of 437 ft in one straight line. Check the distance by taping several times.
   (a) Drive a stake into the ground at a starting point. Drive a nail into the center of the stake to be the starting point.
   (b) Set up a taping party consisting of a *Chief of Party*, *Recorder*, *Rear Tapeperson*, *Front Tapeperson*, and a *Rodperson*.

   Make this measurement using slope taping procedures. It can be checked by the instructor and other taping crews. Be sure to drive another stake and nail at the end measurement, and do not drag the steel tape.
2. Using the same procedures as in problem 1.
   (a) Lay off 310.5 ft. Measure in both directions, then have the party rotate their positions and retape for a check.
   (b) Lay off 623.3 ft. Break tape at least once in this problem. Check by taping in the opposite direction.
   (c) Lay off 1000.7 ft. Tape several times to check for accuracy of measurement.
3. On a building on the school campus measure the exact length and width of the building. Have another crew or the same crew with rotated positions check that the measurements are accurate.
4. Measure the exact distance from one building on campus to another building or to a specific fixed object on the campus. The instructor or another taping party can check the measurement.
5. Tape the distance between at least five exact locations, each separated by not less than one tape length. Tape the distance again, this time going in the reverse order. The exact locations used for this exercise should be points chisled in concrete, tacks in asphalt, firmly set stakes, or any other object that can be securely set and later relocated. Compare results with other taping parties who used the same locations.
6. Perform the same exercise as in problem 5, but this time break tape during at least one of the measurements.

LEARNING ACTIVITY PACKAGE

Read Chap. 18 carefully.

Chapter 18 read ____________ *(date)*.

If after reading Chap. 18 the student has not understood some of the objectives (a) through (i), the paragraphs containing these objectives should be reread.

Objectives read and studied ____________ *(date)*.

Do the student problems. Work the problems assigned by the instructor.

Problem 1 completed ____________ *(date)*.

Problem 2 completed ____________ *(date)*.

Problem 3 completed ____________ *(date)*.

Problem 4 completed ____________ *(date)*.

Problem 5 completed ____________ *(date)*.

Problem 6 completed ____________ *(date)*.

Now take the Chap. 18 quiz. Remove the quiz from the text and complete all the questions.

Chap. 18 quiz taken ____________ *(date)*.

18

QUIZ

1. What is the difference between the two basic methods of taping? ______

   Slope taping

   horizontal taping

2. Why are there 11 taping arrows? ______

   one tape arrow always stay in the grand

3. How is tension prorated if less than a full tape length must be used? ______

4. What is the difference between a plus tape and a minus tape? ______

5. Where is the taping arrow placed when using the horizontal taping method? ______

6. How many times is each distance measured? ______

7. After a given distance has been measured, why do both the front and rear tapepersons initial the field notebook? ______

8. Name at least two of the possible sources of errors in a measurement. ______

9. What is the difference between a systematic and an accidental error? ______

10. Describe each of the three forms of recording field notes. ______

11. Why are erasures forbidden in the field notebook? ______

12. The geometric principle of similar triangles is used in which method of distance measurement? ______

13. What are the three leveling rod values used when measuring distance by stadia?

____

____

____

14. What degree of accuracy can be expected if careful stadia measurements are made? __________

15. What are some of the possible errors which could be introduced into stadia measurements? ________________________

____

____

19 LEVELING

Objectives

a. Understand the meaning of *mean sea level*
b. Know the difference between differential or spirit leveling and indirect leveling
c. Understand orders of accuracy
d. Study differential leveling
e. Learn the meanings of the leveling terms
f. Understand the importance of balancing the foresight and backsight distances
g. Understand curvature and refraction
h. Read how to adjust the level vial
i. Read the adjustment technique for the horizontal crosshairs
j. Understand the field procedure for leveling operations
k. Learn the sequence of steps in taking a level reading
l. Learn the rodperson's duties
m. Know how data from leveling operations is recorded in the field books
n. Study reciprocal leveling
o. Read about trigonometric leveling

Rationale

Measuring the difference in elevation between points on the earth's surface is a fundamental part of surveying. These differences in elevation can be determined by various methods of leveling.

Leveling is the operation of determining the difference in elevation between points on the earth's surface. A level reference surface or datum is established and an elevation assigned to it. Differences in the determined elevations are subtracted from or added to this assigned value and result in the elevations of the points.

A level surface is one on which every point is perpendicular to the direction of the plumb line. It differs from a plane surface, which is flat and is perpendicular to a plumb line at only one point. A body of still water will assume a level surface. If the changes in the surface of the ocean caused by such influences as tides, currents, winds, atmospheric pressure, and the rotation of the earth could be eliminated, the resulting surface would be level.

The ocean's level surface is determined by averaging a series of tidal height observations over a Metonic cycle (approximately 19 calendar years). This average, called mean sea level, is the most common datum for leveling and is usually assigned an elevation of zero. This datum remains in effect until continuing observations show a significant difference, and it becomes worthwhile to change to the new datum. In the United States, the mean sea level datum of 1929 is still in effect.

TYPES OF LEVELING

Leveling operations are divided into two major categories. Direct leveling is usually referred to as differential or spirit leveling. In this method the difference in elevation between a known elevation and the height of the instrument and then the difference in elevation from the height of instrument to an unknown point, are determined by measuring the vertical distance with a precise or semiprecise level and leveling rods. This is the only method that will yield accuracies of third or higher order.

The second method of leveling, indirect leveling, is further subdivided into two separate methods: trigonometric and barometric. The trigonometric method applies the principles of trigonometry to determine differences in elevation; a vertical angle (above or below a horizontal plane) and a horizontal distance (measured or computed) are used to compute the vertical distance between two points. This method is generally used for lower-order leveling where the terrain is prohibitive to direct leveling.

Barometric leveling uses the differences in atmospheric pressure as observed with a barometer or altimeter to determine differences in elevation. This is the least used and least accurate method of determining differences in elevation. It should only be used in surveys when one of the other methods is unfeasible or would involve large amounts of time or money. Due to its limited use, barometric leveling will not be discussed further.

ORDERS OF ACCURACY

When writing the specifications for a survey, it is very impractical to specify the exact degree of accuracy that is to be attained in each of the measurements. For this reason, specifications are based on the minimum degree of accuracy allowed for the particular survey. The range between the allowed degrees of accuracy is known as an order of accuracy. The orders of accuracy for surveys are called first order, second order, third order, and lower order. The measurements for first-order-accuracy surveys are the most accurate, and the measurements for the other orders are progressively less accurate.

Orders of accuracy are specified for triangulation, traverse, and leveling. For the measurements made in mapping, orders of accuracy are also specified for the astronomic observations made to establish position and azimuth. As an example of the range between orders of accuracy, let us consider the allowed traverse position closure. First order specifies 1:25,000 or better; second order, 1:10,000; and third order, 1:5000. The surveys normally associated with this book require third- and lower-order accuracy.

DIFFERENTIAL LEVELING

In direct leveling, a horizontal line of sight is established using a sensitive level bubble in a level vial. The instrument is leveled and the line of sight is adjusted to be parallel to the level vial axis. When leveled, the line of sight of the instrument describes a horizontal plane (see Fig. 19-1). This procedure is referred to as differential or spirit leveling as described below.

Method

The leveling operation (see Fig. 19-2) consists of holding a rod vertically on a point of known elevation. A level reading known as a *backsight* (BS) is then made through the telescope on the rod; this gives the vertical distance from the ground elevation to the line of sight. By adding this backsight reading to the known elevation, the line-of-sight elevation, called *height of instrument* (HI), is determined. Another rod is placed on a point of unknown elevation, and a *foresight* (FS) reading is taken. By subtracting the foresight reading from the height of instrument, the elevation of the new point is established.

After the foresight is completed, the rod remains on that point and the instrument and back rod are moved to forward positions. The instrument is set up approximately midway between the old and new rod positions.

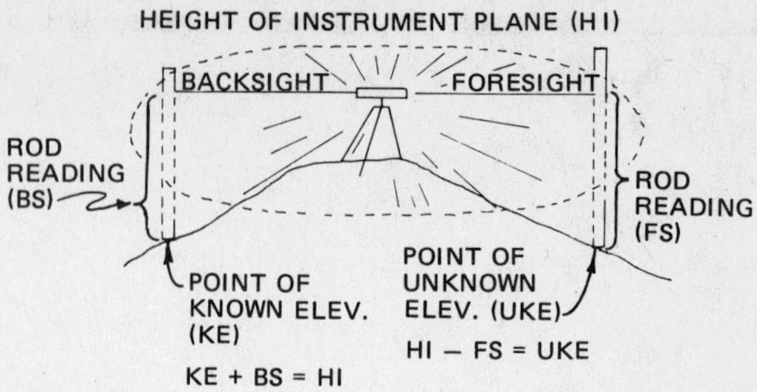

Figure 19-1
Direct leveling.

The new sighting on the back rod is now a backsight for the new height of instrument and the sighting on the front rod is a foresight for a new elevation. The points on which the rods are held for the foresights and backsights are called *turning points* (TPs). This procedure is used as many times as necessary to transfer a point of known elevation to another distant point of unknown elevation. Other foresights to points not along the main line are known as *sideshots*.

Sight Distances. Normally, for third and higher orders, sight distances are kept below 75 meters (m) (245 ft), except when necessary to pass or cross an obstacle. For lower-order lines, the length of sight depends on the optical qualities of the instrument and atmospheric conditions, with the maximum being about 600 m (2000 ft) under ideal conditions.

Before leveling is begun, a reconnaissance of the terrain must be made. Probable locations of turning points and instrument setups can be noted. The slope of the terrain is a prime consideration in leveling. The normal instrument height at any setup is about 1.5 m (4.9 ft). On even downhill slopes, the ground where the instrument is set up must not be more than 1 to 1.5 m (3.3 to 4.9 ft) below the turning point for a level backsight. On the foresight, the extended 4-m (13.1-ft) rod can be held on the ground about 2.5 m (8.2 ft) below the instrument ground level and still permit a reading to be taken. This means that there is a tendency to make foresight distances longer when going downhill. Backsights tend to be longer running uphill.

During the reconnaissance, the line of sight can be estimated by sighting through a hand level. This determines possible instrument and rod setups. The distances between these points are paced in order to balance the foresights and backsights. The procedure is to sight at the uphill point with the hand level, making sure that the line of sight is above ground level. The distance from the proposed turning point to the proposed instrument position is paced, and the same amount is paced to establish the next turning point. Once the distance be-

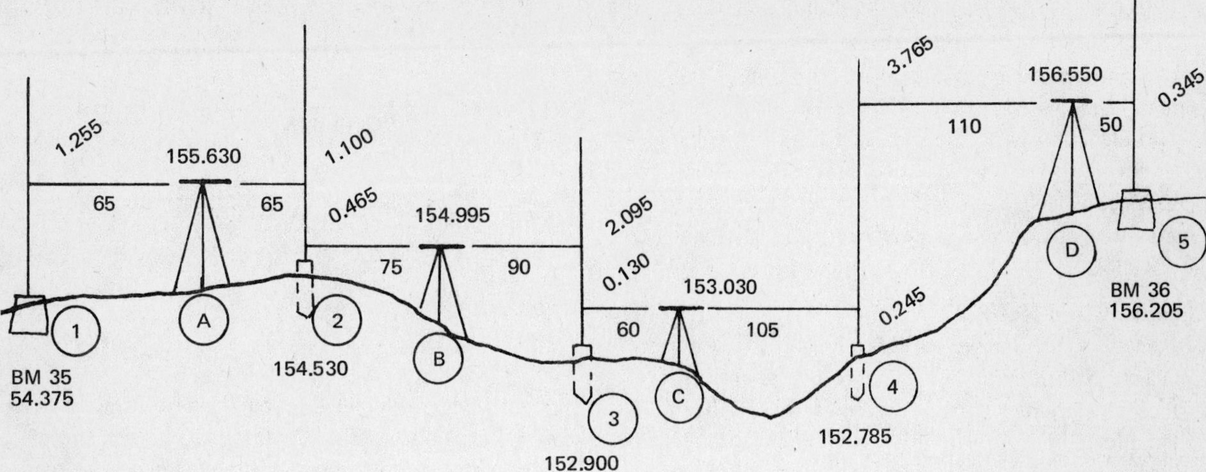

Figure 19-2
Leveling operation.

tween points and instrument is determined, this same amount can be paced repeatedly as long as the slope remains about the same. This procedure balances the distances and makes sure that a level line will fall on the rod. Balancing foresight and backsight distances is very important in leveling.

Balancing Foresights and Backsights. Slight errors in line-of-sight adjusting will distort the horizontal plane into a conical plane above or below the horizontal. Unequal distances between backsight and foresight rod positions will cause an error which will increase in proportion to the distance (see Fig. 19-3). If the same sight (back- or fore-) is consistently longer, the error will accumulate. To eliminate this source of error, the level should be set up midway between the TPs. This is not always possible, and the next best method is to balance backsights and foresights at every opportunity. In practice, the distances from the back rod to the instrument and from the instrument to the front rod are measured at each setup by stadia and then recorded. A separate running total of backsight and foresight distances is kept; the two totals should be continually balanced, not left until the last few setups before closing the line, and not made up by combining one very long and one very short sight. However, if the inequality is introduced by one long sight, then it should be compensated for in one sight before a change in refraction takes place. Balancing backsights and foresights minimizes errors caused by the line of sight not being horizontal. Balancing the sums of the backsights and foresights does not correct curvature and refraction errors, which depend on the square of the distance.

Figure 19-3
Uneven distance error.

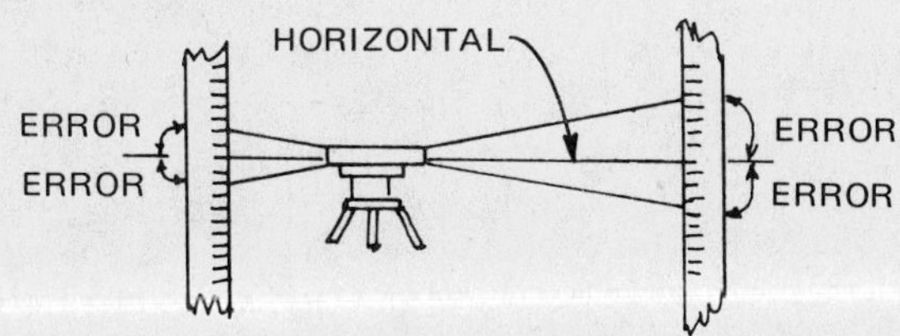

A Leveling Operation

A sample differential leveling run is shown in Fig. 19-2. The rod is held on a point of known elevation, Bench Mark 35, point 1. The level is set up at point *A* midway between point 1 and point 2. The backsight reading is added to the BM elevation; this gives the height of the instrument (HI). The distance is read and recorded for balancing. The rod is moved from point 1 to point 2. The foresight reading on point 2 is subtracted from the HI to get the elevation of point 2. This distance is also read and recorded. The rod is held at point 2, which becomes a turning point, and the level is moved to point *B*. Here the slope becomes a factor. The setup at point *B* requires a longer foresight than backsight, and point 3 must be selected to get across the valley with one setup. The rod still at point 2 is rotated to face the instrument at point *B*, and the backsight and distance are read. Since balancing has been achieved between point 1 and point 2, the new balancing starts again with point 2. When the HI at point *B* has been computed, the rod moves to point 3 for a new foresight and elevation. The process continues (level to point *C*, rod to point 4, level to point *D*, and rod to point 5), and appropriate readings are taken until BM 36 is reached. After point 4 is reached and the valley crossed, instrument position *D* is selected to balance the distances before reaching the next BM.

If BM 36 has a previously established elevation, the elevation computed from the level run is compared to it to determine the amount of error in the line. If BM 36 is being established, the level line must continue until a known elevation is reached and the level run value can be checked against it. This known elevation must have been established to an order of accuracy equal to or greater than the accuracy required for the level line.

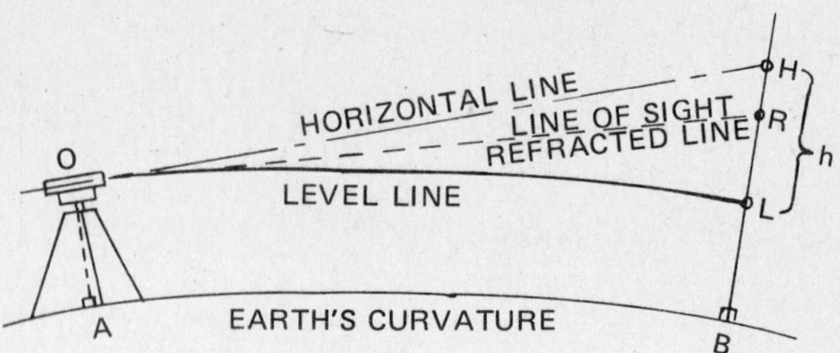

Figure 19-4
Curvature and refraction.

Curvature and Refraction

The level surface defined earlier follows the curvature of the earth. A direct line between two points on this level surface also follows the curvature of the earth and is called a level line. A horizontal line of sight through the telescope is perpendicular to the plumb line only at the telescope and is therefore a straight line, not a level line (see Fig. 19-4). The line *OH* is a horizontal line perpendicular to the plumb line at point *A*. Line *OL* is a level line that parallels the surface of the earth. At each point, *OL* is perpendicular to a plumb line. In leveling, as the distance between points increases, the correction for curvature of earth must be applied to account for the difference between a level line and a horizontal line of sight.

Another correction which must be considered is the atmospheric refraction. The earth's atmosphere refracts or bends a ray of light due to differences in the density of the air between the instrument and the point being viewed. Figure 19-4 illustrates this. Due to the atmospheric density difference, the ray of light will follow the path *OR*. When viewed through the telescope, point *R* appears to be at point *H*.

To make the correction for curvature and refraction, the computations must first locate point *R* from point *H*, and then determine the correction to bring point *R* down to point *L* and establish a level line. In practice, the two corrections are combined. *RH* is about one-eighth of *LH*, and the value is given by the formula:

$$h = M^2 \times 0.0000676$$

where:

h is the correction in millimeters
M is the distance between points in meters.

Adjusting the Level

A check of the instrument's adjustment should be made before it is taken to the field. The adjustment should be checked every day before starting work, anytime the instrument is bumped or jolted, and at the end of each day's work. The instrument should be set up and approximately leveled over both pairs of screws. Since the check also includes the optical assembly, the crosshairs and objective should be focused sharply, using a well-defined object about 50 m (160 ft) away; then the parallax is removed. The check and adjustments are made in three steps described in the following paragraphs. They should be performed in the order listed. *Do not perform these adjustments without your instructor's approval.* Remember that precise adjustment in a precision measurement equipment laboratory is much more accurate than these field tests.

Level Vial. Adjustment of the level vial (see Fig. 19-5) makes the axis of the level bubble perpendicular to the axis of rotation (vertical axis).

Set the instrument over diametrically opposite leveling screws, and center the bubble carefully (see Fig. 19-5*a*).

Rotate the telescope 180° and note the movement of the bubble away from center if the instrument is maladjusted (see Fig. 19-5*b*).

Bring the bubble half the distance back to the center of the vial by turning the capstan screws at the end of the vial (see Fig. 19-5*c*).

Relevel with the leveling screws (see Fig. 19-5*d*), and rotate the instrument 180°. Repeat the previous step if the bubble does not remain at the center of the vial.

Figure 19-5
Adjustments of the level vial.

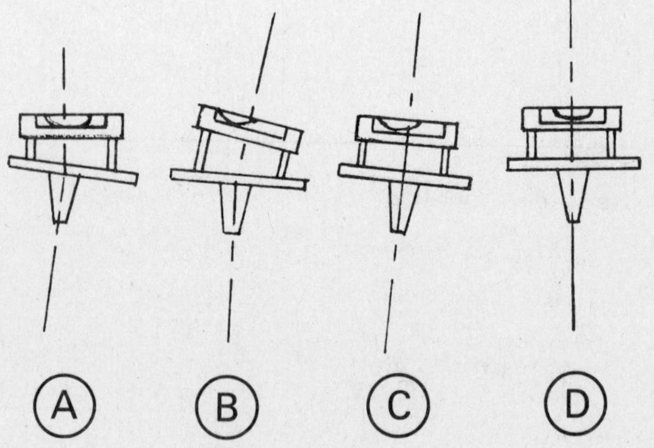

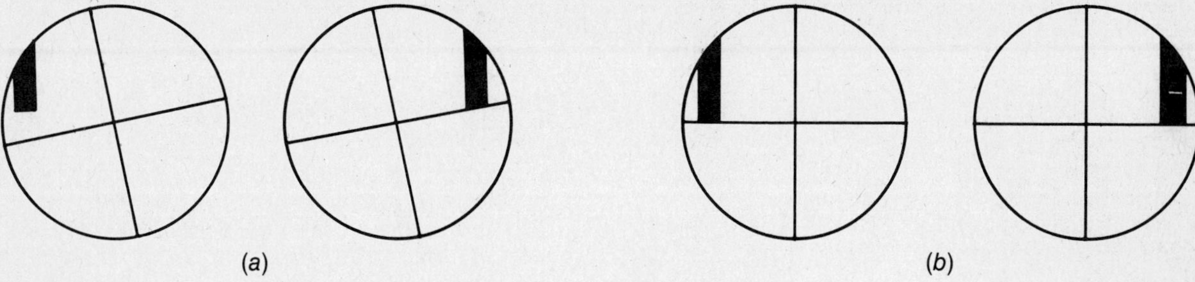

Figure 19-6
Adjustment of horizontal crosshairs. (*a*) out of adjustment (*b*) in adjustment.

Check the final adjustment by noting that the bubble remains in the center of the vial during the entire revolution about the vertical axis.

Horizontal Crosshairs. The horizontal crosshairs are adjusted (see Fig. 19-6) to make the horizontal hair lie in a plane perpendicular to the vertical axis.

Level the instrument carefully.

Sight one end of the horizontal crosshair on a well-defined point about 50 m (160 ft) away. Turn the telescope slowly about its vertical axis, using the slow-motion screw. If the crosshair is in adjustment, the hair will stay on the point through its entire length. If it does not, loosen the reticle adjusting screw and turn the reticle by lightly tapping two opposite screws.

Sight on the point again, and if the horizontal hair does not follow the point through its entire length, turn the ring again.

Repeat this procedure as many times as necessary, until the crosshair stays on the point through its entire length.

Line of Sight. This adjustment (see Fig. 19-7) makes the line of sight parallel to the axis of the level vial. This method is known as the *two-peg* test.

Set up the instrument (see Fig. 19-7, part 1); drive in a stake (A) about 50 m (160 ft) away; drive in another stake (B) at the same distance in the opposite direction.

Take a rod reading a on stake A and a rod reading b on stake B. With the instrument exactly halfway between the two stakes, $b - a$ is the true difference in elevation between the stakes.

Move the instrument close to stake A (see Fig. 19-7, part 2) so that the eyepiece swings within 10 millimeters (mm) of the rod.

Take a rod reading c on stake A through the objective lens, and a rod reading d on the stake B in the normal manner. If the instrument is in adjustment $d - c$ will equal $b - a$.

If the instrument is out of adjustment, calculate what the correct rod reading e should be, ($e = b + c - a$). Move the horizontal crosshair to the correct reading on stake B by loosening the correct vertical capstan screw and tightening the opposite screw.

Check the horizontal crosshair adjustment. The ring may have turned during adjustment of the line of sight.

Rerun the two peg test to verify the adjustment, if one was necessary.

Field Procedure

The leveling operation requires the teamwork of both the instrumentperson and the rodperson at the moment of reading in order to achieve consistent results. The survey accuracy depends upon the refinement with which

Figure 19-7
Two-peg test.

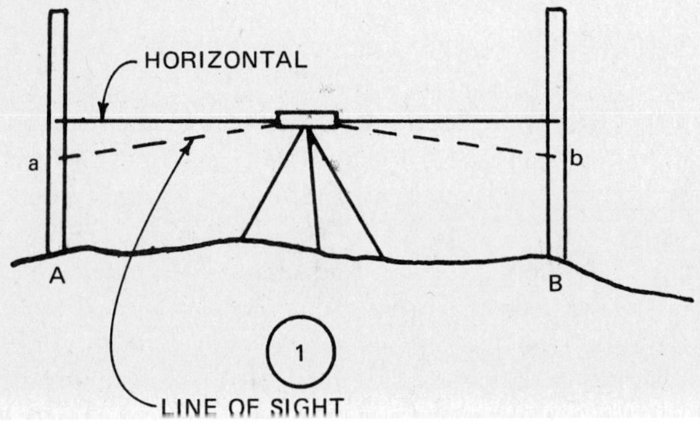

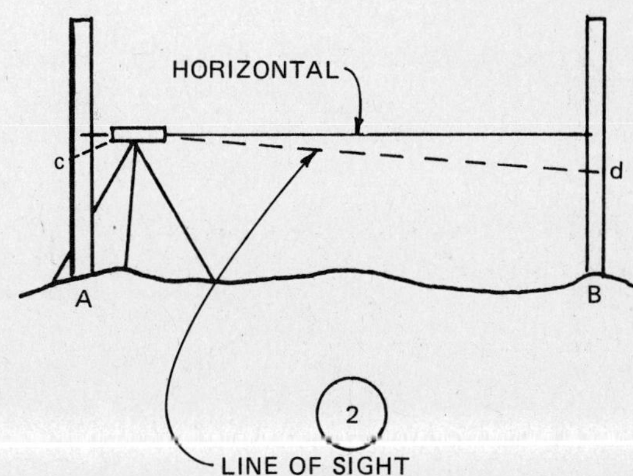

the line of sight can be made horizontal, the ability of the rodperson to hold the rod vertical, and the precision to which the rod is read. Accuracy with instruments using spirit level bubbles must also consider the adjustment of the level vial and the precision with which the bubble axis and the line of sight are made parallel. Self-leveling instruments use a pendulum-prism combination to level the line of sight automatically when the instrument is first brought near level with a circular bubble. Due to the geometry of the prism assembly, the greatest accuracy in leveling the line of sight is achieved when the circular bubble is most accurately centered and the pendulum movement is at a minimum.

Instrument Operation

The level must be in adjustment before starting the leveling operation. Once the instrument is adjusted, operation of the level consists of setting it up, leveling it, and taking the readings to the specified accuracy. Taking a reading consists of determining the position where the crosswire appears to intersect the rod and recording this value. Each instrument setup requires one backsight reading to establish the height of instrument and at least one foresight reading to establish the elevation of the forward point (either a turning point or elevation station). Additional foresights may be made to other points visible from the instrument setup if elevations of these points are also required. Depending on the type of survey and instrument used, either the center wire, all three crosswires, or the micrometer method may be used for taking readings.

The One-Wire Method. In the one-wire method, only the middle crosswire is used. The instrumentperson, looking through the telescope, reads the value where the center wire appears to intersect the rod. If the survey accuracy requires more precise readings, a target and its vernier are used. In this case, the instrumentperson sights through the instrument and signals the rodperson to move the target up or down until the crosswire bisects the horizontal line between the alternate red and white quadrants on the target. When the bisection is achieved, the instrument person signals "OK," and the rodperson locks the target in position until the reading is complete. After locking the target, a check reading is made to see that the target did not slip during the locking operation. The recorder should be near the level to record direct readings or near the rodperson to record target setting operations. Immediately before taking any reading, the instrument person should check the level bubble and bring it back to center if necessary. The tripod may settle slightly, especially if the tripod legs are not set firmly or if the ground is soft. The practice of checking the bubble just before taking each reading will minimize errors.

The sequence for taking a level reading is:

1. The level is set up and leveled.
2. The telescope is pointed so that its vertical crosswire is just off to one side of the rod, and the instrument is clamped.
3. The objective is focused and the parallax is removed.
4. The level bubble is checked for centering and adjusted if necessary.
5. The rod is read and the value recorded.
6. The bubble is rechecked for centering. If it is off center, it must be recentered and the reading repeated.
7. Once the instrumentperson is satisfied that the bubble has remained centered while the reading was taken, the intercept between the upper and lower wires is read to measure the distance from the level to the rod. This distance is used for balancing foresights and backsights and does not have to be read more closely than to the nearest centimeter.
8. The instrumentperson signals the rodperson to proceed to the next position.
9. The telescope is unclamped, revolved, pointed at the next rod position, and focused. Parallax is removed, the bubble centering is checked, the rod is read, and the bubble centering is rechecked.
10. This method continues until the desired number of foresights are taken and a turning point established. The distance to the rod at the turning point is read and recorded. The rodperson then holds the position on the turning point.
11. The level is moved to the next setup position and the procedure repeated.

The target setting procedure requires the levelperson to use hand or voice signals to the rodperson to move the target until the crosswire bisects the target. Figure 19-8 shows some of the more commonly used hand signals. If the rod must be extended, the target is set and the upper section of the rod is moved up or down until the reading is set. Then the rod is clamped. After the instrumentperson has completed the operation and signals "OK," the rodperson reads the rod and vernier if necessary.

The Three-Wire Method. The three-wire method requires the same preparation as the one-wire method. It is good practice to check and clear the parallax very carefully for this operation. The position of each horizontal wire on the rod is read separately. The readings are recorded as the upper, middle, and lower wires. The differences between the upper and middle wires and between the middle and lower wires are known as the half-stadia intervals or thread intervals. The two differences

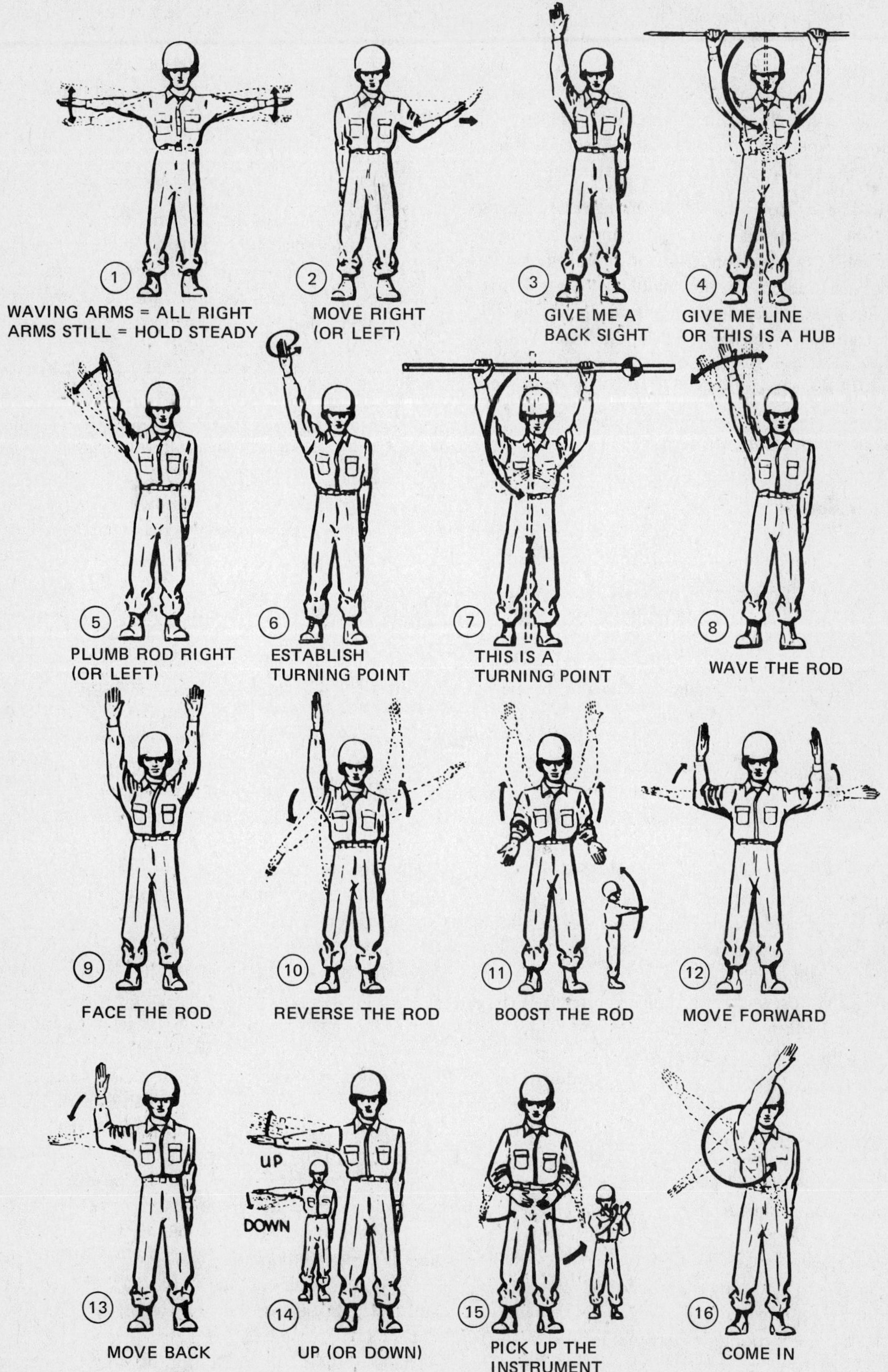

Figure 19-8
Hand signals.

should agree within an allowable amount, or the readings must be repeated more carefully. For example, the readings should agree within 0.003 m (0.01 ft) for second- and third-order accuracy. A separate distance reading is unnecessary in this three-wire method of operation, since the difference between the upper and lower wires multiplied by the stadia factor gives the distance.

The Micrometer Method. The micrometer method also requires the same preparation as the one-wire method. After establishing a horizontal line of sight, the micrometer knob is used to set the middle wire (or wedge-shaped lines) of the reticle to the nearest graduated line (usually centimeter) on the rod. The graduated value of this line is read directly from the rod, and the decimal portion of the reading is read from the micrometer. The distance is found by reading the top and bottom stadia wires as in the one-wire method.

Rod Operation

The action of the rodperson and the care with which the rod is positioned and held will affect the speed and the accuracy of the leveling operation.

Before setting the rod on any point, the rodperson should clean the top of the point and the rod shoe for a good contact. The rod is then placed firmly on the point, and the rodperson stands facing the instrument and slightly behind the rod, holding it with both hands. The rodperson's feet should be spaced about ½ meter (about 1½ ft) apart for a comfortable stance.

The rodperson holds the rod as nearly vertical as possible, places a rod level against the rod, and moves the top end of the rod until the bubbles are centered. When a rod level is not used, the rod is balanced, using the fingertips to prevent it from falling over. A properly balanced rod will stand for several seconds before starting to fall. This process of balancing the rod vertically is known as plumbing the rod.

During a strong wind, it is difficult to plumb the rod and to hold it steady for any length of time. Under this condition, the levelperson may call for the rodperson to wave the rod. The rod is waved by pivoting it on its base and swinging it in a slow arc toward the instrument and away. The shoe should be kept firmly seated during this operation. The motion of the rod permits the levelperson to read the rod when it reaches a vertical position at the top of the arc and the smallest value appears in the eyepiece. Before or after this vertical position, the rod reading will increase.

When setting a turning point, the rodperson should set the turning pin or pedestal firmly in contact with the ground. An unfirm footing can sag under the weight of the rod and result in erroneous readings between foresight and backsight. During freezing and thawing weather, the ground surface can heave in a comparatively short time. Pins and pedestals can be affected by the heave between a foresight and the following backsight. For surveys requiring a higher order of accuracy, the instrumentperson should be aware of this possibility and select firm locations.

Recording

The field notebook is the permanent record of the survey; the notes must be clear and legible and give only one possible interpretation. No survey recording is considered complete until the notes and computations have been checked and initialed by the chief of party or the chief's designated representative.

There is very little difference in format for recording the three types of leveling readings, so only the one-wire method will be discussed here. The recording illustrated in Fig. 19-9 is based on the leveling operation shown in Fig. 19-2.

Leveling notes start with a known elevation or bench mark which is generally described from previous surveys. The identification of this point and its elevation are entered in the proper columns on the left-hand page. The right-hand page must show a reference to the source of the elevation and description. At times a level survey is run to establish grade, and the exact elevation above a datum plane is neither necessary nor readily available. In such a case, a more or less permanent point is selected as a starting point, and a fictitious value is assigned to it for use on the survey. This elevation and all elevations determined from it can be tied in to a known elevation at a later date. The notebook must describe this point and state that the elevation was assumed.

The first reading is a backsight (BS = 1.255), which is added to the elevation (154.375) to obtain the height of the instrument (HI = 155.630).

The next reading is a foresight (FS = 1.100), which is subtracted from the HI to get the elevation (154.530) of the next point (TP 2 in the sample notes).

The first instrument setup *A* was selected midway between bench mark 1 and turning point 2. In the distance column, 65 m appears on the left-hand side to show the distance from the bench mark to the instrument setup and on the right-hand side for the distance from the instrument to the turning point.

The instrument is moved to the next setup *B* while the rod remains at turning point 2. The backsight (0.465) and the distance to the rod (75) are read and recorded, and the HI is computed (154.995). The instrument is then pointed at turning point 3, and the foresight (2.095) and distance (90) are read and recorded. The elevation (152.900) is computed.

This method continues until the survey is tied to the next bench mark. The distance balancing (the sum of the foresight distances should equal the sum of the back-

Proj: 537/US/66/A/70

Des. BM35 to BM36 Date 15 July 70

Party Chief: J Doe
Instr.: W. Coe
Recorder: R. Roe
Rodmen: C. Day & B. Ray

Instr: Mil 10X 2312
Weather: Clear, Calm & Hot

Sta.	B.S.	H.T.	F.S.	Elev.	Dist.	Remarks
	+		−			
① BM35				154.375		Elevation and Description from third order line 2, Pg. 18, Project 537/US/342/70 Book #3 - Recovered as described.
					65	
Ⓐ	1.255	155.630				
					65	
② TP			1.100	154.530	65' 65'	
					75	
Ⓑ	0.465	154.995				
					90	
③ TP (PPM14-3-1382A(v))			2.095	152.900	140' 155'	- PPM14-3-1382A(v) described on page 15 this book.
					60	
Ⓒ	0.130	153.030				
					105	
④ TP			0.245	152.785	200' 260'	
					110	
Ⓓ	3.765	156.550				
					50	
⑤ BM36			0.345	156.205	310' 310'	Elevation and Description from third order line 2, Pg. 18 Proj 537/US/3L/2/70 Book #3 - Recorded as described
	+5.615		−3.785			
	−3.785					
	+1.830					
	154.375					
	156.205	Check				

Figure 19-9
Lower-order level notes.

sight distances) is done as the survey progresses and should be completed before the bench mark is reached.

The recorder's computations can be verified by adding the backsight rod readings and the foresight rod readings separately. The difference between the two totals is the difference in elevation between the starting and final elevation. Applying this total to the starting elevation should give the final elevation. Any disagreement is the result of an error in the computations, which must be rechecked.

In the example, the curvature and refraction correction would not be applied, since the correction for the longest distance would be only 0.8 mm (0.03 in), which is too small to affect any of the readings.

RECIPROCAL LEVELING

This procedure is used for either differential or trigonometric leveling when a long sight must be made across a wide river, ravine, or similar obstacle. A long sight is affected by curvature and refraction and by any small error in aligning the line of sight with the bubble axis. The alignment error can be minimized by balancing the long sight, and the curvature can be computed. Atmospheric conditions vary so much over an open expanse that the refraction correction will be very erratic. Reciprocal leveling is designed to minimize the effect of the atmosphere as well as the line of sight and curvature corrections.

In reciprocal leveling (see Fig. 19-10), the backsights and foresights are balanced as carefully as possible before reaching the obstacle. A turning point (N) is selected close to the edge of the obstruction, so that it is visible from a proposed instrument location (B) on the other side. A second rod is held on the other side of the obstruction at F. Point F should be selected so that distances AN and FB and distances AF and BN are approximately equal. The instrument is set up at point A and leveled very carefully. A backsight reading is taken on the rod at N and a foresight on the rod at F. These readings are repeated several times. The instrument is moved to point B, set up, and carefully leveled. The rods remain at their stations. Once again, a backsight is taken on the rod at N, and a foresight on the rod at F; this is repeated several times. Since instrument leveling is very critical in this procedure, the bubble must be

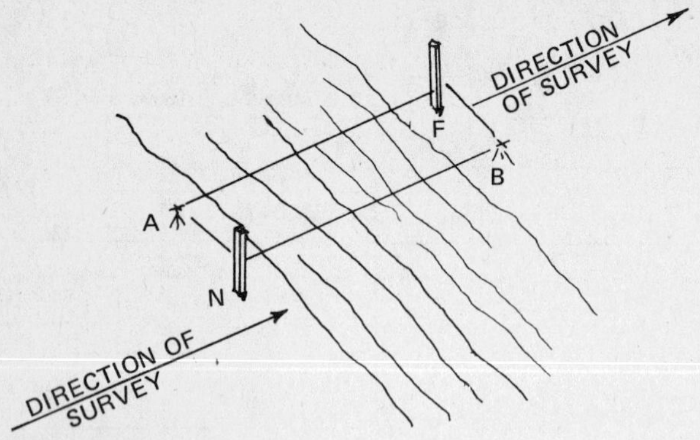

Figure 19-10
Reciprocal leveling.

checked before each reading and centered carefully. If it is off center a slight amount, the procedure must be repeated.

The difference in elevation between *N* and *F* is computed separately from the readings at setup *A* and from the readings at setup *B*. Due to the errors in the long sight, each result will have a slightly different value. Note, however, that the long sight is a foresight from *A* and a backsight from *B*. The true difference in elevation is the average of the two values, since the errors have opposite signs and will cancel each other.

For more accuracy, several long sight readings are made for each short sight and averaged. A target should be used on the rod and should be reset for each reading. Each series of long sights is averaged and combined with corresponding short sights for the computations.

Changes in atmospheric density and temperature affect the refraction of a line of sight. The longer the time interval between reciprocal long sights, the greater the chance of an atmospheric change and a variation in the refraction value. For this reason, the time lapse between the long sights should be kept as short as possible.

Simultaneous Reciprocal Leveling

An excellent method of avoiding the time lapse problem is simultaneous reciprocal observation. The object is to read both long sight values at the same time. This requires two instruments and observers and two rods and rodpersons. Some method of communication or sequence of operations must be agreed upon. For example, the sequence can be to take one short sight and five long sights for two cycles. Both observers read their short sights first, then signal the rodpersons to turn the rods to face the long sight observer. As soon as the observer sees the face of the rod on the opposite shore, the long sightings are started. As soon as five readings have been taken, the observer should make certain that the other observer is also finished. If not, readings should be continued for the same length of time, even though one observer may have six or seven readings to the other observer's five. The seven readings will bracket the time of the five, and the average of each will refer to the same time interval and to the same atmospheric conditions. This procedure can be repeated as many times as agreed upon. The instruments then change stations and the procedure is repeated. The computations will give a mean value for the difference in elevation, minimizing the long sight errors.

Field Notes

The notekeeping for reciprocal leveling is identical to notekeeping for differential leveling. A series of either backsight or foresight readings is taken on the far rod from one setup, with only one sighting on the near rod. The series of readings is averaged, and a single value is used to compute the elevation. Each reading of the series is entered on a separate line in the proper column. The computation is made directly below the last reading of the series, and the average value is marked. From this point on, the recording follows the regular procedure.

LEVEL BENCH MARKS

A bench mark is a relatively permanent object, natural or artificial, bearing a marked point whose elevation is known. A bench mark may be further qualified as permanent, temporary, or supplementary. The purpose of a survey normally governs whether its stations will be permanently or temporarily marked. When it is known that the station may be reused over a period of several years, the station marker should be of a permanent type. Other stations that may never be reused or that will be reused a few times within a period of one or two months are usually marked in a temporary manner. A permanent bench mark is normally abbreviated BM, and a temporary or supplementary bench mark is called a TBM.

Bench marks set to third-order or higher accuracy are intended to form a framework of basic control to which detail surveys are adjusted. The elevations are marked in a permanent manner in locations where they will not be disturbed either by normal native activity or by frost action. The marks are metal caps or disks set in concrete or stone posts, in rock outcrops, or in masonry structures. The disks carry the inscribed name of the organization which set the mark, the name or number of the mark for the future identification, and the date the mark was set.

Bench marks of lower-order accuracy may also be set as permanent markers and referred to as BMs, but the degree of permanence may only be for a few years. Monumenting, as described above, is not required. A concrete-filled iron pipe, or a chiseled square on a permanent structure (bridge abutment, culvert, or building steps) or rock outcrop serves the purpose. This type of mark is not readily visible and should be carefully described for future recovery. Location of these marks from scanty or inaccurate descriptions can waste a tremendous amount of time. An ideal description should lead a person unfamiliar with the original mark to the spot where it was set. If by chance the mark was destroyed, the description should make it obvious that a long search will be a waste of time. Marking this type of bench mark also requires some ingenuity. Since no identification disk is set, the name, number, and elevation of the point cannot appear on the mark. Bench marks can be marked with paint on rock or masonry, if this will not create a nuisance or instill a curiosity in some native who will destroy or remove it for some inherent value. A blaze on a tree, a mark on a nearby fencepost, or a stake lettered with a lumber crayon (keel) can be used as a guide to lead a surveyor with the description to the bench mark.

Temporary bench marks are set for relatively short use, possibly up to several months. A spike or a 30- to 40-penny nail driven into a tree or telephone pole and extending about 1 centimeter (0.4 in) from the surface will serve the purpose. A stake driven into the ground can also be used, especially if no frost action is expected until it is needed. Detailed descriptions of these points are just as important as descriptions of monumented stations.

Bench mark systems or level nets consist of a series of bench marks which are established within a prescribed accuracy along closed circuits; the elevation data are adjusted by computations which minimize the effects of accidental errors and are identified as being of a specific order of accuracy.

ADJUSTMENT OF LEVELING DATA

The error of closure is the amount by which the quantity obtained from a surveying operation fails to agree with the equivalent value accepted from previous surveys. Survey computing is not complete until the closure error is distributed; this process is called adjusting. In precise surveys, the error is adjusted using the theory of least squares, and in some cases, weighted means. The operations discussed in this book normally do not require these precise mathematical adjustments. Instead, they usually use straight line adjusting or prorating. This method assumes that the total error is the result of accumulating a small error at each setup and that the amount of error was the same each time. The total error of closure is divided by the number of setups and applied progressively from the beginning to the end of the survey. For example, if 10 setups were used, the total error is divided by 10. The first station or setup is assigned one-tenth of the total error. The error between the first and the second setup is also one-tenth. Since the first setup was corrected by one-tenth, the correction for the second setup is two-tenths of the total error. The third setup is corrected by three-tenths, and so on until the correction at the tenth or closing point is ten-tenths or the full amount of error. In leveling, the adjustment is distributed over the turning points which carried the elevation through the survey. All elevations determined as sideshots from an instrument setup are also corrected. Their correction is based on the correction at the turning point from which the height of instrument was established.

TRIGONOMETRIC LEVELING

Trigonometric leveling applies the principles of trigonometry to determine differences in elevation (see Fig. 19-11). There are two applications of this method to surveying: on long lines of sight for triangulation and electronic traverses, and on short lines of sight for conventional traverses and level lines. The procedures and techniques in this text pertain only to the short line application. Trigonometric leveling is used only for lower-order accuracies where the terrain prohibits differential leveling or when leveling is needed in connection with triangulation and traverses.

Method and Procedures

Trigonometric leveling requires a transit, theodolite, or alidade to observe vertical angles. This method is particularly adaptable to uneven terrain where level sights would be short due to ground slopes and distance balancing; it is also useful for low-order surveys where time is a consideration. Distances should be kept below 300 m (980 ft) when a stadia or standard leveling rod is used. The curvature and refraction correction is applied only if the survey accuracy requires it. Trigonometric level surveys should be tied in with sideshots to elevations of higher-order accuracy whenever possible.

The instrument is set up and leveled at a convenient location to see the starting point and the first turning point. The rod is held on the starting point. The telescope is pointed at some easily read value (a full meter) on the rod, and the vertical angle is read. The distance between the instrument and rod must be determined either by taping, by a stadia reading, or in some instances by triangulation. Now one side and one angle of a right triangle are known (see Fig. 19-11), so the other sides and angle can be computed. For trigonometric leveling, only the side opposite the measured angle, the difference in elevation DE, is computed. The computation consists of multiplying the measured distance by the proper trigonometric function of the measured angle (sine if the slope distance *OR* is measured, tangent if horizontal distance *OH* is measured). The result is the difference in elevation DE, between the height of the instrument HI and the point on the rod *R*. The rod reading (as in differential leveling) is added on backsights and sub-

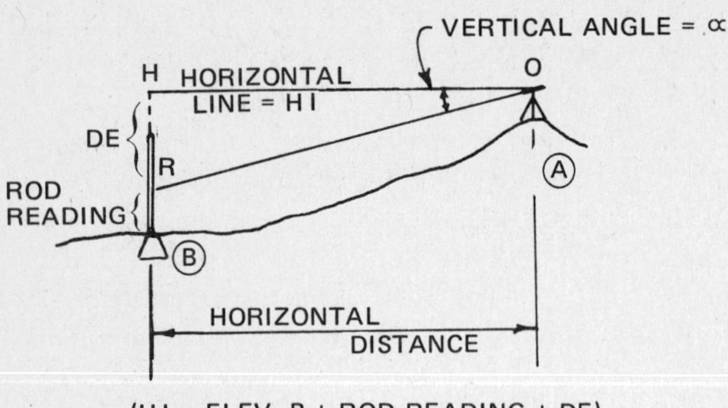

(HI = ELEV. B + ROD READING + DE)

PART 1

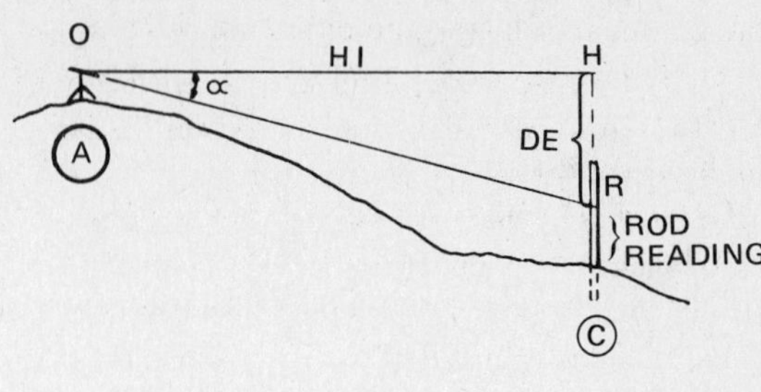

(ELEV. C = HI − DE − ROD READING)

PART 2

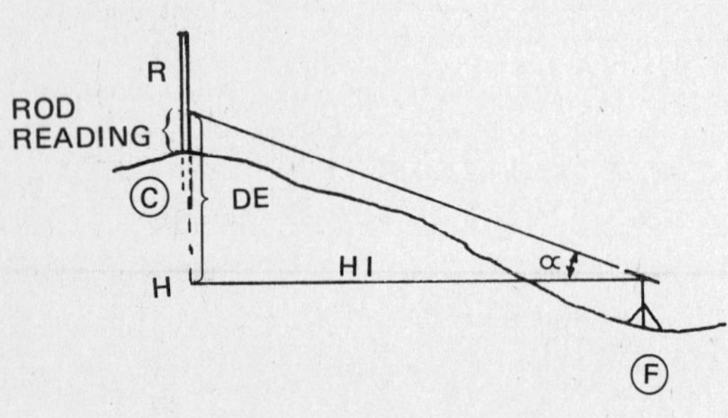

(HI = ELEV. C + ROD READING − DE)

PART 3

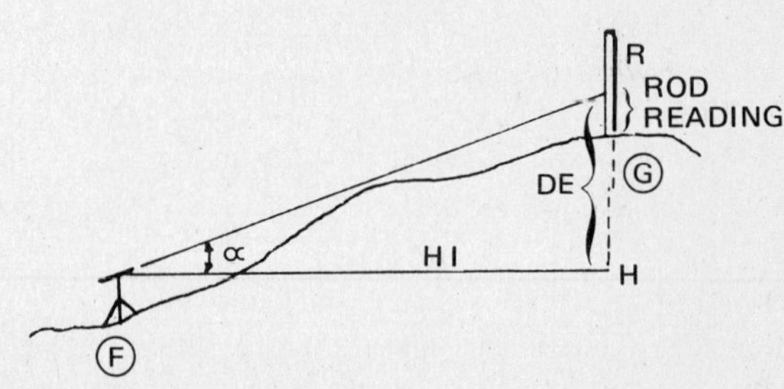

(ELEV. G = HI + DE − ROD READING)

PART 4

Figure 19-11
Trigonometric leveling.

tracted on foresights. The computed difference in elevation is applied in the proper direction (added or subtracted) to obtain the instrument height or the elevation, as required.

Depression Angle Backsight (See Fig. 19-11, part 1). The rod is on a point B below the instrument. The measured vertical angle α is negative (minus) or a depression angle. The measured distance is either slope (OR) or horizontal (OH). The required difference in elevation (HR) equals the distance multiplied by the sine or tangent of the angle α. To compute the height of the instrument, the rod reading RB and the difference in elevation are added to the elevation of B:

$$\text{HI} = RB + \text{DE} + \text{elevation of } B$$

Depression Angle Foresight (See Fig. 19-11, part 2). The rod is below the instrument, and the vertical angle is negative (minus). The difference in elevation is computed as described in the preceding paragraph. The elevation at C equals the instrument height minus the difference in elevation and minus the rod reading RC:

$$\text{elevation at } C = \text{HI} - \text{DE} - RC$$

Elevation Angle Backsight (See Fig. 19-11, part 3). The rod is above the instrument, and the vertical angle is positive (plus). The difference in elevation is computed as described above. The height of the instrument at F equals the elevation at C plus the rod reading RC minus the difference in elevation:

$$\text{HI} = \text{elevation at } C + RC - \text{DE}$$

Elevation Angle Foresight (See Fig. 19-11, part 4). The rod is above the instrument and the angle is positive (plus). The difference in elevation is again computed as described above. The elevation of G equals the height of the instrument plus the difference in elevation minus the rod reading RG:

$$\text{elevation at } G = \text{HI} + \text{DE} - RG$$

Measuring the Distance

The distance between the instrument and the stations must be known in trigonometric leveling to compute the difference in elevation. This distance may be taped, measured electronically, or read by stadia. It may be a part of another survey (such as a traverse) or it may have to be measured during the leveling.

Horizontal distances are simply multiplied by the tangent of the angle to get the difference in elevation. No reduction is required once the proper corrections are applied to the measured distance to get the true horizontal distance.

Slope taping distances must be converted to horizontal distances before being used in this procedure.

Electronic distance measuring devices measure the slope distance between instruments, that is, the straight line distance from unit to unit. If the same setup is used and the electronic equipment is replaced with a theodolite and target or rod, the measured vertical angle can be used to convert the measured distance to a difference in elevation by multiplying by the sine of the angle.

Stadia distances fall into two categories. If the instrument is level when the distance is read, the value is converted directly to a horizontal distance. When the line of sight is moved up or down from the horizontal, the rod reading requires an additional reduction and cannot be converted directly.

Determining the Angle

The vertical angle used in trigonometric leveling is the angle above or below a horizontal plane and is designated by a plus or a minus, respectively.

The transit's vertical circle is graduated from 0° to 90° on each of four quadrants. A horizontal line reads 0° in either the direct or the reverse position. Vertical angle values will increase whether the telescope is elevated or depressed. The vertical angle is read on the vernier; the sign depends on the telescope position: plus if the telescope is elevated and minus if it is depressed.

The 1-minute and 1-second theodolites use zenith distances; that is, a level sight reads 90° on the circle. As the line of sight is elevated, the value on the circle decreases and must be subtracted from 90° to give a positive (plus) vertical angle. The depressed line of sight reading is greater than 90°; the amount greater than 90° is the negative (minus) vertical angle. In the reversed position, the 1-minute and 1-second theodolites read 270° for a horizontal line. The amount above or below 270° is the vertical angle (plus or minus) which is used in trigonometric leveling.

The alidade has a stadia arc with three scales. The center scale is the angle scale and is read by vernier to the nearest minute. Its value for a level line is 30°. Vertical angles are determined by subtracting 30° from the reading. Angles of elevation give a positive result and angles of depression a negative result. The other two scales marked *H* and *V* can be used in leveling.

PROBLEMS

1. Run a level loop from a known or assumed elevation using differential leveling. The course of the level loop should include elevations of at least four intermediate locations and should close on the beginning point. The instrument should be set up at least once between each pair of intermediate locations.
2. If necessary, adjust the field data from problem 1 by using the straight line method of adjustment.
3. Determine the true or assumed elevation of the top of a nearby structure by using trigonometric leveling.

LEARNING ACTIVITY PACKAGE

Read Chap. 19 carefully.

Chapter 19 read ____________ (*date*).

If some of the objectives (a) through (o) are not understood, the student should reread the paragraphs where these topics are discussed.

Objectives read and studied ____________ (*date*).

There are three field problems on leveling.

Problem 1 completed ____________ (*date*).

Problem 2 completed ____________ (*date*).

Problem 3 completed ____________ (*date*).

Now take the Chap. 19 quiz. Remove it from the book and answer all the questions.

Quiz completed ____________ (*date*).

19

QUIZ

1. What is the difference between a level surface and a plane surface?

2. How do direct and indirect leveling methods differ?

3. How is an elevation transferred from one point to another in differential leveling?

4. Why is it important to balance backsight and foresight distances?

5. When is it necessary to check the instrument's adjustment?

6. Within the sequence of actions for taking a level reading, when is the level bubble checked?

7. What is parallax?

8. Why does the rodperson wave the leveling rod?

9. How is a page check performed on the notes kept in the field notebook?

10. What is the best method to use if reciprocal leveling is necessary? ______

11. What type of information can be found on the metal cap or disc of a bench mark set to third-order or higher accuracy? ______

12. Why is adjustment of level circuit data necessary? ______

13. What two items of information are needed in order to perform trigonometric leveling? ______

14. What problem arises if electronic distance measuring equipment is used in trigonometric leveling? ______

15. How do the vertical circle readings on a transit and a theodolite differ? ______

20 ANGLE AND DIRECTION OBSERVATIONS

Objectives

a. Learn how a distance and direction from one known point can establish a point in space
b. Understand that direction is the angular relationship of one line to another
c. Learn about station angles, deflection angles, and interior and exterior angles
d. Understand azimuths: true azimuth, grid azimuth, and magnetic azimuth
e. Understand bearings
f. Read about magnetic declination
g. Learn about vertical angles and zenith distances
h. Learn the procedures for observing angles or directions
i. Become aware of the factors which introduce errors in angle observations

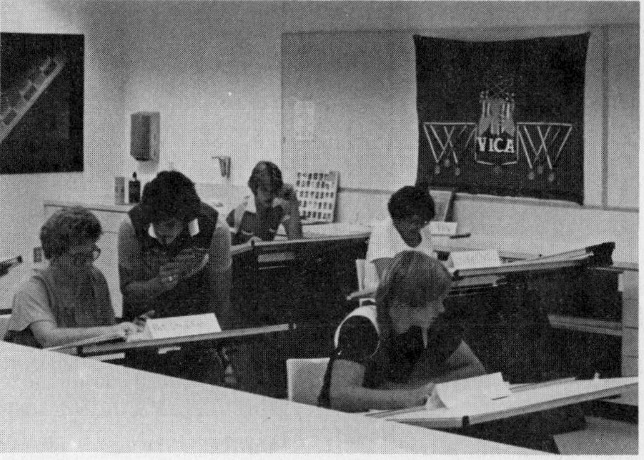

Figure 20-1
A technical school class doing the drafting part of a surveying problem *(Atlantic Vocational Technical Center).*

Rationale

Angles and directions are another fundamental part of surveying information. The student (like those in Fig. 20-1) needs to learn the various systems for measuring directions (horizontal and vertical angles, azimuths, bearings, zenith distances, and so forth) as well as the field procedures for making such measurements.

Surveying is the science of determining relative positions of points or objects on or near the earth's surface. From the study of geometry, it is evident that a point can be located by measuring only the distances from two known points. Surveyors find occasions when this two-distance method is very practical and even highly desirable. However, in many procedures which require locating a point, surveyors use a distance and a direction from one known point or sometimes only the directions (without any distances) from two known points. The discussion of angles and directions in this chapter is simplified in most instances to stay within the scope of plane surveying.

DIRECTION

In surveying and mapping, direction is, by definition, the angular relationship of one line to another. The direction of a line is referred to some other definite line which acts as the zero value, and a dimension must be assigned to show the amount of change from the zero line. A horizontal direction can be observed or measured in two ways—clockwise or counterclockwise. It is common practice in surveying to measure directions or angles clockwise (to the right) from the reference line, unless otherwise designated.

ANGLES

An angle can be defined as the difference in the values of two directions observed from the same initial direction. At times, the directions to several features must be observed from one instrument setup, or the changing directions of a series of connected lines must be determined. The series of lines might represent a boundary which starts from one point, extends around a specific area, and returns (ties in) to the starting point. As another example, the lines might represent a road centerline which starts at one point and extends (traverses) to another location or point some distance away. Direction and angle equipment measure the changes of direction (angles) between the lines in the series. In some types of surveys, only selected angles are observed. To distinguish the different ways the angles are observed, they are given special names, such as station angles, explement angles, or deflection angles in traverse and construction surveys (see Fig. 20-2). In triangulation, only the differences in directions are observed and used as angles in the computations.

Station Angles

When two points of known position are intervisible (for example, *Z* and *A*, in Fig. 20-2) and the survey starts from one of these points (from *A* in our example), the instrument is set up at *A* and backsighted on *Z* as the zero direction. The angle is turned to point *B*, the first point of the new line. As discussed, the angle is normally turned and read clockwise (to the right). This angle is referred to as the station angle. Generally, surveys require at least one direct and one reverse pointing on each station to observe the angle. A direct pointing is made with the telescope in the direct position. A reverse pointing is made with the telescope in the reverse position (plunged). The direct/reverse (D/R) measurement is made to eliminate the collimation error in the instrument. For a complete direct/reverse reading, the station angle is read, then the telescope is reversed and pointed on the forward point (*B* in Fig. 20-2) and read. The angle to the starting point (*Z*) is turned to the right and read; this angle is called the explement angle. The sum of the station angle and the explement angle should equal 360°.

Deflection Angles

Some surveys use deflection angles in their computations. These can be computed from the angles obtained in the paragraph above, or they can be turned directly using a transit or 1-minute theodolite. The instrument is setup at *A* (Fig. 20-2), and backsight is made on *Z* as is done for station angles. The telescope is plunged first instead of being rotated horizontally. The angle to *B* is turned to the left. This is called a left deflection angle; it is recorded with an *L* or minus sign in front of the angular value. Figure 20-2 shows a left deflection angle to *B* and a right deflection angle to *C*, if *C* were the required point. Right deflection angles are recorded with an *R* or plus sign in front of the angular value. When turning and reading deflection angles, special care must be taken to distinguish left and right values and to record them properly.

Interior and Exterior Angles

Some surveys follow the border of a figure or area and close (tie in) to the starting point. The angles which are inside the figure are referred to as the interior angles, while their explements are called exterior angles. Depending on the direction in which the survey is run, either the interior or the exterior angles may be read as the direct or station angles. The other angles (exterior or interior) are then the explement angles. Interior and exterior angles are not recorded in surveys; angles are read and recorded as direct and reverse directions.

Figure 20-2
Angles.

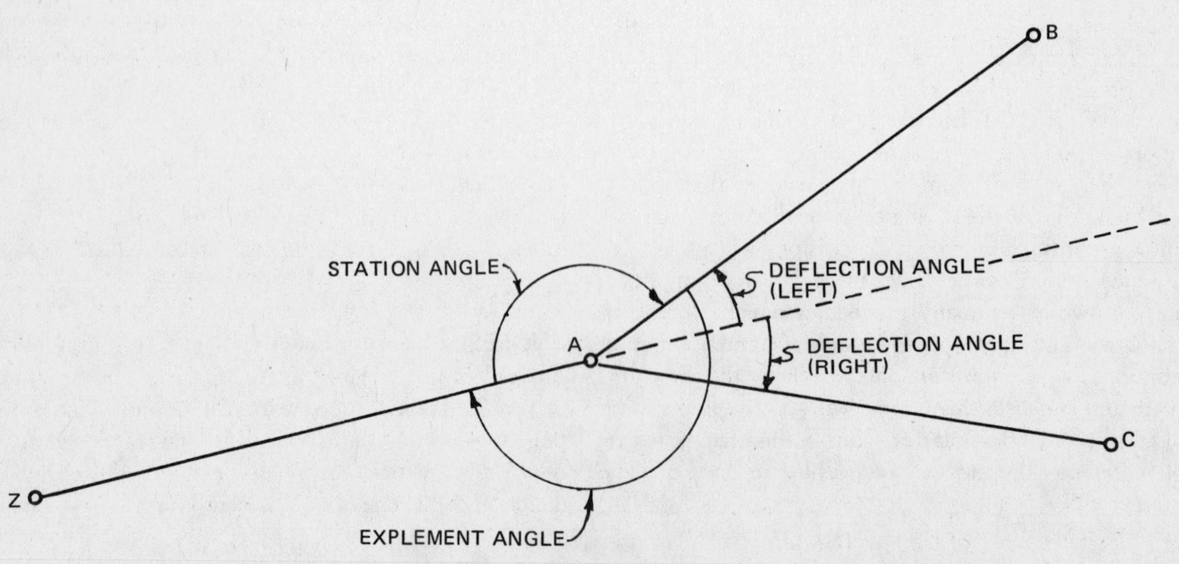

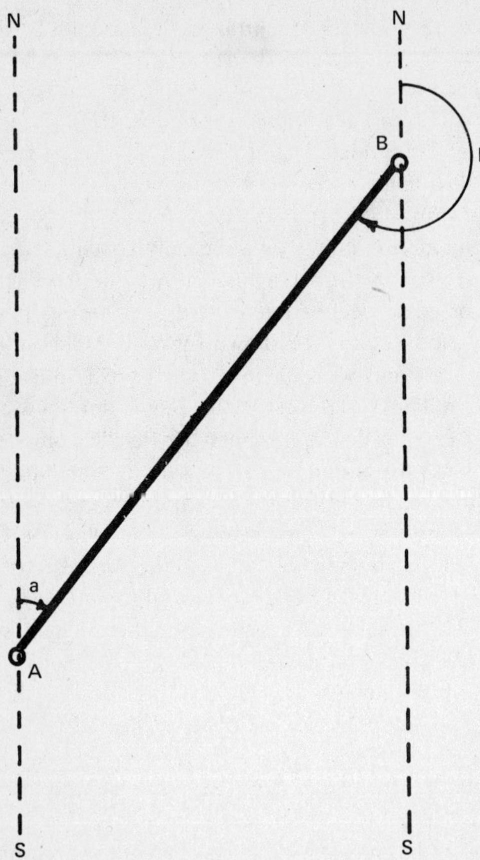

Figure 20-3
Azimuth.

AZIMUTH

One of the methods used to describe direction in surveying uses azimuths. The azimuth is the horizontal direction measured clockwise from a zero line which runs north or south. Every line has two azimuths, depending on the observer's position. For example, in Fig. 20-3 a survey is progressing from *A* toward *B*. Angle *a* is the forward azimuth for this line. To designate the direction from *B* to *A*, angle *b* is used; angle *b* is known as the back azimuth of the line. In plane surveying, the forward and back azimuths of a line always differ by exactly 180°. The zero azimuth line can be based on true, grid, or magnetic north.

True Azimuth

The horizontal direction of a line measured clockwise from a true reference plane, usually the meridian, is a true azimuth. A true azimuth is usually referred to as a true north azimuth or a true south azimuth. A true azimuth can be established by sighting over a line whose true azimuth is known and subtracting the known value or by sighting on the stars. The stars observed are usually circumpolar stars, except in the low latitudes (near the equator), and the resulting azimuth is referred to as an astronomic azimuth. By applying a correction (using the Laplace equation) the astronomic azimuth can be converted to a geodetic azimuth. Both geodetic and astronomic azimuths are considered true azimuths.

Grid Azimuth

Many surveys are computed on a system of plane coordinates. A system of squares called a rectangular grid is superimposed over a small portion of the earth's surface. One line (the central meridian) of this grid coincides with a true north-south line. Other north-south grid lines are parallel to this line, and all east-west grid lines are perpendicular to the north-south grid lines. When survey computations are based on a grid system, the northerly direction of the north-south grid lines is used as the zero grid azimuth. Grid azimuth is defined as the angle measured clockwise between a straight line and the central meridian of the plane-rectangular coordinate system.

Magnetic Azimuth

Magnetic azimuths are based on a zero line established with a magnetic compass. They are used in surveying to obtain approximate values for azimuths. Magnetic north as shown by a compass needle is selected as the zero value; angles are measured from this line and are referred to as magnetic azimuths. Although forward and back azimuths for a line should differ by 180°, the compass-measured difference may vary several degrees because of local magnetic attraction. A detailed discussion of the factors that affect measurements with a magnetic compass is found in the paragraphs on magnetic declination. Magnetic azimuth can be defined as the angle (at the point of observation) between the vertical plane through the observed object and the vertical plane in which a freely suspended, symmetrically magnetized needle, influenced by no transient artificial magnetic disturbance, will come to rest. Magnetic azimuth is generally reckoned from magnetic north (0°) clockwise through 360°.

BEARING

Azimuths are measured from north or south, and the angles vary from 0° to 360° (see the inner circle of Fig. 20-4). Computations using the trigonometric functions of azimuths may require that the angles be converted to equivalent angles of less than 90°. The use of bearings in the measurements automatically keeps the angles below 90° (see the outer circle of Fig. 20-4).

The bearing of a line is its direction (within a quadrant) with reference to a meridian (a north-south line). Bearings are measured clockwise or counterclockwise, depending on the quadrant, from either the north or south line. A bearing is identified by first naming the

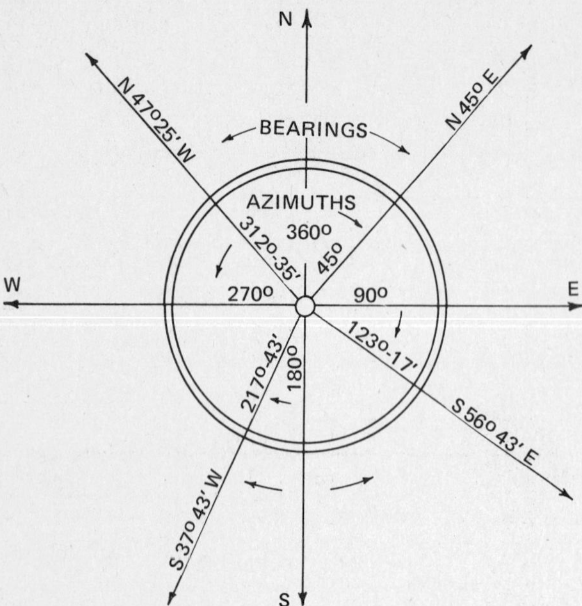

Figure 20-4
Bearings and azimuths.

end of the meridian from which it is reckoned (north or south), then the angle value, and the direction (east or west) from the meridian. Thus, a line in the southwest quadrant making an angle of 37°43′ with the south reference meridian has a bearing of S37°43′W. An angle in the northwest quadrant, 47°25′ from the north meridian has a bearing of N47°25′W.

Bearings, like azimuths, can be true, grid, or magnetic, depending on the reference meridian. If the meridian is a true north-south line, the bearing is true. Grid north-south lines as reference result in grid bearings, and using magnetic north or south gives magnetic bearings.

The compasses included with the transit and the 1-minute theodolite can be used to read magnetic bearings.

MAGNETIC DECLINATION

The magnetic needle of a compass aligns itself with the earth's magnetic field and points toward the earth's magnetic pole. At a few places on the earth's surface, the needle will point exactly north along the true meridian. Everywhere else, the magnetic north line indicated by the needle forms a horizontal angle with the true meridian. This angle is called the magnetic declination.

The magnetic declination is labeled east when the needle points east from true north and west when the needle points westward. An east declination is added to the magnetic azimuth to get a true azimuth; a west declination is subtracted. Magnetic bearings may also be changed to true bearings by adding east declinations in the NE and SW quadrants and subtracting them in the SE and NW quadrants. West declinations are added in the SE and NW quadrants and subtracted in the SW and NE quadrants.

Magnetic declination is not a constant value at any point but is continually changing. This continual variation affects the reliability of magnetic readings. Even at best, the surveyor must not expect results closer than one-fourth of a degree.

Declination is shown on a specially constructed chart called an isogonic chart, which shows lines connecting points of equal declination. These lines are referred to as isogonic lines and are drawn for each degree of declination east and west of zero. The zero line is called the agonic line. Lines west of the agonic line show areas with an east declination, where the needle points east. Lines east of the agonic line show west declination areas, where the needle points west. Such charts are published in the United States once every five years by the U.S. Coast and Geodetic Survey. Due to the five-year interval between printings, a series of annual change lines are added. These lines indicate the amount and direction of the annual change expected in different locations.

Local attraction is a term denoting local influences that cause the magnetic needle to be deflected away from the magnetic meridian for that locality. Some sources of local attraction are: magnetite (loadstone) in the ground, electric power lines, steel structures, railroad rails, surface and underground iron pipes, and other fixed objects of iron or steel. Contrary to common belief, ordinary iron ores do not attract the magnetic needle unless they contain magnetite or pyrrhotite. According to its true definition, local attraction does not include avoidable iron or steel articles which can cause large deflection errors. Some of these avoidable sources are: steel keys, knives, steel rimmed spectacles, spectacle cases, metal buttons, wire stiffeners in hats, steel helmets, surveying equipment such as axes, steel tapes, and range poles and other items such as motor vehicles, radio receivers and transmitters, and power generators. The smaller of these items should be moved from 3 to 10 meters (10 to 33 ft) away from the compass, and the larger items may need to be moved several hundred meters. The surveyor using the magnetic needle should be constantly aware of the influence of surrounding features on the needle.

VERTICAL ANGLES

A vertical angle (see Fig. 20-5*a*) is the angle measured vertically (up or down) from a horizontal plane of reference. When the telescope is pointed in the horizontal plane (level), the vertical angle is zero. When the telescope is pointed up at a higher feature (elevated), the vertical angle increases and is called a *plus* vertical angle. The values of plus vertical angles increase from 0° for a horizontal position to +90° when the telescope is pointed straight up. As the telescope is depressed (pointed down),

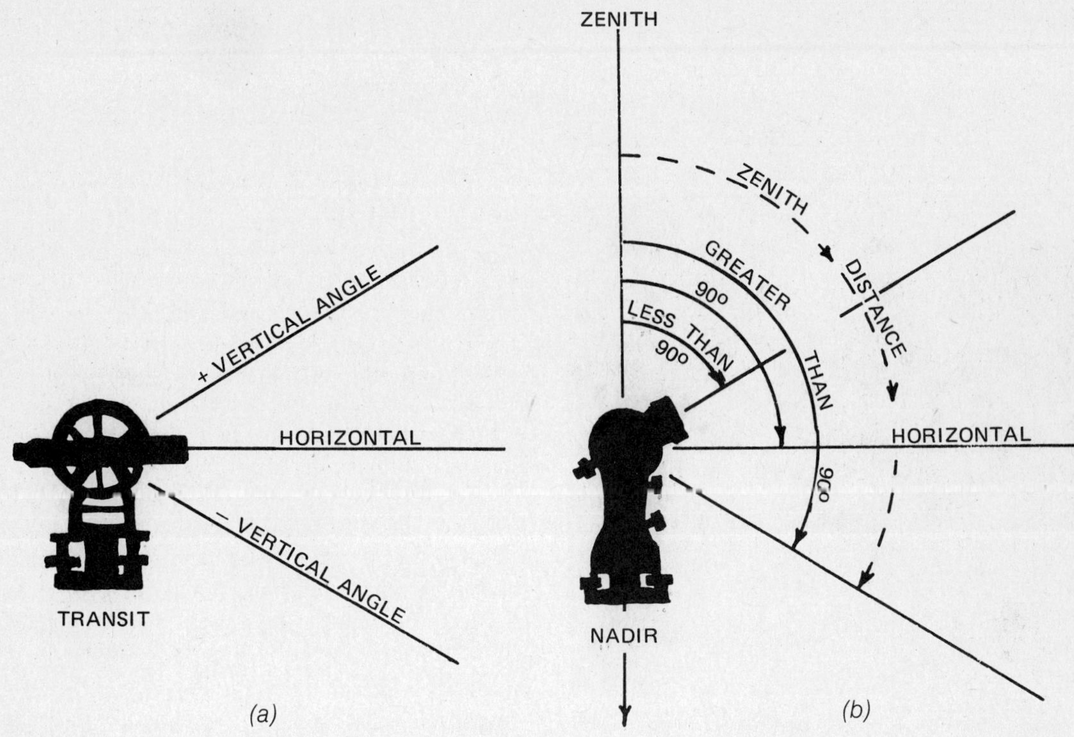

Figure 20-5
Vertical angles and zenith distances.

the angle also increases in numerical value. A depressed telescope reading indicates an angle below the horizontal plane, called a *minus* vertical angle. Numerical values for minus vertical angles reach −90° when the telescope is pointed down.

Zenith Distances

The zenith is an imaginary point directly overhead where an extension of the plumb line intersects an assumed sphere on which the stars appear to be projected. The equivalent point which is directly below the zenith is called the nadir. Use of the zenith permits reading angles in a vertical plane without using a plus or minus. Theodolites, with the exception of the 0.2-second theodolite, have a vertical scale reading zero when the telescope is pointed at the zenith (instead of reading zero when the telescope is in a horizontal plane). With the telescope in a direct position and pointed straight up, the reading is 0°; on a horizontal line, the reading is 90°; and straight down is 180°. Vertical angle measurements with theodolites (see Fig. 20-5*b*) read elevation (plus) angles as values less than 90° and depression (minus) angles as greater than 90°. These angle measurements (with the zenith as the zero value) are called the zenith distances. Double zenith distances are observations made with the telescope direct and reversed to eliminate errors due to the inclination of the vertical axis and the collimation of the vertical circle.

ANGLE OBSERVING PARTY

The angle observing party is very flexible in size, and may vary from 1 to 12 or more people. This party may be a subparty of a triangulation or traverse party, or it may work independently. An instrumentperson is required in every angle party, and a recorder is desirable. A rodperson or light-tender is often required at each point to which an angle is being measured. Sometimes semipermanent targets are erected at some points to avoid stationing a person at each of these points. The chief of the angle observing party decides on the dispersal of available personnel.

The instrumentperson sets the transit or theodolite exactly over the selected station or point and observes the angles (horizontal, vertical, or both) demanded by the survey. If the survey requires elevations by leveling but does not warrant an additional leveling party, the instrumentperson also performs leveling duties. (Notice the difference between the level and the transit shown in Fig. 20-6.)

The recorder records all field notes as they are read by the instrumentperson, makes sketches and descriptions of all stations, and makes all necessary on-station computations. On lower-order surveys when personnel are not available, the instrumentperson may also act as the recorder. However, this is not recommended because of the lack of an on-station check of the field note computations.

Figure 20-6
Level and transit. Notice the difference between a level in lower picture and a transit in upper picture *(David White Instrument Co. and U.S. Air Force).*

The rodperson sets or holds a range pole or plumb bob on the rear or the forward station as directed. When targets are to be erected, the rodperson performs this duty making sure that the target is exactly over the point. When leveling is required, the rodperson holds the leveling rod on the stations. In addition, the rodperson is sometimes a light-tender or radio operator on area triangulation nets.

OBSERVING ANGLES OR DIRECTIONS

The value of a horizontal angle between two lines can be determined by setting an index value (possibly zero) on the transit circle, pointing the telescope at a target placed over the terminal of one of the lines, holding the index and moving the telescope to point at a target over the terminal of the other line, reading the circle for the second pointing, and then taking the difference between the last reading and the index value. For vertical angles, the index is set with the telescope in level position, the telescope is pointed at the target, and the value is read on the vertical circle. The angle value (horizontal or vertical) determined in this manner is only as accurate as the minimum reading possible on the instrument. It is also subject to numerous errors and blunders. Survey techniques have been developed to minimize these effects.

All angles should be measured at least twice, once with the instrument telescope direct and once with the telescope reversed. A greater number of measurements are often made to obtain a mean value with a minimum of residual error.

There are two basic methods for multiple measurements of a horizontal angle—the repetition method and the direction method. The repetition method normally is used with a repeating instrument such as an engineer's transit, but it is always used with a direction-type instrument such as the theodolite. Deflection angles require a different technique but are usually measured using the repetition method.

FACTORS AFFECTING ANGLE OBSERVATIONS

There are three types or errors that affect angle observations. These errors may be due to the instrument, the observer, or the environment. The surveyor should try to reduce these errors or to avoid them completely.

Instrumental Errors

There are several types of instrumental errors that may affect the measured value for a horizontal angle: adjustment errors in the transit or theodolite; eccentricity of the horizontal circle; small errors in the graduation of the circle, the verniers, or the micrometer scale; and an error in the apparent length of the micrometer scale. Except for the last error, the effect of all instrumental errors can be eliminated or minimized by proper adjustment of the instrument and by using systematic observing procedures.

Personnel Errors

There are several personnel errors that affect horizontal angle measurements:

1. Errors in centering the instrument and the targets over their stations.
2. Errors in leveling the instrument.
3. Errors in pointing the instrument.
4. Errors in reading the circle and verniers.
5. Errors in making coincidence for readings.

These errors can all be minimized by using correct procedures and by proper training.

Environmental Errors

Environmental errors affecting horizontal angle measurements are due to differential temperatures within the instrument, horizontal refraction of the line of sight, and phase. Errors due to vertical refraction will not affect horizontal angle measurements within the scope of this book. Vertical angle measurements which can be influenced by vertical refraction are discussed under leveling.

Differential Temperatures. Differential temperatures in the instrument are usually caused by direct sunlight; they result in variable expansion within the instrument. When using a transit or theodolite, the effect can be minimized by shading the instrument with a surveyor's umbrella.

Horizontal Refraction. Horizontal refraction is the horizontal bending of light rays between a target and an observing instrument. It is caused by density differences resulting from temperature variations in the air along the path of the light rays. Under good observing conditions, lines of sight close to the ground and over sloping terrain can be deflected several seconds horizontally. Under extreme conditions, the effect of horizontal refraction might amount to over 1 minute of arc. One situation in which horizontal refraction can cause a large error is when the sun is shining on an open field between stands of timber. In this case, the rising column of warmer air over the open field causes a prismatic effect in the air and deflects the line of sight. The force and direction of the wind has considerable influence. A brisk wind usually reduces the temperature differential and the differences in air density. However, when long lines are to be observed, night observations on lights usually result in greater accuracy than daytime observation.

Phase. Phase, due to the unequal illumination of a target, can often cause an error of considerable magnitude in the measured value of a horizontal angle. The shape of the target and the angle at which the sun's rays intersect the target are the primary causes of phase. When a round target such as a chimney is illuminated from one side by the sun, an observer tends to point the instrument toward the illuminated side rather than toward the center of the chimney. Phase can be minimized by using targets with a flat surface facing the observer.

ANGLE ADJUSTMENT

In spite of the best efforts of the field personnel, there are still occasional errors in angle readings. If the accuracy of the survey will tolerate the error, the readings may still be accepted.

When a series of angles around a point are measured, the sum of these angles should equal 360°. If it does not, an adjustment known as the station adjustment of the angles is applied. This adjustment is made by dividing the difference between 360° and the sum of the angles by the number of angles measured. This prorated error is applied to the value of each angle. When the adjusted angles are added, the sum will be 360°. If the difference is not evenly divisible by the number of angles, the remainder should be divided among the angles closest to 90°, so that the sum will be exactly 360°. The reason for using the angles closest to 90° is that the sines of angles are usually used in computations, and angles near 90° have the smallest change in the sine function per second of angle. For example, assume five angles are measured around a point and the total correction equals 4.7″. The amount to be applied to each angle is 4.7/5 or 0.9″ with a 0.2″ remainder. Thus, the two angles nearest to 90° would have a 1.0″ correction, and the remaining three would be corrected by 0.9″. The total correction is 4.7″.

PROBLEMS

1. Establish four points that are about 30 feet [9 m] apart. Use a two- or three-person transit party to determine the horizontal angles inside this polygon.

   The angles should total 360°00′00″.
2. Establish a point at least 50 feet [15 m] from a vertical surface. Tape the exact distance, and set the transit over the point.

   Determine the positive vertical angle to the top of the surface, and the negative (minus) vertical angle to its base. Use the following formulas to determine the height of the surface.

$$\text{Height of vertical surface} = a_1 + a_2$$
$$\text{where } a_1 = b \cdot \text{Tan}(\angle A+)$$
$$\text{and } a_2 = b \cdot \text{Tan}(\angle A-)$$

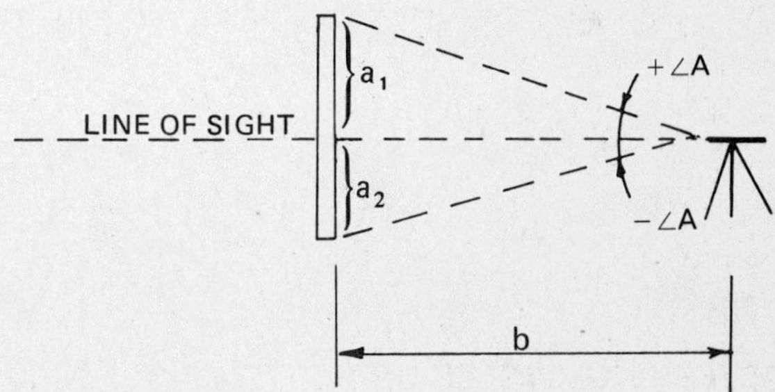

Figure 20-7

LEARNING ACTIVITY PACKAGE

Read Chap. 20 carefully.

Chapter 20 completely read ______________ (*date*).

If some of the objectives (a) through (i) have not been understood after completely reading the chapter, the portions of the chapter which discuss those topics should be reread. An understanding of the objectives listed above is adequate knowledge for a beginning surveyor.

Objectives read ______________ (*date*).

There are two surveying problems for this chapter.

Problem 1 completed ______________ (*date*).

Problem 2 completed ______________ (*date*).

Now take Chap. 20 quiz. Remove it from the text and answer all the questions.

Chapter 20 quiz taken ______________ (*date*).

20

QUIZ

1. A horizontal angle can be measured in two ways. What is the most common method? ______
2. By how much do the forward and back azimuths of a line differ in plane surveying? ______
3. What are the three methods used to establish zero azimuth lines? ______
4. How do bearings and azimuths differ? ______
5. What is the name given to the difference between a true north meridian and a magnetic north line indicated by a compass needle? ______
6. What are some of the possible sources of local attraction for a compass needle? ______
7. When would a vertical circle reading of 90° for a horizontal line be expected? ______
8. Why should every effort be made to have a separate recorder and instrumentperson on each survey party? ______
9. What are the three types of errors that affect angle observations? ______
10. How are angle adjustments distributed? ______

ABBREVIATIONS

A

abandoned	abd
abbreviations	abbr
abutment	abut.
acre	ac
acre-foot	ac-ft
addition	add.
adjusting	adj
afternoon	PM
aggregate	agg
alternate	alt
altitude	alt
aluminum	al
approved	appd
approximate	approx
area	*A*
article	art.
asbestos	asb
asphalt	asph
assembly	asm
assistant	asst
associate	assoc
association	assn
automatic	auto.
auxiliary	aux
avenue	Ave
average	avg
avoirdupois	avdp

B

backsight	bs
back to back	b to b
barrel	bbl
basement	bsmt
bearing	brg
bearing value	B.V.
bell and spigot	b & s
bench mark	B.M.
beveled	bev
bituminous coated corrugated metal pipe culvert	BCCMP
bituminous coated & paved corrugated metal pipe culvert	BCPCMP
bituminous coated pipe arch culvert	BCPA
bituminous coated and paved pipe arch culvert	BCPPA
black	blk
board	bd
board feet	fbm
bottom	bot
boulders	B
boulevard	Blvd
boundary	bndy
brown	brn
building	bldg
bulkhead	blkhd
bushel	bu

C

capacity	cap.
capital	cap.
cast iron	C.I.
cast iron pipe	C.I.P.
ceiling	clg
cement	cem
cemetery	cem
centerline	C.L.
center	ctr
centers	ctrs
center to center	c to c
chain	ch
change	chg
checked	ckd
church	ch
circular	cir
clay	CL
clear	clr
coated	ctd
coefficient	coef
column	col
computations	comp
concrete	conc
concrete pipe	C.P.
construct	const
continuous	cont
continued	contd
contract	cont
contractor	contr
contraction	contr
control	cont
continuation	cont
coordinate	coord
corner	cor
corrugated iron	Corr. I.
corrugated metal	CM
corrugated metal pipe	CMP
corrugated metal pipe arch culvert	CMPA
county	Co.
creek	Cr
cross road	x rd
cross section	x sect
cubic	cu
cubic foot	C.F.
cubic yard	C.Y.
culvert	culv

D

degree	deg
degree of curvature	*D*
department	dept
designed	dsgn
diameter	*D* or diam
dimension	dim.
directional	dir
drawing	dwg
drawings	dwgs

E

each	ea
east	E
elbow	ell
elevation (above sea level)	El

elevation (view)	elev
emergency	emerg
enclosure	encl
end to end	e to e
engineer	Engr
engineering	engg
equal	eq
equation	eq
equivalent	equiv
estimate	est
excavation	exc
expansion	exp
extension	ext
external	ext
external distance	*E*

F

face to face	f to f
federal	Fed.
Federal Aid	FA
Federal Aid Interstate	FAI
Federal Aid Primary	FAP
Federal Aid Secondary	FAS
feet	ft
feet board measure	fbm
feet per minute	fpm
feet per second	fps
ferry	fy
figure	Fig.
fire hydrant	F.H.
flange, flanged	flg
flexible	flex
floor	fl
flow line	F.L.
foot	ft
ford	fd
forenoon	AM
foresight	fs

G

gage	ga
gallon	gal
gallons per minute	gpm
gallons per second	gps
galvanized iron	G.I.
general	genl
green	grn
ground	grd

H

hexagonal	hex
high water	H.W.
horizontal	horiz
horsepower	hp
hour	hr
house	hse or h

I

inch	in.
including	incl
incorporated	Inc
information	inf
inside diameter	id
intermediate	inter.
iron pipe	I.P.

J

joint	jt
junction	jnct
junction box	J.B.

L

latitude	lat
left	lt
length	lgth
length of curve	*L*
length of tangent	*T*
light	lt
lighting	ltg
linear	lin
linear foot	lin ft
longitude	long.
longitudinal	long.

M

manhole	M.H.
material	mtl
maximum	max
mean sea level	MSL
meridian	mer
miles per hour	mph
minimum	min
minute	min
miscellaneous	misc

N

national	natl
negative	neg
north	N
northeast	NE
northwest	NW
number	No.
numbers	Nos.

O

on centers	oc
opposite	opp
orange	orn
ounce	oz
outside diameter	od
outside to outside	o to o

P

page	p
pages	pp
paragraph	par.
parallel	par.
plane	pl
plate	pl
point	pt
point of compound curvature	PCC
point of curvature	PC
point of intersection	PI
point of reverse curve	PRC
point of tangency	PT
portland cement concrete	PCC
pound, pounds	lb
power	pwr
power pole	P.P.
primary	pri
principal meridian	prin mer
project	Proj.

Q

quadrangle	quad
quart	qt

R

radius	*R* or rad
railroad	RR
railway	Ry
range	R
received	recd
reduction	reduc
reference	ref
reflector	refl
regular	reg
reinforced	reinf
reinforcement	reinf
reinforcing	reinf
required	reqd
revision	rev
right	rt
right-of-way	R/W
river	R
road	rd
roadway	rdy
round	rd
route	Rte.

S

sanitary sewer	San. S.
second	sec
secondary	secd
section	sect
separate	sep
service	serv
sheet	sh
signal	sig
south	S
southeast	SE
southwest	SW
spillway	splwy
square	sq
square foot	sq ft
square inch	sq in
square mile	sq mile
square yard	sq yd
standard	std

station	sta
storm sewer	S.S.
stream	str
street	St
structural	str
structure	str
substructure	substr
superelevation (ft./ft.)	e
superstructure	superstr
support	sup.
survey	surv
symmetrical	sym

T

tangent	tan.
telegraph	telg
telephone	telp
telephone pole	T.P.
temperature	temp
terminal	term.
terra cota	T.C.
thousand	M
tongue and groove	t & g
township	Twp
typical	typ

U

underground	ug
upstream	upstr
U.S. Geological Survey	USGS
U.S. Coast & Geodetic Survey	USC & GS

V

variable	var
vertical	vert
vertical curve	V.C.
volume	vol

W

weight	wt
west	W
white	wht

Y

yard	yd
year	yr
yellow	yel

DEFINITIONS

Angle of turn: the angle through which a vehicle travels in making a turn.

Approach nose: an end of an island or neutral area between roadways which faces approaching traffic that passes either on one or both sides.

Arterial highway: a highway primarily for through traffic, usually part of a continuous route.

At-grade intersection: an intersection where all roadways join or cross at the same level.

Auxiliary lane: the portion of the roadway adjoining the traveled way for parking, speed-change, or for other purposes supplementary to through-traffic movement.

Average daily traffic (ADT): the average 24-hour volume, determined by dividing the total volume during a stated period by the number of days in that period. Unless otherwise stated, the period is a year.

Average spot speed: the arithmetic mean of the speeds of all traffic or traffic components at a specified point.

Basic capacity: the maximum number of passenger cars that can pass a given point on a lane or roadway during one hour under the most nearly ideal roadway and traffic conditions that can be attained.

Belt highway: an arterial highway for carrying traffic partially or entirely around an urban area or portion thereof (also called a circumferential highway).

Bus: a self-propelled motor vehicle designed for the transportation of more than eight persons.

Channelized intersection: an at-grade intersection in which traffic is directed to definite paths by islands.

Cloverleaf: a four-leg interchange with loops for left turns and outer connections for right turns (or two-way ramps for these turns). A full cloverleaf has ramps for two turning movements in each quadrant.

Control of access: the condition in which the right to access, light, air, or view in connection with a highway is fully or partially controlled by public authority. *Full* control of access means that preference is given to through traffic by providing access connections with selected public roads only and by prohibiting crossings at grade and direct private driveway connections. *Partial* control of access means that preference is given to through traffic to a degree that, in addition to access connections with selected public roads, there may be some crossings at grade and some private driveway connections.

Cross connection: a connecting roadway between two nearby and generally parallel roadways.

Cul-de-sac street: a local street open at only one end, with special provision for turning around.

Curb loading zone: roadway space adjacent to a curb and reserved for exclusive use of vehicles during loading or unloading of passengers or property.

Dead-end street: a local street open at only one end, without special provision for turning around.

Dedication: the setting apart by the owner of property for highway use and acceptance of the property by the public, in accordance with statutory or common law provisions.

Delay: the time lost while traffic is impeded by some element over which the driver has no control.

Density: the number of vehicles per mile on the traveled way at a given instant.

Design capacity: the practical capacity or lesser value determined for use in designing the highway to accommodate the design volume.

Design speed: a speed determined for design and correlation of the physical highway features that influence vehicle operation. It is the maximum safe speed that can be maintained over a specified section of highway when conditions are so favorable that the design features of the highway govern.

Design vehicle: a selected motor vehicle whose weight, dimensions, and operating characteristics are used to establish highway design controls to accommodate vehicles of a designated type.

Design volume: a volume determined for use in design, representing traffic expected to use the highway. Unless otherwise stated, it is an hourly volume.

Diamond interchange: a four-leg interchange with a single one-way ramp in each quadrant. All left turns are made directly on the minor highway.

Direct connection: a one-way turning roadway which does not deviate greatly from the intended direction of travel.

Directional interchange: an interchange, generally having more than one highway grade separation, with direct connections for the major left-turning movements.

Diverging: the dividing of a single stream of traffic into separate streams.

Divided highway: a highway with separated roadways for traffic in opposite directions.

Drainage easement: an easement for directing the flow of water.

Easement: a right acquired by public authority to use or control property for a designated highway purpose.

Expressway: a divided arterial highway for through traffic, with full or partial control of access and generally with grade separations at intersections.

Fixed delay: delay caused by traffic controls.

Flared intersection: an unchannelized intersection or a divided highway intersection without islands other than medians where the traveled way of any intersection leg is widened or an auxiliary lane added.

Four-leg intersection: an intersection with four legs, for example, an intersection where two highways cross.

Freeway: an expressway with full control of access.

Frontage street (or frontage road): a local street or road auxiliary to and located on the side of an arterial highway for service to abutting property and adjacent areas and for control of access.

Grade separation: a crossing of two highways or a highway and a railroad at different levels.

Headway: the time interval between passages of consecutive vehicles moving in the same direction by a given point.

Highway, street or road: a public way for vehicular travel, including the entire area within the right-of-way (recommended usage: in urban areas, highway or street; in rural areas, highway or road).

Interchange: a grade-separated intersection with one or more turning roadways for travel between intersection legs.

Interchange ramp: a turning roadway at an interchange for travel between intersection legs.

Intersection: the general area where two or more highways join or cross, included within are roadway and roadside facilities for traffic movements in that area.

Intersection angle: the angle between two intersection legs.

Intersection entrance: the part of an intersection leg for traffic entering the intersection.

Intersection exit: the part of an intersection leg for traffic leaving the intersection.

Intersection leg: any one of the highways radiating from and forming part of an intersection. The common intersection of two highways crossing each other has four legs.

Island: a defined area between traffic lanes for control of vehicle movements or for pedestrian refuge. Within an intersection, a median or an outer separation is considered an island. An island may or may not be curbed.

Light delivery truck: a single unit truck, (such as a panel or pick-up truck) with size and operating characteristics similar to those of a passenger car, commonly used for short-haul light delivery service.

Local street (or local road): a street or road primarily for access to residences, businesses, or other abutting property.

Loop: a one-way turning roadway that curves about 270° to the right to accommodate a left-turning movement. It may include provision for a left turn at a terminal to accommodate another turning movement.

Major street (or major highway): an arterial highway with intersections at grade and direct access to abutting property and on which geometric design and traffic control measures are used to expedite the safe movement of through traffic.

Median: the portion of a divided highway separating the traveled ways for traffic in opposite directions.

Median lane: a speed-change lane within the median to accommodate left-turning vehicles.

Median opening: a gap in a median provided for crossing and turning traffic.

Merging: the converging of separate streams of traffic into a single stream.

Merging end: an end of an island or neutral area between roadways beyond which traffic merges.

Minimum turning path: the path of a designated point on a vehicle making its sharpest turn.

Minimum turning radius: the radius of the minimum turning path of the outside of the outer front tire. (Vehicle manufacturers' data books give minimum turning radius to the centerline of the outer front tire.)

Multi-leg intersection: an intersection with five or more legs.

Operational delay: delay caused by interference between traffic components.

Outer connection: a one-way turning roadway primarily for a right turning movement. It may include provision for a left turn at a terminal to accommodate another turning movement.

Outer separation: the portion of an arterial highway between the traveled ways of the roadway and a frontage street or road.

Overall travel speed: the speed over a specified section of highway, determined by the distance by the overall travel time. The average for all traffic or traffic components is the summation of distances divided by the summation of overall travel times.

Overall travel time: the time of travel, including stops and delays on the traveled way.

Overpass a grade separation where the subject highway passes over an intersecting highway or railroad (also called an overcrossing).

Parked vehicle: a vehicle stopped for temporary storage.

Parking lane: an auxiliary lane primarily for the parking of vehicles.

Parkway: an arterial highway for noncommercial traffic, with full or partial control of access, usually located within a park or a ribbon of parklike development.

Passenger car: a motor vehicle designed for the transportation of not more than eight persons. The term includes taxicabs, limousines, and station wagons.

Planting easement: an easement for reshaping roadside areas and establishing, maintaining, and controlling plant growth thereon.

Possible capacity: the maximum number of vehicles that can pass a given point on a lane or roadway during one hour under the prevailing roadway and traffic conditions regardless of their effect in delaying drivers and restricting their freedom to maneuver.

Practical capacity:[1] the maximum number of vehicles that can pass a given point on a lane or roadway during one hour under the prevailing roadway and traffic conditions, without unreasonable delay or restriction to the drivers' freedom to maneuver.

[1]The difference between the levels of possible capacity and practical capacity is accounted for by the effects of traffic density. At practical capacity the lower volume level, the traffic density is not great enough to cause any unreasonable delay or undue restriction on the drivers' freedom to maneuver. As traffic volumes increase beyond practical capacity, a high traffic density results. The high traffic densities cause substantial delay and restriction on the drivers' freedom to maneuver. However, due to lower and more uniform speed, these conditions also result in higher traffic volumes up to a point corresponding to possible capacity values. As traffic density increases above possible capacity, a sharp reduction in traffic volume results.

Radial highway: an arterial highway leading to or from an urban center.

Railroad crossing angle: the angle of 90° or less where a railroad and a highway intersect.

Railroad grade crossing: the general area where a highway and a railroad cross at the same level, within which are included the railroad, roadway, and roadside facilities for traffic traversing that area.

Right of access: the right of ingress to a highway from abutting land and egress from a highway to abutting land (see control of access).

Right-of-way: land, property, or interest therein, usually in a strip, acquired for or devoted to a highway.

Riparian Rights: the rights of an owner of water-fronting lands to the bed, banks, accretions, water, access, moorage, and similar items.

Roadbed: the graded portion of a highway, usually the area between the intersections of the top and side slopes, upon which the base course, surface course, shoulders, and median are constructed.

Roadside: the area adjoining the outer edge of the roadway. Extensive areas between the roadways of a divided highway can also be considered roadside.

Roadway (in construction specifications): the portion of a highway within the limits of construction.

Roadway (general): the portion of a highway (including shoulders) for vehicular use. A divided highway has two or more roadways.

Rotary: a channelized intersection in which traffic moves counterclockwise around a center island ideal of sufficient size to induce weaving movements in lieu of direct crossings.

Rotary interchange: a multi-leg interchange where one highway is grade separated from a rotary on which all turning movements and through movements of all other highways are accommodated.

Running speed: the speed over a specified section of highway, calculated by dividing the distance by the running time. The average for all traffic components is the summation of distances divided by the summation of running times.

Running time: the time the vehicle is in motion.

Scenic easement: an easement for conservation and development of roadside views and natural features.

Shoulder: the portion of the roadway contiguous with the traveled way for accommodation of stopped vehicles, for emergency use, and for lateral support of base and surface courses.

Sight line easement: an easement for maintaining or improving the sight distance.

Skew angle: the complement of the acute angle between two crossing centerlines.

Slope easement: an easement for cuts or fills.

Spacing: the distance between consecutive vehicles, measured front to front.

Speed: the rate of movement of a vehicle, generally expressed in miles per hour.

Speed-change lane: an auxiliary lane, including tapered areas, primarily for the acceleration or deceleration of vehicles entering or leaving the through-traffic lanes.

Standing vehicle: a vehicle stopped for a brief interval, such as for loading or unloading.

Streetcar: a vehicle designed for the transportation of persons and operated on rails (principally in municipalities).

Subgrade: the portion of a roadbed prepared as a foundation for the base or surface course.

T intersection: a three-leg intersection in the general form of a T.

Thirtieth highest hourly volume: the hourly volume that is exceeded by 29 hourly volumes during a designated year. (Corresponding definitions apply to any other ordinal highest hourly volume, such as tenth, twentieth, and so forth.)

Three-leg intersection: an intersection with three legs, where two highways join.

Through street (or through highway): every highway or portion thereof where vehicular traffic from intersecting highways is required to stop before entering or crossing the highway and when stop signs are erected.

Toll road, toll bridge, or toll tunnel: a highway, bridge, or tunnel open to traffic only upon payment of a direct toll or fee.

Traffic control device: any sign, signal, marking, or installation placed or erected under public authority for the purpose of regulating, warning, or guiding traffic.

Traffic control signal: a traffic signal by which traffic is alternately directed to stop and to proceed.

Traffic lane: the portion of the traveled way for the movement of a single line of vehicles.

Traffic marking: a traffic control device consisting of lines, patterns, or colors on pavement, curbs, or other objects within or adjacent to the roadway, or words or symbols on the pavement.

Traffic sign: a traffic control device that is mounted on a support above the level of the roadway and that conveys a specific message by means of unchanging words or symbols.

Traffic signal: a power-operated traffic control device by which traffic is regulated, warned, or alternately directed to take specific actions.

Traveled way: the portion of the roadway for the movement of vehicles, exclusive of shoulders and auxiliary lanes.

Trolley coach: a motor vehicle designed for the transportation of persons and propelled by electric power from overhead trolley wires, but not operated on rails.

Truck: a motor vehicle designed for transportation of property. The term includes single unit trucks and truck combinations.

Truck combination: a truck tractor and a semi-trailer (with or without a full trailer) or a truck with one or more full trailers.

Turning movement: the traffic making a designated turn at an intersection.

Turning path: the path of a designated point on a vehicle making a specified turn.

Turning roadway: a connecting roadway for traffic turning between two intersection legs.

Turning roadway terminal: the general area where a turning roadway connects with a through traffic roadway. *Exit* used as a modifier refers to leaving the through-traffic lanes and *entrance* refers to entering the through-traffic lanes.

Turning track width: the radial distance between the turning paths of the outside of the outer front tire and the outside of the rear tire which is nearest the center of the turn.

Two-way ramp: a ramp for travel in two directions. At a cloverleaf it serves as both an outer connection and a loop.

Unchannelized intersection: an at-grade intersection without islands for directing traffic to definite paths.

Underpass: a grade separation where the subject highway passes under an intersecting highway or railroad (also called an undercrossing).

Volume: the number of vehicles passing a given point during a specified period of time.

Weaving: the crossing of traffic streams moving in the same general direction accomplished by merging and diverging.

Weaving section: a length of one-way roadway designed to accommodate weaving. At one end two one-way roadways merge, and at the other end they separate.

Y intersections: a three-leg intersection in the general form of a Y.

INDEX

Abbreviations, 130–132, 302
Acre, 61
Adjusting the level, 314
Adjustment of leveling data, 321
Alignment, vertical, 127, 165
Alignment of roadway, 122, 137
Ames lettering instrument, 17
Angle and direction observations:
  angle adjustment, 333
  angle observing party, 331–332
  angles, 327–328
  azimuth, 329
  deflection angles, 328
  differential temperature, 333
  direction, 327
  environmental errors, 332
  factors affecting angle observations, 332
  grid azimuth, 329
  horizontal refraction, 333
  instrumental errors, 332
  interior and exterior angles, 328
  magnetic azimuth, 329
  magnetic declination, 330
  observing angles or directions, 332
  personnel errors, 332
  phase, 333
  rationale, 327
  station angles, 328
  true azimuth, 329
  vertical angles, 330–331
  zenith distances, 331
Architect's scales, 5, 144
Atmospheric effects on tape, 300

Back slope, 74
Balancing foresights and backsights, 313
Base line, 244
Beam compass, 3
Bearings, 103–105, 122–123, 329–330
  computing, 123–124
  instructions on taking, 103
Beginning of job, 122
Bench marks, 120–122, 143, 320–321
Board covers, 2
Border lines, 160–161
Bow compass, 3
Box culverts, 84
Breaking the tape, 299

Carbide blades in lead pointers, 6
Centerline:
  of project, 142
  of survey, 162–163
Channels, 73, 78
Chief of party, 296
Cleaner:
  paper, 7
  pen (ultrasonic), 22
Compass:
  beam, 3
  bow, 3
Control points, 126
Conventional signs, 43
Corrections, 302–303
County lines, 57–58
Crest of curve, 129
Cross-section view, 35, 185–189
Cross slope, 74, 110, 112–114
Culverts:
  box, 84
  construction details, 79
  endwalls, 79–81
  height, 84
  pipe, 78, 144, 165
  span, 84
Curbs, 199
Curvature and refraction, 314
Curves:
  control point, 126
  crest, 129
  degree of curvature, 125
  horizontal, 125
  length (*L*), 126
  point of intersection (PI), 129
  reference point, 126
  sag, 129–130
  vertical, 129, 143
  vertical curve data, 129

Definitions, 132–133
Deflection angles, 328
Degree, 103, 125
Delta angle, 123
Depression angle backsight, 322
Depression angle foresight, 322
Design squad, 33
Design squad leader, 34
Determining:
  angle, 323
  taped distance, 299
Difference in elevation method of taping, 301
Differential leveling, 312
Differential temperature, 333
Direction:
  changes of, 123
  in surveying, 327
Direction observations (*see* Angle and direction observations)
Distance measurements (*see* Measurements, distance)
Distances on plans, 109
Ditch requirements, 74
Ditches, special, 74–77, 144
Doric lettering device, 9, 41
Drafter's dustbrush, 5
Drafting film setup, 9
Drafting machine, 2, 4
Drafting powder, 10
Drafting tables, 2
Drafting tape, 7
Drafting technicians, 43
Drainage:
  arrows, 88
  basics, 73
  centerline of project, 86, 88
  ditches, 73–74, 144
  existing structures, 86
  explanation, 84–85
  ground cover, 86–87
  information on map, 85, 87–88, 96
  physical features, 86
  preparation, 85–86
  rainfall intensity, 87
  rationale, 73, 235
  rural drainage map, 95
  storm sewer drains, 145
  symbols, 89
Drainage structures, 79–81, 166
  existing ground line, 236
  flow line grades, 81. 240
  identification of structures, 236

inlets, 82
notes on cross-drain structure sheets, 240
order of systems, 240
ordinary cross drains, 236
preparing drainage structure sheets, 236–239
rationale, 235
on road plans, 235–236
sequence of plotting, 236–239
skewed structures, 81, 236
spacing structures, 236
underground utilities, 240
Drawing board, 2
Drawing mediums, 7
mylar, 7, 43
paper, 7
vellum, 8
Drawing symbols, 89

Earthwork:
balance areas, 231
balancing earthwork quantities, 231
basic earthwork processes, 227
borrow excavation, 229
grading, 229
mass diagram, 230–231
quantities, 229–230
rationale, 227
shrinkage factors, 231
subsoil excavation, 229
summary of quantities sheet, 228–229
types of earthwork, 227–228
Elevation, super (*see* Superelevation)
Elevation angle backsight, 322
Elevation angle foresight, 322
Elevation view, 35
Elevations of proposed roadway, 127
Emery cloth in the lead pointer, 6
Ending of job, 122
Endwalls, 79–81
Engineer's scales, 5, 144
Environmental errors in surveying, 332
Equations:
actual length, 108
apparent length, 108
lengths, 107–108, 140
stationing, 109–110
Erasers:
electric, 10
erasing ink details, 10
Magic Rub, 7
Pelikan eraser, 7, 10
Erasing shield, 5, 7

Fasteners, paper, 7
Fastening the drawing sheet, 10
Fence, 58
Field books, 167
Field notes, 34, 302–304, 320
Field procedure in leveling, 315
Fill sections, 190
Filler squeeze bottle, 8
Film, 8, 43
Flag, 43, 60
Flow line, 81, 240
Forms of recording distance measurements, 302
Fractions, 20
French curve, 5
Front tapeperson, 296

General notes, 144
Grades, 110–112, 127–128, 229
Grid, 160–162
Grid azimuth, 329
Grid system, 243
Guardrail, 198–199
Guidelines, lettering, 16–17, 20–21
horizontal, 17, 20
inclined, 17
vertical, 16, 20
Gutter grades at street intersections, 145

Hand level, 287
High water, 143
Horizontal crosshairs, 315
Horizontal refraction, 333
Horizontal taping party, 296
Horizontal taping procedure, 298
Hourly volume at readway cross sections, 197

Indirect methods of measuring distance, 305
Ink, 8
Inking, elevating triangles when, 43
Inking tools, 8
Inlets, 82–83
Instrument operation, 316
Instrumental errors, 332
Interior and exterior angles, 328
Irregular curves, 5

Jobs for civil drafting technicians, 43

Key maps:
arrangement, 38, 49
city population, 40
Drawing No. 1 (Green River County, Fla.), 38, 49
flagging, 60
index of sheets, 41–42, 58–59
instructions, 36
items on map, 36–37, 49, 57
length of project, 41, 49, 60
lettering size, 40
location map, 37–38, 41, 58
method of drawing, 39
municipal, 33–56
need for key map, 36
north point, 60
physical features, 40, 58
project identification, 41, 49, 60
project location, 38, 49, 58
purpose, 43
range lines, 61
rationale, 33, 57
rural, 57–72
scale, 57–58
specific instructions for drawing, 38–39
state outline, 41, 49
station numbers, 40, 49
stationing of project, 40, 49
township lines, 61

Land development:
base under the land, 259
connecting to city water, 261
connecting piling to grade beam, 269
connecting to sanitary sewer, 259
cutting the pilings, 269
developing the lot, 261–262
driving piling, 268–269
elevation of the property, 259
finding city sewer connection, 260
history of the property, 257–258
legal description of the property, 257–258
locating the piling positions, 265–266
location of the points for piling, 263
marking the stations, 265
nails and tabs, 264
pile driver, 267–268
piling operation, 267
rationale, 257
setting up the transit, 263–265
soil survey, 259
water main, 264
who requires development, 257
Land widths, 198
Lead, electrolytic or filmograph, 6
Lead hardness, 6
Lead holder, 5, 6
Lead sharpeners or pointers, 6
Learning activity package (LAP), 2
Length of project, 60
Leroy lettering device, 9, 41
Lettering:
basic strokes, 18
capitals, 18, 23
compressed, 16
extended, 16
guidelines, 16–17, 20–21
importance, 24
inclined, 21
letters and figures, 16
lowercase, 20
mechanical, 21
normal letters, 16
proportions, 15
rationale, 15
samples on plan and profile sheet, 23
spacing, 16, 21
stability, 16
style, 15
uniformity, 16
Lettering triangle, 16
Leveling, 311–323
adjusting the level, 311
adjusting of leveling data, 321

Leveling (*Cont.*)
- balancing foresights and backsights, 313
- curvature and refraction, 314
- depression angle backsight, 322
- depression angle foresight, 322
- determining the angle, 323
- differential leveling, 312
- elevation angle backsight, 322
- elevation angle foresight, 322
- field notes, 320
- field procedure, 315
- horizontal crosshairs, 315
- instrument operation, 316
- laying off a given distance, 299
- length of tape, 300
- level bench marks, 320–321
- level party, 296–297
- level vial, 314
- leveling operation, 313–314
- leveling signals, 317
- leveling the tape, 298
- line of sight, 315
- measuring the distance, 322–323
- method, 312
- method and procedures, 321–322
- micrometer method, 318
- one-wire method, 316
- orders of accuracy, 312
- rationale, 311
- reciprocal leveling, 319–320
- rod operation, 318
- sequence for taking level readings, 316
- sight distances, 312–313
- simultaneous reciprocal leveling, 320
- three-wire method, 316
- trigonometric leveling, 321–322
- types of leveling, 311

Leveling tools:
- hand levels, 287
- leveling rods, 285–286
- levels, 283–284
- plumb bobs, 290
- rod targets, 286
- roller markers, 290
- scissor clamp, 289
- stadia rods, 286–287
- tapes, 287–288
- taping arrows, 288
- tension scale, 289
- thermometers, 289
- turning pins, plates, and wooden stakes, 289
- umbrella, 290

Line ahead, 106
Line back, 106
Line of sight, 315
Location map for key sheet, 37–38, 41, 58

Magnetic azimuth, 329
Magnetic declination, 330
Manholes, 83, 88
Measurements, distance, 295–307
- abbreviations and symbols, 302
- atmospheric effects, 300
- breaking tape, 299
- chief of party, 296
- corrections, 302–303
- descriptions, 302
- determining the taped distance, 299
- difference in elevation method, 301
- field notebook information, 302
- field notes, 302
- forms of recording, 302
- front tapeperson, 296
- horizontal taping party, 296
- horizontal taping procedure, 298
- indirect methods, 305
- laying off a given distance, 299
- length of tape, 300
- level party, 296–297
- leveling the tape, 298
- measuring distances longer than ten tape lengths, 299
- measuring full tape lengths, 298–299
- measuring partial tape lengths, 299
- method of support, 300
- party organization, 296
- rationale, 295
- rear tapeperson, 296
- recorder, 296
- recording, 302
- recording precautions, 304
- recording procedures, 303–304
- sketches, 302
- slope of tape, 301
- slope taping party, 296
- slope taping procedure, 297–298
- stadia accuracy, 307
- stadia constant, 306
- stadia interval factor, 306
- stadia measurement, 307
- stretcherperson, 296
- tabulation, 302
- tape alignment, 297
- taping, 296
- taping corrections, 299–300
- taping mistakes and errors, 301–302
- vertical angle method, 301

Measuring the distance in leveling, 322–323
Mechanical lead holders, 5
Mechanical lettering device, 9, 22
Median ditch, 74
Median edges, 163
Method of leveling, 312
Method of trigonometric leveling, 321–322
Micrometer method of leveling, 318
Mile, 61
Minute, 103
Mylar, 7, 43

North point, 60, 140–141
Numeral characteristics, 20
Numerals, 18, 20

Observing angles or directions, 332
Observing party for angles, 331–332
One-wire method of leveling, 316
Orders of accuracy, 312
Organization, taping party, 296
Outer road edges, 164

Paper cleaners, 7
Paper fasteners, 7
Parallel rule, 3
Parcels, 245
Pen cleaner (ultrasonic), 22
Pen set (technical), 39
Pencil, wooden, 6
Pencil technique, 18
Personnel errors in direction surveying, 332
Phase in surveying, 333
Pipe culverts, 78, 144, 165
Plan and profile:
- alignment of roadway, 122, 137
- bearings, 140
- bench marks, 120–122
- centerline of project, 142
- centerline of survey, 138
- city limits, 141
- construction centerline, 139
- conventional symbols, 140
- equations, 140
- existing topography, 142
- features of municipal construction plans, 142
- flagging project limits, 142
- fundamentals, 119
- lateral ditch details, 141
- nontypical pavement edges, 142
- north arrow, 140
- number of stations, 138
- plan view, 23, 34–35, 103
- plumb bobs, 290
- point of curvature (PC), 126, 139
- point of intersection (PI), 129
- point of tangency (PT), 126, 139
- points of beginning and ending, 122
- profile grade, 127–128, 165
- project or job number, 60
- project location, 38
- rationale, 103, 119, 137
- reference points, 141
- right-of-way lines, 142
- rural plan view, 138
- scales of drawings, 119–120, 138
- sheet size, 137
- side roads, 141
- tick marks, 139
- topography, 140
- (*See also* Producing a plan and profile sheet)

Plumb bobs, 290
Principal meridian, 244
Producing a plan and profile sheet:
- bearing of centerline, 164
- border lines, 160–161
- centerline of survey, 162
- developing the grid, 160

- drawing the centerline, 163
- drawing the proposed roadway, 163, 165
- drawing sheet size, 159
- fastening the sheet, 160
- horizontal part of the profile grid, 162
- median edges, 163
- need for a T-square, 160
- notes for the roadway, 164
- outer road edges, 164
- rationale, 159
- right-of-way (city and country), 164
- right-of-way lines and station numbers, 164
- scale, 162
- setup procedure, 159
- splitting the sheet, 160
- ticking the centerline, 163
- vertical lines in grid, 162

Profile view for municipal roadway construction:
- general requirements, 144
- gutter grades at street intersections, 145
- marking vertical elevations, 144
- scales, 144
- storm sewer drains, 145
- underground utilities, 144

Profile views for rural roadway construction:
- bench marks, 143
- breaks in stationing, 143
- existing ground line profile, 143
- high water, 143
- profile grade lines, 143
- special ditches, 143
- stationing and scales, 143
- undesirable materials, 143
- vertical curves, 143
- vertical elevation datum, 143

Radius (*R*), 126
Rainfall intensity, 87
Range lines, 57, 61, 244
Range pole, 285
Rapidograph pens, 8, 39, 43
- sizes, 8

Rapidometric lettering device, 9
Rear tapeperson, 296
Reciprocal leveling, 319–320
Recorder, 296
Recording:
- field notes, 302
- leveling readings, 318–319

Recording precautions, 304
Recording procedures, 303–304
Reference points, 126
Right-of-way:
- bench marks and ground elevations, 167
- city and country, 164, 166, 243
- easements, 246
- existing topography, 166
- ditches, 166
- drainage, 166
- drainage structures in the profile, 168
- drawing highway profile, 168
- field book information, 167
- grid systems, 243–246
- information, 243
- marking off elevations on profile, 168
- natural ground line, 168
- parcels, 245
- profile stations, 168
- rationale, 243
- reference points, 167

Roadway cross sections (*see* Typical roadway cross sections)
Roadway ditch, 74
Roadway plan and profile sheets:
- alignment, 137
- bearings, 140
- centerline of project, 142
- centerline of survey, 138
- city limits, 141
- construction centerline, 139
- conventional symbols, 140
- culverts and cross drain pipe, 144
- ditches of uniform but nonstandard depth, 144
- equations, 140
- existing pavement, 140
- existing topography, 142
- features of municipal construction plans, 142
- flagging project limits, 141, 144
- general notes, 144
- lateral ditch details, 141
- nontypical pavement edges, 142
- north arrow, 140
- number of stations, 138
- points of curve and tangent, 139
- rationale, 137
- reference points, 141
- right-of-way lines, 142
- rural plan view, 138
- scale, 138
- sheet size, 137
- special ditches, 144
- topography, 140

Rod operation, 318
Rod targets, 286
Roller markers, 290

Sag of curve, 129–130
Scales:
- architect's, 5, 144
- engineer's, 5, 144

Scissor clamp, 289
Scriber systems, 9
Section, 34, 61, 244
Section line, 41, 58
Sequence for taking a level reading, 316
Shoulders, 198, 222–223
Side roads, 141
Side slopes and ditches, 198
Sidewalks, 199
Sight distances in leveling, 312–313
Signals used in leveling, 317
Simultaneous reciprocal leveling, 320
Sketches, 302
Skew angles, 81
Slope ratio, 112
Slope taping party, 296
Slope taping procedure, 297–298
Slopes, 110, 112
Special ditches, 74–77, 144
Stadia accuracy, 307
Stadia constant, 306
Stadia interval factor, 306
Stadia measurement, 307
Stadia rods, 286–287
Stainless steel blade, 4
Station angles, 328
Stationing, 43, 105–106
Storm sewer drains, 145
Stretcherperson, 296
Superelevation:
- general notes, 223
- normal crown, 213
- rationale, 213
- shoulders, 222–223
- slope rates, 216
- superelevation of roadway, 213–214
- transition length calculation, 215–220
- transitions, 214
- typical sections with curve data, 217–218, 221
- undivided highways, 214–215

Surveying equipment:
- leveling rods, 285–286
- levels, 283–284
- range pole, 285
- rationale, 283
- transits, 284
- tripods, 284–285

Symbols, 89, 140

T-square, 3, 160
- testing for rigidity of blade, 4
- testing for straightness of blade, 3

Tabulation, 302
Tangent length (*T*), 126
Tape alignment, 297
Tapes, 287–288
Taping, 296
Taping arrows, 288
Taping corrections, 299–300
Taping mistakes and errors, 301–302
Technical pen, 8, 39, 43
Tension scale, 289
Test for rigidity, T-square blade, 4
Test for straightness, T-square blade, 3
Theory of stadia, 305
Thermometers, 289
Three-wire method of leveling, 316
Throw table, 2
Thumb tacks, 2, 7
Tick marks, 139, 163
Topography, 140
Township, 41, 57–58, 61, 243–244
Transits, 284

Triangles:
  30–60°, 4
  45°, 4
  correcting accuracy, 4
  standard size, 4
  testing, 4
Trigonometric leveling, 321
Tripods, 284–285
True azimuth, 329
Turning pins, plates, and wooden stakes, 289
Typical roadway cross sections:
  calculating design hourly volume, 197
  cross sections of the natural ground, 185–186
  curbs, 199
    barrier, 199
    median, 199
    mountable, 199
    shoulder gutter, 199
  cut sections, 190
  fill sections, 190
  guardrail, 198–199
  multiple typical sections, 187–189
  pavement cross slope, 198
  rationale, 185
  shoulders, 198
  side slopes and ditches, 198
  sidewalks, 199
  tape alignment, 297
  taping corrections, 299–300
  taping mistakes and errors: accidental, 302
    errors, 301
    mistakes, 301
    systemic errors, 302
  traffic definitions, 197
  traffic lane widths, 198
  typical section, 185–187
  typical section of divided hghway, 187–189
Typical section, 34, 185–189

Umbrella, 290
Underground utilities, 144, 240
Undesirable materials, 143
Unitech lettering device, 9, 41

Vellum, 8
Vertical alignment, 127, 165
Vertical angle method of slope taping, 301
Vertical angles, 330–331
Vertical curve data, 129
Vertical curves, 129, 143
Vertical lines in grid, 162

Water control, 73
  (*See also* Drainage)
Waterproofing field notes, 303

Z type inlet, 82–83
Zenith distances, 331